THE NEUROEDUCATION TOOLBOX

Practical Translations of Neuroscience in Counseling and Psychotherapy

RAISSA MILLER
Boise State University

ERIC T. BEESON
The Family Institute at Northwestern University

Bassim Hamadeh, CEO and Publisher
Amy Smith, Senior Project Editor
Abbey Hastings, Production Editor
Emely Villavicencio, Senior Graphic Designer
Stephanie Kohl, Licensing Coordinator
Kim Scott, Interior Designer
Natalie Piccotti, Director of Marketing
Kassie Graves, Vice President of Editorial
Jamie Giganti, Director of Academic Publishing

Printed in the United States of America.

To all the individuals with whom we have worked. Thank you for inviting us into your stories and for being open to exploring neuroscience as part of our journey together.

Brief Contents

Detailed Contents

Preface

PURPOSE OF THE TEXT

The integration of neuroscience in various fields is increasing rapidly, and the mental health field is no exception. Neuroscience, broadly defined as the study of the nervous system, has been used to evaluate the etiology of mental disorders, measure treatment outcomes, monitor in-vivo changes to process elements of psychotherapy, and, more recently, explore transdiagnostic functional systems underlying all human functioning. Every day, clinicians are exposed to neuroscience research findings through the popular press, academic literature, and professional conferences; however, many ask, "What do these findings mean for my practice?"

This question is at the heart of this book. The purpose of *The Neuroeducation Toolbox: Practical Translations of Neuroscience in Counseling and Psychotherapy* is to share how everyday clinicians interpret neuroscience research and translate it into their practices. Specifically, this text focuses on a type of integration of neuroscience in practice called neuroeducation. Neuroeducation, which can be considered a subset of psychoeducation focusing on neuroscience topics, is a transdiagnostic and transtheoretical process, defined as "a didactic or experiential-based intervention that aims to reduce client distress and improve client outcome by helping clients understand the neurological processes underlying mental functioning" (Miller, 2016, p. 105).

Although many clinicians likely use some form of neuroeducation in their practices, this intervention often lacks a sound model to guide its integration. Too often, neuroscience information is viewed as a panacea and given superior status to other ways of knowing or understanding clients' experiences. This idea could not be further from the truth, and such application comes with real risks to clients. Some examples of haphazard integration of neuroscience include overgeneralized, overstated, or inaccurate information sharing (e.g., Coutinho et al., 2017; Lilienfeld, 2014). Negative client impacts include perceiving the clinician as less warm and empathic and decreased belief in the effectiveness of psychotherapy (Fernandez-Duque et al., 2015; Haslam & Kvaale, 2015; Lebowitz et al., 2015; Nowack & Radicki, 2018; Weisberg et al., 2008). In addition, placing "blame" for struggles in the brain can, at times, reduce client agency and hopefulness for change.

Despite these risks, there is both anecdotal and empirical evidence to support the benefits of neuroscience integration in counseling and psychotherapy. For example, the sound integration of neuroscience can increase intentionality and precision in treatment and lead to various outcomes, such as reduced shame, increased compassion and empathy for self and others, and increased pain tolerance, coping, emotional regulation, and neural integration (Badenoch, 2008, 2018; Cozolino, 2010; Fishbane, 2013; Louw et al., 2011; Miller & Barrio Minton, 2016; Miller, 2016; Robins et al., 2016; Siegel, 2012a). The neuroeducation process presented in this book will help you mitigate the risks and enhance the benefits of integrating neuroscience in your work.

The risks and benefits of neuroeducation are parallel to any other intervention. Some individuals may try to separate neuroscience into a superior class of intervention given the fancy metrics and brain images produced, but we propose that neuroscience is just another lens through which we can view human experience. Neuroscience information should be considered alongside other biological, psychological, and sociocultural information that we already incorporate in our practices. Furthermore, neuroeducation interventions should be continually evaluated and modified to match client needs.

In sum, in this book, we aim to establish a framework to guide the integration of neuroscience in mental health practice through neuroeducation, as well as offer a compendium of resources that demonstrate how real-life clinicians interpret neuroscience research and apply neuroeducation in their counseling and psychotherapy practices. Rather than providing an authoritative reference source on all neuroscience concepts (there are plenty of textbooks that already do this), this book will show neuroscience brought to life in counseling and psychotherapy. If you come across a term you do not recognize, we recommend that you look it up in one of the excellent resources dedicated to explaining in detail various neuroscience terms and concepts.

In addition, it is worth noting that our professional training and practice background is within the field of counselor education, specifically clinical mental health counseling. Thus the terms we use, the perspectives we represent, and the voices we take on in our writing are indicative of this background. The contributors of neuroeducation activities also come from unique professions, such as counseling, psychology, social work, and even physical therapy, among others. Therefore, we use terms like counseling, psychotherapy, and therapy interchangeably in this text and believe that the concepts and ideas presented are applicable to the larger mental health field, including school counseling, rehabilitation counseling, marriage and family therapy, social work, addiction treatment, recovery coaching, life coaching, psychology, psychiatric care, nursing, and related disciplines.

NEUROREALITIES/PRESUPPOSITIONS

There are a couple of neurorealities and presuppositions that are important to review prior to reading this text. The brain is immensely complex, and the more we learn, the more we find out what we do not know. We, as a field, know some things, but we do not know all things, and much of what is heard and communicated about neuroscience has some degree of simplification. Neuroscience research is also rapidly changing, and it is possible that some claims in this book may have morphed since the book entered production. For example, until just a few years ago, neuroscientists considered the brain an immune-privileged organ, meaning that it did not have a strong inflammation response or lymphatic drainage system. Scientists now know that the brain does in fact have an intricate immune response, with previously ignored cells like microglia taking center stage. Evolving knowledge in this area of research has provided new ways of thinking about links between the body and the brain and ways to conceptualize, prevent, and treat brain-based disorders. Much of this primary science has yet to make its way into textbooks or coursework. Further, although we have diligently reviewed the content in this book and clinicians' submissions, the submissions represent interpretations and translations of existing research. It is up to each reader to evaluate clinicians' interpretations and applications in the context of emerging science and revise accordingly.

ORGANIZATION AND CHAPTERS

The first two chapters of the book set the foundational model to guide the application of neuroeducation exercises in the later chapters. Chapter 1 introduces the concept of neuroeducation and its general uses in counseling and psychotherapy. Chapter 2 describes the neuroeducation process, practical strategies, and metaconcepts to guide the neuroeducation process.

Chapters 3 through 9 are the heart of the text, focusing on neuroeducation activities that are grouped according to similar concepts. It is important to acknowledge, however, that just as the brain is highly interconnected, so too are the chapters, and you will see some carryover in concepts from chapter to chapter.

Chapter 3 focuses on the key principles of brain development.

Chapter 4 explores basic brain anatomy and physiology.

Chapter 5 highlights the autonomic nervous system.

Chapter 6 focuses on the enteric nervous system and embodied brain.

Chapter 7 explores the social-emotional brain systems.

Chapter 8 highlights the memory systems.

Chapter 9 focuses on the technological application of neuroscience.

In each neuroeducation activity chapter (Chapters 3 to 9), we begin with an introduction that sets the objectives of the chapter and reviews a sampling of seminal research needed to understand and apply the neuroeducation activities in the chapter and then close with some reflection questions. After the introduction, each chapter includes several neuroeducation activities. You will find that some chapters have more activities than others. Although the brain likes consistency and balance just as we do, the distribution of activities across chapters is perhaps demonstrative of mental health providers' exposure to the concepts.

Neuroeducation is by definition a process. Therefore, each neuroeducation activity is written in a way to bring the activity to life so that you can replicate and/or adapt the process in your practice. Each entry includes the following sections:

- Empirical Justification
- Materials Needed
- Process of the Activity
- Follow-Up
- Neuroscience in Action
- Ethical and Multicultural Considerations

The neuroeducation activities vary in how neuroscience is used. For instance, you will notice that some submissions use neuroscience to justify the activity while others use neuroscience to inform the specifics of the activity. Also, some authors reference explicit neuroscience information in their activity with their clients, whereas others mention it to a lesser degree. Regardless of the degree of integration, it is important to note that the neuroscience information is always secondary to the therapeutic relationship and the delivery of the neuroeducation process. You will even see how some contributors use neuroscience to inform their approach to the everyday therapeutic encounters that we all experience.

Each contributor uses a different writing style in their descriptions of the neuroeducation process and how they show neuroscience in action. Some take a more narrative approach, while others list clear step-by-step procedures. Some include detailed scripts and transcripts of client interactions, while others describe general recommendations and examples of client interactions. Each contributor was responsible for ensuring that ethical standards were upheld when writing about actual client material in their submissions. Rather than impose a consistent style, we embraced these differences to add variety in your review of these activities. Hopefully, this will keep you engaged as you work through the neuroeducation submissions in this text.

This diversity in writing style also influences the way each contributor describes neuroscience concepts. You will find that many neuroscience concepts are referenced multiple times throughout the book, often with slight variations in how they are described or applied. We hope the repetition supports your overall learning process and the differences in explanations or uses deepen your synthesis of the information and spark creative applications.

After moving through 40 neuroeducation activities, Chapter 10 concludes our journey with a discussion of future directions and implications for research of the neuroeducation process.

CONCLUDING THOUGHTS

Before transitioning into the main text, we have some final considerations. We are not neuroscientists, and we do not believe any contributors in this text would consider themselves to be neuroscientists in the purest sense. We are simply mental health practitioners who are trying to make sense of a complex and ever-growing, ever-changing body of neuroscience literature in the work we do. We ask that you practice neurohumility as you journey through this text, embracing the complexity, leaning into the research, and continuing your own study in an effort to be an effective and ethical practitioner who uses neuroeducation as one part of the therapeutic journey you take with your clients.

Acknowledgments

We would like to thank the following people for their contributions, feedback, and tireless work supporting the writing and publishing process:

Eve Rogerson
Jennifer Klein
Emily Cruse Elliott
Jessica Lindsey DeArcangelis
Allen E. Ivey, Professor Emeritus, University of Massachusetts
Damara Goff Paris, Emporia State University
Thomas A. Field, City University of Seattle
Victoria Sepulveda, Mount Mary University
Sheila R. Dennis, PhD, MSW, Indiana University School of Social Work
Dr. Lisa E. Cox, Stockton University, Galloway, NJ
Kathryn S. Woods, Ferris State University
Sky Niesen Smith, DSW, LICSW, Minnesota State University, Mankato
Dr. Alaric A. Williams, Arkansas Tech University
Chad Luke
Cognella staff
Family
Lauren E. Brdecka

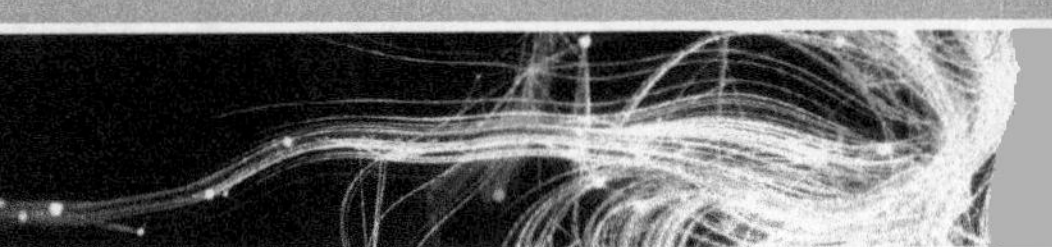

CHAPTER 1

Introduction to Neuroeducation

CHAPTER OBJECTIVES

1. Define neuroeducation and identify potential benefits of neuroeducation in clinical practice.
2. Identify the top uses of neuroeducation in clinical practice.
3. Discuss applications of neuroeducation in practice.

INTRODUCTION

You likely did not become a mental health practitioner because of a deep-seated interest in electrical and chemical signaling, epigenetics, or myelogenesis. It is more likely that you became a mental health practitioner because of an interest in connecting with people in a meaningful manner, offering encouragement and support, and fostering healing and growth (see Figure 1.1).

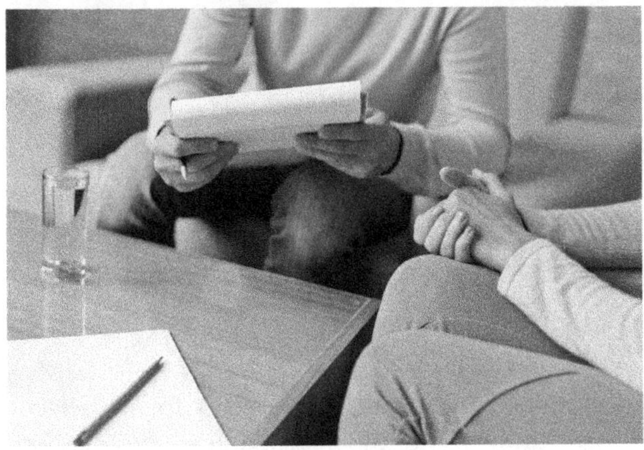

FIGURE 1.1. Counseling Relationship

What if we were to suggest that having some understanding of the former can actually support your ability to do the latter successfully? This notion has been true in our clinical work and serves as the basis of this book.

The field of neuroscience—and its many subfields, including affective neuroscience, cognitive neuroscience, neurophysiology, and so forth—is growing rapidly, and researchers are producing knowledge that both validates existing paradigms and offers insights into new ways of seeing and knowing (Beeson & Field, 2017). Although the brain is infinitely complex (Bassett & Gazzaniga, 2011), researchers' current findings on brain structures, functions, networks, and nodes can help us, and our clients, better appreciate the work of therapy. Exploring neuroscience information with clients, a process we refer to as neuroeducation, can be a powerful component of the therapeutic process.

Neuroeducation is formally defined as "a didactic or experiential-based intervention that aims to reduce client distress and improve client outcome by helping clients understand the neurological processes underlying mental functioning" (Miller, 2016, p. 105). Although sometimes called by a different name (e.g., brain talk, internal education, neuroscience-informed psychoeducation, therapeutic neuroscience education), the concept of neuroeducation has been found in mental health literature for more than a decade (Badenoch, 2008; Cozolino, 2010; Fishbane, 2013; Miller, 2016; Siegel, 2012a). Spurred by the "decade of the brain" (1990–1999), a time when tremendous strides were made in neuroimaging that enhanced the way scientists could study the brain (e.g., use of functional magnetic resonance imaging), practitioners began to translate basic neuroscience research into relevant mental health applications. Daniel Siegel, the originator of interpersonal neurobiology (IPNB) and author of numerous books for clinical and nonclinical audiences, is one of the leading figures in translational neuroscience.

Siegel (2009) described IPNB as a consilient approach combining various branches of objective science and subjective human experience to have a holistic understanding of the mind, brain, and relationships across the life span. Louis Cozolino, therapist and author of the popular book *The Neuroscience of Psychotherapy* (2010), among other books, and Bruce Perry, creator of the neurosequential model of therapeutics, were also early pioneers in translational neuroscience. Most clinicians do not have easy access to the basic science itself and thus rely heavily on translational texts. This book also falls within the larger category of translational texts, as you will be able to read how clinicians across settings and educational backgrounds creatively translate and share their understanding of neuroscience in their work with clients. You will find references to both primary science research and translational texts throughout. It is worth noting that the term neuroeducation has also been used to describe the application of neuroscience within the larger field of education; however, our use of the term is primarily descriptive of applications within the mental health field and mental health training.

Neuroeducation falls within the larger umbrella of psychoeducation, a therapeutic approach that has long-standing empirical support (Donker et al., 2009; Leffler et al., 2008). Neuroeducation is transdiagnostic and transtheoretical. The approach is transdiagnostic in that activities can be applied across diagnostic categories and/or address underlying causal mechanisms present in many diagnoses (Sauer-Zavala et al., 2017). Some activities in this text note specific areas of application (e.g., addiction, post-traumatic stress), whereas other activities focus on more global experiences, such as shame, hypervigilance, and general mood dysregulation. Similarly, neuroeducation activities can be applied within the philosophical frameworks of many theoretical orientations. For example, a humanistic counselor may consider engaging in a neuroeducation activity because they believe that it will strengthen the therapeutic relationship or support the client's personal agency and responsibility. A cognitive therapist may select a neuroeducation activity because they believe it will help a client with reappraisal of automatic thoughts. This versatility across diagnoses, human experiences, and philosophical traditions has aided in our understanding and application of neuroeducation with countless clients in our careers.

As we will discuss in Chapter 2, the process of delivering neuroeducation is as critical, if not more so, than the content itself. Simply teaching clients about neuroanatomy or reducing their experiences of distress to an absence of a certain neurochemical is generally not effective in fostering change. In fact, in some instances, providing a biological explanation for mental disorders can inhibit therapeutic progress by decreasing individuals' sense of personal agency and optimism for recovery (Haslam & Kvalle, 2015). However, based on our clinical experiences and the experiences of many other clinicians cited in this text, we believe that engaging in a collaborative exploration of different ways of knowing, grounded in neuroscience, can have a positive effect on therapeutic outcomes (see Figure 1.2).

FIGURE 1.2. Sharing Neuroscience

Neuroeducation can take many forms. Direct information-sharing and instruction are skills akin to many microskill paradigms in counseling and psychotherapy (e.g., Ivey et al., 2018) that can help promote learning, increase awareness and insight, and develop concrete change strategies. Experiential activities can help clients develop a felt sense of the information coming alive (Miller & Barrio Minton, 2016) that promotes more stable memory construction. Metaphors have a long history of promoting insight and change in counseling (Wagener, 2017) and can support neuroeducation efforts by linking the scientific jargon of neuroscience to clients' everyday language. These are just a few familiar ways you can begin to think about how neuroeducation can be infused into your practice. Regardless of form, it is essential that all neuroeducation is individualized and aligned with neuroscience principles of learning (Cozolino & Sprokay, 2006).

USES OF NEUROEDUCATION IN COUNSELING AND PSYCHOTHERAPY

We have identified five ways neuroeducation is most frequently used in clinical practice. We describe these uses here and offer brief introductions to some of the neuroscience-related concepts that will be further explored in later chapters in this book. We also offer some brief client examples to illustrate the use of neuroeducation, setting the stage for more detailed case studies that apply neuroeducation in clinical practice in later chapters.

TOP-FIVE USES OF NEUROEDUCATION

1. Support positive narratives grounded in science versus a negative view of self.
2. Increase compassion and empathy for self and others while reducing blame and shame.
3. Normalize client experiences and the change process.
4. Support regulation of thoughts, feelings, emotions, and behaviors.
5. Enhance client engagement and motivation.

Supporting Positive Narratives

One of the primary benefits of neuroeducation seems to be that it helps individuals create a narrative grounded in the science of brain development, nervous system functioning, and information processing rather than the more common narratives we encounter in the counseling room—ones of personal worthlessness, incompetence, or inadequacy that seem unchangeable to those with whom we serve. Creating stories to make sense of experience is what our brain does. Cognitive neuroscientist Michael Gazzaniga (2011) refers to this tendency as the interpreter role of the brain. Gazzaniga's experiments with split-brain patients, individuals who have their corpus callosum, the part of the brain that connects the two hemispheres, severed—typically in an effort to relieve seizures—revealed that individuals have an innate tendency to make causal relationships between events, even in the absence of objective evidence of such. Causal relationships about self, others, and the world are determined at a very early age, often before the development of language and the availability of explicit memory or higher level cortical capacities, and thus the narratives feel like truth to the individual but make little factual sense to outside observers.

For example, Raissa Miller (the co-editor of this text) once worked with a young woman whose mother struggled with severe depression when the client was a young child. The client's mother was unable to consistently respond to the client's bids for emotional connection, leaving her alone for hours at a time with minimal eye contact or touch. It was unbearable for the client, as a young child, to internalize a sense that her caretaker was flawed, thus she developed the more common narrative that she was flawed in some way—unworthy of being seen or known. The client never had her internal world reflected in an organized manner, which could have allowed for the development of a coherent and healthy sense of self. Instead, her needs for validation and healthy co-regulation were inconsistently met or not met at all. She did not experience others as trustworthy. Not surprisingly, her concerns in counseling revealed struggles with self-worth, emotional regulation, and interpersonal intimacy.

Raissa was able to share information about how our neural networks related to self and others develop in relationship to early caregivers' ways of responding to us and that those early experiences play a huge role in shaping our perceptions of self and others and automatic ways of responding to the world (Teicher et al., 2003; Twardosz & Lutzker, 2010). This information alone did not lead to spontaneous reorganization of thoughts, feelings, and behaviors; however, it was a starting place that fostered a renewed sense of curiosity and openness to a different way of knowing.

Increasing Compassion and Empathy

Another commonly cited goal of neuroeducation is increased compassion and empathy for self and others

(Badenoch, 2008, 2018; Cozolino, 2010, 2014; Fishbane, 2013; Miller & Barrio Minton, 2016; Siegel, 2012a). As individuals understand basic facts about the brain and nervous system, such as the ways the brain develops in response to experiences or the ways that perceived threat affects information processing, they are often able to loosen the grip of blame and shame. Siegel (2012a) stressed that clients realize "it's not my fault, but it is my responsibility" (p. 10–7) and begin developing curiosity about change from a foundation of kindness and acceptance toward themselves.

Raissa once worked with a young man who blamed himself for not effectively applying his newly learned cognitive therapy techniques in highly charged moments between him and his girlfriend. He reported feeling like he "couldn't even do therapy right" and was beginning to feel like there was something uniquely wrong with him that made him incapable of learning and changing. In an effort to help him develop more compassion for himself, Raissa introduced concepts about how the brain often functions under high stress. Raissa and her client explored how many of the skills he acquired in his traditional cognitive therapy required access to his prefrontal cortex. However, under acute stress, cerebral blood flow is redirected to other regions of the brain, inhibiting the functioning of the prefrontal cortex (Raio et al., 2013). In such moments, our brains begin to care more about survival, leaning on networks and functions in the midbrain and limbic regions rather than regions dominant in social engagement, executive functioning, long-term planning, or rational thought. Raissa suggested that in such moments, he was likely falling back on automatic implicit ways of responding that were adaptive and protective at some point in his life but were no longer as effective at getting him what he wanted in his present adult life. Raissa further shared details about information processing during times of acute stress, integrating Siegel's concept of "flipping your lid" (Siegel, 2012a). As this information was shared and discussed, the client's physical demeanor changed; his shoulders relaxed, his eyes softened, and his tone shifted from one of self-judgment to one of greater self-compassion. As he let go of some of the shame, he embraced new possibilities of change.

Normalizing Experience

A related use of neuroeducation is the normalization of experiences. Helping clients understand that their perceptions, feelings, thoughts, emotions, and behaviors make sense, given a particular set of experiences and typical neural functioning, can be quite validating. One particular experience that frequently needs to be normalized is the change process itself. Many clients, and many practitioners for that matter, expect change to occur quickly in counseling, especially when motivation is high, and insights seem to come readily. Although some changes may occur rapidly, especially in response to bottom-up interventions, such as those in accelerated resolution therapy (Kip et al., 2013), many changes take time and repetition. When clients struggle to consistently translate insight into sustained action, they can become discouraged. Understanding mechanisms of change in the brain, however, can offer more realistic expectations for how long it can take to establish lasting changes. Thus, individuals can foster a greater sense of patience and acceptance of the normal ups and downs of the process.

Raissa worked with a young adult woman who struggled with assertiveness in relationships. The client would often go into conversations determined to share her perspectives and give voice to her needs. Within seconds of being in the room with another person with whom she hoped to have a difficult conversation (e.g., her mother, her boyfriend, her boss), she began to feel shaky, sweat excessively, and lose any memory of what she planned to say. In counseling, initial work focused on soothing her physiological arousal, exploring past experiences that may have contributed to her current ways of thinking and feeling, and practicing high-pressure conversations, thus allowing her the opportunity to give voice to the ideas in her mind and heart for the first time. After being a regular client for a couple of months, one day, she did not show up for her appointment. She did not answer phone calls or emails. After a few attempts at contact, Raissa assumed she would never see her again. Then, a few months later, the client emailed and asked for an appointment. She shared that she had become discouraged with her progress, noting that the night before her session a few months prior, she had tried to stand up for herself to her boss, but after getting a couple of words out, her mind went completely blank, and she left the room humiliated. She said she decided counseling was not working for her. At this moment, Raissa realized that the client likely had unrealistic expectations of what it looked like to change largely automatic nervous system responses and ways of relating to others in high-conflict scenarios.

Raissa introduced the concept of brain plasticity, the various ways the brain changes in response to experiences throughout the life span (Sale et al., 2014). Raissa stressed that plasticity supported the idea that the brain can change but that the speed of that change is not always rapid, especially in adulthood. Raissa knew the client was a student at a local university, so she asked her to think of the walking paths often formed across campus where the grass is beaten down—so much so that there are grooves in the dirt from regular foot traffic. Raissa noted that students rarely make a conscious choice to follow a particular path; they just walk where everyone else before them has walked. It is almost automatic. After asking her to think of spots on campus where the landscaping crew was trying to reestablish grass and had even poured a new concrete path off to the side of the well-worn grass path, she pointed out that many students still used the old path, despite warning signs and a nice new path to the right. Raissa connected the client's narrative related to the well-used walking path to the functioning of the brain, specifically that the easiest and most automatic ways of responding form highly myelinated "paths" of neural networks in the brain and changing those paths takes a lot of time and a lot of repetition. Changing her body's response to stressful conversations would take much longer than a couple of months, but it was possible! This new information helped support her motivation to keep working in counseling.

You may be starting to see that many of the benefits of neuroeducation are connected. Closely linked with the concept of normalization and validation is the benefit of increased empowerment and hope for change. Many clients enter counseling with the implicit or explicit belief that how they are is how they will always be. There is also often a sense that their thoughts, feelings, and behaviors just "happen" and that they have no control over changing them. At a biological level, sometimes this notion is true. Breathing just happens, our eyes just blink, and sometimes we just feel the way we do. However, there are neuroscience-informed approaches, including neuroeducation, which can help automatic processes become more conscious and, as a consequence, regulated. By infusing concepts such as implicit memory or discussing ways they can strengthen prefrontal cortex functioning, clients can begin to envision and take ownership of a different future.

Raissa worked with a young adult female client with a complex developmental trauma history who struggled with emotion regulation. She described times of "falling apart" in which she would suddenly, often unexpectedly, become upset by something her romantic partner said or did. Once upset, she was inconsolable for hours and felt a sense of hopelessness that she would never be able to sustain a romantic relationship. She said she did not blame her previous partners for calling her "crazy" and eventually ending the relationship. In an effort to help the client explore what was likely going on in her moments of upset, Raissa introduced the concept of implicit memory. Raissa explored how our perceptions, behavioral impulses, and emotional responses largely operate below the level of conscious awareness (Baars & Gage, 2010). Raissa suggested that the times of upset were likely responses to her internal implicit world; some embodied memory was being touched (Badenoch, 2018). She was not at all crazy, but rather her responses were adaptive and protective in some way. Raissa assured her that she could gain insight into what was going on in her internal world and learn ways to recognize and develop more flexible ways of regulating her responses. Through this discussion, the client gained a new perspective on her experience and a new sense of hopefulness for her future.

Supporting Regulation

Yet another benefit of neuroeducation is enhanced regulation. Siegel (2010a) referred to the "name it to tame it" effect of understanding brain structures and functions in support of regulation. Many individuals experience some degree of immediate symptom relief from just identifying and naming what is going on in the moment. The act of categorizing and naming requires the concentrated work of the prefrontal cortex, often not the part of the brain that is dominant when we are experiencing states of dysregulation. For instance, when running from a threatening situation, we often do not stop to narrate our escape. Thus calling on that part of the brain to engage can help relieve some of the chaos. Giving some acknowledgment to an experience, such as "I am feeling really sad," or "I am feeling really frustrated," especially when met with an attuned, nonjudgmental listener, can lessen the intensity of the experience. Further, the act of bringing an experience into the realm of consciousness allows for greater response flexibility (Siegel, 2012b). Counselors can use physiological measures (e.g., galvanic skin response, heart rate variability, and so forth) to bring subjective experiences into objective awareness. Counselors can then teach clients strategies for affecting their physiological responses, giving them a greater sense of self-capability to regulate.

When thinking about this use of neuroeducation, we often think about our work with children and their families. Many parents are uncomfortable with emotion and engage in emotion dismissing, failing to help children acknowledge, label, and regulate internal experiences. Ignoring emotion, unfortunately, does not generally lead to positive health outcomes (Flynn et al., 2010; Katz et al., 2012). Raissa worked with one 9-year-old female who was brought to counseling after her teacher reported multiple incidences of bullying at school. In talking with the parents, Raissa learned that they viewed any expression of negative emotion as immature. Raissa approached the conversation about the value of emotions from a neuroscience lens, framing emotions as forms of information that originate from our bodies and subcortical regions of the brain for adaptive purposes. Raissa asked the parents to experiment with "name it to tame it" exercises in which they would help their child acknowledge and accept the experience of an emotion. Although the parents were skeptical, they appreciated the science behind the recommendation and were willing to give it a try. After a few weeks of experimenting with "name it to tame it," they reported that their child seemed more cooperative and less aggressive at school. They noted that their daughter still had occasional emotional outbursts, but that the bursts of emotion tended to dissipate more quickly when they were present with the emotional experience rather than dismissing and shaming.

Enhancing Engagement and Motivation

Lastly, neuroeducation can be useful for engaging clients in the therapeutic process, helping increase understanding of and motivation to follow counselors' clinical recommendations and/or treatment plans. Neuroscience can also lend a degree of credibility to approaches, as long as the neuroscience is accurate and not overstated, thus enhancing clients' belief in their ability to help and investment in following through with exercises. When thinking of neuroeducation in this manner, the popular quote, often attributed to Viktor Frankl, but whose author is actually unknown (Covey, 2008) seems relevant: "Between the stimulus and the response, there is a space and in that space lies our freedom and power to choose." Many people use this quote to champion the power of choice. We can see this use. We also know, however, that many of the people we work with in counseling have very little "space" between an activating event and an automatic way of responding. Certain recommendations we make in counseling, such as mindfulness, physical exercise, or even the therapeutic relationship itself, can greatly expand this "space." These types of experiences can help strengthen the middle-prefrontal cortex, an area of the brain that helps with emotion regulation, response flexibility, fear modulation, and other important functions (Sale et al., 2014). Information processing that influences our appraisals and actions occurs very quickly in the brain, within the realm of milliseconds. Although changes often only effect milliseconds of "space," such changes can mean the difference between dysregulated responses that have unwanted consequences and reflective responses that have more desired consequences. When clients and counselors talk about the purpose of interventions and recommendations from this perspective, clients often become more interested in figuring out a way to integrate such activities into their lives.

Raissa worked with a middle-aged male client who was mandated to counseling for a workplace-related offense. His insight regarding his role in the incident, as well as his motivation to participate in counseling, was very low. Raissa decided to approach the counseling experience from a wellness- versus pathology-oriented perspective. He did not seem interested in acknowledging or addressing particular symptoms, but he did express some curiosity when Raissa mentioned neuroscience-supported activities that enhance brain health. He noted that at the very least, he could learn something to help his young adult daughter be more successful. Raissa introduced the Healthy Mind Platter (Rock et al., 2012) and talked about the brain-based benefits of sleep, physical movement, internal reflection, focused and mastery-oriented tasks, downtime, spontaneous and novel activities, and felt-sense connection. Raissa and the client reviewed one of the components of the Healthy Mind Platter each week and developed goals and tracked progress in each area. A side benefit of using this neuroeducation approach was that the client developed trust in Raissa and the process and began to open up more about other areas of his life that were not going as well as he initially led Raissa to believe.

THERAPEUTIC NEUROSCIENCE EDUCATION LITERATURE

The mental health field is not the only discipline considering the potential uses of neuroeducation. Researchers in the fields of physical therapy and pain management have found positive outcomes associated with neuroscience education (e.g., Louw et al., 2011; Robins et al., 2016). Referred to as pain neuroscience education or therapeutic neuroscience education, such approaches to psychoeducation have been found to increase pain tolerance, regulate emotional responses to pain, and improve overall coping. Research in these fields has also revealed some potentially useful lessons for us to consider when using neuroeducation. Robins and colleagues (2016) highlighted the value of metaphors when teaching neuroscience concepts to patients and the usefulness of group approaches. The researchers also noted that neuroscience education is not always associated with positive outcomes, especially when used as a stand-alone intervention or when given in the form of informational booklets for patients to read on their own at home. As noted earlier, neuroeducation is more effective under certain conditions and when delivered with a process orientation. This process will be further elucidated in Chapter 2.

NEUROEDUCATION ATTITUDES AND INTENTIONS

There are certain attitudes and intentions that we have found helpful in facilitating the neuroeducation process. In Table 1.1, we consider the more and less helpful ways of being and focusing when engaging in neuroeducation with clients. These attitudes and intentions introduce the theoretical rationale, skills, and metaprinciples of neuroeducation that will be discussed in Chapter 2.

The more a neuroeducation exercise can help clients get a sense of the concept within their own bodies and minds the better. Similarly, the more an activity is personalized to the unique culture, developmental level, presenting concerns, experiences, and personhood of the client, the more likely it will seem relevant and useful to the client. You should also strive to keep the whole person in mind when talking about various neuroscience concepts. Although much of the neuroscience research takes a reductionistic perspective of nervous system functioning, our role as mental health professionals is to translate these findings in a way that honors the inherent complexity of human experience and expands the opportunities to intervene. Your decision about neuroeducation should be intentional, fitting with the client's here-and-now presentation, rather than being some interesting fact that you learned at a training or read in a book (like this one!). Neuroeducation is generally more impactful when it occurs spontaneously within a session rather than part of a pre-set agenda you bring into a session.

Further, neuroeducation should be approached from an exploratory lens rather than an absolute truth perspective. Although there are many new and promising discoveries coming out of neuroscience fields, the unknown far surpasses the known. It is also possible that many of the neuroscience concepts outlined in this book will have been expanded or revised during its publication. Therefore, it is both useful and accurate to be tentative in your approach to neuroscience discussions. Neuroeducation should be an exercise grounded in the therapeutic alliance, with clients having agency over the decision to learn about neuroscience and the choice about whether the information ends up being useful to them. Finally, neuroeducation should be approached from the perspective of honoring individuals' current ways of being, as well as acknowledging the adaptive and protective nature of brain and nervous system development and functioning.

TABLE 1.1

Less Helpful ⟵⟶	More Helpful
Disembodied	Embodied
Standardized	Contextualized
Universalized	Individualized
Reductionistic	Holistic
Arbitrary	Intentional
Dogmatic	Hypothesis driven
Unilateral	Collaborative
Predetermined	Emergent
Judgment	Appreciation
Critical	Compassionate

CLOSING THOUGHTS

In this chapter, we introduced the concept of neuroeducation and its application in counseling and psychotherapy. We hope this chapter has sparked your curiosity to learn about the neuroeducation process and exercises that are reviewed in the following chapters. It can certainly be exciting to have information to offer clients that helps reduce judgment, enhance hopefulness, and improve motivation. Neuroeducation is not a panacea to all client concerns, however. As you read the remainder of this book, consider your past personal or professional experiences and how each exercise could have been applied to help enhance some element of the change process. Brainstorm how the concepts in this text can inform your work with current and future clients. Finally, consider how these concepts can influence your own future development as a person and practitioner. As we move forward in the book, we will dive deeper into the process orientation of neuroeducation, as well as some guidelines to consider for the ethical and effective translation of neuroscience principles into clinical practice.

REFLECTION QUESTIONS

1. What are your initial thoughts about neuroeducation—appreciations, concerns?
2. Think of a current or former client who could have potentially benefited from the use of neuroeducation. What would you have shared with the client and why?
3. What barriers might impede your engagement in neuroeducation? What could you do to lessen the barrier(s)?

CREDITS

Fig. 1.1: Copyright © 2016 Depositphotos/pressmaster.
Fig. 1.2: Copyright © 2012 Depositphotos/lightsource.

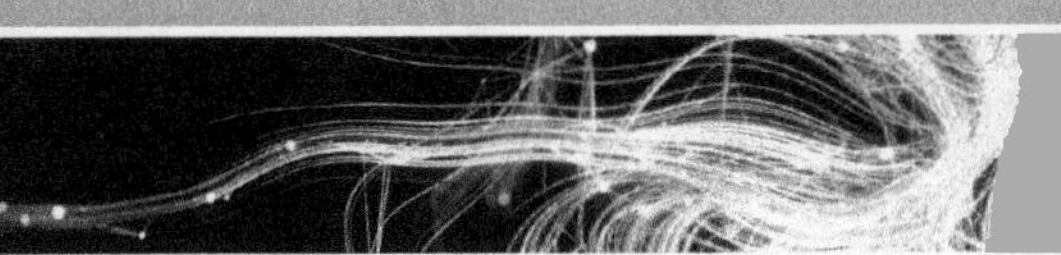

CHAPTER 2

Facilitating the Neuroeducation Process

Theory, Skills, and Metaprinciples

CHAPTER OBJECTIVES

1. Understand the theoretical framework guiding the implementation of the neuroeducation process.
2. Describe how microskill paradigms are used in the facilitation of the neuroeducation process.
3. Recognize ethical and multicultural principles relevant to the facilitation of the neuroeducation process.

INTRODUCTION

In this chapter, we build upon the uses of neuroeducation and the attitudes and intentions of such uses discussed in Chapter 1. We offer a theoretical framework to guide neuroeducation interventions and review microskills that will be necessary for the effective application of neuroeducation exercises. We end the chapter with a review of metaprinciples that includes attention to cultural and ethical considerations.

A Common Factors Theoretical Framework

What makes counseling and therapy work? What leads to the life-changing experiences that we have witnessed in our therapeutic work? These questions have been the source of much debate. Whether it be evidence-based treatments, empirically supported treatments, specific ingredients, or common factors, it is clear that therapy works, but our understanding of how these changes happen, for which clients, and under what conditions continues to evolve. These questions are also important to consider during the neuroeducation process. What accounts for the potential effectiveness of neuroeducation? Is it the neuroscience information itself? Insight? The process? Or something else?

Several books (e.g., *The Heart and Soul of Change: Delivering What Works in Therapy, The Great Psychotherapy Debate: The Evidence for What Makes Psychotherapy Work*) and empirical research (e.g., Orlinsky et al., 2004) have provided commentary on the mechanisms of effective therapy. One method of understanding the mechanisms of change in therapy is referred to as the common factors approach. The common factors approach explores the most influential factors contributing to effective therapy regardless of theoretical orientation or specific treatment paradigm. For instance, a counselor operating from a predominantly cognitive behavioral approach compared to a counselor operating from a primarily psychodynamic approach may both achieve similar therapeutic outcomes. Does this mean that cognitive behavioral and psychodynamic approaches are equally effective?

Proponents of a common factors approach (e.g., Frank & Frank, 1993; Laska et al., 2014; Wampold, 2001) contend that the creation of common factors leads to the positive outcomes, rather than the specific theoretical approach alone. Counselors serve as process experts to facilitate the emergence of common factors in clinical work. Neuroeducation fits well within a common factors model because of its transtheoretical nature. For instance, you might find neuroeducation helpful whether you align with a cognitive behavioral, psychodynamic, or any other theoretical approach. A cognitive behavioral therapist might use neuroeducation to explore the neuroscience of learning and neuroplasticity to promote hope and belief in the power of therapeutic strategies. A psychodynamic therapist might use neuroeducation to explore the neuroscience of early attachments as a means to help clients enhance new attachment patterns and interpersonal satisfaction. The process is bidirectional; neuroeducation can help foster the common factors, and the common factors can aid in the effectiveness of the neuroeducation process. Therefore, we use a common factors approach as a metaframework guiding the implementation of the neuroeducation process (see Table 2.1 for a complete review of the neuroeducation implications of each common factor).

A complete review of the common factors literature is outside the scope of this text. As noted earlier, entire books have already been written about this topic (e.g., Duncan et al., 2011). However, a brief review of the most influential common factors and an emerging model to integrate each into therapy is discussed next. Although several common factors and specific ingredients of effective therapy have been proposed, extensive research has shown that the most influential common factors, from largest to smallest, are goal consensus/collaboration, empathy, alliance, positive regard/affirmation, congruence, genuineness, cultural adaptation of evidence-based treatments, and expectations (Wampold, 2015). These common factors are to therapy as the myelin sheath is to proper nervous system functioning; they aid in the flow of energy from one to another.

TABLE 2.1

Common Factor	Neuroeducation Implication
Goal Consensus/ Collaboration	Neuroeducation is never prescribed or dictated by the counselor. Neuroeducation is presented at the behest of the people being served, which begins a collaborative meaning-making process that compares the neuroeducation information to their past experiences, current challenges/opportunities, and future desires.
Empathy	Empathy is crucial to neuroeducation. Neuroeducation rests on the ability to see another person's experience as they see it rather than how the counselor sees it, reflect this perception, and then share in the emotional experience that follows.
Alliance	Neuroeducation requires an understanding of the potential threats posed by a therapeutic relationship. Therefore, it is essential to foster safe neuroception that drives the therapeutic alliance necessary for the neuroeducation process, and then the neuroeducation process further depends on the therapeutic relationship in which both are affected by one another.
Positive Regard/ Affirmation	Neuroeducation is not about accurate assimilation of knowledge. Rather, it is about exploring what information means within the client's unique developmental and cultural history. In this way, the process is affirmed as clients move closer to the therapeutic gains they desire.
Congruence	Neuroeducation requires the counselor to maintain a balance between their internal experiences and external behaviors. This congruence fosters the neuroeducation process and the synchrony between counselor and client.
Genuineness	Neuroeducation comes from a place of hope to benefit the client's life. Rather than one person holding knowledge and power and bestowing it on another, neuroeducation employs the egalitarian pursuit of knowledge and meaning.
Cultural Adaptation	Neuroeducation, to some degree, is transcultural, although the meaning made from the process is directly linked to and affects the cultural history and intersectionality of the client. In addition, neuroeducation must include metaphors, images, etc., that are culturally aware.
Expectations	Expectations shape experience with neuroeducation, and neuroeducation shapes expectations moving forward. As expectations are explored, processed, and made use of, this bidirectional nature enhances each.

The contextual model (Wampold, 2015; Wampold & Budge, 2012; Wampold & Imel, 2015) has been proposed as an integrated framework to merge historical contexts of healing with decades of psychotherapy research and explain the common factors and pathways to therapeutic outcomes (see Figure 2.1). In therapy, the client and therapist create a two-person ecosystem and an even more complex system in relationship, couples, and family work. Regardless, the first goal is to develop an initial therapeutic relationship. Clients bring first-person accounts of the situations that prompted their visit to therapy and through interactions with the therapist, an initial therapeutic relationship emerges. This initial therapeutic relationship is a prerequisite to three pathways to therapeutic outcomes in the contextual model: (1) development of the real relationship, (2) creation of expectations, and (3) enactment of adaptive change.

The creators of the contextual model (Wampold, 2015; Wampold & Budge, 2012; Wampold & Imel, 2015) describe each component in eloquent detail as paraphrased next. The therapeutic relationship is described as both a top-down (e.g., evaluation of expertise) and bottom-up (e.g., transference, cultural norms) phenomenon that consists of implicit processes and explicit appraisals of various therapist characteristics (e.g., office, dress, nonverbals). This initial rapport enables the ***real relationship***, which is characterized by elements of social connectedness, mutual commitment, secure attachment, norms, and complex empathy. Geller and Porges (2014) added depth to the understanding of the real relationship by identifying neurophysiological mechanisms underlying therapists' ability to foster sufficient safety for components of the real relationship to emerge. They highlighted the role of therapists' embodied presence in supporting clients' *neuroception* of safety.

Grounded in the real relationship, the therapist aims to *cultivate expectations* and hopes that the client will be able to cope and solve problems during therapeutic sessions and that these experiences will translate to independent resolution outside of therapeutic sessions. The creation of expectations also includes an exploration of clients' first-person accounts of what led to their presentation in therapy. As we know, this initial conceptualization is often the tip of the iceberg, and the creators of the contextual model suggest this initial conceptualization is sometimes maladaptive and informed by popular press adaptations of neuroscience. If client conceptualizations lead to more challenges (e.g., I heard my brain is broken, and that is why I will never have a relationship), then to create expectations, an alternative hypothesis (e.g., experiences in early relationships influenced the development of my nervous system and the way I engage in relationships), along with a structure to address the reasons for therapy (e.g., specific ingredients of theoretical techniques), must be developed. This new conceptualization and proposed methods of healing leads to self-efficacy, the mutual creation and acceptance of goals and tasks, and collaboration toward activities that will bring those expectations to life.

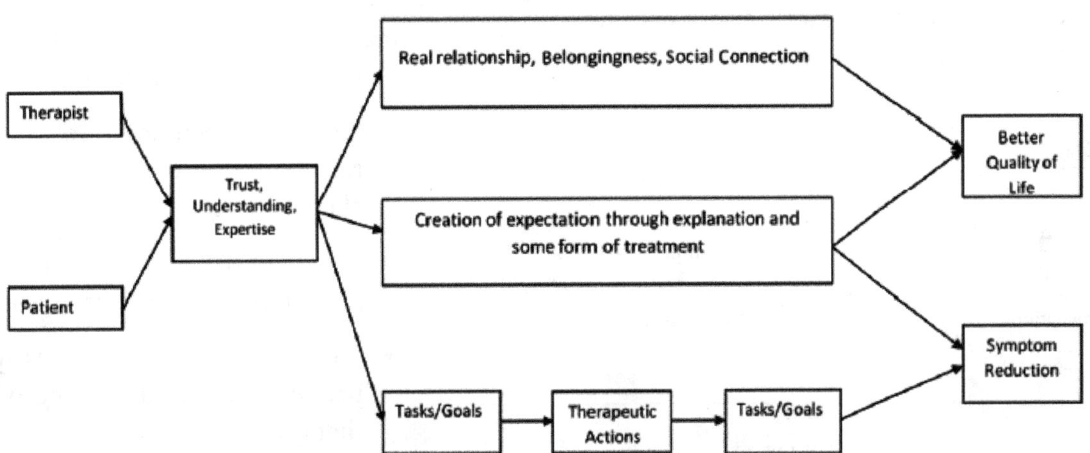

FIGURE 2.1 The Emphasis on the Therapeutic Relationship Within the Contextual Model

Although expectations are valuable, the creators of the contextual model affirm that expectations alone are likely not curative, and the development of *healthy adaptive behaviors* and tasks are necessary to foster therapeutic outcomes. The specific change behaviors use theoretical approaches (e.g., a Gestalt approach might develop somatic awareness and integration with other perceptual levels of awareness) as an organizing structure, but the promotion of the common factors with the goal of wellness remains primary. For example, a Gestalt approach alone will likely be less effective if delivered without consensus, collaboration, empathy, positive regard, congruence, or cultural adaptation.

The contextual model serves as a guide for the implementation of the neuroeducation activities in this book (see Figure 2.2). The initial therapeutic relationship and a sound assessment of the client's perception of the world, themselves, and the reason for presenting in therapy must be fully evaluated using a holistic biopsychosocial model. Microskills are used to explore the client's narrative and build basic trust, as well as foster co-regulation and a neuroception of safety. Once basic trust is established in the therapeutic relationship, then neuroeducation can continue as a method to promote the real relationship, establish expectations, and promote new ways of being. It should be noted that this process is not linear, and the neuroeducation process is recursive throughout the course of therapy. During the entire therapeutic process, neuroeducation might continue as the relationship deepens, new constructed narratives evolve to give meaning to client experiences and promote expectancy for outcomes, and more changes occur, thus promoting human development and wellness.

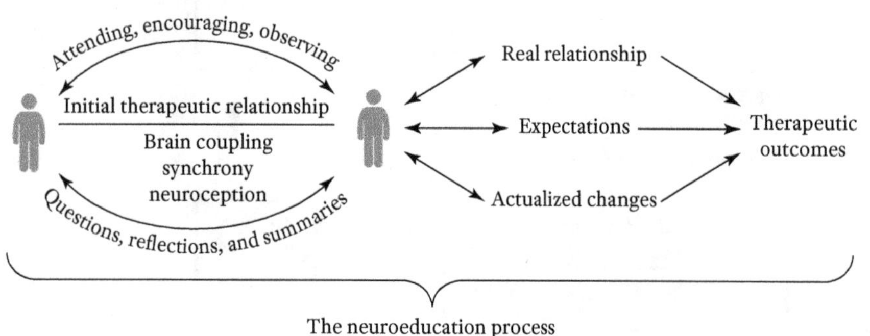

FIGURE 2.2 The Neuroeducation Process Is Informed by the Contextual Model

One closing note is important when considering neuroeducation. Neuroeducation should not be considered a silver bullet or an intervention delivered in isolation of the broader therapeutic process. Rather, neuroeducation is a strategy designed to promote the common factors inherent to the process of effective therapeutic work across disciplines and theoretical orientations. Within the context of a sound therapeutic relationship, neuroeducation is one method to promote expectations and foster adaptive changes.

Using a common factors approach provides a theoretical rationale for the process of neuroeducation. Grounded in this model, we offer the following guidelines for engaging in the neuroeducation exercises that you will find in this book:

- Cultivate a trusting secure base in the therapeutic relationship that is grounded in empathy, collaboration, positive regard, affirmation, congruence, genuineness, and flexibility.
- Elicit clients' narratives of the reasons for counseling and psychotherapy.
- Introduce the neuroeducation exercise as a means of exploring their first-person accounts and theories of their challenges and achievements.
- Promote collaboration and agreement in the goals and tasks of the neuroeducation exercise.
- Be culturally and developmentally responsive.
- Present the neuroeducation exercise tentatively with neurohumility.
- Use microskills to facilitate clients' discovery and meaning making regarding the neuroeducation in relation to previous conceptualizations.
- Ensure the creation of a coherent narrative of the process that translates to clients' lives.
- Evaluate the process using formal and informal methods as appropriate.
- Continue neuroeducation as appropriate throughout the course of therapy.

MICROSKILLS

The common factors approach provides a metaframework to guide the neuroeducation process. *Microskills*, defined as the "behavioral foundations of intentional counseling and psychotherapy" (Ivey et al., 2018, p. 11), are the means—the specific tools—that contribute to successful engagement in the neuroeducation process and promotion of the common factors. Depending on your training, these microskills might have been referred to as active listening skills, basic counseling skills, or some other nomenclature, but no matter the name, these are the basic microcommunication strategies (e.g., reflection, attending) that facilitate the therapeutic process, regardless of theoretical orientation.

There is evidence to suggest that microskills support healthy nervous system functioning. For instance, functional magnetic resonance imaging research has shown that active listening can activate reward and positive valence systems in the brain (Kawamichi et al., 2015), and counselors who use microskills more skillfully are able to promote regulation in their clients by increasing parasympathetic nervous system activity (e.g., Kiema et al., 2014; Kleinbub, 2017). Beckes and Coan's (2011) research found that accompaniment (i.e., being in a relationship with an attuned other) inhibited the body's threat response, including the release of stress hormones and other signs of sympathetic activation. Using a sound microskill paradigm will assist in the process of neuroeducation and reduce the chances of misuse.

Although many microskill paradigms exist, we recommend the framework created by Ivey et al. (2018). This framework outlines the therapeutic process (e.g., build an empathic relationship, elicit a story and strengths, identify goals, restory, and action), as well as the microskills that facilitate this process (see Figure 2.3).

We appreciate this model because of its emphasis on the neuroscience and multicultural applications of basic microskills. Next, we describe the proposed microskill hierarchy that you can use to facilitate the neuroeducation process that is adapted from Ivey et al.'s (2018) basic listening sequence (see Figure 2.4). This process includes several skills: questions, encouragers, reflections, and summarizations. Within this sequence, attending and observation skills are used throughout. Each microskill is explained in more detail next and summarized in Table 2.2.

Attending

Attending skills in therapy and in the neuroeducation process provide the foundation for the therapeutic relationship to evolve. A number of scholars have expanded our understanding of the importance of attending from a neuroscience perspective (Geller

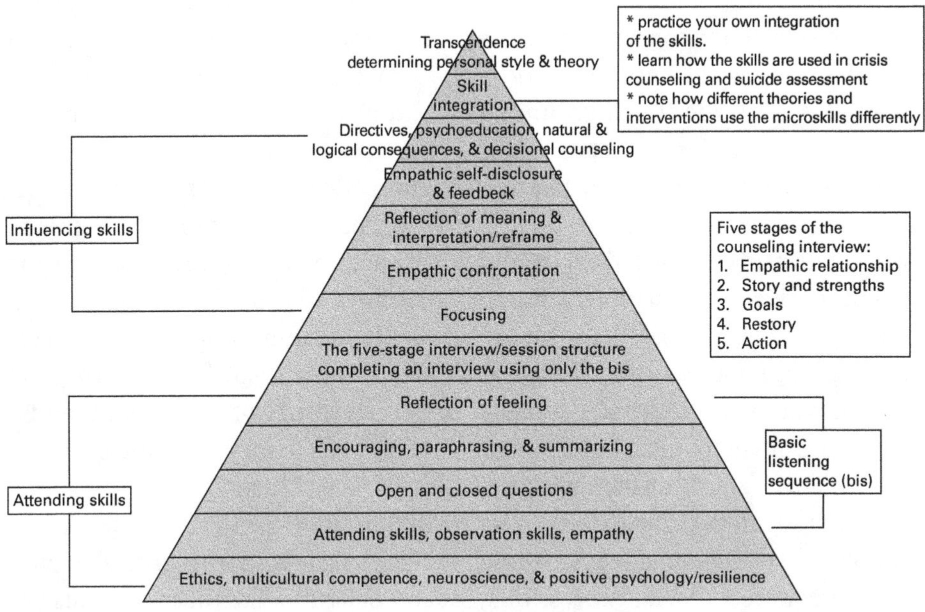

FIGURE 2.3 The Microskills Hierarchy

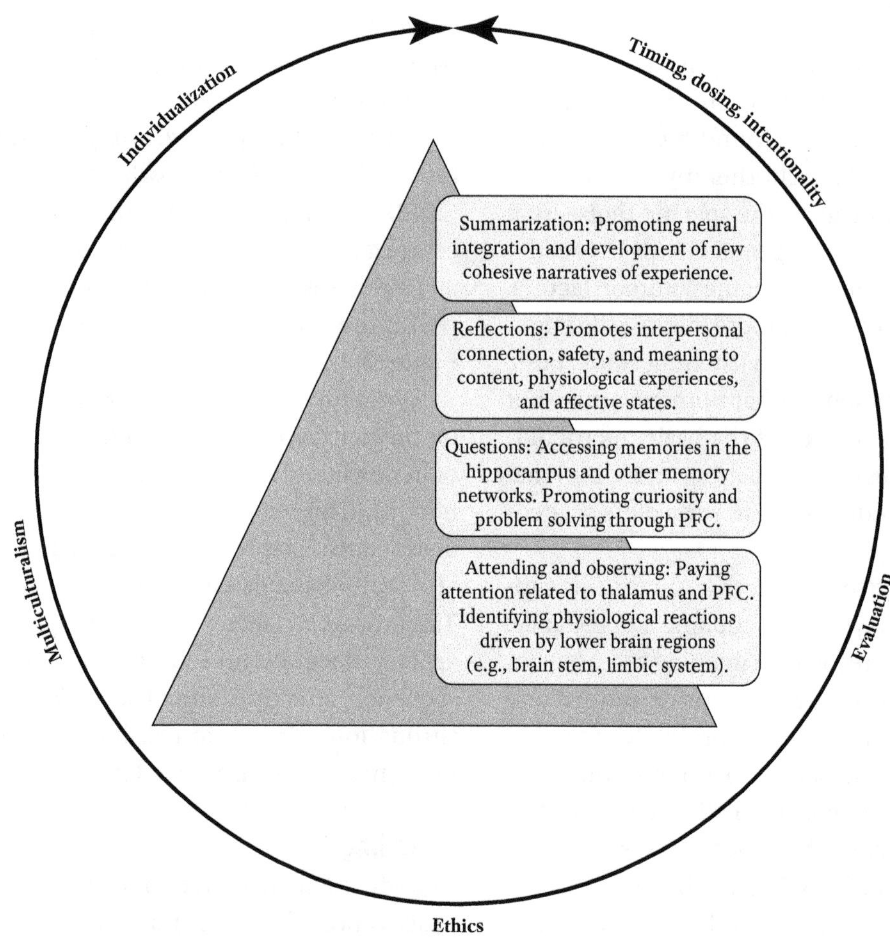

FIGURE 2.4 As You Work Your Way Up the Microckills Pyramid, You Will Need to Consider the Neuroinformed Purpose As Well As How Each Metaprinciple Informs Your Intentional Application

& Porges, 2014; Kleinbub, 2017; Schore, 2014). These authors highlight the role of nonconscious physiological processes in facilitating felt-sense connection. Unobservable attending attitudes (e.g., grounded presence, open receptivity) are just as important as observable behavioral manifestations of attending (e.g., eye contact, open posture). In fact, we contend that if you work on cultivating internal attending capacities, you will not have to worry very much about external attending behaviors. When you are truly present, curious, and open to clients' experiences in the moment, your behaviors will naturally convey such interest and intent to meaningfully connect. Koole and Tschacher's (2016) conceptualization seems to capture both the internal and external foci of attending. They discussed therapeutic synchrony at three levels: movement (e.g., facial expressions, breathing patterns, eye gaze), alliance (e.g., shared language, I-sharing, and affective co-regulation), and emotion (e.g., explicit and implicit self-regulation).

Attending attitudes and behaviors promote synchrony with your clients, in which you begin to mirror your clients, and they begin to mirror you. Hasson and colleagues (Hasson et al., 2012) talked about the idea of brain-to-brain coupling, noting that the connection of two brains allows for the emergence of states that neither person could have obtained alone. In counseling, we see this as the therapeutic relationship fostering a secure base that allows for the emergence of new insights and the development of new regulatory capacities.

Observation

Observation is another critical microskill. Our observable behaviors and those of clients provide insight into the underlying functioning of the nervous system.

TABLE 2.2

The Neuroeducation Microskill Pyramid

Microskill	Domain	Skill
Attending Skills	Attitude	Be open, curious, respectful, humble, and congruent.
	Movement synchrony	Connect and regulate with your client's facial expressions, breathing patterns, eye gaze, and posture.
	Verbal synchrony	Develop a shared language in a tone and words that incorporate I-statements or your experiences in the session.
	Emotional regulation	Promote your own self-regulation to couple with the client's and co-regulate one another.
Observation	Evidence of sympathetic activation	Notice physiological hyperarousal, such as perspiration, pupil dilation, accelerated heartbeat, chest breaths, psychomotor agitation, and sweaty/cold hands.
	Evidence of parasympathetic activation	Notice physiological hypoarousal, such as pupil constriction, decelerated heartbeat, belly breaths, resting psychomotor activity, and warm hands.
	Observe with technology	Consider observing with peripheral technological measures of physiological activation, including heart rate, skin temperature, and galvanic skin response, among others.
	Provide feedback	Notice and wonder aloud about the potential meaning in these observations using a new brand of immediacy.
Questions	Open	Use more open questions to promote exploration of the client's experiences (e.g., what, how, can you tell me more).
	Closed	Use closed questions to clarify content or express hesitancy in your statements (e.g., is, are, do).
	Memory and connections of present to past	Use past-oriented questions (What was that like for you? How does what we have been talking about compare to your past experiences? What does this remind you of? What's familiar about this process?).
	Attention and awareness of the process	Use present-oriented questions (As we talk about this, what is it like for you now? What are you noticing about yourself right now? In the past it was this way, what is it like for you now?).
	Planning and creating meaning	Use future-oriented questions (What will it be like for you later? What does this mean for you moving forward? How will this experience impact your life moving forward?)
Reflections	Basic structure	I hear you saying that... (insert domain of experience). Am I close?
	Content	Sounds like you have experienced many traumas in your life.
	Emotion—physiological	I heard you describe this tightness in your throat, and I see you get choked up when talking about your experience.
	Feeling—cognitive label	Sounds like you are connecting to this fear in a very physical way.
	Meaning	It seems like to you this fear means that you are defective and will never achieve the expectations that your family has set for you.
Summarizing	Connecting all domains of experience to promote neural integration	Can we recap a few things that I have experienced so far? I listened to the story of your trauma and the events surrounding them (content). I have noticed your throat tighten up and your gaze avert when discussing these details (emotion, behaviors), almost as if you were outside of yourself (observation of sympathetic arousal/ emotion), and you named this as a common reaction to fear and terror (cognitive feeling label). Now it seems like you are paralyzed (extreme sympathetic arousal leading to a shutdown/immobility) in a place of uncertainty regarding your ability to meet the demands of your family and culture (meaning). Am I tracking that closely?

If the sympathetic nervous system is activated, the pupils might dilate, heartbeats could accelerate, breaths might come from the upper chest, and the legs might bounce up and down. If the parasympathetic nervous system is activated, the pupils might constrict, heartbeats slow down, breaths might come from the abdomen, and legs might come to a rest. The operation of these functions is generally outside of conscious control.

Imagine that you had to consciously remind your heart to beat faster or the kidneys to secrete epinephrine when you needed to escape a dangerous situation? What would happen?

Well, you probably would not be around to tell us about this experience because the functions of the autonomic nervous system (ANS) are generally automatic to promote quick responses for survival. Much of what is observable in therapy can be traced back to physiological functioning throughout the nervous system. Observations provide us with insight into the potentially subconscious experiences of our clients that are generated by implicit associations in the subcortical brain networks and even into the body through the vagus nerve. As this unconscious material seeps into the observable world through behaviors such as leg bouncing, shallow breaths, flushed faces, or even tears, we gain a clearer insight into the lived experience of our clients and their physiological functioning. This makes observation a critical skill for understanding, attending to, and responding to the client's experience.

Although adaptive initially, the ANS can sometimes become unbalanced. This is especially true in times of chronic stressors and trauma when the sympathetic branch promotes heightened arousal, which makes dysregulation more common. This activation of our ANS often happens so quickly that by the time we are aware of dysregulation, it is generally too late to intervene. For instance, if we encounter a bear when camping, we are likely running before we have a chance to think about it. In a clinical setting, if clients unintentionally encounter traumatic material or transfer insecure attachment figures onto us, they likely engage protective systems (e.g., dissociation) or become quickly dysregulated before they have a chance to think about it. What if we could observe these physiological reactions before they became dysregulated? What if clients could notice the activation of the sympathetic nervous system prior to entering a mode of fight, flight, or freeze?

Thankfully, technological advances in therapy have provided additional means of collecting observational data. Various professional (e.g., BrainMaster Discovery—https://www.brainmaster.com/) and home use devices (e.g., Muse headsets—https://choosemuse.com/) provide clinicians with peripheral measures of ANS functioning, such as electroencephalography, galvanic skin response, and skin temperature that can identify physiological arousal before it is observable to the counselor and client. Using technological methods of observation brings these preconscious reactions into the room sooner, prior to the dysregulation that could follow. This therapeutic exchange provides an opportunity to infuse the neuroeducation exercises that you will find later in this text.

Regardless of whether you are using technological or nontechnological forms of observation, the skill is critical to not only assess but also regulate the client's physiological arousal during the neuroeducation process. We can use our observation skills to identify potential areas of the client's story to explore further, assess the effect of the intervention, and improve our timing and dosing (two concepts that are discussed further next). As we provide feedback to our clients through the skill of immediacy (e.g., I noticed your galvanic skin response increased; I noticed you averted your gaze), we enhance the neuroeducation process while also promoting the common factors of effective therapy and eventual self-regulation. We also use observation to notice when clients are not benefiting from the neuroeducation exercise. Perhaps their eyes glaze over with boredom or confusion. Perhaps their levels of emotional arousal increase beyond the point that new learning is taking place. In such instances, you should abandon the neuroeducation process and reconnect with clients' here-and-now needs. In doing so, you promote collaboration in the process of neuroeducation.

Questions

Appropriate use of questions can be a tricky microskill to learn: too many questions and the client feels interrogated, too few questions and you may find the back-and-forth dialogue becoming stalled, and/or you may miss eliciting key details from the client's story. In truth, little research exists on the effect of questions on the therapeutic encounter. In general, open questions (e.g., what and how) are most helpful to promote longer disclosures, and closed questions (e.g., is, are) are useful to elicit shorter disclosures of very specific clarifying information. Sklare et al. (1985) provided a foundational model to evaluate types of questions in counseling. In their model, the most effective questions are those that promote exploration (Could you tell me more about...?), understanding (What is that experience like for you?), and action (What would it be like if you had more control of this reaction?). In addition, previous research (Bishop & Fish,1999) has also found that clients preferred solution-focused questions (What is life like when you believe yourself to be at your best?) to Socratic and diagnostic questions.

Questions have an effect on various functions of the nervous system. In general, questions activate the systems responsible for memory (past oriented—what was that like for you then?), attention (present oriented—what is it like for you as you talk about it now?), and planning/decision making (future oriented—what will it be like for you in the future?). Questions can help engage the cognitive cortical regions of the brain and sometimes promote regulation in the ANS. Questions can also aid in self-awareness and reflection as we ask clients to reflect on the process of therapy.

As with all interventions, questions are best used with intention. Past-oriented questions can promote connections between the client's past experiences to the current information being experienced in the neuroeducation process (How does what we have been talking about relate to your past experiences?). Present-oriented questions can help the client reflect on the process (As we talk through this, how are you doing?) and create new memories that edit old ones (In the past, you said you had no control, what is it like for you now?). Future-oriented questions can help the client capitalize on the gains in neuroeducation by collaboratively setting tasks for future application in the client's world (e.g., now that we have had this experience, what does this mean for you moving forward?). As you use questions intentionally during the neuroeducation process, you can help clients realize the expectations created in the early phases of treatment as well as plan for and practice new ways of fostering a sense of wellness.

Reflections

If you look in a mirror, what do you see? Well, unless you are at a carnival looking in one of those distorted mirrors, you will likely see a clear reflection of yourself, at least visually. In the therapeutic process, we act as mirrors for our clients that not only attend to their experiences but also begin to reflect them to the client, thus promoting more synchrony and the real relationship.

The skill of reflection is a process in which we can communicate our empathic understanding to our clients. The nonverbal attunement increases the connection between client and counselor, and the verbal responses continue to deepen the relationship. Although most microskill paradigms focus on the reflection of content (paraphrasing), feeling (e.g., sad, angry), and meaning (e.g., values, valence, salience, appraisals), we contend that this might not capture the complexity of the client experience, specifically in the domain of affect.

Affective neuroscience has made significant contributions to our understanding of constructs such as feeling and emotion. Much debate exists regarding the definition of affect, emotion, and feeling (e.g., LeDoux & Hofmann, 2018), and even though the evidence is not conclusive, it is clear that multiple components (e.g., physiological, cognitive, spiritual, social) make up the human experience of an affect. Therefore, words like "fear" alone might not capture the totality of one's affective experience. Some research suggests (e.g., Montag & Panksepp, 2017), that physiological experiences (i.e., emotion) arise first and are then evaluated via multiple pathways in the brain and given a name (i.e., feeling). The social construction of words such as "feeling" and "emotion" leads to some inconsistency, but what remains true is that there is a need to reflect all levels of the client's experience. Therefore, during the neuroeducation process, it is important to engage all levels of the client story through reflection: content, emotion (physiological experiences), feeling, and meaning.

When facilitating the neuroeducation process, a simple formula, such as, "I hear you saying that (insert content, behavior, emotion, feeling, or meaning), am

I close?," can suffice, although the need for the final checkout of your understanding is a matter of timing and intentionality based on how much confidence and connection you want to show. This formula provides the basic building blocks of verbal connection that will later be integrated with well-formed summaries. As we track and attend to the client's holistic experience leading up to therapy and during the neuroeducation process, we foster the real relationship driving therapeutic outcomes. Depending on the phase of treatment and using clinical judgment and intentionality, the reflections should occur at a higher frequency than questions, especially early in the development of the initial therapeutic rapport and the real relationship.

Summarizing

The final microskill we would like to address is summarizing. Many client challenges, especially those related to traumatic experiences, include some elements of disruption in the memory encoding process (e.g., Bisby et al., 2018; Lee et al., 2017). The process of reactivation of the old memories before reconsolidating and reconstructing them into a new coherent narrative is critical to most treatments of trauma and fear-based memories (Welling, 2012). In many ways, the construction of a coherent narrative is important to develop neural integration and psychological well-being. The skill of summarization is one method to promote the development of such a coherent narrative.

Whereas the structure of the summary is identical to a reflection (e.g., as we have been talking, I have heard connections between ...), the length and intention is different. A summary helps the client see the integration of all levels of their story (e.g., content, behavior, emotion, feeling, and meaning). When old memories are activated during therapy and the neuroeducation process, regular summaries help connect the pieces of the coherent narrative that is evolving. As we offer well-timed and intentional summaries, the narrative of the client becomes coherent and well-formed, helping the client see patterns, make meaning, and consider changes.

Influencing Skills

The basic microskills provide counselors and therapists with foundational skills that aid in the development of the real relationship essential to the organizing framework for neuroeducation. This alone can promote therapeutic change. In addition, Ivey et al. (2018) propose more direct skills, which they call influencing skills that go beyond active listening to promote creative change. Two of these influencing skills, information sharing and interpretation/reframe, fit well within the contextual model that serves as a guiding framework for neuroeducation.

Reflection of meaning helps us identify the existing conceptualization that clients have for the challenges that brought them to therapy and their expectations for how change will occur. Interpretation/reframe often uses some theoretical lens to make sense of clients' experiences and offers a new theory of who they are, who they desire to be, and how they will pursue the things that are most important to them. Various neuroeducation exercises can be used as a framework guiding the interpretation of the client's presenting challenges and perhaps reframe the preexisting conceptualization that brought the client to counseling. Some clients enter counseling believing that they are the only one to blame for their challenges, and using neuroeducation (e.g., impact of trauma on stress response system) as an interpretation/reframe skill could shift the preexisting narrative of shame and guilt to a narrative that includes a variety of internal and external contributing factors, thus opening up to various methods of intervention to aid in their pursuit of what's important to them. This aids in cultivating expectations and hope that are essential to the contextual model reviewed earlier in this chapter. As referenced in the contextual model, the expectations alone are often not curative, and some adaptive behavioral tasks and collaborative tasks often follow in the pursuit of therapeutic goals. Therefore, Ivey et al. (2018) advocate for information sharing related to stress management techniques (e.g., biofeedback, imagery) and therapeutic lifestyle changes (e.g., exercise, nutrition) to aid in therapeutic outcomes. Neuroeducation exercises then become a strategy to explore this information and promote therapeutic outcomes.

METAPRINCIPLES

In addition to the common factors and basic microskills, there are a few metaprinciples to consider during the neuroeducation process: individualization, timing, dosing, intentionality, evaluation, ethics, and multicultural considerations. Each metaprinciple will be further explored in the following sections and summarized in Table 2.3.

Individualization

Have you ever tried a technique with one client, and it worked beautifully but then tried the same technique with another client, and it fell flat? We certainly have, and this has been especially true for our infusion of neuroeducation. Eric (the co-editor of this text) remembers one case in which neuroeducation was used to discuss the physiological "set point" within the ANS with a client having panic attacks at school. The client quickly said to Eric, "You sound like my biology teacher." This response specificity underscores the importance of neuroeducation to be individualized to the client. Clients are diverse and come with unique worldviews, developmental histories, and cultural identities. Therefore, our skills need to be consistent with clients' unique selves, linguistic systems, and developmental levels. The use of neuroeducation with an 8-year-old will look different than neuroeducation with a 54-year-old client who is also a neuroscientist.

In all neuroeducation, there should be an attempt to use the client's language and customs to ground the activity. For instance, if the client is a mechanic, then neuroeducation can be grounded in the construction and functioning of motor vehicles. Even though you might present concepts to your client, it is important to ask the client to connect these concepts to their lived experience (In what ways have you

TABLE 2.3

Metaprinciples	
Individualization	Be patient and flexible, remembering that what works with one might fail with another.
	Be consistent and capitalize on the client's beliefs, values, development, language systems, customs, hobbies, etc.
	Use metaphors that align with the client's natural ability (e.g., if the client is a baseball player, then use baseball-related imagery).
Timing, dosing, and intentionality	Ensure that you have enough context about the client's history to identify how their story relates to specific neuroeducation activities. Use it sparingly with intentionally and purpose while checking in with your client throughout.
Evaluation	Evaluate the process by eliciting client feedback (How are we doing? How is this process working for you so far? How is the relationship? When were we more/less connected?).
	Evaluate the outcomes with formal and informal methods as well as tracking the generalization of changes and benefits outside of the session.
Ethics	Ensure that the neuroeducation falls within your competency level and scope of practice. Consider bringing in outside resources (e.g., videos, websites) and using the process to facilitate the exploration of this experience.
	Beware of neuromyths and the seductive allure of neuroscience information.
	Value the client's ultimate authority and autonomy by collaborating throughout.
	Be tentative and honor the evolving nature of neuroscience research.
Multiculturalism	Be aware of and explore the effect of social injustices on the client's current experiences.
	Use your own physiological reactions as a potential indicator of biases.
	Appreciate and capitalize on the universality of some neuroscience principles (e.g., physiological responses to threat), as well as the uniqueness that each person brings to the therapeutic encounter.

seen this process in your life?). For example, after discussing myelination of neurons, the mechanic might make the connection to oil in the vehicle. The vehicle analogy then becomes the foundation for future neuroeducation that originated from the client's unique experience. As Field et al. (2017) state, it is important to distill concepts without diluting the accuracy or power in the neuroeducation concept being used.

Timing, Dosing, and Intentionality

You have heard the adages "everything has a time and a place" and "everything in moderation." These statements remind us of some key principles in therapeutic interventions. The timing, dosing, and intentionality (e.g., Gibson & Tantam, 2018; Lee et al., 2017; Levitt et al., 2016) are just as important as the actual delivery of the skill. The timing of the intervention and its dose and intention are often factors that can separate the more from the less effective use of a specific skill. For instance, research suggests that immediacy promotes more collaboration later in the counseling session as opposed to earlier (Li et al., 2016). These findings are especially relevant given the emphasis on the process and physiological orientation of neuroeducation.

All neuroeducation should follow the creation of the initial rapport, a complete biopsychosocial assessment, and a clear view of the client's first-person theory of their distress. If delivered too early, neuroeducation could impair the therapeutic relationship by creating an unnecessary power differential, inducing unhelpful transference, or setting a precedent that you are a knowledge holder responsible for educating the client. As the initial therapeutic relationship is established, we continue to assess and conceptualize until a neuroeducation exercise matches the client's experience. For instance, if they seem to be experiencing primarily bottom-up processes (e.g., subcortical and outside of conscious awareness), then neuroeducation might focus on the organization of the brain in response to threat and subsequent regulation of the subcortical processing. If the client seems to be experiencing cognitive thought loops generated by a top-down process (cortical and consciously aware), then the neuroeducation might focus on how the threat-scanning features of the left hemisphere of brain seem to be stuck. The key feature in all neuroeducation is to continue to check in with the client, be flexible, and maintain collaboration throughout this process. If any feature is off, then collaboratively recalibrate. Also, neuroeducation should never be delivered haphazardly because the concept sounds revolutionary, or it had a significant effect on previous clients or your own life. The neuroeducation process requires intentionality that is guided by the first-person account of the client's experience and then filtered through their meaning-making systems through ongoing formative and summative evaluation.

Evaluation

An evaluation of our therapeutic work is essential not only for third-party payer sources and our own development but also for the curative effects that progress brings to clients. How do you evaluate the process and outcomes of your current practice? Regardless of the methods of evaluation, evaluating the process and the outcome of neuroeducation is important. From a process perspective, it is important to evaluate the ongoing development of the real relationship and other common factors. The use of client feedback is one method of evaluation that has consistently shown large effects on outcomes (Kivlighan et al., 2016; Reese et al., 2009; Shaw & Murray, 2014). Eliciting client feedback provides an accessible method of real-time process evaluation that also further promotes the common factors (e.g., collaboration, fostering expectations). Process outcomes can be assessed using formal (e.g., Session Rating Scale; Duncan et al., 2003) or informal methods (How well do we seem to be working together?). Using client feedback can promote collaboration and effectiveness of an approach and ensure neuroeducation aligns with the wishes of clients.

There have been times when our facilitation of the neuroeducation process has not gone well. There may be times when you assume a style that is too directive in the facilitation of the neuroeducation process. You might find yourself turned into the client's biology teacher, like Eric was, which significantly impairs the therapeutic relationship. Thankfully, process evaluation has helped us identify these ruptures early and provided the opportunity to readjust expectations and strategy in the therapeutic process.

In addition to the process of neuroeducation, it is important to evaluate the outcome of neuroeducation. How are neuroeducation and the resulting changes helpful to the client? Is neuroeducation alone the curative factor, or does it facilitate the pathway to change? The emerging evidence for the effectiveness of neuroeducation in pain management (e.g., Louw et al.,

2016) creates hope for neuroeducation in other forms of therapy. The outcomes of neuroeducation in therapy can be evaluated using both formal (e.g., Outcome Questionnaire-45; Lambert et al., 1996) and informal evaluation (How has your life been affected by the experiences we have had in therapy?). In sticking with the common factors approach, the neuroeducation process can lead to the creation of healthy behavior change, and this change should continue to be evaluated to reinforce expectations for change, client self-efficacy, and therapeutic outcomes.

Ethical Considerations

What are some ethical considerations in the infusion of neuroscience in practice? What ethical considerations apply to the neuroeducation process? It is important to consider the ethical codes of your discipline when considering the neuroeducation activities in this book. Whether it be the American Mental Health Counselors Association, National Association of Social Workers, American Counseling Association, American Psychological Association, or another discipline, it is essential to ensure that you are practicing neuroeducation in accordance with your unique code of ethics. Regardless of discipline, whether you are a counselor, social worker, psychologist, marriage and family therapist, or a member of another mental health profession, be mindful of upholding all meta-ethics of autonomy, nonmaleficence, beneficence, justice, fidelity, and veracity.

The neuroscience evolution in our fields has led to much debate on alignment with theoretical orientations and scope of practice (e.g., Beeson & Field, 2017; Bott et al., 2016; Wilkinson, 2018). Although therapist competence is not an influential common factor in most research (Wampold, 2015), accurate comprehension of the concept being illustrated with neuroeducation is essential. You do not need to be a neuroscientist to use neuroeducation, but it is essential to know the basic science underlying your illustration. You can also rely on outside experts, videos, and worksheets to help with this illustration and then use the microskills to facilitate the meaning-making process of the client integrating this information into their narrative.

There is an emerging body of literature focusing on neuromyths in both education (e.g., Macdonald et al., 2017) and counseling (e.g., Beeson et al., 2019) that raise our awareness of the potential inaccurate portrayal of neuroscience concepts in the therapeutic process. Neuromyths are a "misunderstanding, a misreading and in some cases a deliberate warping of the scientifically established facts to make a relevant case for education or for other purposes" (Organisation for Economic Co-operation and Development, 2002, p. 71). Some of the most common neuromyths among therapists include the belief of false statements, such as the following:

> Short bouts of motor coordination exercises can improve integration of left and right hemisphere brain function; Children have learning styles that are dominated by particular senses (i.e., seeing, hearing, touch); and Individuals learn better when they receive information in their preferred learning style (e.g., auditory, visual, kinesthetic). (Beeson et al., 2019)

In the age of the internet, many clients have access to tremendous information that guides their interpretations of symptoms, and they may present with a pop-psychology view of the brain. This view can sometimes be facilitative, but at other times, it can lead to difficulties in the neuroeducation process. Some parts of the neuroeducation process explore editing maladaptive narratives of distress with more adaptive ones. To do so, these adaptive conceptualizations must be grounded in actual science rather than popular press translations of these principles. In this same spirit, it is important to balance complexity with oversimplification, and as mentioned earlier, personalize the information with your client.

In addition, counselors are often eager to apply neuroscience interventions and techniques but might not always rely on sound assessment strategies first (e.g., Field et al., 2018). Assessment becomes a critical part in the provision of any counseling intervention, including neuroeducation. Neuroeducation exercises should not be applied because we think they are remarkable nor should we assign more credibility to them. The neuroeducation process should be informed by a complete and holistic biopsychosocial assessment. The assessment identifies potential areas of neuroeducation that are then tentatively proposed as an option in the therapeutic process, which, ultimately, clients have the autonomy to veto or consider in light of their first-person experiences that brought them to therapy.

Finally, there is potential for counselors and psychotherapists to assign empirical superiority to neuroscience research (e.g., Lilienfeld, 2014), leading to what some have described as neuroenchantment and neurorealism (Coutinho et al., 2017) or the tendency to overstate, overgeneralize, or overbelieve findings based on neuroscience. Neuroscience can have a "seductive allure" (Weisberg et al., 2008), and we must critically evaluate primary sources of neuroscience information rather than passive application of existing translations of basic neuroscience. In addition, the science changes daily, and what was true yesterday may not be true today. Therefore, we propose a tentative approach to the neuroeducation process that introduces the concepts as merely one option to understanding and making meaning of clients' experiences. When presenting ideas to clients, indicate an understanding that the brain and nervous system are complex, and even though there is some empirical support for what you are proposing, there are also other possibilities for their experience. Therefore, the constructivist shared meaning-making process of neuroeducation is very important. Consider asking clients to reflect on this experience and compare the neuroeducation with their lived experiences to create a coherent narrative with your clients.

Multicultural Considerations

Culture is important to the therapeutic process. Multiculturalism, cultural humility, cultural responsiveness, and intersectionality are important concepts when planning and delivering neuroeducation. Cultural neuroscience has explored the effect of sociocultural factors on health and well-being, and countless findings have suggested that injustices, such as racism, discrimination, and marginalization (e.g., Berg & Sarnyai, 2015; Ivey & Zalaquett, 2011), to name a few, have negative influences on health outcomes that are disproportionately distributed across racial and ethnic groups. These social injustices are strong epigenetic factors influencing the way that genes are expressed and diseases progress, but they also have the potential to edit the genetic code for future generations (Goosby & Heidbrink, 2013).

As therapists, we bring our own explicit and implicit biases to the work we do (Boyson, 2009) and can inadvertently recreate inequitable systems. These biases can emerge through microaggressions in our therapeutic relationships. Given the importance of synchrony in both verbal and nonverbal communication, bias and the related microaggressions become a significant threat to the development of the most predictive element of therapy: the therapeutic relationship (Owen et al., 2018; Owen et al., 2014). Owen (2013) advocated for a multicultural approach that is reminiscent of and promotes the common factors—namely, practicing with curious cultural humility, responsiveness to multiple identities, and willingness to explore cultural context in relation to clients' subjective experiences of their reasons for presenting in therapy. Therefore, we must be mindful, humble, and honest in our exploration of our own identity development and how we respond to these themes in our therapeutic work. It is helpful to recognize your physiological arousal during sessions and seek supervision, consultation, and personal therapy when that arousal poses risks to the therapeutic process.

An intersectional lens also becomes important to the integration of neuroeducation; however, the infusion of intersectionality in psychotherapy is a complex task (Adames et al., 2018). Crenshaw (1989, 1991) discussed intersectionality by elevating the need to be cognizant of intragroup differences and the various sociocultural factors (e.g., race, gender, sexuality, nationality, socioeconomic status) that influence identity development, potentially leading to compounded discrimination and oppression (Grzanka, 2014). However, simple awareness and focus, referred to as weak intersectionality, is only the first step, as there is a greater need to explore the systems of inequity experienced by people with multiple socially constructed identities, referred to as strong intersectionality (Grzanka, 2014). This elevates the need to not only explore the multiple identities that intersect to describe the client but also the way in which systems interact with those identities—namely, through inequity, discrimination, and oppression. In therapeutic practice, it is important to include critical and often tense conversations about race, class, power, and privilege, alongside the more comfortable discussions of inclusion (Kuri, 2017). It is important to talk about race, as well as racism (Adames et al., 2018), in the way the client experiences the world. Kuri (2017) recommended several factors to help therapists practice from an intersectional lens: self-reflexivity regarding personal power, privilege, and oppression;

emphasis on the therapeutic relationship; preventing otherness; and awareness of internalized attitudes of prejudice. Intersectionality helps promote the common factors (Wampold, 2011) of effective therapy by eliciting narratives that honor both subjective experiences and the effect of external structures on presenting issues (Adames et al., 2018).

Despite the challenges we might face to be culturally responsive therapists, there are some intriguing benefits of cultural neuroscience to the therapeutic process. Many theorists and researchers have explored the cross-cultural universality and variation in emotional experiences. For instance, it is possible that some physiological experiences and basic emotions (Panksepp & Watt, 2011), such as the response to a threat, are universal and evolutionarily wired, but various epigenetic factors (e.g., culture, trauma, oppression) shape the way these primal drives are expressed and interpreted. There are certain elements of emotion and physiological experiences that can be considered universal (Elfenbein & Ambady, 2002; Lim, 2016); however, the social construction and meaning in such emotion add texture and cross-cultural variability that must be explored.

Cross-cultural recognition of some emotions (e.g., happy) is more accurate via facial expressions, while others (e.g., anger) are more accurately recognized by voice (Elfenbein & Ambady, 2002). A smile to one person can indicate happiness, and yet another person might perceive a smile as an aggressive advance. This again supports the need to expand the reflection paradigm to include more elements of emotion rather than the simple label of a feeling. If there is some universality in our emotional experiences and a substantial portion of our relationship building occurs at a preverbal level through right-hemisphere to right-hemisphere connection (e.g., Schore, 2014) and synchrony, then it is possible that some relationship building can occur despite certain cultural differences—namely, language barriers.

There are many multicultural considerations in the process of counseling (e.g., Davis et al., 2018; Hutchison & Gerstein, 2017) that apply to the neuroeducation process. The common factors research suggests that even evidence-based treatments require some cultural adaptations (Wampold, 2015). Culture influences the incoming explanations of client distress, as well as different conceptualizations of the mind, body, spirit, and science in general; therefore, neuroeducation should be aware of and affirm these beliefs. Care should be taken to connect the neuroeducation to the unique worldview and experiences of the client. In addition, the educational component might shift the therapeutic relationship and power dynamics in the room. Therefore, it is important to maintain the collaborative process orientation that is essential to the neuroeducation process.

CLOSING THOUGHTS

The purpose of this chapter was to introduce a metaframework for the implementation and use of neuroeducation in counseling and psychotherapy. Although these considerations are important, it is crucial to remain flexible during the neuroeducation process. As you read the following chapters, you will see many neuroscience concepts come to life. Remember the principles outlined in this chapter to consider how you can and will use these activities to promote health and wellness in your clients.

REFLECTION QUESTIONS

1. How do you currently promote the common factors of therapeutic work? What role can neuroeducation play in the promotion of the common factors?
2. What client indicators might suggest that the neuroeducation exercise is not going as intended and prompt you to abandon or adjust your approach?
3. In addition to the guidelines for neuroeducation that we outlined in this chapter, what principles, factors, and/or considerations do you think might be important to follow or be mindful of when engaging in neuroeducation?

CREDITS

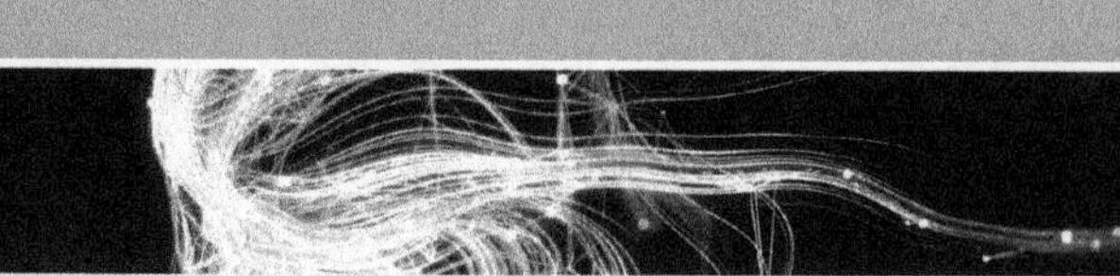

CHAPTER 3

Key Principles of Brain Development

Early experience shapes the regulation of synaptic growth and survival, the regulation of response to stress, and even the regulation of genetic expression.

—Dan Siegel

CHAPTER OBJECTIVES

1. Identify key principles related to brain and nervous system development.
2. Examine the effect of environmental experiences on brain development.
3. Apply brain development concepts in neuroeducation.

INTRODUCTION

Our brains are pretty amazing. Just think about the way you came into this world—completely helpless and dependent on your caregivers for every aspect of your existence. Then, in just a few short years, you learned how to walk and talk, as well as increasingly manage your emotions and behaviors (See Figure 3.1).

FIGURE 3.1 Childhood Development

As an adult, you are now able to perform many daily tasks without much intentional thought or effort. Even complex activities, such as driving a car or navigating an emotionally charged conflict, likely occur automatically. Take a moment to list five activities you did in the last few hours. How much thought did each activity require? To what degree were you consciously focused and making intentional decisions about your thoughts, feelings, and behaviors? Our guess is that your answer is "not very much." The question remains, is this automaticity a good thing? Is it comforting to think about how little intention, evaluation, and decision making is required for many of our daily activities?

If you are like us, at first, you might think "oh no, that is not good"; however, we would like to offer a contrary idea. The fact that our brains operate so automatically and outside of conscious awareness much of the time is actually very adaptive and generally helpful (Gaskill & Perry, 2012). Our brains use a significant amount of energy, especially the parts of our brains, such as the prefrontal cortex, that play a primary role in higher order tasks, often referred to as the CEO of

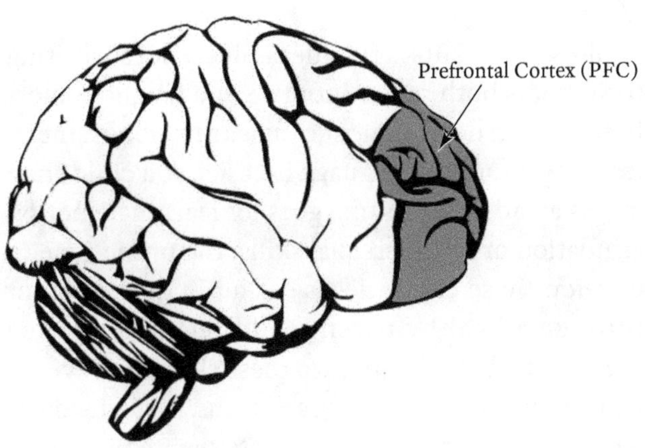

FIGURE 3.2 Prefrontal Cortex

the brain for its role in executive functioning (e.g., long-term planning, focus, rational thought, and so forth; see Figure 3.2).

When tasks can be relegated to more automatic, implicit processes of the brain, our CEO is freed up to focus on other novel or emergent tasks and issues. In fact, you could say one of the major developmental roles of the brain is to learn from experience to predict and move toward greater functional efficiency. Understanding the way our brains develop and change can foster greater insight and empathy for the way we think, feel, and behave and inform ideas for ways to heal and grow.

The brain is an adaptive organ that is largely shaped, and reshaped, by its environment (Galvan, 2010). A person who grows up in a violent and unpredictable neighborhood will develop neural circuits that are especially primed for threat detection and hypervigilance. This person has to devote a lot of neural energy (e.g., increased blood flow and brain wave activity) to being alert and staying safe (see Figure 3.3).

FIGURE 3.3 Fearful Child

A person who grows up in a relatively safe and predictable environment, however, will be able to devote that same neural energy to other tasks, such as learning complicated math equations or inventing a new gadget. If you took images of these two individuals' brains, they would likely show differences in the size of certain anatomical regions (e.g., prefrontal cortex, amygdala, and hippocampus) and degree of interconnection between the regions. These individuals' behaviors will also differ because of the structural and functional differences. Just as experience influenced the development of these patterns in structure and function, so too can experience change the patterns. This idea is broadly referred to as neuroplasticity.

Kolb et al. (2013) identified three types of brain plasticity: experience-independent, experience-expectant, and experience-dependent. The first two types of plasticity occur as part of normal early development, providing the initial framework for future neural structures and functions. When you hear neuroplasticity talked about in the context of counseling, individuals are generally referring to *experience-dependent* neuroplasticity. This type of neuroplasticity refers to changing aspects of the brain that already exist either through addition or pruning (e.g., making new or pruning neurons, synaptic connections, molecular structure, genetic expression, and so forth; see Figure 3.4).

FIGURE 3.4 Brain Plasticity

A 2009 National Institute of Health Blueprint for Neuroscience Research workshop brought together leading scientists from around the world to discuss the latest advances in understanding neuroplasticity and translations of the concept into clinical practice (Cramer et al., 2011). These scientists formally defined neuroplasticity as "the ability of the nervous system to respond to intrinsic and extrinsic stimuli by reorganizing its structure, function, and connections" (Cramer et al., 2011, p. 1592). They further noted that neuroplasticity "can be described at many levels, from molecular to cellular to systems to behavior and can occur during development, in response to the environment, in support of learning, in response to disease, or in relation to therapy" (Cramer et al., 2011, p. 1592). This definition is important for counselors to understand because it highlights the fact that a number of factors can contribute to change, including therapy. The reality is that everything we do impacts, and potentially changes, brain structures and functions to some degree. As counselors, our hope is to support clients in making positive changes that are long-lasting. Cramer and colleagues (2011) specifically reviewed evidence of plasticity related to mental and addictive disorders. They noted that individuals struggling with neuropsychiatric disorders typically show brain differences in limbic, prefrontal, and frontostriatal circuitry and that therapeutic experiences have been shown to influence positive changes in these areas. The scholars caution, however, that changing the brain is not always quick and easy. Especially in the case of neuropsychiatric and addictive disorders, many complex environmental factors influence the development and perseverance of dysregulation and distress. For long-lasting brain changes to occur, counselors must also attend to neurodevelopmental history, environmental stressors and supports, and internal beliefs about self, others, and the world. The scholars also identified brain stimulation, neuropharmacology, physical training and exercise, and specific types of cognitive training as promising clinical approaches to promote neuroplasticity.

One important aspect of neuroplasticity for counselors to understand is "sensitive periods" in brain development (Galvan, 2010). Change does not occur with the same ease and speed across the life span. The brain is most plastic (i.e., open and receptive to change) during early childhood and in adolescence (Kolb & Gibb, 2014). This idea is likely not surprising to you; it is both rather intuitive and taught in most basic human development courses that, for example, learning a foreign language is easier as a child than it is as an adult. The same goes for learning emotion regulation or interpersonal skills; the prime time to develop these capacities is earlier in development through a healthy parent-child relationship (see Figure 3.5). Adults can learn these skills; however, it will take more time, energy, and focus. For individuals who did not learn how to regulate their emotions as children, doing so as adults may always feel a little more difficult or unnatural, but it is possible.

FIGURE 3.5 Parent–Child Attachment

The timing of certain negative experiences during development (e.g., parental alcohol use, physical abuse, neglect, bullying) is also relevant. Awareness of the links between early childhood experiences and adult well-being has grown in recent years in large part because of public health campaigns centered on sharing research findings from the Adverse Childhood Experience studies. The original study and the many studies that have followed have provided evidence of the long-term physical and mental health effects of toxic stress experienced in childhood (Felitti et al., 1998; Merrick et al., 2017). Part of the explanation for this observed phenomenon is that the brain develops in a sequential manner, beginning with lower subcortical structures, including the brain stem and diencephalon, and then progressing to middle brain regions, such as the limbic systems, and upper brain regions, including the cortex (Gaskill & Perry, 2012).

Each of these brain regions is dominant in certain functions and thus the timing of environmental inputs affects the brain differently. For example, traumas occurring between the ages of one and three when the limbic region is experiencing its most rapid growth period will often result in functional problems related to attachment and affect regulation. Traumas occurring during early adolescence, a time of neural reorganization and integration, can result in impaired cognitive functioning, including impulse control, long-term planning, and value-guided action. In addition, childhood traumas have been associated with other biological factors influencing brain development and functioning, including cell damage (e.g., shortened telomere length) and chronic inflammation (Chen & Lacey, 2018; Schaakxs et al., 2016).

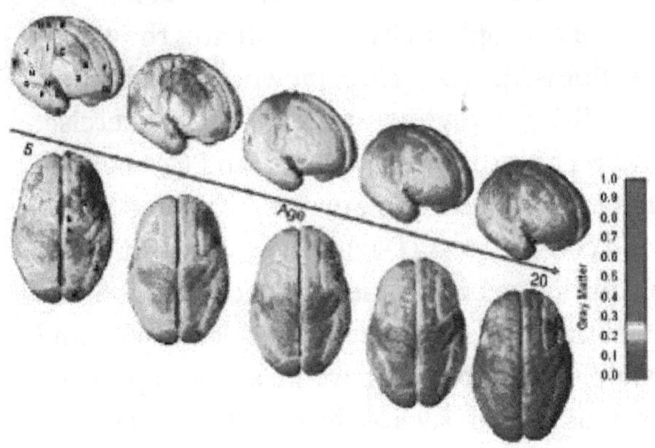

FIGURE 3.6 MRI Scans of Healthy Children and Teens Shows 15 Years of Brain Development Ages 5–20 and the "Pruning" Process. Red Indicates More Gray Matter, Blue Less Gray Matter

Information about brain development, both typical and atypical, can be normalizing and encouraging to share with individuals in counseling. Understanding the possibilities and challenges inherent in supporting brain development throughout the life span can also guide the selection and dosing of therapeutic interventions. The neuroeducation activities described in this chapter offer ideas about how to bring the concepts of brain development and neuroplasticity to life for clients in ways that will support healing and growth.

NEUROEDUCATION ACTIVITIES

This chapter includes seven neuroeducation activities geared toward integrating principles of brain development into the counseling experience. These individual and group activity ideas are experiential and reflective in nature and are grounded in strength-oriented, wellness-based perspectives.

BRAIN WELLNESS (B-WELL)

Susan M. Long

Brain-based health and wellness is an emerging area of focus in counseling (Beeson & Field, 2017). Despite a long-standing belief that the adult brain was largely fixed and incapable of change, regeneration, or reorganization (Doidge, 2007; Rosenzweig et al., 1972), neuroscientists now view the brain as malleable throughout the life span, capable of structural and functional changes in response to new learning experiences. Changes in the brain may occur positively or negatively (Chapin & Russell-Chapin, 2014; Doidge, 2007). Examples of positive changes include challenging the brain with new tasks (e.g., learning an instrument, physical exercise, and counseling) or adopting healthy lifestyle behaviors (e.g., good sleep hygiene, healthy nutrition, meaningful connection; Chapin & Russell-Chapin, 2014; Davidson & McEwen, 2012). Conversely, examples of negative brain changes include exposure to toxic environmental conditions (e.g., poverty, violence, natural disasters, and so forth), adoption of negative thinking patterns (e.g., beliefs of worthlessness), and experiences of trauma (Chapin & Russell-Chapin, 2014; Cozolino, 2010; Perry, 2009).

The purpose of the *Brain Wellness* (*B-Well*) activity is to provide clients with a framework to establish healthy lifestyle behaviors to support their brain health and overall well-being. The *B-Well* activity introduces clients to the fundamentals of neuroplasticity and facilitates the exploration of a variety of strategies for optimum brain wellness. The *B-Well* framework includes four domains: (1) mental strategies (e.g., learning new skills), (2) physical strategies (e.g., exercise, healthy diet, sleep), (3) social strategies (e.g., positive relationships with others), and (4) environmental strategies (e.g., playtime, spending time in nature). These domains are grounded in the literature about neuroplasticity, holistic wellness, and eco-wellness (Davidson & McEwen, 2012; Myers & Sweeney, 2004; Reese & Myers, 2012). In addition to brain-based psychoeducation, the *B-Well* emphasizes collaboration between counselor and client to establish goals for brain wellness. This approach extends previous models, such as the *Healthy Mind Platter* (Rock et al., 2012), through the inclusion of assessment and goal-setting components throughout.

MATERIALS NEEDED

- *B-Well* worksheet
- *TB-Well: A Survey for Brain Wellness*
- Diagram or model of the brain

PROCESS OF THE ACTIVITY

The *B-Well* activity may be used in initial counseling sessions to introduce and explore how the brain changes in response to a variety of mental, physical, social, and environmental interventions. It may also be introduced whenever it is relevant to the clients' presentation (Miller, 2016) or when the counselor and client want to integrate interventions for overall wellness. The steps that follow describe how the *B-Well* activity may be used in counseling.

Step 1—Introduction to Brain Wellness and Neuroplasticity. The first step in the *B-Well* activity is eliciting feedback from clients about their knowledge and levels of interest about neuroscience principles and, if clients' desire, sharing information about the principles of neuroplasticity. Example prompts include the following: "What do you know about how the brain changes, if anything at all?" "What is your interest in exploring how to improve your brain function?" If clients express an interest in learning about how the brain changes, introduce the *B-Well* worksheet and facilitate an initial discussion about neuroplasticity and how each area within the model contributes to positive brain changes and/or functioning. It may be helpful to have a diagram of the brain and nervous system and/or a model of the brain to refer to when talking about how elements of *B-Well* affect brain regions and functioning.

Step 2—Assessment of Brain Wellness. The next step in the activity is establishing a baseline of clients' current behaviors associated with brain wellness via the *B-Well* Survey. This brief questionnaire can also be given at various times during the therapeutic process to measure progress. As part of the survey process, clients will have the opportunity to identify strengths and areas of growth. After completing the survey, you can ask the following open-ended questions to transition into goal setting: "What was it like for you to engage in this assessment process?" "Tell me about the strengths and growing edges that you see within the *B-Well* model?"

Step 3—Planning for Optimal Brain Wellness. The next step is supporting clients in identifying two areas they would like to develop or enhance (e.g., physical and mental strategies). Help clients brainstorm specific strategies they are interested in implementing, both in and out of counseling, to support their development of the identified areas. Then, using the Simple, Measurable, Achievable, Realistic, and Time-bound (S.M.A.R.T) framework (Doran, 1981), help clients establish goals. These goals can be part of clients' formal treatment plans or conceptualized as supplemental to larger treatment plans.

FOLLOW-UP

The final step of the *B-Well* activity is to evaluate progress toward brain wellness. Moving forward, check in with clients regularly, eliciting feedback about successes, barriers to progress, and any other concerns. You can also use the *B-Well* Survey to assess progress more formally in various areas, comparing pre- and post-treatment responses. Another way to evaluate progress is to encourage clients to keep a journal related to their progress and review journal entries in session. Example prompts for open dialogue around progress include the following: "Tell me how engaging in this process is influencing your wellness." "Based on your baseline with the *B-Well* Survey compared with your post-test, you have made progress with your goals! What are your thoughts about this progress?" "What supported your progress the most?" Prompts that elicit discussion about areas of continued struggle include the following: "What strategies have been more difficult to implement?" "What strategies are not working as well as you would like?"

NEUROSCIENCE IN ACTION

Mary was a 23-year-old female who presented to counseling with symptoms of depression. She reported increased irritability, low mood, low energy, difficulty concentrating, and a poor self-image. The following is a sample transcript of our dialogue using the *B-Well* framework:

Counselor: Mary, in our work together, we have talked about how your thoughts, feelings, and behaviors interact and influence your depression. I think it might be helpful to explore these connections further by integrating neuroscience. What are your thoughts about doing that?

Mary: Sure, I think that could help me better understand why I feel and think the way that I do.

Counselor: Right. Well, what do you know about how the brain changes, if anything at all?

Mary: Not much. I guess I always thought that the brain you are born with is the brain you are stuck with.

Counselor: That is a common misconception when it comes to our brain! So, with that in mind, I'd like to explore some information with you about the concept of neuroplasticity.

Mary: Okay. I've never heard of that before.

Counselor: Neuroplasticity refers to the brain as plastic rather than fixed, and so, this means that the brain has the capacity to change structurally and functionally with learning and experience.

Mary: Ok, how do I learn to change my brain?

Counselor: Great question! I'd like to share an activity with you that will help us to explore this idea of neuroplasticity and brain wellness a bit further; it's called *Brain Wellness* or the *B-Well* [shares *B-Well* handout with the client]. You will see four domains; each of these domains includes strategies that can help you positively change your brain function.

Mary: Wow! So, I can change my brain by doing all of these things?

Counselor: Yes, you can. You can integrate activities within the *B-Well* framework to support your brain wellness. The activities can support the brain reorganizing in different ways. Let's take a look at this diagram of the brain, and I can point to the different parts of the brain that are impacted by various activities. Mindfulness meditation has been shown to decrease amygdala reactivity and strengthen connections with parts of the brain responsible for emotion regulation (e.g., ventromedial prefrontal cortex). This means you are likely to feel less reactive or fearful. Physical strategies like exercise and a nutritious diet strengthen our brain in many ways. Exercise increases the brain's volume of gray matter and white matter, which not only produces more neurons but also strengthens the connections between them. Think about diet as fuel for the brain; about 95% of the neurotransmitter serotonin, our mood-regulating chemical, is produced in our gastrointestinal tract, so what we eat can directly affect our emotions. This really highlights how important physical health is as it relates to our brain. Also, connecting with others can reduce depression and improve your brain health overall. Social support is positively correlated with the right medial prefrontal cortex, an area of the brain that is involved in memory, decision making, and emotional responses. The final domain in the model is environmental strategies. An example of this would be spending time in nature. Nature affects the prefrontal cortex, the brain's command center, and allows the brain to relax and rest, like an overused muscle. So, you might consider walking in nature to reduce stress and increase your focus and concentration, which you expressed was a concern for you.

Mary: This makes a lot of sense when you explain it to me this way. I can see how this could be helpful for my depression. How should I start?

Counselor: Let's start with an assessment. It's a quick survey that gives us an idea of where you are with your brain wellness currently and can help us identify some initial areas of focus. [Introduces *B-Well: A Survey for Brain Wellness*].

Mary: Okay [completes survey].

Counselor: What was it like for you to engage in this assessment process?

Mary: It was good. I can see that I am stronger in some areas than others.

Counselor: Yes, that is pretty normal; all of us tend to have areas of strength and areas of growth. Let's start by talking about what you are doing well. Tell me more about your areas of strength.

Mary: I have close relationships, so I think the social domain is one strength.

Counselor: Okay, that is an important one for sure. What other strengths do you notice?

Mary: Well, I also try to meditate every day, like we talked about, and I've noticed that's been helping me feel more grounded. I'd say that's one of my strengths too.

Counselor: I am happy to hear you are finding the meditation helpful! It sounds like you are already active in some ways that support your brain wellness! What about your growing edges or areas you'd like to enhance? [Begins planning for optimal brain wellness.]

Mary: Definitely the physical and environmental domains.

Counselor: Okay. Let's take another look at the *B-Well.* What strategies within those two domains would you be interested in adding to your life?

Mary: I would like to exercise more and spend more time in nature.

Counselor: Considering those two areas, let's see if we can get more specific and set some S.M.A.R.T goals. What is one goal you could set for each domain? Consider the type of exercise you will try. How many times a week?

Mary: I will try yoga and cardio. I think at least twice per week for 30 minutes.

Counselor: Great. How about for spending time in nature?

Mary: I will walk my dog in the park at least twice a week to start. There's a nice park down the street from my house.

Counselor: It sounds like you have some very clear ideas of what would work for you and what you would enjoy. Some next steps that will support your goals is journaling your progress. If you feel up to it, write about your successes and any areas of challenge as you go through the week. For example, if you didn't make it to exercise one day, what got in the way? That way, we can talk about and address any barriers. Does that make sense?

Mary: Yes. I will bring my journal in here too, so I can talk about it.

Counselor: Yes, I think that's a nice idea. Also, in about one month, I am going to encourage you to retake the *B-Well* Survey, so we can compare with your original assessment. How does that sound to you?

Mary: That sounds good to me.

[Evaluation of Progress for Brain Wellness—1 Month Later]

Counselor: I'd like to start a discussion about your progress with your brain wellness. Let's begin with you taking the *B-Well* Survey, and then we can discuss what you notice.

[Administers post-test]

Mary: I notice changes in my responses and definitely in how I feel.

Counselor: Let's take a closer look, pre-test post-test. What stands out to you?

Mary: I circled "Strongly Disagree" in the physical domains and now I circled "Agree."

Counselor: I see that too! What else?

Mary: Same thing with the environmental domain. I picked "Disagree" in spending time doing fun activities, and now it's "Strongly Agree"!

Counselor: Great! Can you tell me about how this process has influenced your wellness?

Mary: It's been helpful for me. I think the idea that I could change my brain inspired me to do more about it.

Counselor: Nice! Tell me more about that.

Mary: I have noticed that I have more energy, and overall, I feel better; my mood is better. I have definitely seen a difference with exercise and yoga and spending time with my dog in the park.

Counselor: Tell me more about what you've noticed.

Mary: Well, I had a lot of trouble concentrating in general, and being outside gave me clarity. I don't know, I was able to focus more and be more present.

Counselor: And that makes sense! We know that being in nature allows the prefrontal cortex to rest and use less energy, so you can have more focus. Isn't that cool?

Mary: Absolutely! I will definitely continue that practice long term. It's been transformational.

Counselor: Wow! That sounds like a powerful experience!

Mary: It really is.

Counselor: Great. Will you tell me a bit about how the exercise component has influenced your brain wellness?

Mary: Sure. I noticed improvement on my low mood, mainly I am not feeling that tired or as much sadness.

Counselor: That makes sense too. Like we've talked about before, exercise is an excellent strategy to change our brain and mood. Exercise stimulates the brain to grow and strengthen in important cortical regions, and that makes it easier for the brain to make new connections and also produce nourishing hormones in the brain. It's like that runner's high people experience with vigorous exercise!

ETHICAL AND MULTICULTURAL CONSIDERATIONS

The *B-Well* activity is designed to work for clients with diverse backgrounds and experiences, including various demographic factors: age, ability, social class, educational levels, and the intersection thereof. Despite the wide range of uses of this activity, an important consideration of *B-Well* is that individuals vary significantly in their experiences, worldviews, and reported symptoms; thus, clients may respond differently to the intervention.

Further, it is important to consider clients' readiness and openness to neuroeducation and integrating neuroscience principles into their lives. Client readiness can determine the effectiveness of the *B-Well*. For example, a client with limited knowledge of neuroscience may feel intimidated about learning more about the brain and therefore reject the *B-Well* activity. However, this may be managed by introducing neuroscience principles to clients in a way that is relevant to them and their unique presentations. Emphasizing the experiential component of the model can also assist clients in becoming more open to integrating the *B-Well* in their counseling experience; counselors could integrate relaxation techniques in session to assist clients in integrating this activity outside of counseling. Another consideration may include clients' perceptions about change; clients who hold a deterministic view of their experiences may believe that they are unable to change their brains and may not engage in the activity. This could be managed by introducing additional neuroeducation resources (e.g., neurobiology, neuroplasticity) and facilitating a discussion with clients about what topics are most interesting and relevant to their lives.

B-Well: A Survey for Brain Wellness

Please select which best describes you.

Domains:	Always	Frequently	Sometimes	Never
1. Mental Strategies for Brain Wellness				
I use relaxation techniques to manage my stress.	1	2	3	4
I learn new skills.	1	2	3	4
I am able to cope with my emotions.	1	2	3	4
2. Physical Strategies for Brain Wellness				
I engage in physical exercise at least three times a week.	1	2	3	4
I feel well rested.	1	2	3	4
I make healthy dietary choices.	1	2	3	4
3. Social Strategies for Brain Wellness				
I have a strong social network.	1	2	3	4
I have a sense of belongingness with my community.	1	2	3	4
I have at least one person I can confide in.	1	2	3	4
4. Environmental Strategies for Brain Wellness				
I take time to appreciate nature.	1	2	3	4
I engage in environments that stimulate learning.	1	2	3	4
I take time to appreciate my surroundings.	1	2	3	4

Brain Wellness (*B-Well*)

Mental Strategies

- Learn about a new topic that interests you.
- Learn a new skill (e.g. playing a musical instrument, dancing, painting).
- Practice mental imagery (e.g., follow a guided imagery script for relaxation)

Physical Strategies

- Engage in physical exercise (e.g. 40 minutes at least three times a week).
- Make healthy dietary choices (dietary supplements; Vitamin D, Omega 3 fatty acids).
- Achieve adequate sleep (consistent sleep/wake times, 7-8 hrs/night).

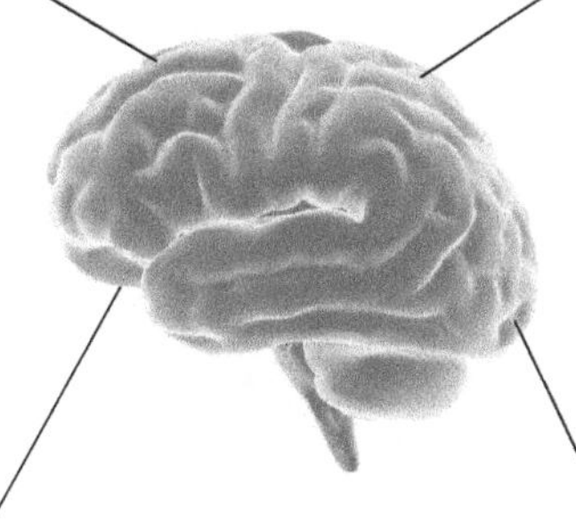

Social Strategies

- Interpersonal connections with friends and partner (e.g. meaningful intimate relationships).
- Social engagement (e.g. community membership, religious or spiritually affiliations, join an organization that interests you).
- Engage in client-centered therapy with your counselor.

Environmental Strategies

- Play time (e.g. engage in a fun activity).
- Spend time in nature (e.g. hike in park, go on a picnic, etc.).
- Engage in a stimulating environment (e.g. sensory information, activities that involve concentration and learning).

What are your strengths in the *B-Well* model? ______________________________

What are your areas for growth? ______________________________

List two domains you want to improve:

Goal 1: ______________________________

Goal 2: ______________________________

THE A-MAZE-ING BRAIN

Chad Luke

Clients commonly fear making changes in their lives. They feel stuck and struggle with motivation. This challenge reflects, in some ways, the principle of Hebb's learning rule (c. 1949), related to brain plasticity and processes for learning and memory. Neuroscientist Carla Shatz paraphrased Hebb's rule as "cells that fire together, wire together" (Shatz, 1996, p. 604), highlighting the role of timing and proximity in the formation of synaptic connections. One of the brain's priorities is making itself as efficient as possible so that it can move everyday tasks to background processes and devote more resources to new and emerging issues. Through a process of associative learning, which Hebb's rule undergirds (Yee et al., 2017), various stimuli become automatically paired with certain neural and psychological responding. Although this tendency can be quite helpful in many situations, when it comes to thoughts, feelings, and behaviors we do not like, it can make the process of change difficult. For example, after experiencing a car accident on a bridge, bridges can become associated with danger and fear, and the mere thought of a bridge invokes a sense of dread or panic. Similarly, after spending months drinking alcohol with a group of friends, merely being around the same group of friends triggers an urge to drink. For an even more common example, think of traveling the same way to work or school for weeks, months, or years, and then changing homes, jobs, or schools. What happens in those first days or weeks after that change? Often, we will have the impulse or actually follow through with making a wrong turn as if the move or change had never happened.

Even when we develop unwanted associations and patterns of thinking, feeling, and behaving, there is clear hope for change. Hebb's rule can work in a positive direction as well! Neuroplasticity, including neurogenesis (growth of new neurons) and synaptogenesis (growth of new connections between neurons) demonstrates that the brain can reorganize itself for growth and change, in part by making new associations. Installation of hope is a crucial therapeutic element in counseling, yet clients often attend counseling with little hope.

The purpose of the *A-MAZE-ing Brain* activity is to illuminate the processes that keep us stuck in ineffective behaviors and then present the hope for change from a brain-based perspective. Specifically, I use mazes to help illuminate the principle of brain plasticity. Mazes have a rich history in psychological research, often to measure cognitive processing abilities and/or personal characteristics (Pasek, 2016). Mazes can be fun and challenging, as well as frustrating and discouraging. All of these experiences are useful for the counseling process. Mazes activate parts of the brain responsible for executive functioning and emotion regulation, thus stimulating growth in brain networks and functional capabilities that are often a focus of treatment. Ultimately, through repetition and reflection, clients can gain new perspectives on the possibility of change.

MATERIALS NEEDED

- Three printed copies of a maze
- A pen or pencil
- A timer (a phone will work well)

As an alternative, and to take the activity further, you can use three different mazes of increasing complexity. In this case, you will need three copies of each of the three mazes.

PROCESS OF THE ACTIVITY

The *A-MAZE-ing Brain* activity can be completed in an individual or group counseling setting. Begin the activity by asking if the client would be willing to participate in an experiment. I often make a light-hearted comment about it being harmless and noninvasive. Then, present the client with a basic maze (see Luke, 2016, for an example) with little or no explanation other than an

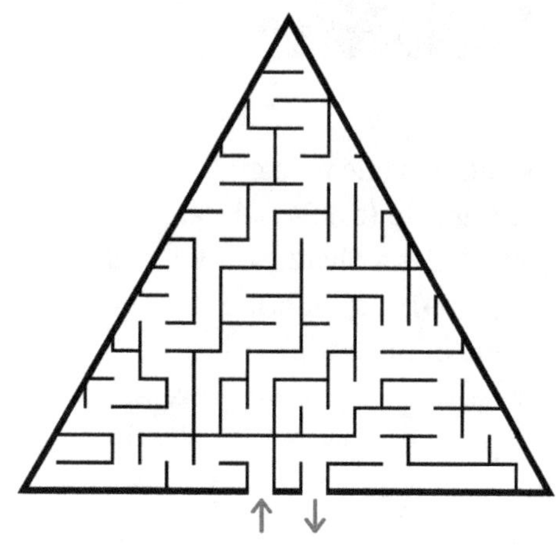

FIGURE 3.7 Brain Maze 1

invitation to attempt it. The maze has a clear entry point and a clear exit. Using a basic timer (cell phone works great), ask the person to simply complete the maze and time them (see Figure 3.7). Then, ask them to complete the exact same maze a second and third time, timing each trial. Write down the time taken on each trial. The majority of individuals are able to show improvements (i.e., complete the maze faster) in their times during each successive trial.

In 80%–90% of the cases, participants experience increases in performance of the maze task from trial one to trial three. For these folks, the impact is almost immediate—success through repetitive, effective behaviors. After completing the timed maze trials, ask clients to share their observations. Example reflection prompts include the following: "What did you notice about your times?" "What was is like completing the same maze over three times?" You can then briefly discuss what they think accounted for the improvements. Responses tend to include "practice," "experience," and "trial and error." At times, I make the learning point, and the activity concludes with a neuroscience-informed debrief, as illustrated in the case study that follows. In some cases, it may be appropriate to add the steps described next.

In a minority of cases, clients' times get worse or remain about the same. This outcome can be extremely helpful in understanding an individual's approach to completing tasks and solving problems, or potential challenges in cognitive processing. In such cases, you can pose the following prompt: "Tell me about each of your attempts, the similarities and differences between each." The most common response is, "I did not know I could solve it using the same path; I thought I had to find a new one each time." You can then explore why building on their previous successes and using what has worked for them in the past seemed like cheating.

FIGURE 3.8 Brain Maze 2

As a further variation of the activity, in subsequent sessions, you can switch to the second and third mazes, which get progressively more difficult. This approach demonstrates learning and scaffolding, particularly for clients who first responded to the maze activity with statements such as, "I'm not really a maze person," or "I can't do mazes" and associated attitudes.

The second maze (See Figure 3.8) is significantly more complex and is not marked with "enter" and "exit" arrows. Rather than using three trials, process their reaction to this increased complexity, as many either give up or take a very long time to complete it. Next, introduce the third maze, which, in addition to missing the entry and exit points, has multiple entry and exit points and no obvious paths through the maze, if they only try to follow the white space. In the sample maze provided in Figure 3.9, the black lines are the only way to complete the maze.

Clients make quick associations in their experiences with mazes two and three. Following maze two, discuss what they could use from the maze one trials and what adjustments they may need to make to their thinking. This is often a good time to share how neuroplasticity is related to the experiment—making new connections using previous experiences and novel situations to learn new strategies. For example, I might say, "Since the brain likes patterns, it modifies itself using experience to become more efficient, like learning the maze. This is helpful in making mundane processes automatic (not a lot of thought involved in brushing our teeth) but it does make changing those behaviors more challenging (like adding flossing to the dental hygiene regimen after years of not flossing or brushing with the opposite hand). "What are some ways you've tried to add 'flossing' to your life routine?" In processing maze three, you can invite clients to explore what it means to create their own definitions of success and how not having clear goals or even knowing where to begin can limit their growth and chances of success.

FIGURE 3.9 Sample Maze

Regardless of the outcome of the maze completion exercise, you can frame client attempts in a positive manner. For example, you can note that sometimes the hardest part about change is that it doesn't happen immediately and requires practice, patience, and perseverance. At the end of the exercises, you can also begin to explicitly generalize to the client's life via information gained in the assessment and ongoing counseling process. The client can also self-identify personally meaningful examples of changes they have made in the past and/or are trying to make in the present.

FOLLOW-UP

The primary follow-up approach to the *A-MAZE-ing Brain* is the post-maze reflective prompts described in the process questions earlier.

NEUROSCIENCE IN ACTION

"Manny" entered the intensive outpatient group struggling with depression. He reported that he felt like he could not "shake" the down times and was exhausted from trying. He said he tried medication and was afraid that he was permanently broken. The group tried to encourage him but with little avail. During one group session, I brought in the *A-MAZE-ing Brain* activity, distributing a blank copy, along with a pencil, to each member. I asked group members to work in pairs, taking turns timing one another during maze completion and then discussing their results. In the whole-group debrief, Manny's partner described feeling hopeful as her times improved with each attempt, musing, "I wonder how fast I could get if I could practice a little more!" Manny's times actually got slower, and he lamented that his depression would not let him focus and therefore prevented him from being successful. When a group member asked Manny about his approach, he explained that he thought it was against the rules to use the same route during each trial. This resulted in him taking more time to find an alternative, leading to unnecessary frustration. One group member shared that they started from the exit and worked their way backward to find success. Another group member shared Manny's frustration, so I invited both members to attempt the activity again, but with a new understanding of the rules, along with an invitation to approach the maze creatively. Both clients improved their times on each trial and remarked how nice it was to be able to repeat a task they understood. The group then processed how rigidly held assumptions had limited their successes in life and then provided examples of effective strategies in managing their symptoms. Manny reported feeling more connected to the group than he had thus far and that previously he viewed himself as "not a maze" person. He stated, "I felt good being able to practice and experience success even with something so simple."

Following the experiential portion of the activity, I took about 3 minutes to explore neuroscience concepts related to their learning experiences—namely, Hebb's rule and synaptogenesis:

"Neurons communicate with one another to get us to take action, and these neurons get used to 'firing' together. This makes it easier to form habits, but harder to break old habits and form new ones. The flexibility of the connections between neurons makes change possible, but their routine firings make change challenging. When you want to make changes in your life, it is important to have patience and expect that you will likely have to practice new ways of thinking, feeling, and behaving many, many times before that new way of being becomes automatic. Despite the difficulty, it can be encouraging to know your brain is capable of making new automatic patterns."

ETHICAL AND MULTICULTURAL CONSIDERATIONS

In most cases, *A-MAZE-ing Brain* can be viewed as values neutral, in that the first maze is very simple and straightforward. However, it can and should still be presented as an "experiment" that works for some and not for others. This approach can serve to destigmatize clients with impaired intellectual or spatial functioning. Because the activity is considered a "challenge by choice" activity, clients can feel free to opt out of it as well. It is important to use the activity after establishing rapport with the client and not as an icebreaker, given that there is a low-level risk associated with "performing" *A-MAZE-ing Brain*. As currently designed, this activity may not be accessible to individuals with visual impairments.

ANCILLARY MATERIALS

- Hebb's law (although not explicitly stated as such) and neuroplasticity for clients: https://www.youtube.com/watch?v=tfifTUYuAYU
- Memory system with Hebbian implications. Cute and concise, for clients: https://www.youtube.com/watch?v=TUoJcONPajQ
- Video of Rick Hanson (*Buddha's Brain*) talking about self-directed neuroplasticity mediated by attention: https://www.youtube.com/watch?v=1_yB-AYG6Eg&nohtml5=False
- Ted-Ed quick video comparing/contrasting classical and operant conditioning in four minutes: https://www.youtube.com/watch?v=H6LEcM0E0io&nohtml5=False

PLAYING OUT YOUR BRAIN WORLD

Savannah Cormier

The translation of neuroscience research into counseling practice is growing, and thus counselors are increasingly faced with the challenge of sharing neuroscience principles in ways that excite learning systems and inspire hope rather than overwhelm and confuse. Creative methods, such as metaphor and sand tray, can be useful and nonintimidating ways to distill information and introduce clients to neuroscience principles (Bear et al., 2007; Field et al., 2017). Further, creative forms of expression tap into right-hemisphere processing, which is understood to play a major role in emotional responses, imagination, creativity, and holistic thinking (Luke, 2016; McHenry et al., 2014). Creative expression prioritizes novel, fun, multisensory processing over literality, reasoning, and logic, which can sometimes keep clients stuck in surface-level intellective discussions that are less helpful to healing embodied pain (Carson & Becker, 2004; Gladding, 2008; Hecker & Kottler, 2002; Luke, 2016). The *Playing Out Your Brain World* activity focuses on using the therapeutic properties of sand tray and creative expression to explore and process topics related to the client's brain.

The primary goal of *Playing Out Your Brain World* is to illustrate the brain's ability to change and reorganize through neuroplasticity (Cramer et al., 2011; Goldapple et al., 2004; Hübener & Bonhoeffer, 2014; Purves & Hadley, 1985). Counselors facilitate client's creation of their current "brain worlds" and struggles in the sand tray and then share about ways the brain makes connections and changes through the process of neuroplasticity. As clients physically and visibly change the metaphorical "brain" connections in the sand, it is hypothesized that their actual brains begin to change too as they imagine new associations and possibilities in their minds (Ratey, 2002).

MATERIALS NEEDED

Counselors should work in collaboration with their clients to decide which materials would be the most therapeutic to touch. Ideally, it is helpful to provide clients with a variety of options and allow them to choose. Options can include various types of sand (e.g., fine-textured sand, kinetic sand, riverbed sand, and so forth), small rocks, dry rice, or dry beans. Counselors will need a medium-sized container to hold the chosen medium. An 8.5" x 10" baking sheet or generic plastic storage box can work well as a sand tray container. Finally, counselors will need a variety of items for clients to choose from when creating their brains in the sand (or another medium). These items can include the following:

- Toy miniatures (available for purchase at https://www.childtherapytoys.com or at various children's toy stores)
- Magazine cutouts
- Rocks or stones
- Cutout client drawings
- Tangible items that clients can use to represent characters in their brain worlds and physically manipulate

PROCESS OF THE ACTIVITY

Before beginning the activity, counselors should consider their own competency regarding the neuroscience concept or principle they hope to explore with the client. You can facilitate this activity at various stages of the therapeutic process—from information gathering and relationship building to implementation and outcome assessment. The steps that follow provide a generic outline of the overall process:

1. **Assess therapeutic goals and objectives to determine if *Playing Out Your Brain World* is appropriate.** This activity should begin with intentionality. My own intentionality has been grounded in a belief that a sand tray can serve as a creative "canvas" to explore neuroscience concepts with a client, often supporting the development of insight and instillation of hope. I have found it particularly helpful when clients feel "stuck" or seem to need a more visual or embodied learning experience.

2. **Introduce *Playing Out Your Brain World*.** Offer your client the opportunity to try a different way of working with their struggles. For example, you could say, "I am wondering if you would be interested in trying something a little different with me today? I would like to explore some neuroscience principles with you that I think might help you understand your experience a little better. What do you think?" If a client responds with interest and/or a willingness to try the activity, you can move forward with introducing the various mediums and objects and providing an initial prompt. An example of an open prompt is as follows: "Thinking about your current struggles, choose objects that you feel drawn to and place them in the sand." Other more directive prompts include, "Create your brain's world in the sand," or "Thinking about the anxiety you have been experiencing and talking about with me, choose miniatures that represent different aspects of what anxiety is like for you and your brain. As you choose, place the miniatures in the sand tray almost as if to set up a story." I share with clients that there is no right or wrong way to go about the activity and that there will be time to add to their sand trays after the initial choosing time. I also encourage them to ask me any questions they may have along the way.

3. **Observe the client choosing and placing objects.** As your client is choosing and placing their objects in the sand, notice their process. Is the client taking a long time to choose their objects, or did they choose instantly? Does the client seem embarrassed or unsure in their choosing? Is the client quiet or narrating their process aloud? Is the client asking you many questions? Does it seem as if they are trying to do the activity "right?" What might this mean in regard to the client's anxiety level for trying new things? Counselors may choose whether to give more guidance based on what they assess to be helpful to their clients. More nondirective counselors may choose to just repeat the original prompt and remind their clients that they cannot do the activity "wrong."

4. **Once your client feels their brain world is complete, ask them to share what they created, reflecting and asking clarification questions as needed.** An example reflection prompt is, "Tell me about the world you created." Again, there is no "right" way to share a sand tray. With some clients, you may need to help them share their sand trays by asking follow-up questions such as, "I'm curious what's happening in this area," or "I notice this figure is far away from all the other figures."

5. **Throughout the client's sharing, as you hear connections and themes, draw lines and connections in the sand tray—making lines deeper depending on how often a theme or connection is repeated.** Before touching the client' sand tray, let them know that you would like to draw lines in the sand as they share and ask if that would be okay. Ask specific questions about the connections between objects such as, "I notice you said every time you experience (corresponding object) you also start to experience (another object). Say more about that."

6. **Once the client is finished talking about their sand tray and you have no more clarification questions, share that the lines in the sand may represent the connections the client's brain makes.** Note that just as you made lines in the sand tray, repeated experiences and focused attention make connections in our brains. As you discuss neuronal connections, introduce

the term neuroplasticity—the brain's ability to change itself in response to new and repeated experiences. Focus on highlighting the possibility of change and hope for the future. Before moving on, pause to allow the client to share their thoughts and ask questions. You can say, "What do you think about this idea?" Or, "What sense does this concept make to your life?" After this discussion time, introduce the second prompt by asking the client to create a new tray that represents what they would ideally like their brain world to look like.

7. **Repeat previous steps of asking the client to share their sand tray, reflecting and asking questions for clarification, and creating lines in the sand.** Ask clients to be as specific as possible and help them expand on their sharing to include deeper and deeper descriptions. Notice differences between the first and second sand trays and offer clients the opportunity to reflect on those differences.

8. **Summarize.** Bring everything back together by summarizing the main themes and processes. Highlight specific neuroscience concepts, such as neuroplasticity and the brain's ability to change with the repetition of new associations. Do not immediately clean up the sand tray. This allows for the metaphor of the new brain world to remain open as the client leaves the session.

9. **Take a picture of each sand tray to include in the client's file.** Ask permission from the client to take a picture of the trays to keep in their file. You may also suggest to the client that they take a picture themselves to keep for their own reflection. If the client chooses to take pictures for themselves, it might be helpful to open a dialogue about who could potentially see the pictures and what, if anything, the client would like to do to ensure privacy. You may clean up the sand tray after a picture is taken and/or the client has left your office.

FOLLOW-UP

Following this activity, you can ask open-ended questions to help clients reflect on their experiences. Example prompts include the following: "What was it like to create an inner experience in the sand tray?" "What was it like to change things in the sand tray?" "To what degree has your thinking about your struggle or your brain shifted?" "What ideas do you have for how you can start creating more neuronal changes?" And, "What, if anything, do you wish you could have put in either sand tray but didn't?"

NEUROSCIENCE IN ACTION

Hunter (pseudonym), a 30-year-old female, reported struggling with anxiety. As she explained how she was "just an anxious person," the following dialogue emerged:

Client: I feel like I'm just crazy.

Counselor: When I listen to you talk about anxiety, it sounds like you see anxiety as a character flaw in you. A part of you, you don't like and have little hope it can be changed.

Client: Well yeah. I've always been told we just have anxiety in our family. This is just how I am.

After more discussion, I believed that Hunter could benefit from some exploration of how anxiety had been reinforced in her brain, as well as some education on neuroplasticity to provide hope. I also thought Hunter was so connected to her anxiety that it might not be useful to rely solely on talk therapy. After Hunter agreed, I pulled out a sand tray and a bag of toy miniatures and explained to Hunter that I wanted her to pretend her brain was its own world in the sand tray. As Hunter touched the sand, I noticed her calming down and starting to smile.

Counselor: I noticed you smiled when you touched the sand. Your brain's world seems enjoyable right now.

Client: Well that's because its calm right now. There's no anxiety in it yet.

Counselor: That's a good point. Right now, it's just your brain. Before we've added any connections to anxiety.

FIGURE 3.10 Cormier Case Study 1

I handed Hunter the bag and asked her to choose miniatures to represent different aspects of her experience with anxiety and place them in the sand tray. Once all the characters were set up, I asked Hunter to tell me about what she had created in the sand tray. As Hunter told her story, I began drawing soft lines in the sand, connecting the characters. As I listened for connections and repeated themes, I reinforced the lines in the sand by making them deeper (Figure 3.10). Once Hunter finished her story, I explained that the lines in the sand were similar to how her brain makes neural connections; the more the "characters" create stories together, the stronger the connection between them.

Counselor: If you were to try to go from any of these characters to anxiety, it would be pretty easy because your brain already has these well-paved connections. It makes sense to me that you feel like anxiety is just a part of who you are. It's been strengthened in your brain.

Client: (sigh) So you're saying my brain is stuck like this?

Counselor: Actually, no. We can change it in the sand tray, like we can change it in your brain. Both have the ability to change and move.

We then spent some time talking about why changing our habits, behaviors, and neuronal connections is so difficult. I shared, "These deep 'ruts' in the sand represented years of repetition. The more these connections were repeated, the deeper the 'rut' got, the stronger the connection became." Going with our newly created metaphor, Hunter sighed.

Client: I'm definitely stuck in a rut.

Counselor: You feel stuck. And it also sounds like you feel like these "ruts" are keeping you trapped. The good news is, we can change that "trap" and those "ruts." Those "ruts" are a creation of your brain trying to make associations to keep you safe. Unfortunately, sometimes we get stuck in patterns that are no longer helpful to us. When that happens, we can create new connections in time with that same repetition.

FIGURE 3.11 Experience Instead of Anxiety

I then asked Hunter to choose new miniatures to represent what she would ideally like to experience instead of anxiety (Figure 3.11). Using the same process, I drew new connections in the sand, explaining that the work of change involves creating new connections and then reinforcing them so that they are as deep or even stronger than the connections we had discussed before.

Together, we created a new visual brain world, with new connections and fading old connections. Following-up with our activity, we used a shared language of "getting out of the rut," "changing old patterns," and "reinforcing new connections" to discuss why change feels so difficult but also how it is possible. Most importantly, Hunter began to believe that she was capable of change with the new realization that her brain was not fixed and unchangeable but plastic and adaptable.

ETHICAL AND MULTICULTURAL CONSIDERATIONS

Although *Playing Out Your Brain World* is helpful for a diverse range of clients presenting with a variety of concerns, clinicians should always be thoughtful and intentional when using it, as it may not be appropriate, or may need to be adapted, for some clients. For example, some clients may not enjoy or be willing to engage in creative or sand tray counseling for a variety of reasons. Rather than immediately conceptualizing this reluctance as client resistance, clinicians can embrace the mindset of creativity to think outside of the box and find a method that works better for their clients. If using play therapy miniatures, be sure to include a variety that your clients can relate to, such as a variety of races and genders. In addition, given the powerful nature of creativity to stimulate vulnerability, counselors should be prepared and inform their clients that traumatic or emotionally painful experiences may arise from the use of the sand tray.

It is important to note that ethical counselors always represent their training, licensure, and credentials accurately to their clients and the public (American Counseling Association, 2014). Incorporating sand tray or play into counseling does not mean counselors are doing "play therapy" or are "play therapists," unless they have undergone the play therapy training, supervised direct experience, and other requirements outlined by the Association for Play Therapy (n.d.). Non-play-therapist counselors who incorporate sand tray or play into their counseling practices must accurately describe their use as incorporating creative interventions or creativity into counseling. Additional training or certification in play therapy or expressive arts counseling is recommended to those interested in professional development but not considered a requirement to use this activity.

THE CREATIVE MINDFULNESS TECHNIQUE

Corinna Costello

Historical and/or current exposure to traumatic events is common among clinical populations (National Institute of Mental Health (NIMH), 2013). Many individuals with such experiences report problematic neurophysiological symptoms (e.g., startle response, altered perceptions and behaviors, and disassociation). The body's adaptive responses at the time of the trauma can sometimes get "stuck" in chronic hyperarousal and are unable to return to pre-trauma homeostatic levels (Szeszko et al., 2018). Understanding how trauma affects the brain and body is important for case conceptualization and treatment planning (Bicknell-Hentges & Lynch, 2009). Just as the brain can alter its response when exposed to traumatic experiences, it can also shift the neuronal pathways within the brain toward healing through growth-promoting experiences.

Researchers have demonstrated that neuroplasticity in the brain occurs when new neural networks adapt to new experiences, learn new information, and create new memories (Siegel, 2010a). The process of neuroplasticity is modulated by genetics but dependent on outside experiences. The reshaping of neuronal circuitry is also affected by emotions, cognitions, and behaviors connected to the experience (Davidson & Begley, 2012). The *creative mindfulness technique* (*CMT*) is an original strength-based approach that reworks and reshapes the trauma experiences within the counseling process. The goal of *CMT* is to embrace the natural process of neuroplasticity to aid in physiological regulation and strength-based approaches of resilience. Concepts like body awareness, resilience, creativity, and mindfulness are commonplace in contemporary trauma treatments, especially interventions incorporating a neuroscience perspective (Follette et al., 2006; Goodman & Calderon, 2012; Hass-Cohen et al., 2014).

The concept of building resilience is a common focus of treatment for traumatized individuals. Resiliency is a process defined as "adapting well in the face of adversity, trauma, tragedy, threats, or even significant sources of stress" (American Psychological Association, 2013a, p. 2). It is an adaptive response to struggles that is strengthened by proactive strategies of coping, problem solving, and facing one's fears (Feder et al., 2010). When scholars talk about resilience in the neurological context, they often refer to balance or an ability to return the individual's system back to homeostasis (Hass-Cohen et al., 2014).

Creative activities, such as art making, music, and movement, as well as mindfulness, can enhance learning and provide opportunities for novel insights and the process of integration of traumatic experiences (Gladding, 2011; Leckey, 2011; Rappaport, 2014). Schmid (2005) defined the act of creativity or being creative as an "innate capacity to think and act in original ways, to be inventive, to be imaginative and to find new and original solutions to needs, problems and forms of expression" (p. 6). The engagement with art materials, along with the concrete visual imagery, may allow for easier access to emotional material, more so than verbal approaches (Czamanski-Cohen & Weihs, 2016). Further, creativity can be an inherent predictor and possible facilitator of resiliency (Hass-Cohen et al., 2014; Metzl & Morrell, 2008).

Researchers have also found that specific activities, such as mindfulness, can alter the stress response and support healing from traumatic experiences (Follette et al., 2006). Mindfulness exercises help strengthen parts of the brain that are often most affected by trauma and are critical for fear modulation and emotion regulation (Goodman & Calderon, 2012). The axonal fibers at the prefrontal region strengthen links to other areas of the brain. For example, the cortex or the higher functioning region of the brain influence aspects of thought and action concerning the traumatic moment. The limbic area or the emotional region of the brain that includes the amygdala, hippocampus, thalamus, and hypothalamus focus on the emotional response surrounding the traumatic experience. Finally, the deeper region of the brain stem communicates with the spinal cord and controls breathing and the body functions that are interwoven into the individual's physical experience of the trauma (Siegel, 2012b). Ultimately, mindfulness teaches attentiveness to the body's physical sensations so that "we can recognize the ebb and flow of our emotions, and with that, increase our control over them" (Van der Kolk, 2014, p. 208).

Researchers have been exploring various options of creativity and mindfulness, as well as the integrative process of creative activities with mindfulness techniques. For example, Kalmanowitz (2016) studied two refugee women from different countries who took part in the *Inhabited Studio*, an art therapy and mindfulness studio approach. Elbrecht and Antcliff (2014) explored the integration of body awareness into psychotherapy through a focus on sensorimotor processes. Other researchers, such as Monti et al. (2006), combined mindfulness and creative arts to identify significant decreases in distress symptomology. Finally, Hass-Cohen et al. (2014) developed an art therapy neurobiological-based trauma protocol designed to facilitate the processing of the trauma narrative and aid in rebalancing the dysregulated responses of the participant. When delivered to individuals experiencing post-traumatic stress after witnessing the September 11, 2001 attacks on the World Trade Center, the intervention resulted in a reduction in anxiety and avoidant behaviors.

The *CMT* is an integrative process that uses creative activities with mindfulness techniques to promote body awareness, embrace aspects of neural integration through creativity, build strength through resilience, and practice and empower emotional regulation within the treatment of trauma-related symptoms. The *CMT* builds on the brain's natural capacity for neuroplasticity to help clients move toward enhanced neurophysiological regulation and resilience.

MATERIALS NEEDED

To facilitate the *CMT*, you will need art supplies that promote a sense of control and emotional expression. Art supplies that allow the client to "feel in control" include the following:

- Pencils
- Markers
- Crayons
- White or colored paper
- 8 ½ x 11-in. white/colored papers provide a natural outline and boundary

Items that provide for more opportunities for emotional expression include the following:

- Magazine images that are precut and that visually and thematically connect with the client's culture, interests, or concerns. Images of individual people, groups of people, and items of relevance support the client in their creative experience
- White glue or glue sticks
- Construction paper of various colors
- Age-appropriate scissors
- Lightweight tactile items, such as sticker, feathers, or felt

PROCESS OF THE ACTIVITY

The *CMT* can be used in a single-session or multisession format. The *CMT* approach is most suitable for individuals over the age of 5. Adaptations are needed for children and adults according to ability level.

Step 1. The first step of the *CMT* is exploring basic information about the brain and brain functioning with clients. For example, share information like the following: *"Under calm situations, our rational brain sends information to other parts of the brain, which allow us to think things through and make decisions based on the information presented. This is a top-down process that allows for* *conscious and rational decisions to be made. In optimally functioning brains, the rational part of the brain, the prefrontal cortex, regulates brain structures in the limbic region, the emotional part of the brain. However, when we are under stress, our brain alters its functioning approach. When a threat is perceived, the body becomes activated, and the rational part of the brain becomes less active."* After you introduce any neuroscience information, it is important to engage the client in processing this information. Some example prompts include the following:

> Which part of your brain seems to be more active? What does it mean to you to hear this information about how the brain communicates and responds to threat?

Step 2. In the second part of this activity, transition from sharing general information about the brain to sharing specific neuroscience information relevant to the client's stress or trauma experience. For example, you might say, "*When our body senses something stressful, the information travels up the central nervous system through the thalamus region of the brain. The brain sends chemical signals directly to the amygdala which releases hormones. When these chemicals are sent down through the nervous system into the body, the body responds by releasing adrenaline (i.e., epinephrine). This chemical activates the sympathetic nervous system and the pituitary gland which releases a flooding of cortisol hormones throughout the body. This level of activation serves to prepare the system for a survival action. Peter Levine (2010) described the various ways we respond to threat as: Arrest (increased vigilance, scanning), Flight (try first to escape), Fight (if the animal or person is prevented from escaping), Freeze (fright-scared stiff), and Fold (collapse into helplessness)*" (p. 48). Follow-up prompts during this step can include the following: *What level of activation do you find yourself in most often? When have you been in each of these levels, and what was the outcome?*

Step 3. The direct sharing of neuroscience information in Steps 1 and 2 prepares the client for the heart of *CMT*. Provide a brief rationale for how the intervention could be helpful to integrate the rational and emotional parts of the brain to help the client access multiple levels of responding depending on the necessity of the context of the situation. Facilitate a discussion about the potential risks and benefits of the intervention. The discussion should focus on the level of activation the client may experience and what type of support will be necessary.

For a Single-Session Activity

The next step is to engage in mindfulness and breath work (see script), as well as support the client's body awareness and focused breathing for 30 seconds to 2 minutes, based on the client's tolerance level for the experience. After completing the mindfulness and breathing component, provide the following directive to the client: "*Create an artistic expression about what coping and wellness looks or feels like using the presented materials.*" Allow the client enough time to complete the presented task and at the end of the activity, provide the client with an index card to title their piece of art on one side and write out a written description on the other side. Once that process is completed, respectfully secure the piece of art to a wall or arrange and display it on the table away from the materials. Allow the client time to examine the experience and the completed work through visual and verbal processing.

Creative Activity Prompts to Continue With Multiple Session Applications

If you wish to keep the *CMT* going throughout multiple sessions, then you can use the following prompts as the focus for each session.

Session 2. *"Create an artistic expression about your strengths and your struggles in the context of the trauma."* This directive serves to support the inherent strengths of the client and to identify any perceived struggles the client may have during the treatment of trauma exposure.

Session 3. *"Create an artistic expression about who you are, who you want to be, and how others see you."* This directive allows the client to identify how they see themselves and how others might experience them.

Session 4. *"Create an artistic expression of nurturing and support."* This directive brings this process back to strength aiding the client in identifying what they need for moving through the trauma experience.

Session 5. *"Create an artistic expression of how you believe your brain has become an ally in your journey."* This directive integrates the learned and intentional behaviors of mindfulness and visualizes strength and empowerment into one's being.

FOLLOW-UP

When clients complete their artistic expressions, you can use the following prompts to encourage reflection: *What is the title for this piece and why? What was this self-expression process like for you? Tell me a story about this image. How did your body respond to this CMT? If you were to do this again, what would you change about the experience?*

A formal approach to assessing the effectiveness of this process can include a resiliency scale of the clinician's choice, such as the Connor-Davidson Resiliency Scale (CD-RISC; Connor & Davidson, 2003), the Resiliency Scale (Wagnild & Young, 1993), or the Scale of Protective Factors (Ponce-Garcia et al., 2015). You can provide a pre- and post-test of your chosen measure.

NEUROSCIENCE IN ACTION

A 20-year-old female client named Toni sought counseling to address high levels of anxiety related to her required emergency surgery 4 months prior. At that time, she was also diagnosed with chronic inflammatory bowel disease. She expressed anxiety related to school, long-term career goals, and relationships. She had to consider life-altering issues, such as not having the medication when required, how the illness would affect her social life, and long-term family considerations, such as genetics and her future children.

This initial session served to familiarize Toni with the rationale for the *CMT* approach. The clinician discussed the potential risks and benefits within the *CMT* approach and the level of activation the client may experience. Focus was placed on the type of support the client might require during or after the session.

> Counselor: *Toni, I am so glad you came in today and are acknowledging the struggles that you are having. The Creative Mindfulness Technique is an approach to support you in acknowledging your struggles and recognizing your strengths. This process can help you build resilience. The potential risks with this approach include feelings of vulnerability that can come with creating art and self-expression. Please let me know if you are experiencing any negative reactions as we progress.*

I then administered the CD-RISC (Connor & Davidson, 2003) to evaluate her level of resiliency at the beginning of treatment. Toni's total score was 67/100, with higher scores indicating higher levels of reported resilience. This baseline CD-RISC score was later compared to CD-RISC scores of future administrations during the *CMT* approach. I then introduced the mindfulness and breathing step by saying, *"Please get yourself comfortable in the chair and place your feet firmly on the ground. Take deep breaths and allow yourself to keep your eyes open or closed during this mindfulness moment.*" The mindfulness and breathing script lasted about 2 minutes and was read in a calm and slow manner to support relaxation and comfort.

After the mindfulness and breathing step, I introduced the artistic expression portion of the *CMT*. She responded well to the presented art materials and demonstrated visible excitement in her body language and level of animation. I offered the following directive: "*Create an artistic expression about what coping and wellness look or feel like using the presented materials.*" She chose markers and colored on 8½" x 11" white paper and entitled the piece "Spiral of Recovery." She was given enough time to complete the work, and when presented with the index card, she described the work in writing as follows:

> Recovery is just a never-ending spiral. There are no real ups or downs, just emotions that can get heightened or dulled as time goes on. There is no real end in sight, but with chronic disease, there is no change in shape. And beyond the spiral of recovery is all of the other life events and emotions—not as prominent, but still present. And their colors and significance end up leaking into the recovery spiral.

Once that process was completed, I respectfully secured the artwork to the wall. I then provided time to examine the experience and the completed work through visual and verbal processing. I asked the client to answer the following questions:

What is the title of this piece and why? The client explained what was written on the index card and discussed what it felt like to get sick and shift from a healthy young woman with her life in front of her to a woman with a chronic illness. She identified that she would always be concerned with her health, her medications, and her future.

What was this self-expression process like for you? The client discussed her excitement about being creative and the freedom it provided. She discussed the opportunity for her feelings to be expressed but identified concern for the level of disclosure within her artwork and wondered how much she could or should share.

Tell me a story about this image. The client examined the image of the downward spiral and how it represented her own personal situation. She identified the emotionality of the reflections of the colors and the ability to, as she stated, "place a color into a feeling as they played off of each other." She continued to compare it as a color spectrum versus the emotional spectrum.

How did your body respond to this Creative Mindfulness Technique? The client reported feeling a release of energy and tension in her body as she engaged in the *CMT* process. The client acknowledged feeling tingling in her body and light-headed. She acknowledged her breathing was calm and the tightness in her shoulders was reduced. Ultimately, she identified feeling higher levels of focus and concentration, as well as motivation to complete one of her personal goals for that day.

If you were to do this again, what would you change about the experience? The client wanted to have more time to engage in the *CMT* approach, as she was comfortable with the process and the product, but she could recognize that other clients might need more time to feel comfortable with it.

ETHICAL AND MULTICULTURAL CONSIDERATIONS

Clinicians should have some training and supervision in using expressive arts interventions before implementing the *CMT*. The *CMT* approach requires an active and highly empathic demeanor. It is necessary to acknowledge the client's fears and support those concerns throughout the process.

The act of being creative involves risk-taking and leads to vulnerability. Developmentally, this approach is highly relatable to children, as much of their learning occurs in a creative sphere that combines cognition with creativity and play. Adolescents may have more hesitation over engaging in the creativity, which they may perceive as childish or immature; however, this approach may still be effective by replacing the primacy of face-to-face dialogue with a counselor with a tactile and self-expressive exchange that is still relational. Adults may also have more hesitation that requires attunement and exploration to enhance motivation.

Ultimately, the strength of the *CMT* is that it goes beyond the verbal processing of an experience. It provides more opportunities for brain activation and integration across structures, systems, and networks. The cautionary approach to the clinician is to closely monitor and support the process. It is important to watch the client for stress activation and the reexperiencing of the trauma event. The clinical goal is to coordinate the pacing of the *CMT* to the client's traumatic processing of the trauma events.

The *CMT* is highly effective in honoring clients' perspectives and their multicultural experiences. Integrating the approach with mindfulness allows for a decrease in the stress response and demonstrates an openness to new experiences engaged in collaboratively. This process supports the building of resiliency within the traumatized client. In fact, "many different cultures have healing traditions that activate and utilize physical movement and breath" (Ogden et al., 2006, p. xxiii). Clinicians should make sure to have a variety of materials available so that individuals of various cultural backgrounds and experiences can find items to represent their worlds.

ANCILLARY MATERIALS

Mindfulness and Breathing Script

Get comfortable on the seat or the floor. Take a big deep breath and relax with your eyes open or closed. Be aware of sounds coming and going and let them be whatever they are. Know that you are taking this time to meditate. You can drop all other concerns during this period, like setting down a heavy (bag) (box) (load) before plopping onto a comfortable (chair) (couch) (bed). After the meditation, you can pick those concerns up again—if you want to. Bring your awareness to the sensation of breathing. Don't try to control the breath; let it be whatever it is. Sense the cool air coming in and warm air going out, the chest and belly rising and falling.

Try to stay with the sensations of each breath from beginning to end. You may want to softly count your breaths—count to 10 and then start over; go back to one if your mind wanders—or note them quietly to yourself as "in" and "out." It's normal for the mind to wander, and when it does, just return to the breath. Be gentle and kind to yourself. See if you can stay attentive to 10 breaths in a row. After your mind settles down during the first minutes of the mindfulness, explore becoming increasingly absorbed in the breath and letting go of everything else. Open yourself to the simple pleasures of breathing; give over to the breath. With some practice, see if you can stay present with the breath for dozens of breaths in a row.

Using the breath as a kind of anchor; be aware of whatever else is moving through the mind. Be aware of thoughts and feelings, wishes and plans, images and memories—all coming and going. Let them be what they are; don't get caught up in them; don't struggle with or get fascinated by them. Have a sense of acceptance—even kindness—toward whatever passes through the open space of awareness.

Keep settling into the breath, perhaps with a growing sense of peacefulness. Be aware of the changing nature of what passes through the mind. Notice how it feels to get caught up in the passing contents of awareness—and how it feels to let them go by. Be aware of peaceful, spacious awareness itself.

In the next few moments, we will bring this meditation to an end. Notice how you feel and take in the good of your mindfulness moment. Allow yourself to enjoy those feelings throughout the rest of your day.

PLANTING SEEDS AND WATCHING THEM GROW

An 8-Week Psychoeducation and Process Group to Foster Post-Traumatic Growth

Charmayne Adams and Eve Rogerson

Traumatic events can have a significant and lasting effect on emotional regulation, engagement with others, and daily functioning in occupational and personal tasks (Kira et al., 2015; Layne et al., 2011). Most counselors will work with at least one client, and in most cases many clients, who have experienced a traumatic event (Greene et al., 2016). As practitioners, it is imperative that we use a neuro-informed approach to appreciate the effect of trauma and the complexity of the trauma response. This includes a foundational understanding of neurobiological mechanisms and how those mechanisms can aid in effective interventions that foster healing and growth.

NEUROBIOLOGICAL STRESS RESPONSE

The human stress response system evolved as a way to enhance safety in times of threat. The brain experiences stress as a whole system event (Luke, 2016). The autonomic and endocrine responses (accompanied by an emotional component) prepare the body to respond quickly by secreting epinephrine, norepinephrine, and steroid stress hormones. This release of epinephrine affects glucose metabolism, causing the nutrients stored in the muscles to become available for strenuous movement (Kumar et al., 2013). This release of stress hormones in the body and the brain begins a chain of events, including increased heart rate, elevated startle response, perspiration, and difficulty accessing higher order cognitive functioning that leads to "racing thoughts" (Carlson, 2013). This system is intended for short-term use to evade threat, but in some cases, the threatening situation is continuous (e.g., domestic abuse, high violence communities) and leads to a prolonged stress response. When working with clients who have experienced a traumatic event, it is foundational to support their exploration of the unique ways they respond to the traumatic experience and promote a spirit of normalization to the adaptive nature of these responses (SAMHSA, 2014).

THE NEUROSCIENCE OF POST-TRAUMATIC GROWTH

Post-traumatic growth (PTG) has been one of the most important concepts regarding the changes following trauma and adversity (Joseph & Linley, 2008). PTG is a response to a traumatic event that results in a positive change in how a person sees the world and increases a sense of psychological well-being (Joseph & Linley, 2008). PTG consists of five domains: (1) relating to others, (2) new possibilities, (3) personal strength, (4) spiritual change, and (5) deeper appreciation of life (Tedeschi & Calhoun, 1996). PTG is often fostered by several skills or conditions, such as optimism, positive reappraisal, social support, and spiritual well-being (Prati & Pietrantoni, 2009; Sehgal, Sethi, & Vaneet, 2016). The potential for not just healing but growth after trauma can be fostered in a therapeutic relationship, and counselors are well-suited to facilitate this process.

Although there are studies that support the existence of PTG in people who have experienced a variety of traumas (Arpawong et al., 2017; Helgeson et al., 2006), research examining the neurobiological process of PTG and its five domains is in its infancy. Nonetheless, it is important to review a few empirical and conceptual links between neuroscience and the PTG domains to facilitate our neuroeducation exercise.

Social engagement is one of the five domains of PTG. The dorsolateral prefrontal cortex (DLPFC) has been shown to be the main neural correlate of relating to others, and individuals have shown increased regional gray matter volume in the prefrontal cortex (PFC) after experiencing trauma (Nakagawa et al., 2016). This finding could support a link between DLPFC activity and the relating to others' dimension of PTG. In addition, social encounters affect the way our bodies respond to stress. Socialization, or how those around us respond to adverse events, can affect how we perceive danger or threat (Carlson, 2013). For instance, if those around us dictate that we are not in danger, then the body is less likely to release hormones to ready us for action, and vice versa.

In addition to the role of the PFC in social connection, there is evidence for its involvement in the consideration of new possibilities. The activation of networks primarily responsible for working memory and executive functioning have been shown to be stronger in individuals with higher psychological growth following an adverse experience (Fujisawa et al., 2015). Although this is a retrospective correlation, it supports the idea that the consideration of new possibilities is influenced by neural network connectivity and, by extension, that promoting neural integration in a counseling setting may enable clients to begin to consider new possibilities and increase their PTG.

The use of positive reappraisal has also shown consistent alterations in the height and length of activation of emotional centers of the brain (Waugh et al., 2016). In addition, structural connectivity in cortical regions of the brain have been correlated with positive reappraisal (van der Werff et al., 2017). Consistent reappraisal and reframing of the trauma and practicing this reappraisal in daily life can cultivate neuroplasticity and neurogenesis that taps into Hebb's (1949) seminal thought that Shatz (1992) adapted into the clever phrase "neurons that fire together, wire together" (p. 64).

Counselors with an understanding of the neurobiological function of the stress response system and an awareness of the five domains of PTG can help clients place their symptoms into the context of adaptability instead of dysfunction. Given the growing neuroscience evidence for the process of PTG, it is important to develop interventions that are informed by this evidence. Group psychotherapy is one intervention with growing evidence for the development of PTG (Ramos et al., 2016; Zhang et al., 2015). Given this evidence, along with the importance of social connection to foster PTG, we created an 8-week group intervention entitled *Planting Seeds and Watching Them Grow: An 8-Week Psychoeducation and Process Group to Foster Post-Traumatic Growth.*

By providing accessible neuroeducation about the possibility of PTG and strategies to develop PTG, the *Planting Seeds* intervention supports clients' awareness of the neurobiological correlates of their unique trauma responses and PTG, reframing their past coping behaviors as strengths and identifying new strategies based on the five domains of PTG. This helps reduce the shame that clients often feel when they do not cognitively understand their responses (e.g., I don't know why I keep responding in this way) and promotes flexibility in response selection.

PROCESS OF THE ACTIVITY

Planting Seeds is an 8-week group intervention that aims to increase awareness of trauma responses and possibilities for developing PTG. As with all group interventions, it is necessary to begin with recruitment and selection of participants for the group. The selection criteria should consider the type of trauma experienced and current level of distress and/or PTG. Counselors can administer a formal PTG assessment, such as the Posttraumatic Growth Inventory-Short Form (PTGI-SF; Cann et al., 2010). We advise that group members should have similar trauma experiences since most of the group work research for PTG has focused on homogenous groups of individuals (Ramos

MATERIALS NEEDED

- An accessible space and location conducive for group work
- Chairs (preferably in a circle)
- Clipboards
- Pens
- Access to amenities, such as restrooms and water
- A whiteboard for brainstorming
- An outline for each of the eight sessions
- Copies of the *Let It Grow* worksheet for all group members
- Copies of the Posttraumatic Growth Inventory (PTGI; Tedeschi & Calhoun, 1996)

et al., 2016; Zhang et al., 2014). We recommend a group size of four to eight members to provide space for each group member to share their experiences and process the weekly activities. During the first four sessions, the clinician creates awareness around the phenomenon of trauma and the effect it is having on various neurobiological systems (affect/feeling, cognitive/thought, somatic/body sensations, and behavioral/actions). In the final four sessions, PTG is introduced and used to explore how the concept could increase a sense of wellness for clients.

In **Sessions 1, 2, and 3**, the group facilitator helps the participants build community, establish group norms, and explore the neurobiological concepts connected to trauma. The information presented in the rationale section earlier can be used as a touchstone, but the facilitator is also encouraged to supplement with additional literature that aligns with the developmental level and unique trauma experiences that were used for participant selection. At the conclusion of Session 3, the group should have a firm understanding of what trauma is and how the body responds in times of adversity. This foundational knowledge will be impactful in the subsequent weeks as the information is applied to the unique experience of the participant during Session 4.

In **Session 4**, the counselor opens the group by checking in with participants and reviewing the trauma material covered in the previous weeks. The facilitator then introduces the *Plant the Seed* section of the *Let It Grow* worksheet. The participants can read through the psychoeducation portion at the top and ask questions, elaborate, or take notes about what they have learned about trauma in the previous weeks. The *Plant the Seed* section completed during the session highlights aspects of the definition of trauma and stress that will be helpful for clients to use as they move forward in the activity. Open-ended process questions are useful during this group session to help members begin to integrate previous group sessions and life experiences with the current activity. (*Counselor*: "Over the past three weeks, we have talked about the brain and body science of trauma. I am wondering what parts of this hit home or stuck out for each of you?")

Next, guide the group members through identifying their own emotions, thoughts, bodily sensations, and behaviors that are a result of the traumatic experience. Depending on the group's familiarity with these concepts, the group facilitator may need to offer extra support to help members generate ideas. It is advised that the group facilitator be ready to provide examples or bring awareness to symptoms that were mentioned in previous groups. (*Counselor*: "Jane, in group last week, you said that you were experiencing more headaches after your car accident; this could be an example of a somatic impact from your traumatic experience.") Encourage participants to connect these symptoms to what they learned about trauma and stress, including the neurobiological aspects of trauma and the physical impact of the prolonged stress response. It may also be helpful to remind members that the body's stress response is just its way of responding to environmental circumstances. Avoid suggesting that all physiological responses are caused by the traumatic experience and ensure an adequate medical evaluation has been conducted.

After each member has generated a few items, begin to process how cultural aspects may influence the way they were affected by the traumatic event (*Counselor*: Trevor, I remember you mentioning in a previous group that you felt a lot of shame and guilt about being afraid to walk at night in the dark after your assault. I'm wondering if there is some connection to your sense of "being a tough man," which you mentioned being an important part of your cultural identity?). From the cultural impacts, the group members move into ways they have coped with the effect of the traumatic event. It is important here to help maintain a nonjudgmental space where coping activities are not viewed as all good or all bad but rather that activities are their best attempts at managing a traumatic experience and its effect on their lives. (*Counselor*: "I know sometimes we label our ways of coping with stressful events as "good or bad"; I want to encourage everyone to think of all the ways they have coped with the traumatic event in a nonjudgmental way so we can get a full picture of how our bodies and minds are trying to adapt to the situation.")

This entire session is guided by the *Plant the Seed* section of the *Let It Grow* worksheet with the facilitator allowing time for participants to fill in each section as the growth progresses. The utility of these worksheets is that they allow participants to individualize the psychoeducation they have learned and provide a tangible guide for them to keep after the group is completed. If there is not enough time to complete the entire *Plant the Seed* section, group members are encouraged to continue completing it in between sessions, and you can review it during the beginning of the next session if necessary.

In **Session 5**, the counselor will open by finishing up any material that was not completed in Session 4 and asking clients to share their previously effective coping strategies with the group. Some of these strategies will have been identified in Session 4, but the focus of Session 5 is to focus on the resources that clients can use, which will lay the foundation for learning about building resiliency and the possibility of PTG. The participants can again read through the psychoeducation portion at the top of the *Watch It Sprout* section of the *Let It Grow* worksheet and ask questions or discuss their initial thoughts on PTG. The psychoeducation aspect of this session focuses on information about the growth that can come from adverse experiences without discounting the significant negative effects of trauma. Specifically, clients will be introduced to the domains of PTG (i.e., relating to others, new possibilities, personal strength, spiritual change, and deeper appreciation of life) in the context of existing coping skills, by asking clients to categorize these skills and generate ideas for new coping skills in each category. After answering questions and discussing the key tenets of PTG, guide the group through identifying the strengths and skills they already use for coping; they can write this information down on their worksheets. (*Counselor*: "When we begin to introduce new activities in our lives to build resilience we have the potential to form new neural pathways, this is all neurogenesis. We will be spending the next couple sessions flexing our brain muscle and working with each other to problem solve, highlight strengths, and explore possibilities to promote integration between all the parts of our brains and bodies that we explored to this point.") It may be useful to have group members brainstorm their ideas together on the whiteboard, sharing things they do that they have in common, as well as more individualized strategies.

When each member has identified at least one coping skill and how it has benefited them, the counselor can lead the group in connecting cultural components from the last session to their effective coping behaviors and identifying ways to overcome barriers to adopting new strategies that can lead to PTG. From here, ask the group to generate at least one coping strategy for each of the five PTG domains. Counselors should encourage clients to operationalize their strategies fully. (*Counselor*: "Spending more time one-on-one with your partner is a great way to work on relating more to others, Amira. I'm wondering if you can pick one or two activities for you both to do and how often each week you could do them?") Clients will then set goals to adopt at least two of these strategies for the remaining sessions of the group.

In **Sessions 6 and 7**, clients will be asked to do round-robin feedback as a group, reflecting on their experiences of implementing their PTG strategies. Discussions around what has worked and what has not, as well as suggestions between group members, can be facilitated by the counselor. (*Counselor*: "Over the past week, we have practiced implementing new strategies to increase our sense of wellness and PTG. Who would like to share what they have tried so far?") These two sessions of the group focus on processing and integrating the psychoeducation that was learned throughout the group, the personal experiences group members have reflected on, and the actions taken to apply them. It is a supportive space to explore what is working and what is not working and to continue to generate ideas to build resilience and PTG.

In **Session 8**, as part of termination and evaluation, clients will be asked to complete the same PTG scale administered before group counseling began. This assessment will allow counselors to assess any increase in PTG more objectively. As with all therapeutic groups, counselors should take time to reflect on the group process and be mindful of attending to group members as they reflect on spending 8 weeks together sharing their struggles and triumphs. (*Counselor*: "Today is our last session, I would like to spend some time talking about what everyone will carry away from this experience after it is done.").

FOLLOW-UP

The evaluation of this group begins informally in Session 6 and continues to a more formal evaluation in Session 8. The group process emphasis in Sessions 6 and 7 allows the counselor to gain an understanding of how group members are integrating material. In Session 8, counselors administer the same PTG scale that was completed during the first session (e.g., PTGI-SF) to objectively assess client increase in PTG. After completing the PTG scale, the group facilitator should move into eliciting feedback on the group content and process to gain qualitative information on areas of strength and improvement for the entire intervention. (*Counselor*: We are going to end by completing the same PTG scale that we completed in the first session. Please let me know if you have any questions or concerns. I encourage you to be as honest as possible. After it is completed, I would like to have a conversation about your reactions to the group as a whole. I would love to know if there were parts you enjoyed or feel could be improved.)

NEUROSCIENCE IN ACTION

This case study focuses on the fourth and fifth sessions of the *Planting Seeds and Watching Them Grow* group that were facilitated by Charmayne and Eve. We hope this case study will help demonstrate what dialogue may look like when connecting the neurobiological concepts to the experiences of participants. In this illustration, the intervention group consists of six participants and two group facilitators; the group members were chosen because they all shared the experience of being survivors of domestic violence. During the screening process for the group, Charmayne and Eve ensured that the group members were not still in a domestic violence situation and had resolved any immediate safety concerns, such as housing, finances, and/or medical attention that may have resulted from the initial traumatic experience. The purpose of this vignette is to demonstrate how Charmayne led a conversation about stress response and how Eve led a conversation about PTG. Care is given to provide examples of how to explore complex concepts with clients in a relatable manner.

Example Conversation From Group Session 4

Charmayne (*Counselor*): I want everyone to take a moment and think about the different ways that your domestic violence experience has impacted you. You can start with any of the impact areas on the *Plant the Seed* side of the *Let It Grow* worksheet: feelings, thoughts, physical sensations, and actions.

Jenny (*Group participant*): You know, I hadn't really thought about it, but every time someone slams a door, my heart races. It seems to get worse at night.

Charmayne: So, you notice your heart rate increasing when you hear a door slam, especially at night.

Robin (*Group participant*): I feel really jumpy also, but for me it is yelling. When I hear people yell, it's like my heartbeat is in my ears.

Charmayne: Robin, you have experienced this also. Do either of you remember how that might be connected to your stress response system that we talked about?

Robin: Something to do with the body getting ready to move?

Jenny: Yeah, my mind thinks that the door slamming is a threat, which it was. I always knew that Ben [former partner] was drunk when I started to hear doors slamming in the house. When that started, I knew it was only a matter of time before he would come find me.

Charmayne: Your body was moving into survival mode; it was trying to keep you safe in that moment. Get you ready to move quickly.

Jenny: Yes, I had to do that for so long, it's hard to shut it off.

Robin: I feel the exact same way, it's like I know I'm safe, but I can't turn it off.

Charmayne: Let's look back at the information on the top of the *Plant the Seed* worksheet; it seems like this is an example for both of you of a lasting negative impact. It's gone on longer than the threat. So what category would we put this one in?

Jenny: Physical.

Robin: And I could put jumpy in the behavioral.

Charmayne: Go ahead and write those in the boxes that you think they fit in. How is everyone else doing? Does anyone have an example of an emotional or cognitive impact?

Example Conversation From Group Session 5

Eve (*Counselor*): In our last session, we began to consider what kinds of coping strategies have been helpful in the past when dealing with stress. Would anyone feel comfortable to share theirs with the group?

Robin (*Group participant*): I can share. I find that calling a friend and talking to them about how I'm feeling, especially when I can't seem to calm myself down, is really soothing. Just knowing someone else is on the end of the line who can remind me that I'm safe—it helps.

Eve (Writing group member's answer on the whiteboard)**:** So, you find that connecting with another person is an effective way to manage those symptoms of stress, especially when they can help remind you that you're safe.

Jenny (*Group participant*): Sometimes I find that helps too, but other times, I just feel stupid having to ask someone to help me feel better about something going on in my head. For me, I'd rather put on some relaxing music and do a short yoga practice. It helps me breathe and think about something else.

Eve (Writes this answer on the whiteboard also)**:** While you too have experienced that connecting with someone else can be helpful in managing your stress response, oftentimes, you would rather engage in a mindfulness practice like yoga, which sounds like it both reduces some of those physiological responses we talked about, as well as reframes your mind in a positive way.

Jenny: Yes! It's like it makes it possible to focus on looking forward rather than always dwelling on the past.

Eve: That's a powerful image, Jenny, the idea of being able to look forward with hope away from the distress of the past. When we introduce new activities like this, we start to form new neural pathways—the brain is making new connections and building resiliency. If we take a look at the second part of the worksheet, *Watch It Sprout,* there is a section that splits these kinds of activities into different categories, all of which have been shown to promote neurogenesis, that brain growth, that can lead to healing. Looking at the two examples we have here, in which category would you put "calling a friend"?

Robin: That sounds like "relating to others."

Jenny: Agreed. And yoga and music are "mindfulness."

Eve: Both great examples of activities that can promote growth and increase neural connections. How is everyone else doing? Does anyone have an example we could put into one of the other categories?

ETHICAL AND MULTICULTURAL CONSIDERATIONS

When considering the *Planting Seeds and Watching Them Grow* group, it is important to remember that regardless of the theoretical orientation or the intervention being used, all counselors should practice from a trauma-informed lens. Clients often feel disempowered, overwhelmed, and helpless after a traumatic event, and practicing from a trauma-informed perspective can help maintain a sense of safety, instill autonomy, and encourage mastery at a time when clients need it most (SAMHSA, 2014). Clinicians must remain vigilant to not inadvertently disempower clients by using neurobiological terms and concepts that send a message that the client's brain is "broken" or "damaged." Neurobiology is a tool that can be used within the wellness and developmental counseling framework to help support, rather than replace, basic counseling skills and interventions; we are not neurobiologists but rather wellness professionals who use neuroscience to inform our practice.

This activity requires cultural awareness to address the unique needs of participants as they attempt to make meaning of their traumatic experiences; empirical research supports the notion that cultural factors, such as age, gender, health status, and resources, have a great effect on how individuals respond and cope with traumatic events (Marsella, 2010). Developmental and cultural considerations should be considered during the participant selection stage of *CMT* to ensure that participants are able to safely engage in this activity. Maintaining confidentiality is challenging in a group counseling format, but the counselor should encourage participants to respect the information that is shared in the group and help maintain a sense of trust among group members. Setting clear expectations concerning confidentiality, including the mandatory reporting status of the counselor, is a best practice in facilitating therapeutic groups regardless of the topic.

Let It Grow

The stress response system is the body's *normal* way of coping with a circumstance that is perceived as a threat to survival. This whole-body reaction can be initiated by any number of situations and is dependent on the way that we *perceive* the event (which is different for everyone!). When the body perceives a threat, it switches into a mode where all systems focus on *survival*, this is exactly what the body is supposed to do during these times. Our stress response is something to be appreciated, but the catch is, it is meant to be used *short term*. In conditions where the stress response is engaged and the situation is perceived as so far outside of the "norm" that the body struggles to "turn the system off," it crosses the line into what is called a *traumatizing situation*. Traumatic experience has *a lasting negative effect* on our physical and mental health because the stress response system is more easily triggered and thus experiences this impact more often. This is why it is important to be ***aware*** of how we are responding to our environment and the function that these neurobiological systems serve so that we feel *more empowered* and *in control* of our bodies and minds!

How has the traumatic event affected me? Be sure to think of examples that have increased and decreased your sense of wellness.

Emotionally (Feelings)	Cognitively (Thoughts)	Somatically (Physical Sensations)	Behaviorally (Actions)

How has my culture affected the way I understand the traumatic event? (e.g., sex, race, ethnicity, place of residence, gender)?

How have I coped with the impact?

Emotionally:

Cognitively:

Somatically:

Behaviorally:

Watch It Sprout

The negative effects of prolonged stress can have many different impacts for different people. An awareness of both how we respond to triggers in our environment and why the body is designed to respond neurobiologically in the way it does helps develop *resilience* following trauma. Many of us will already be creating opportunities to do this by connecting with friends and family and looking for ways to be more mindful in taking care of ourselves, and all of us are here today courageously *sharing our stories*. It is actions like these that can help the brain to recover from trauma, and even generate *new neurological pathways* that connect more strongly to recovery and growth. Emotions we view as positive can help to reduce the effect of our ongoing stress response, and even *reverse emotions we view as negative* altogether. This is why it is important to look at what coping skills we already have and work to develop those into actions that can promote *not only healing but also growth*!

What healthy coping behaviors have I used in the past (before this incident) that have been successful?

What new activities can I use to build my resilience?

Relating to Others	
Personal Strengths	
Spirituality/Mindfulness	
Appreciation of Life	
New Possibilities	

Additional Material for Group Facilitator

TABLE 3.1

Destructive	Facilitative
Using more drugs or alcohol than intended	Deep/slow breathing
Denying any problem	Talking to someone
Self-harm	Going for a walk or run
Withdrawing from others	Writing a list of strengths
Reckless behavior	Volunteering
Extended screen time	Learning something new

TABLE 3.2

Therapeutic Lifestyle Change	Benefits
Physical exercise	Decreases worry symptoms and makes relapse into depression less likely
Social relations	Promotes physical well-being
Cognitive challenge	Creation of new neural networks
Sleep	Brain functionality and development of neural networks
Meditation and relaxation	Helps promote calm throughout the day, increases gray matter, and promotes immune system functioning
Multicultural pride and cultural identity	Strength building around family and community, free and able to change self
Positive thinking	Build new neural structures, reduce influence of negative neural networks
Beliefs, values, and spirituality	Reminders of basic value systems and positive role models, optimistic attitude
Nature breaks	Increase memory, attention, and mood
Relaxing and having fun	Releases dopamine into nucleus accumbens
Continuing education	Develop neural networks and lessen chances of dementia
Helping others and social justice action	Reduction of stress hormones and lengthening of telomeres (protects chromosome deterioration), positive differences to helper and helpee

Adapted from Ivey et al. (2018).

ADVANCING DESPITE ADVERSITY

Building Neuro-Informed Resilience

Jurie Rossouw

Resilience can help people manage uncertainty more constructively. Resilience is a psychological and a physiological concept—both the body and mind are involved in building resilience capacity (Rossouw & Rossouw, 2016). Summarized broadly, resilience is defined as advancing despite adversity. The word "advancing" highlights that resilience is a progressive concept, helping individuals achieve something meaningful—a deep sense of satisfaction. The word "despite" suggests that adversity does not have to impede advancement or well-being. The word "adversity" is about all the large and small life challenges we face, those that must be overcome for us to advance. Resilience equips an individual with a set of skills and tools to not only overcome adversity but also to enact strategies to prepare for and avoid unnecessary challenges ahead of time.

THE NEUROSCIENCE OF RESILIENCE

Our capacity to be resilient is primarily enabled through the brain. Physiological health contributes to a healthy brain and the adaptability of neural circuits; however, it is the neural circuits themselves that we are interested in understanding and enhancing to build client resilience. Of course, the brain is the most complex system known to us, so any discussion of neuroscience is an oversimplification, but to form a basic conception of resilience at a neurological level, it helps to start with something that is accessible for clients that could lead to that "aha" moment from where they can build a more nuanced conception of resilience and link together the various strategies presented.

In our simplified model, resilience is essentially about the connective relationship between the limbic brain (LB) and the prefrontal cortex (PFC). The PFC houses the personality, ability to think strategically, critical thinking and executive functions. It contains many executive circuits that give us the ability to modify our own behavior when engaged. The LB is the older part of the brain and contains a number of different structures that are aimed at survival. The most well-known of these structures is the amygdala, having gained infamy for its role in the fear response, and activation of the fight-or-flight system through the hypothalamic pituitary adrenal (HPA) axis. In addition to the amygdala, the LB houses less well-known structures, such as the bed nucleus of the stria terminalis (BNST), which is arguably even more important than the amygdala (Lebow & Chen, 2016).

From an evolutionary perspective, the LB was crucially important to keeping us alive and thus has great overriding power in the brain. Fear activation quickly downregulates blood flow to the PFC, reducing the ability to think strategically—that type of thinking is slow, and the LB is all about reacting fast. The problem, of course, is that the vast majority of challenges we face these days require complex problem-solving skills. Hence, frequent LB activation is no longer productive in typical modern life.

Activation and integration of the LB and PFC are crucial, but in this very short tale of two brain structures, we want less LB activation and more PFC activation. If we can do this, then we can respond to challenges in more constructive ways. We can be resourceful; we can rely on friends; we can take adversity in our stride. This is a resilient outcome. So how does it come about?

IT'S ALL ABOUT CONNECTION

Neural pathways connecting the PFC to the LB are what is critically important. Strong regulatory connections between the PFC and LB enable greater self-control in adverse situations, leading to less LB activation and, therefore, a less acute fear response. This is because the LB effectively "checks in" with the PFC and other association areas in the brain to determine if an unusual situation presents a threat to the self. The LB does this very quickly, and if it finds no answer suggesting to "not worry" about the situation, then it activates the fight-or-flight response, downregulating the PFC and increasing impulsive emotional decision making.

And if the LB activates very strongly, in a single shot, it can create a memory so traumatic that it can take decades to overcome. It's here where many people think about resilience the wrong way; they tend to think resilience is what you develop in response to adversity, when really resilience should be developed *ahead* of adversity. Why? Because by developing resilience skills proactively, we start to build these regulatory neural pathways between the PFC and the LB so that when we face a big challenge and the LB sends out that signal to check if we are in danger, the PFC can come back and say, "Hey, it's OK, we're fine," unless, of course, a formidable life threat and quick response is needed. It is there that we drastically reduce the risk of the formation of traumatic memories. Building these pathways ahead of time reduces the level of LB activation and, therefore, helps us bounce back faster after a setback because the PFC can stay engaged to help us react in a more strategic and constructive way. This is why resilience is such a good protective factor against depression and is suggested to be a key part of overcoming the growing mental health challenges the world faces (Edward, 2005; Elisei et al., 2013).

From this proactive perspective, building resilience is about building connections between the PFC and the LB. Stronger connections mean an increased capacity to engage our critical thinking skills and generate a constructive outcome versus the alternative where LB activation causes fearful or perhaps anxious responses that leave us feeling defeated, worthless, and generally less interested in taking on new challenges. As there are many different types of challenges we might face through life, there are also a large variety of strategies that we can employ. How can we categorize these strategies?

THE SIX DOMAINS OF RESILIENCE

Our research, which included a meta-analysis of the top resilience psychometrics, found that overall, there are six key domains that broadly create resilience capacity (see Figure 3.12; Rossouw & Rossouw, 2016): (1) vision, (2) composure, (3) reasoning, (4) tenacity, (5) collaboration, and (6) health. These domains provide a useful framework to both assess and develop resilience. Let's briefly run through each domain to help you build a framework through which you can evaluate and build resilience in your clients.

Vision. This domain is about your sense of purpose, goals, and personal vision for yourself. Our research shows that this is the most important of all the domains (Rossouw et al., 2017) because all other domains are guided by your sense of purpose. Having clarity in this domain allows you to be decisive when facing tough choices and to maintain perspective when facing challenges. Whether your goals relate to family, to work, or a side project, what's important is being specific and clear.

Neural correlates include the ventral striatum through its role in higher order decision making and risk/reward cognition (Davidson & Begley, 2012). The interplay of memory storage and retrieval by the hippocampus and meaning assignment by the PFC plays a part in maintaining a hopeful sense of the future, and this is reinforced by goal directedness (Preston & Eichenbaum, 2013).

Composure. This domain is about regulating emotions, as well as staying calm and in control. The fight-or-flight response of the brain loves to flare up when you are facing a conflict or hearing about a sudden change at work. But being able to overcome that instinctive emotional response and maintain your composure often means being able to recognize hidden opportunities and solve problems in novel ways. As we saw earlier, LB activation prevents you from properly accessing your ability to think critically.

Composure is primarily about regulating the LB. This relates neurologically to the ability of the insula to interpret emotional signals effectively and enable regulation of the HPA axis (Davidson & Begley, 2012), which by extension connects to the PFC to regulate the threat assessments done by the amygdala and over time activation of the BNST.

Reasoning. Being resourceful, solving problems creatively, and anticipating and planning for challenges is what reasoning is about. Here we see how resilience is not only about applying critical thinking during a crisis but also about taking action ahead of time to prevent things from going wrong in the first place.

From a neural perspective, the prerequisite here is downregulation of the LB, primarily through deployed composure strategies. This allows for upregulation of the left and right PFC, activating functions in conjunction with the anterior cingulate cortex to screen for errors rapidly and optimize subsequent responses (Peterson et al., 2014).

Tenacity. Persistence is increasingly shown to be more important than intelligence in goal achievement (Duckworth et al., 2007). And within this ability to persist, we find many components, including having the ability to learn from mistakes constructively, being realistic about how difficult a task will be while still being hopeful to achieve success, being able to manage and incorporate criticism, and many more small skills that add up to create tenacity.

Various neural aspects relate to our ability to be persistent. These include the availability of dopamine acting as a motivator for action, although directed through the vision domain, toward constructive goals and behaviors. This links in with the PFC's ability to downregulate LB and subsequent HPA activation, reducing the chance to retreat emotionally when we face difficulties along the way.

Collaboration. We are social beings. The brain has a deep fundamental need for connection with others to be able to thrive. The brain has dedicated neural structures to recognize facial expressions, while mirror neurons fire within the brain to help us empathize with others. We are, after all, in this together, so what we do and focus on is not only for us but also to help our communities and improve our world. This connection is what the collaboration domain is about.

The right PFC plays a key role in secure attachment through receiving cues interpreted by other neural regions (Schore, 2000). It has been suggested that the fusiform gyrus plays this interpretive role through facial expression recognition and has been shown to be able to affect the amygdala in response to emotional faces (Pujol et al., 2009).

Health. A newly added domain validated through our research, the domain of health is about physiological wellness, including sleep hygiene, regular exercise, good nutrition, and generally looking after physical factors. A healthy body provides a strong foundation for resilience so that focus can be placed on a sense of purpose and goals. Good health is not the ultimate goal itself but instead acts as an enabler to achieve a larger personal vision.

There is extensive evidence linking these health hygiene factors to the production of brain-derived neurotrophic factor (BDNF), which plays a key role in aiding neuroplasticity that is necessary for resilient adaptation and growth. This includes how unhealthy food and alcohol downregulates BDNF (Heffernan, 2008; Molteni et al., 2002), how exercise increases BDNF and hippocampal function (Cassilhas et al., 2012; Cotman & Berchtold, 2002), and how good sleep enhances BDNF (Giese et al., 2013). These affect cognitive functions and by extension connect to resilience capacity.

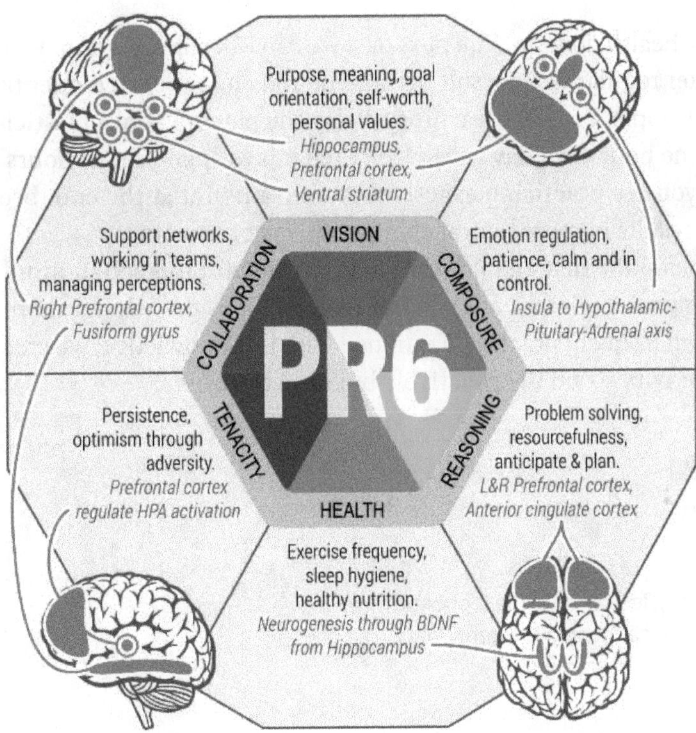

FIGURE 3.12 Six-Factor Neuroscience Model of Resilience

Figure 3.12 provides a graphical summary of the domain concepts, and neurobiological correlates are presented next. Notable is the placement of two of these domains—namely vision and health. Vision attains the position at the top of the model given its aspirational nature, helping us to aim higher and pursue meaningful goals. This also reflects its position as the most important of the six domains, providing guidance for all other domains. Sitting at the bottom of the model is health, noting its function as a foundational domain. As with a good house, resilience requires a strong foundation, and here the health domain provides that foundation on top of which all other domains can thrive. While good health may not be the ultimate goal, failing health undermines all other pursuits and quickly redirects focus to itself until resolved.

THE WHOLE BRAIN IS INVOLVED

While the foundation of resilience is simple—PFC regulatory connection to the LB—as soon as we look a little deeper, we see that many different structures in the brain are involved with developing resilience capacity. Practically, this means that there are many different skills that contribute to resilience. Think through each of these domains and what you work on with your clients—helping to understand their goals, building skills to stay calm, thinking through challenges, looking after their health, not giving up, and building strong support networks. These are all groups of skills related to each domain, highlighting strategies to develop resilience.

One last lesson from the neuroscience of resilience is how the mechanics of neuroplasticity embed these skills within the brain. After all, we need plasticity to build new pathways and break down old pathways to achieve lasting behavioral change. Rather than dive into a detailed explanation of how this works, I'll give you a quick summary of the key takeaways.

Pathways in the brain are reinforced when they are used repeatedly, meaning practice builds pathways. In this process, physical changes occur in the synapses connecting neurons, and BDNF is used to facilitate change. As BDNF runs out, so does our ability to learn, and replenishment is needed through the health domain. The next day, we can learn more again. What does this mean? Quite simply, shorter regular tasks result in more neural change than longer tasks all at once.

As a practical example, consider learning to play the piano. From a plasticity perspective, it's better to practice one hour each day for a week then it is to spend seven hours practicing on one day. Even though you are practicing exactly the same amount at the end, breaking up the task over multiple days results in more neural change and faster learning.

Given the various skills that enable resilience, it's helpful to keep in mind not to overload a client with too many strategies all at once but instead focus on helping them learn and embed smaller skills through frequent practice. Equipped with this knowledge, we created the *Advancing Despite Adversity* activity to aid in proactively building resilience.

MATERIALS NEEDED

- Pencil or pen
- Paper
- Smartphone
- Predictive 6 Factor Resilience Scale (optional)
- Hello Driven resilience training tool (optional)

PROCESS OF THE ACTIVITY

Three key phases encompass the process of this *Advancing Despite Adversity* resilience training activity: innervate, act, and adapt. The first phase sets the context for the training, while for the remainder, we alternate between phases two and three. Applicability of this resilience training is suggested for subclinical populations and individuals who are deemed stable enough to take on more advanced techniques to build holistic resilience as a protective measure against future hardship. We have used this approach with many different cohorts, including professionals, executives, new parents, students and children 14 years and up, and even top athletes.

Innervate

Innervation refers to neural pathway stimulation, which in many ways is the aim of this initial phase. Our goal is to prime the brain of our participant to motivate lasting action—that is to say, innervate the client! We achieve this by building a simple and easily referenceable concept of resilience.

Start with the neuroscience of resilience as the basic concept of resilience. Here we use the simplified model of resilience as essentially the PFC connection to the LB. While this binary concept is a vast oversimplification of the neuroscience of resilience, the pure simplicity of the concept helps clients develop a context within which they can understand and relate to activities provided through the training.

At this point, ready your pen and paper to draw the concept. Fortunately, absolutely no artistic skill is necessary, and it is even helpful to draw this in a very simple way to make the concept more approachable. On the paper, draw a kidney bean shape that forms the cortex of the brain. Next, draw the brain stem coming out the bottom, and then draw a small cerebellum to the right of the brain stem. Just like that, you have a brain ready for clinical use. It's less important for these diagrams to be anatomically correct, so just sketch it out quickly to get set up.

From here you can draw a bubble at the front of the brain to denote the PFC and a bubble in the middle of the brain that represents that LB. Here you can explain the role of each and relate the unhelpful behaviors to LB activation. To illustrate the pathways of regulation between these areas, you can draw arrows going from one to the other. If you have colors available, you can use red for the LB and green for the PFC. As you do this, you can explain the effect one has on the other. In the end, you should have a diagram such as mine in Figure 3.13.

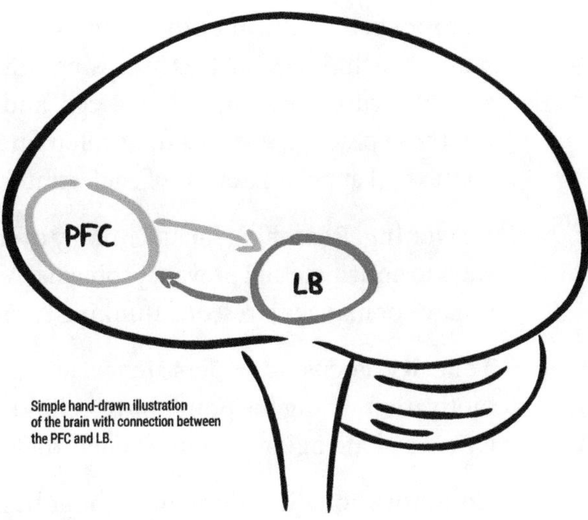

PFC
LB
Simple hand-drawn illustration of the brain with connection between the PFC and LB.

FIGURE 3.13 Example Drawing of PFC to the Limbic System

Take some time with this to ensure that the client can relate regulatory behaviors to PFC activation and, less helpful, automatic, impulsive behaviors and thoughts to the LB. Also ensure that there is sufficient understanding that stronger regulator pathways from the PFC keep the LB calm, helping the participant stay calm and in control, even in difficult circumstances.

Next, you can briefly explain each of the six domains of resilience. At this point, it's not necessary to go into detail on each but rather we have two purposes here:

First, we want to foreshadow for the participant what we'll be working on together over the coming months by giving them a broad tour of the six domains that enable resilience capacity.

Second, we also want to get quick insight into which domains might be more important to work on first. While we do have the PR6 as a psychometric that performs this function, you can also accomplish this in a more organic way by asking the participant about each of the domains as you go through and make an assessment based on the answers provided.

For example, when explaining the composure domain, you could ask if the participant gets angry more easily than they like. Or with the vision domain, do they have clear goals that they are working toward? Questions such as these can be used to broadly assess the resilience of the participant across the domains. With these answers, you can choose to start with the more pressing areas first, or if you feel the client is somewhat vulnerable, you can also choose to start with a stronger domain to build on strengths as a pathway to support weaker domains.

Lastly, in the innervate phase, explore how we will be building new neural pathways, namely through regular action to build the regulatory pathways from the PFC to the LB. To illustrate this, you can draw more arrows from the PFC to LB, explaining that each time you practice a strategy, you strengthen the pathway (drawing over it again to visually show the pathway getting stronger).

Act

With the client now primed (and innervated!), we can focus on taking action. Using your assessment from the innervate phase, you can now choose a domain to start with and take action to build resilience. The activities to focus on here should be short and relatively easy to do. An ideal time is something that takes 5 minutes or less to complete, requiring little or no material. Preparing activities in this way helps to remove excuses for noncompletion and sets the client up for success in achieving behavioral change. Undoubtedly, through our own experience, you can think of quite a few activities that fit in each of the domains. Still, here are a few ideas around each that could be employed, depending on the client context:

Vision. These strategies relate to a sense of purpose and goals. Activities could focus on investigating what time is spent on currently. Taking time to reflect on personal values. Clarifying personal goals. Setting out goals and investigating conflicts (building congruence). Being mindful about time spent and taking time to reflect on how everyday life relates to larger goals.

Composure. This is mainly about staying calm and in control. Activities include many of the popular techniques, such as breathing control to regulate LB activation. Mindfulness techniques, such as focused awareness, body scan, and open monitoring can be helpful as well. The client may use these practice sessions to develop finer internal awareness to recognize the capabilities and contextual appropriateness of each strategy.

Reasoning. Reasoning includes many of the forward-looking aspects in which activities focus on ways to anticipate and prevent problems. Activities here can include identifying ways to proactively remove or manage stressors, thinking through future challenges and visualizing helpful reactions.

Tenacity. Focusing on persistence, activities here can include setting up workspaces to increase motivation. Using the pomodoro technique (time boxing) to practice focus and complete a task. Or even challenging personal beliefs to develop a realistic sense of optimism.

Collaboration. This domain is about building strong support networks. Activities here could be as simple as spending a few minutes a day walking over and saying "hello" to a colleague the participant hasn't spoken to in a while. Or practicing verbal and nonverbal communication skills (perhaps keeping better posture and saying "like" less).

Health. Important as a foundational domain, activities here can include taking a quick walk (for exercise), setting up the bedroom for better quality sleep (remove light sources, going to bed on time), or nutrition (keeping a food log, buying healthy snacks, cleaning sweets out of the pantry).

Focus on one domain at a time, with only one type of strategy to practice for the next week (as an example). Importantly, use some practical way to trigger the practice of the strategy. As you are likely well aware, simply relying on memory for practice reminders is quite ineffective. Therefore, we need outside help to trigger these sessions.

One reliable way of doing this is to have the participant use their phone to set an alarm or reminder to practice the strategy at a particular time of day. The rule of this reminder is that the participant is not allowed to dismiss it until they have practiced. Therefore, if the participant can't do it right away, they are only allowed to snooze.

For other activities where a reminder might not be appropriate (for example, techniques to stay calm in traffic), another visual reminder could work. This could be a piece of green tape stuck to the top of the steering wheel of a car—something that stands out without being a distraction—can be a reminder to practice mindful awareness and nonjudgment while driving.

After all, for our strategies to build stronger regulatory pathways, we need frequent activation of those pathways. By incorporating a novel external trigger, we can strengthen the pathway to the point where it becomes a habit and triggers naturally.

Adapt

Each time your client returns for a new session, you observe results from the act phase, and you adapt. After all, a major component of resilience is about adaptation to the challenges we encounter in order to constantly evolve. In addition, all the skills and strategies that the client learns may slightly alter their understanding and implementation of previous behaviors. Therefore, it is important to recognize this evolution that they are achieving and to successively adapt and incorporate new insights into healthier habits and behaviors. Think of it as the benefits of compound interest through ongoing investment in resilience building.

On each visit, keep reiterating how valuable the practice sessions are in building the regulatory pathways. This is the anchor concept to serve as a central reminder to the client of the value of continuing with the practice sessions and following through with each of them. Where practice sessions were not completed, work through the difficulties experienced, adapt to compensate, and try again until a practical way is found to establish reliable adherence.

Gradually work through each domain as necessary and based on your assessment of the client's needs, essentially cycling between the act and adapt phases. Focus on continual integration of the strategies, highlighting how they each help build overall resilience as a holistic way to stay on top of life, regardless of challenges along the way.

FOLLOW-UP

Evaluation of the *Advancing Despite Adversity* activity primarily focuses on the client's improvement in each of the domains of resilience. The domains are designed to be "learnable," allowing the client to progressively build resilience through the practice of skills and strategies related to each domain. Formal assessment of these domains can be conducted using the PR6 resilience psychometric. The PR6 produces a score for each domain, providing an ongoing assessment of progress. Reassessment is recommended every 3 months; however, more frequent measures can be performed if deemed necessary because of rapidly changing personal circumstances.

Aside from using the PR6, you can simply continue to ask questions regarding the domains that are being practiced and look there for clues of whether the participant is gaining confidence and exhibiting improvement through embedding strategies and developing new behaviors. A useful follow-up indicator here is the completion of the practice sessions provided, reflection on stories of the successful application of the techniques, discussion of the results obtained, and expression of the client's thoughts about new ways to adapt using the new skills.

NEUROSCIENCE IN ACTION

Tyler (not his real name), a 42-year-old professional, sought counseling after being urged to by his partner. He often found himself getting unreasonably angry when facing small inconveniences and was unsure where these feelings come from. This behavior had become more frequent in recent years, and sometimes these episodes resulted in destructive behaviors, such as verbal outbursts, harming relationships with those around him, and adding to feelings of guilt and shame experienced through periods of reflection. Initial assessments showed no clinical diagnoses, and the PR6 Resilience Assessment was selected as a pathway to further explore the origin of this behavior and take practical action to shift behavior patterns.

Phase 1—Innervate

The first resilience sessions started with the explanation of the neuroscience of resilience, using pen and paper to draw the brain and connection between the PFC and LB, thus putting the behaviors into context to understand the activation of the LB in relation to anger outbursts. On invitation, Tyler took the pen and used it to illustrate what it felt like, drawing big spikes coming out of the LB. An explanation was then provided about how the PFC can downregulate the LB, with arrows being drawn from the PFC to highlight its importance. The concept of connection and how practicing activities build regulatory connections was explained. Tyler commented, *"I like that I can understand how the real changes are happening in my brain, like a computer connecting new wires. It helps me understand what the effort is adding up to."*

Phase 2—Act

Next, the six domains were explained, with a few questions posed around each domain to inspect both general feelings around the domains, alongside specifics regarding the behaviors currently exhibited. Two key findings were made:

First, as expected, the composure domain currently presented a challenge. Tyler noted that over the last few years, he seemed to be increasingly on edge and angry with "everything." As a practical example, he often got upset in traffic, getting angry at other drivers pushing in front of him and cars that seem to drive "irrationally." Anger generated here did not quickly dissipate, staying with him and bleeding into subsequent interactions with people encountered afterward, particularly with friends and his partner, with whom he felt less inhibited.

Second, it was noted that Tyler had high goals for himself (such as rising to be an executive in his workplace), although he felt that he was not where he wanted to be, indicating a need for assistance in the vision domain. He said that time is going by and he's just not accomplishing as much as he should be, noting goals he set over 10 years ago which he was not much closer in achieving.

Phase 3—Adapt

With these initial insights, the next steps were determined. The challenges regarding the vision domain were more complex and took more time to unravel. Composure domain interventions were a practical short-term measure to help mitigate the damages caused by behaviors, providing an opening to then explore the vision challenges in more detail.

As an initial intervention, the traffic scenario was chosen with the suggestion of a practical action. Tyler agreed to put on some of his favorite music and turn it up in the car. He would do this every time he gets in the car, providing an automatic way to ensure this strategy is enacted. To reframe the behavior of others, he agreed, "*When someone cuts me off in traffic, instead of getting angry, I will think about how they might be having a medical emergency, and I will let them get through just in case. No need to get angry. I will just breathe, listen to some music, and move along.*"

To increase the likelihood of implementation, Tyler discussed which artist he would listen to (removing uncertainty and potential avoidance) and set an alarm to remind him while at home to make sure he has the music set up in his car.

In the following session 2 weeks later, Tyler discussed how he did eventually follow through after the reminder came on, and he had been using the strategy while driving. He noted that he still found himself getting angry initially at other drivers, although thinking about how they might be in a rush because of some emergency helped him have more compassion toward others, and he used that feeling to then focus on listening to the music instead. After doing this for a few days, Tyler noted that he had become slightly less reactionary to the scenario. Further activities, such as breathing and reappraisal strategies, were practiced over subsequent weeks.

Moving on to the vision domain, the hypothesis was that Tyler had become increasingly frustrated with his lack of achievement over the years, feeling that his chance to achieve his goals was disappearing. Rather than compromise on his goals, the frustration contributed to self-loathing and procrastination because of an inability to find a practical pathway to achieve his goals.

Exploring this mindset and the emotional consequences started with acknowledging that this was a contributing factor to the growing feelings of frustration, matching with the perceived closing of the goal achievement window. Practical activities included a values reassessment to explore what success means to Tyler, as well as setting an "appointment" with his partner to take stock of their lives so far and what they have accomplished together.

By continuing the cycle through act and adapt, Tyler improved his ability to implement practical strategies to reduce causes of stressors while slowly addressing his mindset regarding historical goals. He gained an appreciation for where his life is and what it took to get there. Tyler started working on new goals around health and fitness. By focusing on an area of his life that adds more directly to his enjoyment and that of his partner, Tyler found greater levels of motivation.

Overall, Tyler started with a reluctance to initiate treatment, although the urging of people close to him helped to highlight problematic behavior. PR6 resilience assessment provided a starting point to delve into specific areas. This assessment also helped Tyler realize that he had specific opportunities to improve his own resilience, particularly in the comparison to population scores. With an impetus created to explore methods of change, the neuroscience approach provided a simple way to frame problematic behaviors, combined with skill building to both proactively and reactively manage these situations. Tyler's willingness to implement these skills, in particular the proactive strategies, helped change the environment and his reaction to various stressors. This process was continued with the ongoing exploration of various resilience domains. After 6 months, another PR6 assessment was conducted and showed significant improvement in the initial focus domains of composure and vision. Tyler said, *"I can feel myself handling these situations better, and I do feel a bit more calm in general, so it's great to see on the report that the scores actually confirm things are changing."*

ETHICAL AND MULTICULTURAL CONSIDERATIONS

This activity is not recommended for people actively suffering from major depressive disorder, post-traumatic stress, or severe clinical diagnoses requiring active treatment. It is suggested that clients completing the PR6 assessment not have scores revealed to them if they are deemed vulnerable or might have a negative reaction to the scores. Instead, the scores obtained can be used to inform implementation of the technique without revealing them.

Currently, the youngest population this approach has been used with is 14-year-old students. Any age younger than this may require additional guidance and explanation to ensure concept comprehension and follow-through, involving parents and/or guardians.

As resilience building is often used to help subclinical populations go from "good" to "great," there is wide applicability to various audiences. The author primarily suggests caution when working with clinically diagnosed patients where traditional clinical practices are advised and appropriate.

ANCILLARY MATERIALS

- Further reading on the resilience domains can be found in the open-access research published on the PR6 Scale and the book *Executive Resilience—Neuroscience for the Business of Disruption.* https://www.amazon.com.au/Executive-Resilience-Neuroscience-Business-Disruption/dp/0994241232
- Information about the PR6 resilience assessment and access https://home.hellodriven.com/
- 2017 Research paper—"PR6 and Job Satisfaction" https://www.researchgate.net/publication/320750193_Predictive_6_Factor_Resilience_Scale_-_Domains_of_Resilience_and_Their_Role_as_Enablers_of_Job_Satisfaction
- 2016 Research paper—"PR6 and Neurobiological Foundations" https://www.researchgate.net/publication/303365936_The_Predictive_6-Factor_Resilience_Scale_Neurobiological_Fundamentals_and_Organizational_Applicatio

THE THICK WALLS THAT SURROUND US

Exploring the Neurobiology of Dissociative States With Clients With Dissociative Identity Disorder

Sinem Akay-Sullivan

Dissociative identity disorder (DID), defined as the presence of two or more separate identities with their own ways of relating to and thinking about themselves and their environment (American Psychiatric Association, 2013), is consistently linked to relational trauma and severe abuse in childhood (Dorahy et al., 2014). According to this perspective, individuals cope with and/or protectively respond to the trauma by creating multiple self-states that are separate from each other (Hart, 2013). These self-states, otherwise known as alters, have their own ways of thinking and behaving, as well as containing their own memories. Individuals with DID often struggle with confusion and fear related to their dissociative experiences (Steele et al., 2017). They may show phobic avoidance of what they experience as intolerable, especially when they face the reality of having alter personalities that were created because of severe childhood trauma. This phobic avoidance can be overcome by reducing fear and shame through neuroeducation. Understanding the effect of trauma on brain development can normalize individuals' experiences of dissociative states and help them to reduce their fears of working with their alters to achieve integration.

Wheeler, et al. (1997) proposed that the prefrontal cortex allows individuals to have a special type of consciousness called autonoetic consciousness that constitutes the ability to mentally represent and become aware of their experiences in the past, present, and future (as cited in Forrest, 2001). According to Forrest (2001), the prefrontal cortex is theorized to be involved in the development of DID through the fragmentation of autonoetic consciousness. Forrest (2001) proposed a neurodevelopmental model that focuses on the impairment in the functionality of the orbitofrontal cortex in particular. This model emphasizes the effect of inhibited functioning in the orbitofrontal cortex on the development of alter states. The orbitofrontal cortex is one of three major parts of the prefrontal cortex. This part of the brain influences the inhibitory function that protects the structure of thoughts, speech, or behaviors from external or internal influences, which supports the integrative functions of memory by not allowing detraction from the current goal-directed organization of behavior. Researchers propose that childhood traumatization alters the functioning of the orbitofrontal cortex (Reinders et al., 2018) and the inhibitory function of orbitofrontal cortex may create amnesia as a way to cope with trauma (Forrest, 2001). Even though more research is needed to support the proposed cause-and-effect relationship, recent studies support this model by showing decreased functioning of the orbitofrontal cortex in clients with DID (Reinders et al., 2018; Sar et al., 2007).

The *Thick Walls That Surround Us* activity is intended to help clients understand the development of alter states by exploring the relationship between the orbitofrontal cortex and integrated self. Before using this activity and discussing the neurobiology of DID with clients, therapists need to make sure that clients have the coping skills to stay within the "window of tolerance." Clients with trauma history attend therapy with different windows of tolerance: the ability to handle distressing events without disconnecting from their emotions or having an extreme sense of anxiety or fear (Briere & Scott, 2006). Staying within the window of tolerance allows clients to be grounded in the present instead of fully experiencing the lack of safety during past traumatic events while discussing their trauma-related symptoms (Katz, 2016).

MATERIALS NEEDED

- The *Thick Walls That Surround Us* worksheet
- Colored pens or markers

PROCESS OF THE ACTIVITY

The *Thick Walls That Surround Us* activity is intended for older adolescents and adults, ages 15 and up, who are diagnosed with DID. Information about the role of the orbitofrontal cortex in the development of DID is adapted from Forrest's (2001) article on the orbitofrontal model of DID. For more information about this model, refer to *Toward an Etiology of Dissociative Identity Disorder: A Neurodevelopmental Approach* (Forrest, 2001). Before starting the activity, clinicians need to consider the readiness level of their clients. Clinicians should focus on building a therapeutic relationship with their clients before talking about topics that may trigger less desirable emotions. In addition, clinicians should not use this activity with clients, or any alters, if they are unaware of their diagnoses or in denial of their childhood trauma, as the activity includes information about the effect of trauma on DID development.

Clinicians can get their clients prepared for this activity by saying, "I would like to provide you with some information that can clarify the questions that you have about how your alters got created and why you have gaps in your memory." Clinicians can also let their clients know that it is important to ask any questions that they may have during this activity, as it can be challenging to understand some of the concepts. This introduction may help clients to become more interested in listening to explanations related to their brain functioning and feel free to ask questions to enhance their understanding.

Step 1: Getting Familiar With the Orbitofrontal Cortex

Clinicians begin the activity by sharing that the orbitofrontal cortex seems to play an important role in the development of alters in DID, and the goal of this activity is to discuss this connection and explore what the connection might mean to the client. Clinicians share that the orbitofrontal cortex is the part of the brain that stands right above their eye sockets. To support the visualization process, it might be helpful to say, "If you could look straight up and see what is inside of your skull, you would see your orbitofrontal cortex right above your eyes."

Step 2: Explaining the Function of the Orbitofrontal Cortex

Clinicians then explore an overview of the importance that the orbitofrontal cortex plays in the development of an integrated self and use the *Thick Walls That Surround Us* worksheet to provide examples.

The orbitofrontal cortex supports several important functions in our lives, such as making sure that our memories work properly; helping to regulate our bodily functions, such as breathing and heartbeat when we experience different situations in our lives; and facilitating the development of attachment to our caregivers. It also helps us to regulate our emotions and organize our behaviors.

This part of our brain keeps an eye on how we emotionally react to different situations, negative or positive, and tries to help us to recover from disruptions to our regular state of being, which we will call the "global self." For example, if one of your good friends doesn't invite you to his or her party, your angry or sad part (or self) may come out for a while. But, eventually, you will recover from it and go back to your regular way of being, global self, so that you can continue with your day.

The clinician will then show the client the part of the worksheet called "Fully Integrated Orbitofrontal Cortex" and ask the client if he or she can come up with other parts to add to the chart that are either different emotional states (joy, fear, confusion, etc.) or different behaviors because of changes in the environment (at home, at school, at a party, etc.) and write them in the boxes.

Our orbitofrontal cortex develops the ability to recover from disruptions and go back to our global self through having nonthreatening and caring attachment figures early in our lives. As children, if we can anticipate certain interactions with our caregiver as being consistent and supportive, we will develop an orbitofrontal cortex that allows us to move between our global self and the other parts that are related to different situations and moods. Being able to go back to the global self will allow us to continue planning things out for that day and carry out our goals rather than being stuck in one of the other states.

The clinician will go back to the worksheet and explain to the client that these different states are like having different rooms in a house with wide-open doors that the client can freely go in and out of (point at the arrows that represent free movement between the "rooms" and the global self).

If our caregivers create a chaotic environment that won't allow us to regulate ourselves, then our orbitofrontal system may become rigid and struggle to shift between these internal states. This is a way that the orbitofrontal cortex protects us from getting hurt. For example, if a caregiver is hurting us, we may need to be stuck in the "calm" self to avoid feeling anger or pain, which may cause us to get hurt even more. It will also help us to contain those negative memories that can be extremely overwhelming to deal with when we go to school or hang out with friends. So, living in an unpredictable and scary environment will inhibit our orbitofrontal cortex from creating the global self that allows free movement between different parts (or selves).

If the client has discussed any history of trauma in previous sessions, the clinician can make connections between the client's story and the effort of the orbitofrontal cortex to protect the client from getting hurt more as a child. Then the clinician will show the part of the worksheet called "Inhibited Orbitofrontal Cortex" to the client and point out the thick walls that surround the rooms without the doors, explaining that these are the walls that protected the client from moving between the rooms and getting hurt more, but they also cause the client not to have the integrated or global self that contains all the memories. Then the clinician will ask the client to think about the parts that they are aware of having and write them down in different rooms. The clinician can ask the client to choose different colors that represent each part, which may allow further discussions related to what that part means to them.

The clinician can ask the client the following process questions:

1. What are your thoughts and feelings about how your orbitofrontal cortex was affected by the traumatic situations that you experienced in your childhood?
2. How do you think these walls are affecting your life today in both positive and negative ways?
3. How would you like to see your "rooms" organized?

FOLLOW-UP

Clinicians can use a Likert scale to assess how much understanding their clients have gained after this activity. Before they start the activity, they can ask their clients to rate their level of understanding of why they experience dissociative states on a scale 1 to 5 (1 = Very Poor, 2 = Poor, 3 = Fair, 4 = Good, 5 = Very Good). After the activity, clinicians can give the same scale to their clients to see whether this activity improved their understanding of their dissociative states. It can also be helpful to attend to the turmoil that this understanding can bring while exploring how to make meaning of this to bridge into the future relief that will come.

This activity is not intended to explain every aspect of DID symptoms, and there is limited research that fully explains neurodevelopmental processes that cause these symptoms. Thus it is expected for clients to rate their understandings of the dissociative states as less than 5 on the Likert scale. Clinicians can ask their clients a question, such as, "What makes it a 3 instead of a 5?" Or, "What makes it a 3 instead of a 1?" This will allow clients to discuss their understandings and ask questions related to their dissociative states or other symptoms. This may also allow clients to process their feelings and thoughts related to their diagnoses.

NEUROSCIENCE IN ACTION

This is the illustration of the use of this activity with a female client in her 20s, who was referred to therapy for hearing voices and having gaps in time. The client was extremely confused about the voices she heard when she first started therapy, as she said that the voices belonged to her, but they were not really her voice. After formal and informal assessments, she met the criteria for DID. I first focused on helping the client build better coping skills before discussing her diagnosis, as people may experience extreme fear, confusion, or shame when they hear that they have dissociative states that they cannot remember. Steele, et al. (2017) suggest that to gain better coping skills, clients can practice mindfulness techniques, deep breathing, and come up with a calm place that they can visualize when they feel distressed. I helped all the alters that presented themselves in session to create a calm and safe place that they can visualize when they struggle with negative feelings during the treatment process. I asked the alters to think about a place that will be safe and calm for them to be in and encouraged them to give me details about what they see, feel, and hear in the places that they created. This exercise made it easier for them to visualize the place that they created when needed.

Before talking with the client about her diagnosis, I decided to engage the client in *The Thick Walls That Surround Us* activity, as I believed that it would help with a softer transition to the conversation about her diagnosis. The client was very interested in learning about the reason she had gaps in her memory, as it was one of her presenting concerns that led her to seek therapy. The client seemed to be both relieved and embarrassed when she realized that she has alters that have their own ways of thinking and behaving. She said, "This explains a lot about why people say hi to me sometimes and I am sure that I never met them before," and she told me that understanding how her brain developed this problem helped her to feel less "crazy." The realization that she is not "crazy" and that there are other people who struggle with the same issue seemed to help her in the process of better understanding and accepting her alters later in her treatment.

After I showed the client the part of the worksheet labeled "Fully Integrated Orbitofrontal Cortex," she was able to come up with other parts to add to the chart that are different emotional states. She added fear, confusion, and sadness to the boxes in the worksheet, stating that these are the feelings that she experiences the most. When asked to think about the parts that she is aware of having and write them down in different rooms on the *Thick Walls That Surround Us* worksheet, she chose pink to represent the child that she said she hears in her head sometimes and drew a circle around the word "child" with a blue pen. She reported that pink represented the playful part of the child and blue represented the sadness and fear that she believes the child feels sometimes. The client then picked the red pen to write "Angry Woman" in one of the rooms and told me that red represents the anger that this adult female seemed to feel toward her. I did not want to ask her for more details, as this activity is intended to be an introduction for the client to the neuroscience of DID rather than a way for me to get information about her alters.

At the end of the activity, I asked her about her thoughts and feelings related to how her orbitofrontal cortex was affected by the traumatic situations that she experienced in her childhood. She reported feeling sad about her brain not being fully integrated, but she also added that realizing how her past trauma caused some of her issues helped her to feel a little less ashamed of herself. When asked about how the walls are affecting her life, she stated that she feels glad about the walls not allowing her to remember all the details about her past trauma. She then added that she wanted to get rid of some of the walls, as they do not allow her to remember parts of her day, and she has to "play detective" to figure out what she was doing during those "lost times."

As the therapy progressed and the client became more aware and accepting of her alters, she referred to the neuroknowledge that she gained through this activity. For example, when the client gained more awareness about the alter that was created when she was 5 years old and experienced most of the abuse, she said, "I can see how my orbitofrontal cortex protected me by allowing my brain to create this child. I know the walls between me and her protected me from all that pain." The neurobiology knowledge gave her a foundation to explain why each of the alters was created and played a role in her survival and provided a sense of relief that she was not the one to blame for the development of this disorder.

ETHICAL AND MULTICULTURAL CONSIDERATIONS

This activity is created for adults and older adolescents with DID, as children and younger adolescents may not have the cognitive skills to fully comprehend some of the concepts. Also, cognitive delays need to be considered when deciding on the cognitive capacity of the client to understand this activity. Clinicians should be careful about not introducing this activity early in the treatment process. Individuals with DID may not be aware of their alters when they first start therapy, although they may be aware of gaps in time and hear voices in their heads. Some clients may first need to better develop coping skills before receiving detailed information about their diagnosis. In addition, clinicians need to use their clinical judgments to decide whether it will be beneficial to share this activity with different alters.

ANCILLARY MATERIALS

Clinicians can benefit from additional readings, such as *Treating Trauma-Related Dissociation: A Practical, Integrative Approach* by Steele, Boon, and Hart (2017) and *Dissociation and the Dissociative Disorders: DSM-V and Beyond* by Dell and O'Neil (2009), to gain a better understanding of DID and find answers to questions about DID symptoms and the treatment process.

Thick Walls That Surround Us

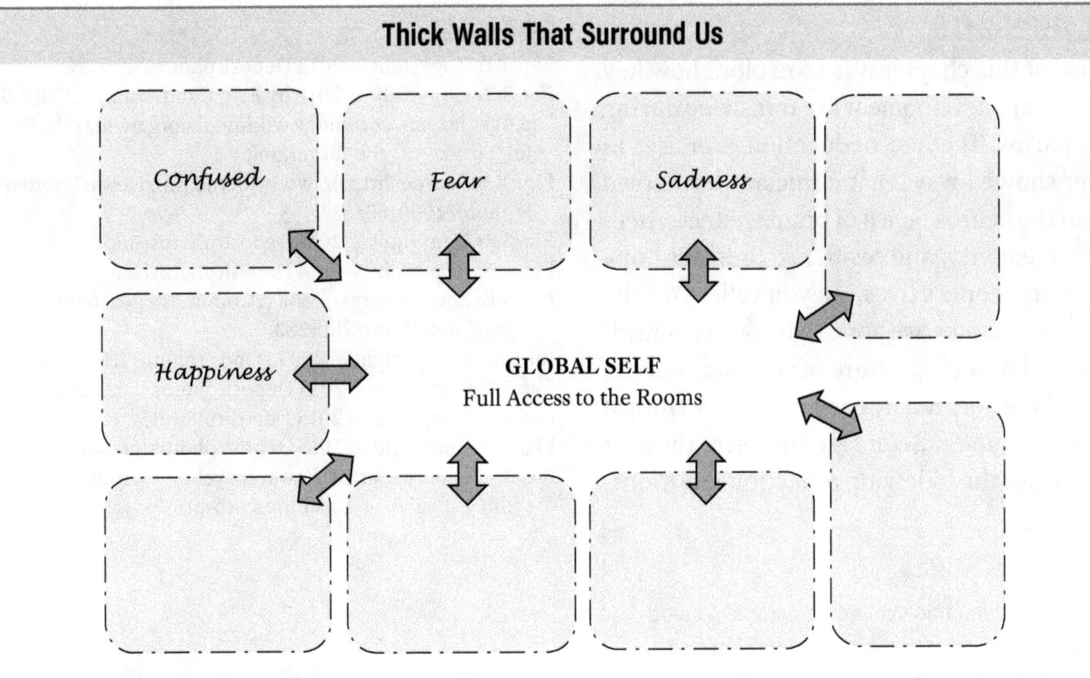

Fully Integrated Orbitofrontal Cortex

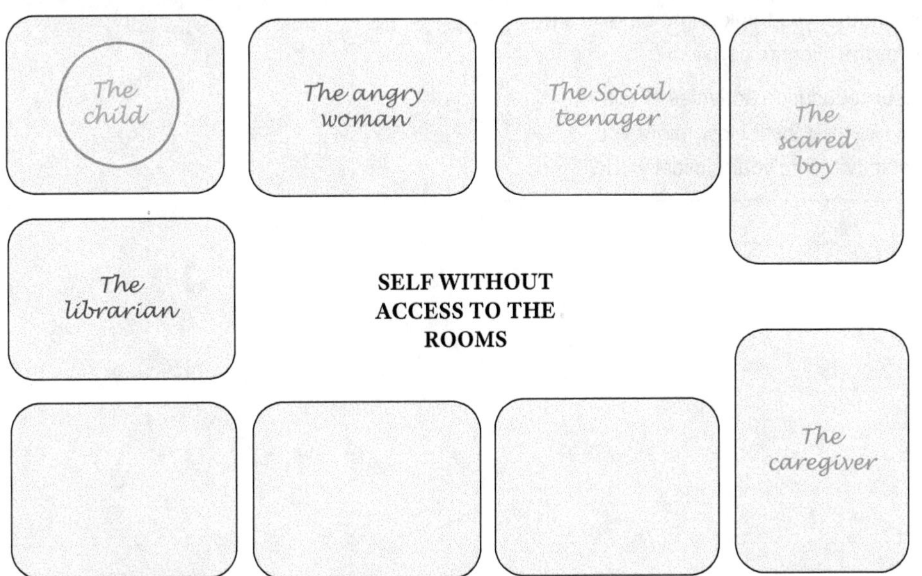

Inhibited Orbitofrontal Cortex

**Please note that some clients may not fill out all the boxes because of not having as many alters or being unaware of all alters. Other clients may need more boxes than provided in this worksheet, so using two worksheets may be necessary.*

CLOSING THOUGHTS

The purpose of this chapter was to explore how key principles of brain development are translated during clinical scenarios. The neuroeducation exercises in this chapter showed ways that clinicians harnessed the power of the neuroscience of brain wellness, neuroplasticity, creativity, and resilience to foster hope and changes in people's lives. As you reflect on the activities in this chapter, we hope that you are considering the ever-developing nature of your brain as you walk into and are affected by each and every clinical scenario you encounter. Before moving on to the next chapter, consider the following reflection questions:

REFLECTION QUESTIONS

1. What effect do you think your own early childhood experiences had on your brain development and current functioning?
2. Think of a specific client. What is one principle of brain development that you think might be relevant and/or helpful for the client to consider?
3. Which of the neuroeducation activities in this chapter did you like the most? How might you incorporate the activity into your clinical work?

CREDITS

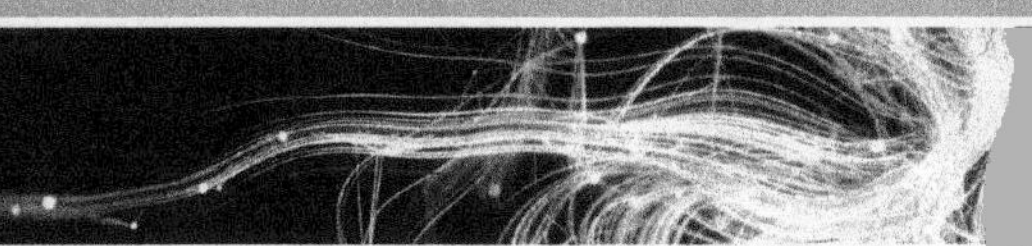

CHAPTER 4

Brain Anatomy and Physiology

There are billions of neurons in our brains, but what are neurons? Just cells. The brain has no knowledge until connections are made between neurons. All that we know, all that we are, comes from the way our neurons are connected.

—Tim Berners-Lee

CHAPTER OBJECTIVES

1. Identify basic brain anatomy and physiology relevant to mental health work.
2. Discuss ways individuals and experiences can influence biology and physiology.
3. Apply brain anatomy and physiology concepts to neuroeducation activities.

INTRODUCTION

The brain is a complex system with a multitude of interconnected structures and emergent functions (see Figure 4.1; Bassett & Gazzaniga, 2011; Siegel, 2012b).

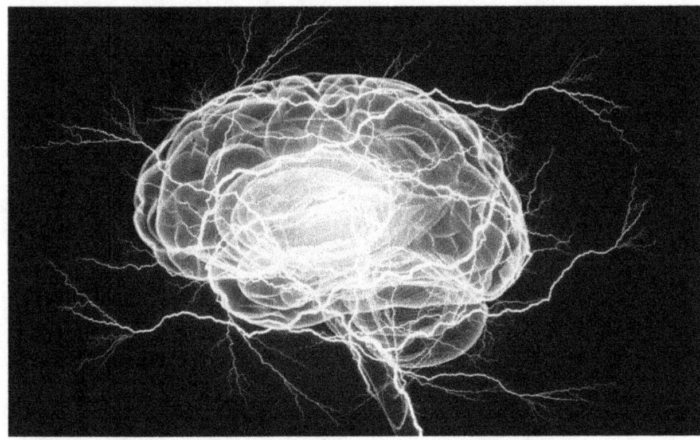

FIGURE 4.1. Brain Complexity

As a counselor, having a comprehensive understanding of brain anatomy and physiology may not be necessary; however, having a general idea of these concepts may be useful. Think of a modern-day automobile; the average driver does not need to know the intricate inner workings of their car. For example, you do not need to know how the engine relies on a spark to ignite a mixture of petrol vapor and compressed air that when inside a momentarily sealed cylinder will cause it to burn rapidly, creating necessary power to drive the car. Or that when you push the brake pedal, in the case of a hydraulic braking system, it depresses a piston in the master cylinder, forcing fluid along the pipe, which then travels to other cylinders at each wheel and fills them, forcing the pistons out to apply the brakes. Really, you just need to know some details, such as a car has an engine that requires fuel to run and has a breaking system that requires your manual force to activate and that at times, we need to consult with others that do know the intricacies of these inner workings to help us optimize, maintain, and even repair the functioning of the car (i.e., mechanics). Now think about the brain and all its anatomical structures and connections. Within the context of counseling, knowing how internal and external stimuli strengthen or weaken these brain structures and connections can guide interventions and support behavioral changes.

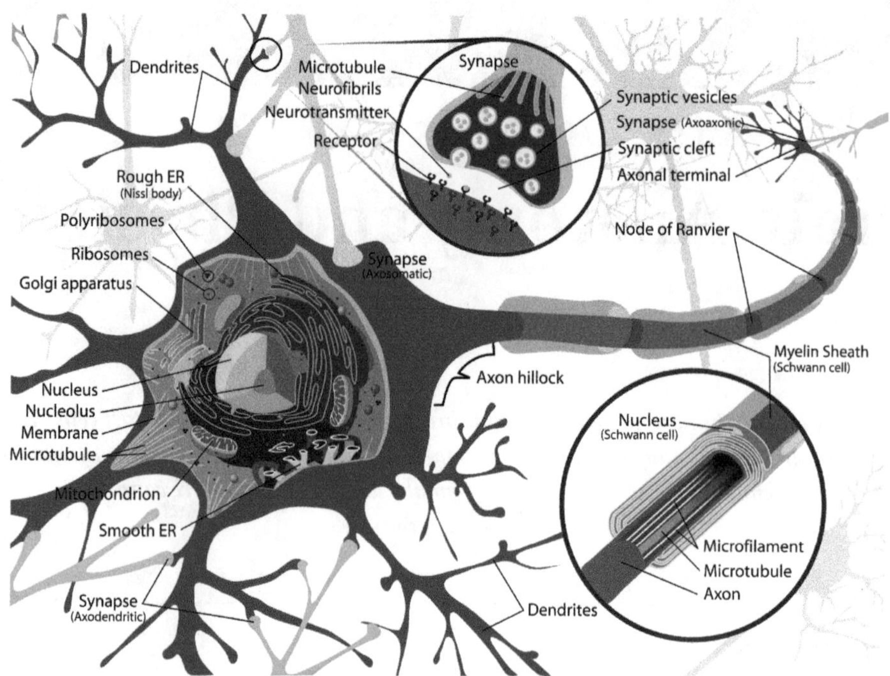

FIGURE 4.2 Neurons and Synapses

Although a complete review of anatomy and physiology is outside the scope of this applied text, the following is a brief review of some basic anatomy and physiology concepts most relevant to clinical work and the neuroeducation activities introduced in this book. Scanlon and Sanders (2015) stated that the brain is part of the nervous system. One of the most basic elements of this system is neurons (i.e., nerve cells), which are transmitted via chemical and/or electrical signals across synapses, resulting in what we experience as thoughts, feelings, or behaviors (see Figure 4.2).

Neurons release chemical messengers, called neurotransmitters, at synapses to communicate with other cells. Common neurotransmitters include glutamate, y-aminobutyric acid, dopamine, serotonin, noradrenaline, and endorphin. Scanlon and Sanders (2015) estimated that our brain is "made of approximately 100 billion neurons and contains trillions of synapses, all of which function as an integrated whole" (p. 198). A number of factors directly affect the creation of new neurons and synapses and the release of certain neurotransmitters, including medications, foods, drinks, and behaviors. In counseling, individuals can learn to modify what they put into their bodies and what they do to influence these biological and chemical brain processes. Clients are often encouraged to learn that they can do things to stimulate the growth of new neurons and synaptic pathways! Individuals might also benefit from learning about how the development and functioning of these biological systems were affected by earlier developmental experiences. For example, drug and alcohol use during adolescents can impede healthy synaptic development and alter neurotransmitter functioning.

A second area of anatomy and physiology that is relevant to counselors is knowledge of major brain structures and/or regions. The broadest conceptualization of brain structures and regions includes a simple division between the lower, middle, and upper brain (Figure 4.3; Siegel, 2012b).

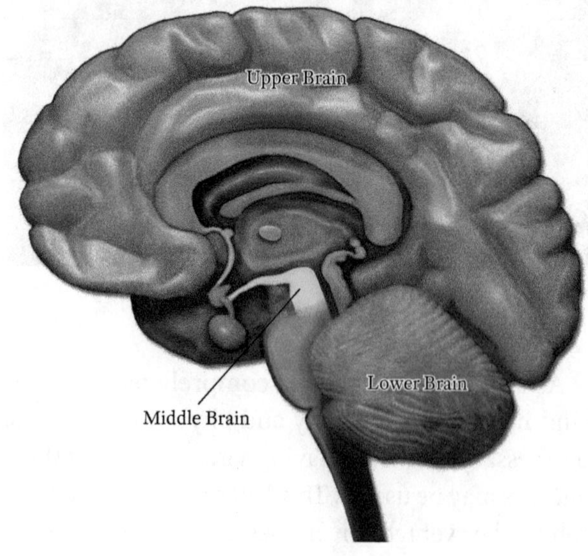

FIGURE 4.3 Brain Regions

Scanlon and Sanders (2015) identified the brain stem (containing the medulla, pons, and midbrain), the cerebellum, the hypothalamus, and the thalamus as key parts of the lower brain. Lower brain structures generally function below the level of consciousness and play a vital role in basic regulatory and rhythmic processes, including heart rate, blood pressure, breathing, body temperature, arousal, appetite, and reflexes. The middle, or central part, of the brain, often referred to as the limbic region, includes key parts of the brain, such as the hippocampus and amygdala. The parts of the brain in this region play key roles in attachment, emotion, reward, and memory. This part of the brain is often talked about in the context of threat detection, as the amygdala constantly scans our environment to assess safety and signals other parts of the brain and nervous system to respond when danger is detected. This largely automatic system helps us to move away from perceived danger and toward perceived pleasure. The cerebral cortex, which is divided into four lobes, each with unique functions, is considered the upper brain (see Figure 4.4).

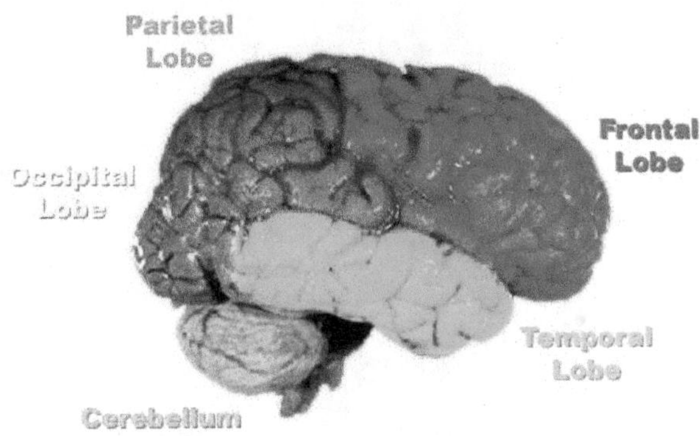

FIGURE 4.4 Brain Lobes

The prefrontal or orbitofrontal cortex is the part of the frontal lobe most often discussed within counseling literature and will thus be elaborated on here. An excellent description of the functions of each lobe can be found in the anatomy and brain development chapter of the counseling text *Neurocounseling: Brain-Based Clinical Approaches* or in related anatomy resources. The primary roles of the prefrontal cortex are often labeled as "executive functions." Scanlon and Sanders (2015) noted that "the prefrontal cortex greatly contributes to what makes us human and able to enjoy the humanity of others" (p. 203). Barbas and Zikopoulos (2007) indicated that the prefrontal cortex is important in selecting relevant stimuli to respond to, as well as recognizing what stimuli are unimportant and should be ignored (i.e., attention and focus). Other functions include response flexibility, affect regulation, and fear modulation, as well as planning, empathy, and morality (Siddiqui et al., 2008; Siegel, 2012b).

Counselors and clients can benefit from this basic understanding of brain structures and functions in many different ways. Some counselors who work with clients who have had traumatic brain injuries or strokes may become experts in this area, as the clients' struggles will often be directly related to the parts of the brain affected by the injury or stroke. Counselors who practice neurofeedback will also likely learn quite a bit about brain structures because the brain wave training protocols require such specified knowledge for correct electrode placement and overall treatment planning. Other counselors may just use the general knowledge of the brain regions and functions to talk about the effect of certain developmental experiences on current functioning (e.g., neglect during early childhood often affects the integration of the limbic region, leading to lifelong struggles with attachment (i.e., healthy interpersonal relationships) or to provide a rationale for certain interventions (e.g., mindfulness has been shown to strengthen certain prefrontal regions and promote focus, attentional control, and emotion regulation).

Related to brain structures and functions is an understanding of information processing in the brain. Generally, information is processed from the bottom-up (i.e., lower brain regions to upper brain regions) or top-down (i.e., upper brain regions to lower brain regions). Information processing is influenced by development (e.g., young children rely more on bottom-up processing because upper regions are not fully formed or integrated), ongoing biological factors (e.g., amount of sleep a person has had and/or the degree of hunger a person is experiencing), and threat detection (Ochsner et al., 2009; Raio et al, 2013; Sussman et al., 2016). A healthy adult who has adequate rest and food and who is not under a state of threat detection will be able to process information in a top-down manner, resulting in reflective responses that align with their values, long-term goals, and consideration of others' needs and perspectives.

An individual who does not have adequate rest or food and/or is under a constant state of perceived or actual threat will be more likely to process information in a bottom-up manner, resulting in more reactive and survival-oriented responses. This information can provide insight into decision making, emotions, and behaviors, as well as guidance for the types of interventions selected. For example, if individuals struggle with bottom-up reactivity, counselors can focus on interventions that enhance body attunement and physiological regulation. Doing so can downregulate the hyperactivity in the lower and middle regions of the brain, which upregulates activation in the upper regions of the brain and promotes neural integration, or balance between all brain regions. Counselors can also focus on improving sleep and nutrition, as well as reducing overall stress, in an effort to help a person's upper brain stay fully engaged in its role to inhibit lower brain reactivity. To revisit our car analogy, many factors influence the performance of our vehicles (e.g., type of gas, maintenance schedule, accidents), and many factors influence the development and functioning of our nervous system. Luckily, we can visit our "mechanics" (professional counselors) to help optimize, maintain, and repair the functioning of our vehicles, brains, and bodies.

NEUROEDUCATION ACTIVITIES

In this chapter, you will be introduced to eight unique neuroeducation activities that demonstrate various ways to incorporate anatomy and physiology information into sessions to support clients' understanding of self and/or others and promote therapeutic growth. From worksheets and checklists to metaphors and mindfulness, your clinical imagination is sure to be sparked with these novel activity ideas.

FOSTERING COMPASSION FOR CHILDREN WITH FETAL ALCOHOL SPECTRUM DISORDERS THROUGH NEUROEDUCATION

Szu-Yu Chen, Saranya Sundaram, and Tilman Schulte

When mothers consume high doses of alcohol during pregnancy, several health complications can arise. One particular complication is the development of fetal alcohol spectrum disorder (FASD; Popova et al., 2017). Children with FASDs can have deficits in executive control, reward processing, and memory functions, as well as attention and language (Kodituwakku, 2009; Kodituwakku et al., 2001; Mons & Beracochea, 2016; Rasmussen & Bisanz, 2009). Neuroimaging techniques have allowed researchers to identify specific structural and functional brain differences associated with FASD. Examples of such structural abnormalities include smaller cerebellar volume and enlarged ventricles (Moore et al., 2014). Reduced volume in the corpus callosum is the most commonly found neural abnormality, affecting almost all areas, except the occipital lobe (Lebel et al., 2011). Additional compromised structures include the hippocampus, basal ganglia, and limbic system (Archibald et al., 2001; Astley et al., 2009a; Astley et al., 2009b; Fryer et al., 2007; Kalberg et al., 2006; Lebel et al., 2008; O'Hare et al., 2005). Without intervention, these deficits can persist throughout the life span.

The aim of this *Fostering Compassion* activity is to provide resources and a framework for mental health professionals to use when talking with caregivers about the potential effects of prenatal alcohol use on children's developing brains. Introducing caregivers to these ideas can be useful for fostering greater empathy for children and their challenging behaviors. Caregivers operating from a place of understanding and compassion are much more effective in their parenting than caregivers operating from a perspective of judgment (e.g., "this child is bad," or "this child is manipulative"; Bratton et al., 2006).

Furthermore, this information can be used to help caregivers understand the importance of early interventions to support social, emotional, and behavioral changes. Targeted interventions, such as behavioral therapy, nutritional counseling, and exercise-based interventions can improve some impairments resulting from developmental alcohol exposure (Murawski et al., 2015). Although more research is needed to achieve a better understanding of the neural, cognitive, and behavioral variation of the spectrum of FASD to improve the diagnosis and to tailor interventions to the individual's context (e.g., school-based interventions), counselors can begin sharing some of the research now to support caregiver understanding and compassion.

MATERIALS NEEDED

- Worksheet 1: A Visual Understanding of Prenatal Exposure to Alcohol. This worksheet provides images of a neurotypical brain and a brain with prenatal exposure to alcohol.
- Worksheet 2: Checklist for Understanding Prenatal Exposure to Alcohol. This worksheet provides a checklist for clinicians to keep track of brain areas shared with caregivers and allows caregivers to rank their level of understanding related to each area.
- Worksheet 3: Relationship between Developmental Effects of Prenatal Exposure to Alcohol and Areas of the Brain. This worksheet provides the expected developmental effects of prenatal exposure to alcohol and the location in the brain in nontechnical language.

PROCESS OF THE ACTIVITY

Typically, *Fostering Compassion* is used when the counselor is seeing a child in individual therapy and regularly consulting with the parent. This activity can be used at any point during ongoing caregiver consultations. The activity includes two stages: (1) building relationships and setting goals and (2) integrating neuroscience information into caregiver consultations.

Stage 1: Building Relationships and Setting Goals. The goal of Stage 1 is to foster trusting relationships with caregivers. Individuals who are caretakers for children with FASDs have unique challenges and stressors. They are often foster or adoptive parents and may be new to those roles. They may be experiencing disappointment and even anger when what they thought the parenting experience would be like does not match their reality of the parenting experience. They will have unique goals for themselves and for their children that are grounded in cultural backgrounds, identities, and family dynamics. Furthermore, they will have varying degrees of knowledge of child development and parenting. Biological parents may experience unique challenges of their own, including struggling with guilt or shame over their behaviors during pregnancy, which led to the child's current struggles. For all these reasons, you should prioritize expressing empathy for the caregivers' concerns, communicating mutual understanding and respect for the caregivers' knowledge of the child, and collaborating on individualized needs and goals. It is also crucial to provide caregivers with support and encouragement through the identification of the child's positive attributes and provide hope for change. It is through these lenses in particular that neuroeducation on the impact of prenatal exposure to alcohol and the potential benefits of early interventions can be useful.

Stage 2: Integrating Neuroscience Into Caregiver Consultations. Once the initial trusting relationship is established, you can begin exploring information about the effects of prenatal alcohol exposure on the brain. You should use a scaffolded approach. We recommend starting with worksheet one, introducing neurotypical brains through visual images, and then sharing about how a parents' prenatal alcohol use can alter typical brain development via Worksheet 2. As caregivers go through the consultation process, mark the information that you all explore together and rate their understanding. You can then use Worksheet 3 to elaborate on expected developmental effects (e.g., difficulty in decision making) and visual pictures on Worksheet 1 where those effects are located in the brain (e.g., in the front part of the brain that helps with decision making).

FOLLOW-UP

We recommend using both formal and informal assessments during this activity. *The Parenting Stress Index™*, 4th edition (PSI-4; Abidin, 2012) can be administered before and after the child's treatment and caregiver consultations.

The PSI-4 measures the stress a parent/caregiver experiences as a result of the interaction with the child. The questions are divided into three domains: (1) parental distress, (2) parent–child dysfunctional interaction, and (3) difficult child, which combine to form a total stress score. The assessment results may indicate what behaviors are most problematic for caregivers and if the integration of neuroeducation resources in the ongoing caregiver consultations helps caregivers decrease their stress levels.

We also recommend facilitating informal assessment during caregiver consultations. Informal assessment includes checking in with parents to ensure that they are able to connect the neuroeducation information with the child's social-emotional needs and behavioral issues and provide support and empathy for the child. A few open-ended questions or prompts include the following:

- "What does this neuroscience information mean to you?"
- "How does this information relate to the concerns about your child?"
- "Which aspect of this information do you consider helpful or unhelpful in supporting your child's needs?"

NEUROSCIENCE IN ACTION

The following clinical example illustrates how I (Szu-Yu) provided *Fostering Compassion* during caregiver consultations with a foster parent. Sasha (pseudonym), a 5-year-old African American girl, has lived with her current foster mother, Ms. Smith, since she was 3 years old. Ms. Smith was an African American single female raising three other foster children, all older than Sasha. According to Ms. Smith, Sasha seemed to get angry or frustrated easily when things did not go her way, leading to a temper tantrum. Sasha appeared to have difficulty in regulating herself when Ms. Smith tried to calm her down. Sasha also showed some signs and symptoms of learning disabilities as evidenced by her inadequate school performance and atypical development of visual-motor skills. Ms. Smith was also seeking an evaluation for Sasha's learning disabilities. Sasha had been admitted to inpatient and outpatient services because of her excessive risky and impulsive behaviors, such as physical aggression toward people and running away from the home and school. She was diagnosed with a mood disorder and attention-deficit/hyperactivity disorder (ADHD) and prescribed ADHD medications by a psychiatrist at the psychiatric hospital. Sasha was referred for play therapy services in the community agency where I worked after she was discharged from an intensive outpatient facility. I provided Sasha with weekly play therapy and regularly conducted caregiver consultations to support Ms. Smith.

Stage 1: Building Relationships and Setting Goals

My primary goal in Stage 1 was to build a safe and trusting relationship with Ms. Smith by listening to her concerns about Sasha's presenting issues, providing empathy toward her parenting stress, gathering Sasha's developmental history, and setting therapeutic goals. Some developmental questions I asked included the following:

- What do you know of Sasha's prenatal and birth history?
- Was there any drug or alcohol use during pregnancy?
- When did Sasha know how to talk, read, and write?
- Did you notice any difference in Sasha's development compared to other children?
- How is Sasha's academic performance?
- How are Sasha's interpersonal relationships with peers, teachers, and families?
- How does Sasha respond to your parenting?
- Is there any other notable medical history?
- What medication is Sasha taking, if any?
- Has Sasha experienced any traumatic events?
- How do you think school is going for Sasha?
- What are Sasha's typical eating, exercise, and screen time habits?
- What are Sasha's interests and strengths?

Although Ms. Smith was not able to provide a full history of Sasha's development, I learned that Sasha might have been prenatally and environmentally exposed to unknown drugs and/or alcohol. Ms. Smith reported that Sasha's biological mother had a history of unknown substance use and that Child Protective Services intervened when Sasha was around 1-year-old. Ms. Smith suspected that the biological mother started using drugs and alcohol when she was pregnant.

Sasha exhibited increasingly aggressive behavior toward peers, teachers, Ms. Smith, and siblings. Based on Ms. Smith's concerns, Sasha seemed to show various problems of a child who was exposed to alcohol prenatally. Yet Ms. Smith did not appear to have knowledge of the effect of alcohol use on the child's development. Hence, I considered integrating neuroeducation activities and providing supplemental materials in the following caregiver consultations. I was hoping the information would increase her empathy and compassion toward Sasha and further enhance the parent-child relationship and decrease parenting stress. I also planned to explore some parenting strategies with Ms. Smith to further support Sasha's behavioral changes. I asked about Ms. Smith's willingness to explore some neuroscience concepts before I started integrating neuroeducation activities into the ongoing caregiver consultations. I first acknowledged Ms. Smith's effort in participating in Sasha's counseling services. I then asked her goals and hopes for the counseling and explained the process of parent consultations, as well as explored her interests in learning some parenting information and skills to improve Sasha's behavioral problems. Here is an example of one of our conversations:

Counselor: I appreciate you sharing your concerns and Sasha's developmental history with me. It seems that you are worried about Sasha's aggressive behavior toward others and her impulsive behavior, such as running away from home when she was mad. It sounds like you have put a lot of effort into finding effective ways to help Sasha. You mentioned you have tried to calm her down by talking to her or having a time-out in her bedroom when she was angry and out of control, but it did not work most of the time.

Ms. Smith: No, none of these work. She would cry and scream louder and louder, and I would feel my frustration. The medication has been stabilizing her mood, but it really depends on the day. I have also tried to ask her if she thinks it is the red light or green light (the traffic light system Sasha learned from the inpatient and outpatient setting), but she has a hard time calming down and doing what I ask when she is upset. This causes more arguments between us.

Counselor: You sound overwhelmed and exhausted and not sure what else you can do. In addition to providing weekly play therapy, I will also schedule a parent consultation with you every three to five weeks. We will discuss how things are going with Sasha and what progress is being made. We will also use this time to address your concerns and explore some effective parenting skills based on Sasha's progress. Earlier, you said that Sasha's biological mother might have used drugs and alcohol since she was pregnant. When you described Sasha's behavior and developments, some of her symptoms sound like the effects of prenatal alcohol exposure. I have some materials about the consequences of prenatal alcohol exposure on children's brain development. I wonder if you are interested in getting more information about it. We can discuss it in next the parent consultation.

Ms. Smith: Really? I heard about it but haven't had time to search for the information. I think it would be great if you can show me some information. I would like to learn what else I can do to help Sasha.

Stage 2: Integrating Neuroscience Into Caregiver Consultations

Following the interaction and relationship building with Ms. Smith in the first caregiver consultation, I noted Ms. Smith's concerns and prepared three worksheets to help her explore the possible developmental effects of prenatal exposure to alcohol on various areas of a child's brain. After four play therapy sessions with Sasha, I scheduled another caregiver consultation and integrated neuroscience information into the feedback. Here is an example of how I facilitated Stage 2 of *Fostering Compassion* in the caregiver consultation:

Counselor: I would like to check in. How has everything been going with Sasha since the last time we met?

Ms. Smith: Sasha still argues with me and does not follow my directions when things do not go her way. However, her meltdowns seemed to become less frequent last week. Her teacher said she would yell at her peers and want them to go away if her peers did not let her get what she wants (e.g., she insists on having a red marker or she doesn't want to take turns and wait while others are having their turns). I am afraid she will continue to show these behaviors at school, as I already got several notices from her teachers.

Counselor: So you have seen a few positive improvements at home, but you are still concerned about how she interacts with other people at school. Last parent consultation, you seemed worried about Sasha's level of aggression toward peers and family members and hoped to see some improvement in her behavioral problems through play therapy. When you talked about Sasha yelling and having a meltdown when things did not go her way, I was thinking that I have seen some of these behaviors in the play therapy sessions. She seemed to increase her frustration when I set limits several times. I could see she was trying hard to gain control by clenching her fists tightly.

Ms. Smith: Yes, she would do that when she was angry, and she did not know how to verbally express her feelings or thoughts.

Counselor: Last time, you said you were interested in getting more information regarding the impact of prenatal exposure to alcohol on the child's brain development. I prepared some worksheets for today and think this information can help you get a better understanding of Sasha's development. What are your thoughts?

Ms. Smith: That's wonderful.

Counselor: A child in the womb of a mother who is using drugs or alcohol is exposed to harmful substances. Some of the risks of such exposure include birth defects, neurological impairment, and developmental delays. Worksheet 1 is the brain image showing how prenatal alcohol exposure can affect executive, attention, language, and memory functions in each area of the brain [counselor simultaneously pointed to those areas of the brain on Worksheet 1].

Ms. Smith: Wow, this looks overwhelming. I never saw this before.

Counselor: That is a completely normal reaction. I found the brain concept complicated when I first learned it. It is just like learning a new language. I'm going to show you what each area means one at a time and explore with you how this might help us understand Sasha's behavior better.

Ms. Smith: Okay, this sounds better.

Counselor: This sheet [Worksheet 2] is for you to check each brain area we explore. You can rate your understanding level and write down any questions on this sheet [counselor simultaneously pointed to those areas where the parent can mark on Worksheet 2]. We will go through each brain area affected, and feel free to ask me any questions while I am sharing the information.

Ms. Smith: Sounds good.

Counselor: Let's start by talking about the left hemisphere. The perspective of the left hemisphere is logical, linguistic, and literal. You can see the image here [counselor simultaneously pointed at the language area of Worksheet 1]. The right hemisphere's perspective is emotional, experiential, and nonverbal. Young children are right-hemisphere dominant, especially during the first three years. As children get older, their left-hemisphere capabilities develop more. The corpus callosum is at the center of the brain. Just like a bridge connecting the right hemisphere with the left hemisphere. It helps children balance both their logic and emotions. However, because of the exposure to harmful substances, such as alcohol, the development of the left hemisphere and corpus callosum can be interrupted. These children are at risk for cognitive impairments and learning disabilities. This means Sasha might have a difficult time using socially appropriate behavior to communicating with others, expressing herself verbally or nonverbally with others, and comprehending what she is being told.

Ms. Smith: This is exactly like Sasha. When I tried to explain why it is dangerous to run away or what the consequences of hitting people are, she would look blank and not respond to me. I would get very frustrated after explaining to her a couple of times because she did not look like she was paying attention to me.

Counselor: This can be frustrating, especially if you did not know that she has difficulty in understanding what is being said to her. Other effects include difficulty learning and holding the information that they hear. This may explain why Sasha feels challenged and discouraged in learning new things and completing tasks at school. This could lead to her poor academic performance and low interest in participating in classroom activities.

Ms. Smith: This is very helpful. I think lots of her behaviors make sense to me now. I hope her teachers know how to help her as well.

Counselor: I think it is important for you to know this information so that you know how to advocate for Sasha's educational needs. Another brain area that might be affected by prenatal exposure to alcohol is the limbic region, which is located in the lower parts of the brain [counselor simultaneously pointed at the emotion area]. This area is responsible for innate reactions, impulses, and emotions. Limbic system damage predisposes children to emotional dysregulation. This can cause some emotional and behavioral problems, such as anxiety, depression, ADHD, mood swings, and tantrums.

Ms. Smith: I can't believe it; these symptoms are very similar to Sasha's situation. I should have noticed this earlier. I knew something was wrong with her because she is different from my other children. You know parenting foster children can be difficult sometimes because of their various behavioral and emotional problems, but I think taking care of Sasha is especially challenging to me.

Counselor: It can be very challenging. You did not have an opportunity to learn what is going on with Sasha. I can see you really care about her, and you have sought different mental health and behavioral help to improve Sasha's situation. Sasha needs developmental and mental health interventions and a nurturing and caring caregiver. I think your consistent involvement in Sasha's treatment can impact her ability to improve and make a difference in the outcome. Next time, we can discuss other strategies to help Sasha's development. I know we have discussed a lot of the brain effects, and I would like to check if you have any questions or concerns so far.

Ms. Smith: I think you explained them in a very simple way, so I still get what you said. I just need some time to process what you just shared.

Counselor: That's good. As I said, this sheet is for you to note how much you understand the concept, and we can always come back to check the area you are not quite sure about. Now, I would like to show you the prefrontal cortex [counselor simultaneously pointed at the executive control area]. This area is located behind your forehead. This is your executive functioning, including decision making, planning, emotional/behavioral control, inhibition, attention, and memory. If there is damage in the frontal lobe and prefrontal cortex, it will impact all areas of functioning. When children's executive functions develop well, they can regulate their emotions, consider consequences, think before acting, maintain focus on tasks, and shift between different tasks. However, Sasha might show some deficits in her executive functioning aspect, so you would observe her not knowing how to regulate her emotions and behavior when she has meltdowns or tantrums, increasing her physical aggression when feeling mad, showing risk-taking and rule-breaking behavior, or other behavioral symptoms may resemble ADHD. In fact, it is one of the last parts of the brain to develop, so Sasha's prefrontal cortex has not fully developed yet.

Ms. Smith: This sounds like a lot, but Sasha does show these symptoms. I always thought it's because she doesn't want to listen to me, and she is forgettable. She has a hard time making eye contact with me or standing still when I talk to her. I feel drained dealing with her behavior every day. I need to work and take care of other children as well.

Counselor: I agree. This information sounds overwhelming. It can be a lot for you to take in at one time. We definitely can explore the rest of them next time. What do you think?

Ms. Smith: I appreciate you preparing these worksheets. It is very helpful, and I think I understand Sasha's behavior better. I am not sure what else I can do now, but at least I have a better idea why she has difficulty in various aspects at home and in school.

During the second caregiver consultation, Ms. Smith and I were able to discuss the effects of prenatal exposure to alcohol on children's language, emotion, and executive control. In addition to exploring different areas of the brain, I aimed to link these developmental consequences to Sasha's presenting issues, which helped Ms. Smith make connections between the neuroeducation and her experiences parenting Sasha. I scheduled the third caregiver consultation after 3 weeks to update Ms. Smith on Sasha's progress in play therapy. I conducted an informal assessment regarding the neuroeducation activity during the parent consultation. We further discussed the last brain area—motor development—and explored some feasible interventions together. Here is an example of how we continued *Fostering Compassion* in the third parent consultation.

Counselor: Last time, we explored prenatal alcohol exposure effects on the developing brain. I wonder if you have been able to connect these effects with Sasha's impulsive aggression behavior and other behavioral concerns. Do you have any questions about what we discussed last session?

Ms. Smith: I have been thinking about Sasha's behavior since the last time we met. I found it interesting that I used to be getting very frustrated or upset when she doesn't follow my directions. She would get mad at me as well when she doesn't know how to verbally communicate with me. I think now I am more able to understand her difficulties, and this helps my frustration as well. I feel more patient to repeat and slow down my directions, and she seems more capable of responding to my questions. I have seen some progress in her behavior at home when she interacts with her siblings. She would walk away and get markers to draw pictures when she was about to have arguments with her siblings.

Counselor: Sounds like you are more empathetic to her behavior, and you have noticed the way you interact with her is different. This sounds encouraging. We have one more area to talk about today, and then we can discuss what parenting strategies you can do to help Sasha.

Ms. Smith: Absolutely.

Counselor: Children with a history of prenatal alcohol use might show fine motor skill delays, such as writing and tying shoes. The basal ganglia and cerebellum are primarily responsible for motor control [counselor simultaneously pointed at the motor area on the Worksheet 1]. You may observe that Sasha's fine motor skills are not typical for her age. I have observed her writing and drawing skills are not matured yet. She also shows difficulty in dressing up the dolls in the playroom. I think this is consistent with what you shared about her physical development in our intake session. This may be another developmental effect of the prenatal exposure to alcohol.

Ms. Smith: I know she has shown some developmental delays, and her teachers have provided her extra time to improve her reading and writing skills.

Counselor: Although children exposed to alcohol often have damage in the developing brain, many can succeed despite their developmental deficits. Sasha may still have some long-term impairments and delays because some parts of the brain are recoverable, and some are not. This worksheet [Worksheet 3] also lists expected developmental effects of prenatal exposure to alcohol. We have discussed the majority of them. You can review these consequences when you have time. Each child's situation is different, but having appropriate stimulation, such as play therapy, speech therapy, and occupational therapy in Sasha's early life can ameliorate the effects of exposure to some extent. Compared to her previous living environment where it might be chaotic and unsafe, your nurturing, patient, and consistent interaction and care is especially crucial for Sasha. She will be able to develop a healthier attachment with you in a safe and stable home environment. For example, you can find ways to initiate appropriate levels of physical and emotional contact, such as hugs, eye contact, and active listening. Creating predictable rules and routines will help to reassure her that she will be safe, and her needs will be met. It is also important to continue to monitor and communicate effects of medication with her psychiatrist and follow up with her teachers on Sasha's academic, social, and behavioral progress. How does this sound to you?

Ms. Smith: I think it's reassuring to hear there's hope for Sasha's development, and yet it may not be possible for me to provide full attention for her while having a full-time job and taking care of three other children.

Counselor: I understand, you have a lot of responsibilities and you cannot give Sasha your undivided attention all the time. That's okay, there are a lot of small things you can do that can help. In the following parent consultations, I would like to explore some skills to enhance your interaction and relationship with Sasha. These skills could also promote Sasha's developing brain by reconnecting and redirecting different parts of the brain. Hopefully, she will learn better coping mechanisms to regulate her feelings and behavior and communicate herself better.

Ms. Smith: That's great. I feel stuck with my parenting skills, and I would like to learn more skills so that Sasha can improve her behavior.

Counselor: I know it might sound like Sasha has a long way to go, but it is important for us to accept the many unknowns about her development because of her history and respect her abilities. I would like you to be patient with yourself and Sasha, and we will work together to support Sasha throughout the counseling process.

I provided 21 play therapy sessions for Sasha and six caregiver consultations for Ms. Smith, including neuroeducation activities. During the caregiver consultations, Ms. Smith was able to explore a variety of effects of prenatal exposure to alcohol on children's brains. She seemed capable of integrating what we discussed with Sasha's symptoms and was able to increasingly provide understanding and empathy toward Sasha's difficulties as evidenced by her report of finding the worksheets really helpful and experiencing that her perception and interaction with Sasha had changed.

In addition to the informal assessment, I asked Ms. Smith to complete the PSI-4 assessment at the beginning of the treatment and a week prior to termination. The PSI-4 looks at characteristics of the child and the parent that may be contributing to stress in the parent-child relationship, so I was able to evaluate the progress of Ms. Smith's parenting stress in her relationship with Sasha. The parent domain consists of seven subscales: (1) competence, (2) isolation, (3) attachment, (4) health, (5) role restriction, (6) depression, and (7) relationship with spouse/partner. Ms. Smith's initial responses scored in the clinical range on attachment and role restriction, indicating that she experienced the parental role as restricting her freedom and frustrating her attempts to maintain her own identity, and she did not feel a sense of emotional closeness to Sasha, as she felt unable to understand Sasha's feelings or needs accurately. Her post-test scores fell in the normal range on all subscales, indicating that Ms. Smith did not experience characteristics of her parenting as significantly contributing to stress in the parent-child relationship with Sasha. This was valuable progress in her relationship with Sasha. In addition, Ms. Smith's total stress scores decreased from the borderline range to the normal range, indicating that by the time we terminated counseling, Ms. Smith had average amounts of stress in the parent-child relationship. This supports the idea that the neuroeducation seemed to foster Ms. Smith's understanding of Sasha's behavior and thus enhanced the parent-child relationship and decreased her parenting stress.

ETHICAL AND MULTICULTURAL CONSIDERATIONS

When incorporating *Fostering Compassion* in the treatment process, mental health professionals need to ensure their competence in providing caregivers neuroeducation and protect clients from possible harm by seeking appropriate neuroscience training, education, and supervision. It is critical to maintain awareness of current scientific and professional information regarding neuroeducation. It is recommended that mental health professionals establish therapeutic and trusting relationships with caregivers, ensure that caregivers are open to learning neuroscience concepts, and monitor the effectiveness of the activity. Mental health professionals also need to consider that some individuals may prefer audio or video materials in addition to or in place of the worksheets.

In addition, mental health professionals need to consider caregivers' diverse backgrounds. For example, Ms. Smith in the clinical example reported having little knowledge of neuroscience concepts; hence, I tailored my wording by avoiding advanced terms of different areas of the brain when providing feedback. I applied the brain development to Sasha's presenting issues so that Ms. Smith would find it simple, accessible, and practical. In general, I observe caregivers' verbal and nonverbal responses during the parent consultations. If they look overwhelmed and have a difficult time following me, I use two to three parent consultation sessions to introduce Worksheets 1 and 2.

When providing effective parenting strategies and recommendations, it is imperative to take caregivers' living and/or working environment into considerations. For instance, given that Ms.

Smith had three other foster children and worked full time, we needed to brainstorm practical ways for her to spend one-on-one time with Sasha, as a nurturing relationship may facilitate her growth. It was not realistic to suggest that Ms. Smith have weekly special playtime with Sasha. Yet Ms. Smith mentioned that she would be able to let Sasha prepare dinner with her. I considered this a great idea because it helps Ms. Smith and Sasha enjoy their time together without pressuring Ms. Smith to do something in addition to her regular housework.

ANCILLARY MATERIALS

- http://adai.uw.edu/fasdtoolkit/index.htm
- http://faculty.washington.edu/chudler/introb.html
- https://www.gov.mb.ca/healthychild/fasd/fasd_caregivers.pdf
- https://ncsacw.samhsa.gov/resources/substance-exposed-infants.aspx
- http://people.virginia.edu/~rra/psi.html

Worksheet 1

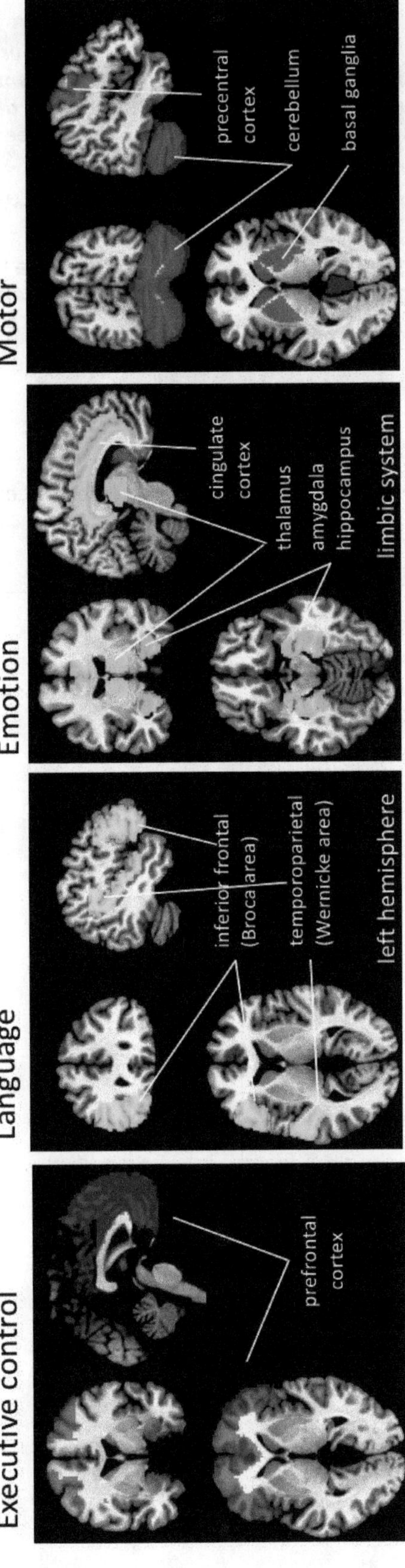
Executive control
prefrontal cortex
Language
inferior frontal (Broca area)
temporoparietal (Wernicke area)
left hemisphere
Emotion
cingulate cortex
thalamus
amygdala
hippocampus
limbic system
Motor
precentral cortex
cerebellum
basal ganglia

Worksheet 2: Checklist for Understanding Prenatal Exposure to Alcohol

Mental Health Professionals : Go through each brain area affected using Worksheet #1 and check mark the information reviewed.		*Caregivers : Rate your level of understanding (scale=0% - 100%) and note any further questions as you go through the information provided in Worksheet #1.*	
✓	**Brain Areas/Functions Affected**	**%**	**Level of Understanding/Further Questions**
	Executive Functions/Attention/ Concentration/Working Memory		**Executive Functions/Attention/ Concentration/Working Memory**
	Prefrontal cortex		
	Frontostriatal network circuitry		
	Verbal Learning and Memory		**Verbal Learning and Memory**
	Left Hippocampus		
	Temporal lobe		
	Visuospatial Functioning		**Visuospatial Functioning**
	Parietal lobe		
	Language		**Language**
	Broca's Area		
	Wernicke's Area		
	Left Hemisphere		
	Motor Skills		**Motor Skills**
	Cerebellum		
	Basal Ganglia		
	Emotion		**Emotion**
	Limbic System		

Worksheet 3: Relationship Between Developmental Effects of Prenatal Exposure to Drugs and Alcohol and Areas of the Brain

This worksheet provides the expected developmental effects of prenatal exposure to drugs and alcohol and the location in the brain in layman's terms.

<table>
<tr><th colspan="3">Executive Functions & Recommended Interventions</th></tr>
<tr><td>Inhibition</td><td>Acting without thinking
Impulsive behavior</td><td rowspan="8">Work with the teachers to modify expectations, based on the child's abilities
Educational and cognitive interventions
-Multi-modality instruction (e.g. use picture cues or songs/music)
-Use concrete language instead of abstract explanation
- Incorporate structure in the environment
- Provide predictability in the schedule
-Monitor the level of stimulation in the environment
-Repetition of the learning information
-Break down assignments into smaller tasks</td></tr>
<tr><td>Set-Shifting</td><td>Difficulty switching from one task to another
Losing focus when multitasking
Inflexible or rigid in their thinking</td></tr>
<tr><td>Working Memory</td><td>Difficulty holding onto information and manipulating it over a relatively short period of time
Forgetting or misplacing information/ objects</td></tr>
<tr><td>Attention</td><td>Distracted
Losing focus on the task at hand
Difficulty focusing for a long period of time</td></tr>
<tr><td>Planning and Organization</td><td>Disorganized
Poor time management
Difficulty learning from past mistakes</td></tr>
<tr><td>Abstraction</td><td>Thinking in a concrete manner
Difficulty thinking "outside of the box"
Interpreting information literally</td></tr>
<tr><td>Reasoning and Judgment</td><td>Difficulty with decision-making
Trouble finding solutions to problems
Engages without thinking of consequences</td></tr>
<tr><td>Self-Regulation</td><td>Difficulty controlling behaviors
Lacking awareness of their actions
Trouble tolerating frustration</td></tr>
</table>

<table>
<tr><th colspan="3">Verbal Learning and Memory & Recommended Interventions</th></tr>
<tr><td>Verbal learning</td><td>Difficulty learning and holding onto information that they hear</td><td rowspan="4">Educational and cognitive interventions
-Use concrete language instead of abstract explanation
-Repetition of the learning information
-Increase timeframe to complete tasks</td></tr>
<tr><td>Verbal recall/memory</td><td>Trouble remembering what is said to them after a long period of time</td></tr>
<tr><td>Perseveration</td><td>Uncontrollable repeating of information or thought that has previously been stated</td></tr>
<tr><td>Intrusions</td><td>Difficulty remembering old vs. new information</td></tr>
</table>

Visuospatial Functioning & Recommended Interventions		
Spatial Perception	Difficulty knowing where objects are located in space in relation to each other	Educational and cognitive interventions - Allow extra time to complete tasks -Provide opportunities to enhance attention to visual detail (e.g. puzzles or construction projects) Occupational therapy

Language & Recommended Interventions		
Social Skills	Difficulty initiating social contact and using socially appropriate behavior to engage or communicate with others	Group play therapy Social skills group (e.g. Good Buddies program or Children's Friendship Training (CFT))
Expressive Language	Difficulty using verbal or nonverbal methods to express or communicate with others	Speech-language therapy
Receptive Language	Difficulty understanding or comprehend what is being said to them	

Motor Skills & Recommended Interventions		
Fine Motor Skills	Difficulty with small muscle movements (e.g., tying their shoe, writing)	Occupational therapy

Emotion & Recommended Interventions		
Emotions	Difficulty expressing how they are feeling and understanding and responding to how others are feeling	Play therapy Parent education and training (e.g. child-parent relationship therapy or parent-child interaction therapy) Families moving forward (FMF) program Parents and children together (PACT) program

BRAIN AS A RIVER METAPHOR

Justin Jacques and Jennifer E. Mostafa

Promoting emotional regulation capacities is often a goal for clients in counseling. In our practice, we often use a continuum of chaos/rigidity—regulated/integrated/flexible as a framework to aid in developing the capacity for emotional regulation. We believe over time and with diligent practice, clients can move from rigid or chaotic states to more regulated, integrated, and cognitively flexible ways of being.

There are many brain structures implicated in experiences of chaotic and/or rigid emotional dysregulation (e.g., fear, anxiety, anger, and so forth). Fear, which is composed of fear response and extinction, is implicated in the amygdala, the medial prefrontal cortex, and the hippocampus (Sah & Westbrook, 2008). Anxiety is associated with the bed nucleus of the stria terminalis, ventral tegmental area (VTA), basal amygdala, parabrachial nucleus, and hypothalamus regions of the brain in research on mice (Johansen, 2013). In addition, anger has been very recently linked to the ventral medial prefrontal cortex (Jacob et al., 2018). Finally, the origination of potentially chaotic feelings, such as irritability, sadness, and panic, have been connected to multiple regions of the brain: the insular cortex, the orbital frontal cortex, the medio anterior temporal cortices, the ventral basal ganglia, the hypothalamus, the brain stem complex, and the somatosensory cortices (Damasio et al., 2012). It is worth noting that adolescents and individuals with unresolved trauma histories are more vulnerable to states of chaos because of potential differences in brain structure and functioning (Chao et al., 2013; D'Andrea et al., 2013; Somerville et al., 2011).

Cognitive flexibility is composed of many complex systems and areas. From a neuroscience perspective, the frontal cortical region has been implicated as an important area that houses the neural circuits of cognitive flexibility (Amodeo et al., 2017; Barrus et al., 2017; Trow et al., 2017). Furthermore, researchers have discovered that other regions of the brain, including the prefrontal cortical region, dorsal striatal circuit system, thalamus, lateral habenula, and cerebellar regions, are important areas supporting cognitive flexibility (Baker et al., 2017; Bissonette & Roesch, 2017; Dickson et al., 2017; Guo et al., 2017; Prasad et al., 2017;). Flexibility paves the way for integration, which is described as the linkage of differentiated sections that aims to harmonize the responses of the brain, mind, and body using conscious awareness (Siegel, 2014).

Given the complexity of the neuroscience behind these experiences, metaphor may be a helpful way to explore these concepts with clients. This *Brain as a River* activity aims to help clients gain insight and awareness regarding their physiological and psychological experiences of chaos and rigidity. As individuals gain awareness and knowledge, they can begin to enhance integration, therefore decreasing experiences of rigidity and chaos. Using the *Brain as a River* activity, we offer clients a relatively easy-to-understand framework for thinking about distressing experiences and conceptualizing new, more integrated ways of being.

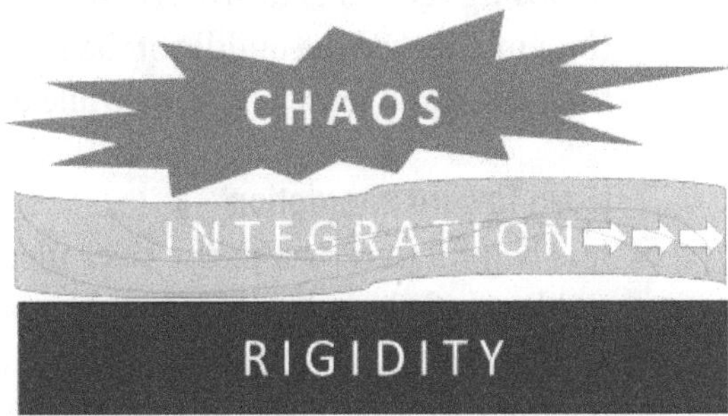

FIGURE 4.5 River of Integration

MATERIALS NEEDED

- River of Integration handout (see Figure 4.5)
- Blank piece of paper and pencil or pen (if you would like to draw the metaphor)

PROCESS OF THE ACTIVITY

Complete a Biopsychosocial Assessment

Prior to the activity, the counselor should complete a thorough biopsychosocial assessment. Specifically, look for significant rigidity in clients' thought patterns or inappropriate comfort with chaos and disorder in their emotional and behavioral experiences. A simple example of rigidity is an individual having significant anxiety regarding the rigid idea that they *must* make all As in their classes to be successful in life. An example of chaos for the same individual might include fear of turning an assignment in late or not at all, leading to an immobilized response that limits the ability to achieve the As they believe they must obtain. These two competing drives can invoke varied emotions, such as a feeling of control versus helplessness.

Introduce the Brain as a River Metaphor

Once the assessment is complete, you can introduce the *Brain as a River* activity using the *River of Integration* handout. You might introduce the activity by asking if the client can imagine kayaking on a river or creek. Continue by explaining that the body of water can be shallow with areas that are difficult to paddle and rushing water that can sweep up anything in its path. Provide opportunities for the client to connect with the metaphor and proceed by sharing that behaviors, thoughts, and feelings are often like the image of the river in that they sometimes require constant work or maintenance to sustain movement or to navigate unpredictable obstacles, such as rocks that appear in the rapids of fast-moving white water. Proceed by asking the client to reflect on their own cognitive and behavioral tendencies (chaos or rigidity) and identify patterns in their experiences. For example, "I hear you say that you feel like it is difficult to control your emotions when you experience stress, which side of the river best describes your reaction to stress?" "Can you describe ways in which you 'control' your stress and ways in which you feel 'out of control'?" During this process, it is helpful for both the client and the clinician to begin assigning behaviors, thoughts, and feelings to their corresponding sides of the riverbank.

To continue with this example, a client might forego meals, physical fitness, and sleep to complete assignments, which enables them to feel like they are "controlling" their stress (rigidity) and adversely experiencing panic attacks when feelings of being "out of control" arise (chaos). These opposing reactions to stress can now enable the client and the therapist to discuss integration (moving toward the middle of the river) by processing the client's reaction to the idea of releasing their perceived sense of control while managing the fear of impending chaos experienced in the past.

Move Toward Integration

It is helpful to return to the river metaphor once again and describe the idea of balancing both rigidity and chaos by describing the principles of integration. The therapist helps clients become empowered by brainstorming strategies to move away from both rigidity and chaos and toward the middle of the river. This helps the client uphold their values of hard work and dedication to their goals and avoid chaotic feelings of being out of control. An intervention at this step can include a discussion of how self-care can aid in moving toward a more integrated state of being. For example, the brain requires rest and recuperation, which is achieved through self-care, such as sleep, diet, and exercise. If an individual does not regularly initiate these self-care activities, the body will enter a deficit state. An individual in this state will use habitual strategies to regain and return to previously learned chaotic or rigid habits, thus emphasizing that self-care is essential in maintaining an integrated state of being.

Develop Hope for the Future

At this stage, it is useful to normalize experiences and offer hope for change, noting that although these patterns are largely automatic, they can be changed through interventions that support neural integration. Examples of such interventions include various mindfulness practices, behavioral experiments, and attention to lifestyle behaviors (e.g., nutrition, sleep, physical activity). The *River of Integration* worksheet can be a helpful framework to aid in treatment planning, as well as ongoing outcome evaluation.

FOLLOW-UP

The effect of *the Brain as a River* activity can be evaluated informally and formally. The easiest way is with an informal discussion after delivering the intervention. Continually checking in with the client during the process of defining their identified ways of rigid and chaotic behaviors, emotions, and thoughts can be an effective method for staying attuned to the client. Prompts might include the following: "What is it like for you to use words such as 'control' and 'out of control'?" "How is this metaphor working for you?" "We've covered a lot of ground in this session, I am wondering what has been the most helpful for you in terms of understanding your current behaviors?"

Formally, you could use the Session Rating Scale Version 3 (Duncan et al., 2003) or another satisfaction survey. In addition, we work in a university counseling center, and the Counseling Center Assessment for Psychological Symptoms (CCAPS; Locke et al., 2011) is a common assessment used to evaluate change over time in symptoms such as depression and anxiety. Using CCAPS, you can identify numerical value changes and consult with the client regarding their perception of symptom improvement.

NEUROSCIENCE IN ACTION

A 24-year-old male, Tanner, presented to a university counseling center reporting feelings of inadequacy, shame, and embarrassment regarding his medical condition: ulcerative colitis (UC). Tanner shared that he was disheartened with his poor physical condition and worried that his symptoms may never improve. He scored high on the CCAPS for generalized anxiety and social anxiety with specific symptoms, including accelerated heartbeat, feeling self-conscious around others, racing thoughts, and spells of terror or panic.

During the first two sessions, Tanner shared his thoughts, feelings, and behaviors related to his health condition. He said he isolated himself from social connections for fear of embarrassment and rejection. Tanner also noted that he no longer participated in athletic activities because of his UC-related symptoms and fears and thus was experiencing a loss of identity. The client acknowledged feeling exhausted, lonely, and a prisoner to his lifestyle.

At this point, I decided to introduce the *Brain as a River* metaphor to guide our discussions about chaos, rigidity, and integration. I asked Tanner if he had kayaked in a river, and he indicated that he had. I talked about various parts of a river: the more advanced areas such as fast-moving whitewater areas with debris (representing chaos) and the shallow slow-moving areas that require more effort to navigate to keep moving down the river (representing rigidity).

We talked about the client's previous experience navigating these parts of the river. He connected most with the state of rigidity, noting that he worked hard each day to avoid his fears by isolating and limiting his time away from his apartment, as well as spending large amounts of time ruminating on his diagnosis and symptoms. He also noted that he sometimes felt himself in a state of chaos. Such times included being overwhelmed by anxiety about losing control of his bowels in public or simply leaving his apartment without a laid-out plan of control measures in place to manage his fears. When discussing the chaotic nature of his behaviors, thoughts, and feelings

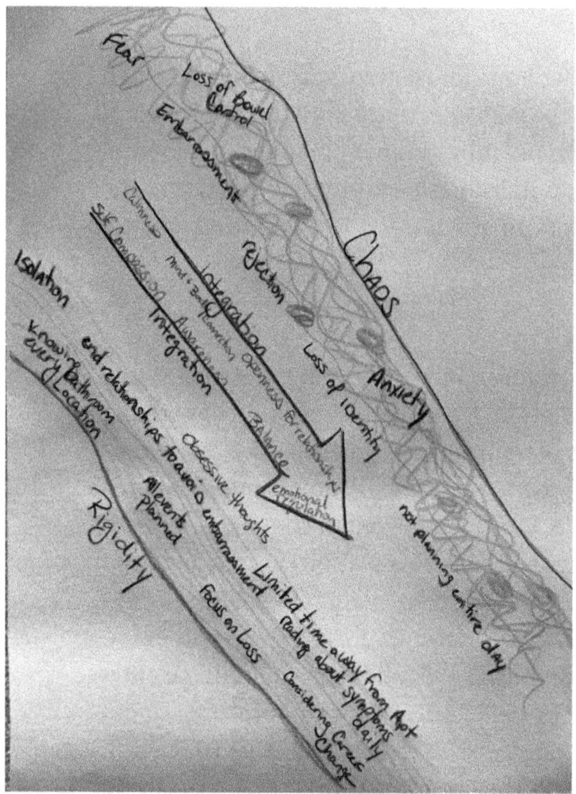

FIGURE 4.6 River of Integration Handwritten Tool Completed With Client

Tanner identified that even in the safe environment of the counseling office, he felt his heart rate increase and was overwhelmed by the idea of being controlled by his disease. Through awareness of the here and now, we were able to negotiate the pace at which the session continued by using short mindfulness techniques for grounding.

Engaging in a mindfulness activity while in session was helpful for Tanner, who was not familiar with mindfulness practice. The intervention used during this session was "mindful listening" by using a bell. The therapist asked Tanner to sit with his eyes closed and complete a series of deep breathing exercises. I then introduced him to the mindful bell as part of the activity. The therapist instructed Tanner to raise his hand when he no longer heard the sound of a bell. Acknowledging this valuable awareness aided Tanner in identifying his underlying resistance toward stability, which was processed and allowed for movement in establishing what integration could look like for him.

Tanner expressed relief in being understood. He also said he felt connected to the concepts of the *Brain as a River* metaphor and felt more self-compassion. He said he understood that he had experienced real embarrassment because of his condition and that his current rigidity was just his brain working to protect him from such experiences in the future.

In the final stage of the activity, I introduced the idea of integration and again used the *River of Integration* tool, which we co-constructed. Tanner shared that he felt a sense of losing control (chaos) even during counseling while discussing the process of letting go of part of his current behaviors and thoughts. I suggested the practice of mindfulness as an aid in this journey toward integration to reduce his identified fears and their effects within his body and mind. Tanner also planned to refrain from spending large portions of his time seeking information about his disease through various websites and forums, which seemed to increase his symptoms of distress and fear. When he felt the urge or found himself seeking medical information regarding his diagnosis on the internet, Tanner agreed to make a note in his mobile phone app that simply stated "medical search" under the date. This simple exercise encouraged Tanner to make a conscious decision about his participation in the activity.

Lastly, Tanner expressed appreciation for the therapeutic alliance and committed to seeking continued counseling upon returning to his home state during breaks from college. Upon follow-up, his scores in both the generalized anxiety and social anxiety columns of the CCAPS dropped. During this activity, we identified ways in which Tanner increased his suffering and anxiety by adhering to rigidity, as well as fears that held him in his state of isolation. I was able to use the depiction of the *River of Integration* in a way that not only made practical sense to the client but also reflected the therapeutic goals of the client to maintain relationships amid treating and living with his diagnosis.

ETHICAL AND MULTICULTURAL CONSIDERATIONS

One important ethical consideration is clinicians' neuroscience competency. Clinicians should have training in basic brain anatomy and neuroscience principles to be proficient enough to share these more complex abstract ideas without unintentionally doing harm. Advanced training may be needed and can be obtained through professional development workshops, graduate courses, reading materials, and supervision.

Regarding multicultural considerations, caution should be used when using the intervention with individuals with disabilities and particularly individuals with autism or borderline intellectual functioning. Although this intervention could be used with autism spectrum clients, it is important that the counselor also have expertise with autism. Individuals with borderline intellectual functioning or students who are more concrete may struggle with the abstractness of the intervention. Finally, individuals with conservative religious backgrounds may be hesitant about interventions that embrace science, mindfulness, or meditation because they may see these ideas or interventions as in opposition to their spiritual beliefs or practices.

ANCILLARY MATERIALS

We recommend the following books and websites as supplements to the activity described here:

- Dr. Daniel Siegel's books including *Mindsight, Brainstorm, The Mindful Brain, and Aware.*
- 3D Brain App (http://sciencenetlinks.com/tools/3d-brain/)
- Woebot (https://woebot.io/)
- Calm (https://www.calm.com/)
- Headspace (www.headspace.com)

WE'VE GOT ROOTS

Using Horticultural Imagery to Explain Neurobiology in Attachment Theory

Danica M. Rodriguez and Joy S. Whitman

Humans, from infancy to older adulthood, feel the need to belong. Attachment theory suggests that mental health is tied to one's early attachment to caregivers (Bowlby, 1988). An infant's primal need to belong is either met with security (love, support, stimulation) or insecurity (abuse, neglect, trauma). One's experience in infancy begins the foundational attachment to others and the world around them (Bowlby, 1988).

Research in neuropsychology reinforces the principles of attachment theory with brain-based evidence. The brain expands as it receives stimuli from a person's environment (Siegel, 2010b). Tube-like neural pathways grow and sprout branches called dendrites and axons (Sullivan, 2013). These pathways meet other neural pathways, and within the space between them (synapses), there is a transfer of information. These circuits form the basis for various human functions.

As a child grows, circuits of attachment are activated, reinforced, or pruned (Schore, 2017). For example, if a child is neglected and the secure attachment circuitry is not reinforced, these neural pathways could become susceptible to pruning (removal). In parallel, new pathways might wire together that help the child adapt to the neglect (Sullivan, 2013). This child might learn that reaching out to others is not helpful and so rely only on themselves for emotional regulation. Although adaptive in infancy, this becomes isolating and problematic in adulthood. On the other hand, healthy secure attachments in infancy stimulate brain growth and integration that promote social engagement and healthy regulation (Schore, 2017).

Attachment theory is an integral focus of many neuroeducation interventions (Sullivan, 2013). However, the language mental health professionals use can often leave clients feeling disconnected and with more questions than answers (Marshall et al., 2011). Technical language, such as the terms and concepts related to the neuroscience of experience, can cause further confusion and stress at a time when clients are already struggling to regulate thoughts and emotions. Therefore, there is a need to develop creative strategies to bring the neuroscience of attachment to life in counseling sessions.

Horticultural imagery during therapy is one creative avenue that I (Danica) have found useful when exploring concepts related to neurobiology and attachment. Nature and plants have been used for medical treatment (Ho et al., 2016), group therapy for schoolchildren and the elderly (Ho et al., 2016), and meditation (Relf, 2005). Baker (2009) described many benefits of horticultural therapy, including stress reduction, increased confidence and self-esteem, reduction of symptoms of depression, and overall balance of mood. However, no literature has been found that connects horticulture imagery to the neuroeducation process in counseling. The *We've Got Roots* activity provides a creative method of sharing neuroscience and attachment theory principles with clients by replacing technical language (e.g., neurological pathways, synaptic connections, pruning, and neuroplasticity) with horticultural imagery and terminology.

MATERIALS NEEDED

The following materials are recommended:

- A small plant
- Images of the sun, water, fertilizer, soil, shade, and poison bottle (see the following)

PROCESS OF THE ACTIVITY

Step 1: Explore Existing Knowledge of Plants

Begin the activity by showing the client a plant and discussing the different parts of the plant. We recommend using a plant that has visible roots (e.g., orchid) because such plants provide a clearer illustration of the neurobiological underpinnings of attachment. If a live plant is not accessible, you can use a clip art image (See Figure 4.8) or sketch a plant with your client (see Figure 4.7). Be sure to include all plant parts that will be relevant in connecting the concept of attachment. The most important plant parts for this exercise are the roots, stalk, flowers, and leaves.

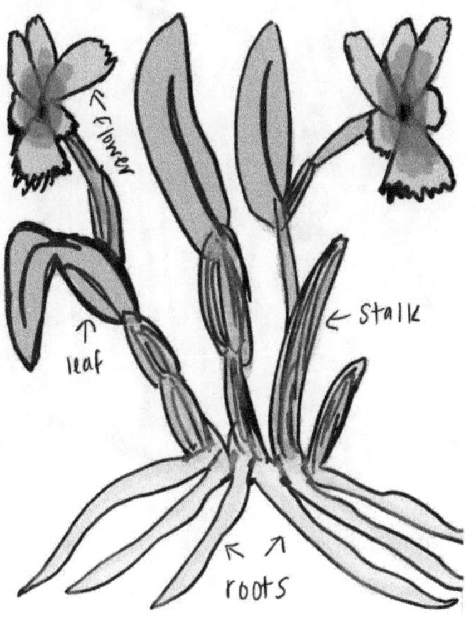

FIGURE 4.7 Basic Plant Parts

Step 2: Discuss the Growth Process of Plants

After describing basic plant parts, you can share about the growth process as follows:

> A plant has roots that are used to attach to the earth and soak up the nutrients around them. The plant has a stalk that is used to steady the plant. It has leaves used to reach for sunlight. A plant starts as a seed and then begins to grow leaves, a "body" (stalk), and, finally, begins to grow roots. The purpose of the roots is to take in the necessary nutrients and to hold the plant firmly in its environment. When the plant is young, its roots are small and fragile. However, if it is given sunlight and water, the roots begin to grow. A plant that is given extra minerals and nutrients grows roots that are thicker and healthier, and it is able to firmly hold on to its surroundings.

You can then show the client images of the sun, water, and fertilizer as examples of a supportive environment.

After exploring factors that contribute to healthy development, transition to sharing about factors that may inhibit optimal development:

> If the plant is deprived of healthy nutrients, its roots are stunted. An unhealthy plant has thin, frail roots that are not firmly attached. The plant survives, but it is not the strongest or healthiest version of itself.

You can show the client images of poison or shade to represent a lack of nutrients for the plant.

Step 3: Connect the Analogy to the Neuroscience of Attachment

The next step in the activity is connecting the metaphor of a plant and plant growth to the neurobiology of attachment:

> Much like the roots of a plant, infants need "nutrients and water" to facilitate optimal growth of their bodies and brains. Like a seedling, the nature of the environment greatly influences the growth and connections of the "roots" or neural pathways of a child. Specifically, the nature of relationships in the child's life affect the neural circuitry related to secure or insecure attachments.

Step 4: Connect the Neuroscience of Attachment to the Client's Past Life

This is a good time to pause and ask the client to reflect on the types of relational experiences they think can help a child feel secure and trust the world around them. After the client shares, you

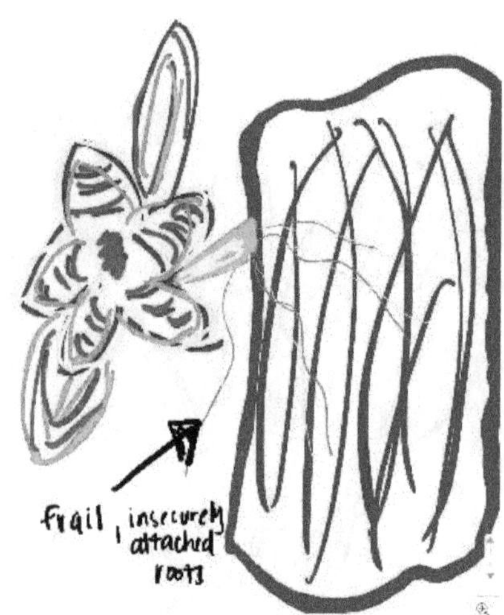

FIGURE 4.8 Plant in Nonoptimal Environment

can follow up by noting that, in general, experiences that allow the child to feel seen, safe, soothed, and secure are supportive of healthy attachment and brain development. This type of interaction supports emotional regulation, allowing individuals to feel grounded, or *rooted*, even in the midst of strong emotions.

You can then note that some experiences have a different effect on children's developing view of self, others, and the world. Some examples include toxic stress, neglect, abuse, or unpredictable caretakers. These experiences may lead to certain pathways (roots) wiring together to create adaptive defenses. These defenses are ways that individuals protect themselves to survive. Sometimes defenses cause individuals to become disconnected from their environments. For example, when an individual feels sad, instead of reaching out, they may bottle up their emotions and decide not to call a friend or someone they trust to help them regulate. This may lead to other habits, such as disconnecting from others or lashing out at them. These ways of responding not only fail to alleviate sadness, but they can also lead to other distressing emotions, such as loneliness.

FIGURE 4.9 Plant in Optimal Environment

Connecting it back to the plant analogy, you can say something like, "Think about a plant that requires sunlight but has been planted in the shade. The leaves may begin to wither, and its roots retreat to reserve energy, leaving the roots disconnected and unattached from the soil. Although the plant is doing its best to protect itself by disconnecting to reserve energy, it is reducing its only access to the sunlight (leaves). This response means the plant is isolated from the potential of receiving help from its environment. Just like the plant's roots, our "roots" might begin to wire together in ways that build protections against an environment we deem unsafe."

It is important to note that not all stress is toxic stress. A certain amount of stress can be healthy. Orchids, when placed under severe stress, produce a keiki. Keiki is the Hawaiian word for "little one." This tiny replica of the mother plant is created so that the plant can live on and flourish. Just like orchids, people are resilient and can even bloom through stressful experiences.

Step 5: Connect the Analogy to the Hope for the Client's Future

To summarize the activity, we suggest saying something like, "As adults, our 'roots' are impacted by our upbringing, environment, experiences, and relationships. The pathways that formed in our brains as children often become the automatic ways of being in adulthood. These pathways can be difficult to change because they are created in our attachment (early growth) phase; however, they are not impossible to change. Older plants that have a change of environment can adapt and grow new 'roots.'"

At this point, check in with clients to see what connections they are making to their own experiences. You might ask an open-ended question like, "How does this idea relate to your own life?" As clients connect their lives to the plant metaphor, it becomes a vehicle of shared language to explore past attachments and foster new attachments. If the neuroscience of attachment is true, then this vehicle becomes a tremendous asset to our clients' neural development and future growth; it strengthens their roots.

FOLLOW-UP

This initial activity description is just the start of using horticultural imagery and language to help clients more deeply understand their attachment histories. The evaluation of outcomes is primarily informal through observation and collaborative process evaluations (e.g., how is this imagery helping you?). You can refer back to, adjust, or expand the plant/attachment metaphor depending on the client's feedback. For instance, you can introduce other plants (e.g., resilient cacti or succulents) that represent resilience and mirror the client's progress or forecast future development.

NEUROSCIENCE IN ACTION

The client was a 13-year-old cisgender Latina female who reported symptoms of depression and anxiety. She reported a history of sexual trauma between the ages of 5 and 8 perpetuated by her half-brother. As a young teen, she engaged in risky sexual activities with many of the males at her school. I (Danica) spent four sessions talking about these risky behaviors with her. Although she reported that she wanted a stable relationship, she said she did not feel she could attain this level of commitment. She reported that she struggled to say no to sexual advances.

In sessions, the client struggled to connect her current behavior to her past trauma. In session six, I used the *We've Got Roots* activity to explore attachment theory and the potential effect of stressors that she experienced early in life.

I began by asking the client if she was familiar with gardening or plants. The client responded that she remembered growing small plants in the second grade. I took note of the client's limited knowledge of horticulture and began by describing the anatomical structures of the plant (leaves, body, roots). The client remembered planting a seed in soil and watching it grow with her classmates. I used this information to engage the client in discussions regarding the growth of the plant. I noted that the roots grew because the plant received sunshine and daily watering and the soil was full of nutrients. I described how this seedling (infant plant) was able to grow strong because it was cared for. It was given water, proper sunlight, and bugs were removed, and it was given other healthy vitamins and minerals to aid in its growth. I then asked the client what might have happened to the plant if it lacked healthy nutrients. The client's response was along the lines of "it would not grow." I affirmed the client's suggestion and followed up with the idea that the plant would not grow strong or firmly attached. Its roots would be fragile and less able to soak up the necessary "good" nutrients. The client agreed and became pensive about the analogy.

I then began the process of connecting this analogy to attachment and neuroscience. I described children as being similar to these seedlings. I shared that their brains have pathways (or roots) that are impressionable and shaped by the environment. If something "poisonous" or harmful is introduced, the child's brain begins to send distress signals. The brain's "roots" wire together and create pathways that lead to certain behavioral defenses. If the child experiences something harmful, such as abuse, the roots become rigid defensive pathways that are difficult to change. This is because the body has learned to protect itself from painful feelings. I then asked the client for her thoughts. The client instantly connected her trauma to her current behavior. The projection of her experience on the plant analogy seemed to provide her with enough distance and safety to make this connection in the present moment. She explored the idea that her ability and choice to say "no" was taken away from her at such a young age. I suggested that she learned that saying "no" didn't help protect her from feelings of fear and sadness. The client agreed and remembered that she stopped saying "no" to her half-brother because it "never worked." She instinctively learned to stop fighting when her pleas were ignored, and instead, she began to dissociate from the encounters. I took care to share that she was young and influenced by her environment and that it was not her fault. The words "no" were dismissed by her perpetrator, and, therefore, her brain formed a new "root" or pathway to help her cope.

I then shared how this "root" still exists and her brain struggles to break this cycle. This realization was emotional and profound. The client reported that sexual activities were numb for her and that she was bothered by her inability to feel anything about the experiences. The client became angry and tearful as she realized how her brain was so strongly affected by the trauma. I engaged the client in processing the emotions that she was previously unable to feel. Finally, before the end of the session, I offered the client hope through the explanation of neuroplasticity and neurogenesis through horticultural language. I explained that plants grow new roots as they age, and these roots can help them to more firmly attach and seek healthy nutrients. The client smiled and reported that she hoped to grow "new and stronger roots" that help her to make different decisions. The horticulture imagery became a shared language through which she could safely process her experiences during subsequent sessions.

ETHICAL AND MULTICULTURAL CONSIDERATIONS

When working with various age groups, it may be important to change the language used to explain the activity to fit the cognitive development of the client. For example, the ability of children to use emotionally competent language is directly linked to their self-efficacy (Beck et al., 2012). Although language centers of the brain are not fully formed, language helps to shape the emotional competence of children. Using language that is appropriate for the developmental stage of the client will help in the efficacy of the activity. This is also important to consider for clients with cognitive disabilities or limitations.

Clients who are ethnic minorities are less likely to use counseling services, and one potential barrier is the difference in native language (Casa et al., 2012). The technical language of neuroeducation may not be the most useful approach with clients whose native language is not English. Therefore, we suggest that the language and imagery of horticulture can address this potential gap in language. In addition, a counselor should be aware of clients' varying experiences with plants, as well as any allergies to specific flowering plants.

MINDFUL MEDICATIONS

Jennifer Reckner

Professional counselors are encouraged to approach counseling in a holistic manner, promoting the highest level of wellness and behavior change through the integration of mind, brain, and body. Increasingly, this holistic view includes consideration of the effect of pharmacology on the counseling process (Kaut, 2011). Although most counselors do not rely solely on a biomedical view of mental health, understanding common medications and their effect on thoughts, feelings, and behaviors is important. Given counselors' specialized knowledge relating to forming and maintaining therapeutic relationships, counselors are perhaps uniquely qualified to explore basic information about the neurobiological processes of medication to support medication management alongside the counseling process.

This *Mindful Medication* activity describes the process of incorporating neuroeducation about medication within an existing wellness framework: the Healthy Mind Platter (Rock et al., 2012). The Healthy Mind Platter includes seven "nutrients" that are needed to foster optimal brain health: (1) sleep time, (2) physical time, (3) time in, (4) playtime, (5) connecting time, (6) down time, and (7) focus time. Each nutrient has ample empirical support regarding its benefit on various neurophysiological outcomes. Rock et al. (2012) discussed how to concentrate on the nutrients, how to accomplish the desired goal with each nutrient, and how to assess and overcome barriers in integrating that nutrient into daily life. Miller (2016) described how this framework could be used during counseling to promote experience-dependent neuroplasticity. The *Mindful Medication* activity extends the conceptualizations of both Rock et al. (2012) and Miller (2016) by including how medications might influence each category of the Healthy Mind Platter.

Although any class of medication could be used, I will specifically focus on the medication management of attention-deficit/hyperactivity disorder (ADHD) with Vyvanse in the Healthy Mind Platter activity. Individuals with ADHD appear to have abnormal levels of norepinephrine and dopamine in the prefrontal cortex and striatum (Durston, 2003; Heal et al., 2009). Thus Vyvanse, a central nervous system stimulant, works to increase the number of certain neurotransmitters (e.g., dopamine and norepinephrine) in the brain by inhibiting dopamine and norepinephrine transporters, which then increases catecholamine availability (Heal et al., 2009; Hutson et al., 2014). Helping clients explore the neuroscience of the medication, its intended benefits, and more or less desirable effects using the *Mindful Medication* activity can increase informed decision making regarding medication management and use of other "nutrients" in the promotion of healthy brain development and functioning.

MATERIALS NEEDED

The following materials are needed to complete this activity:

- A copy of the Healthy Mind Platter via Dr. Dan Siegel's website: http://m.drdansiegel.com/resources/healthy_mind_platter/
- A copy of the Healthy Mind Platter Self-Care Evaluation (Page 109)
- Handout specific to medication (optional)
- A piece of paper or whiteboard to illustrate the mechanism of the drug on the brain (optional)

PROCESS OF THE ACTIVITY

Begin the neuroeducation activity with an open discussion about the client's knowledge of the medication and their reason for taking it. This discussion presents an opportunity to provide psychoeducation about the diagnosis, help the client conceptualize the condition, and emphasize the possible advantages and disadvantages of medication management in conjunction with psychotherapy.

Once the client understands the condition that the medication targets, then neuroeducation about the medication itself can take place. It is important to keep in mind your client's literacy and comprehension levels and to tailor the conversation appropriately. Some clients will appreciate discussions about specific neurotransmitters, agonists, and antagonists, and some will simply want to know how it works in the most basic sense.

Once the client expresses enough understanding about the medication and reason for taking it, you can transition to a discussion about the larger picture of the individual's treatment. You can note that although the medication can be helpful, it is only one part of what is needed for the client to achieve greater well-being and should be continually monitored for both desirable and undesirable effects. This open and neutral exploration of the effect of medication on the client's life can promote more informed decision making regarding the role of medication in the achievement of the client's goals.

The Healthy Mind Platter is a helpful model to facilitate the client's understanding of their situation, effect of medication, and additional changes necessary alongside medication. I recommend that you first introduce the Healthy Mind Platter and briefly review each domain. Then continue by exploring the Healthy Mind Platter Self-Care Evaluation (see page 109). Allow time for the client to complete the evaluation and then open a discussion about strengths and areas of desired change. During this discussion, integrate considerations related to the client's medication. Specifically, explore how the medication might positively or negatively affect each Healthy Mind Platter category. Some important considerations include the following:

- Will the medication help the client sleep or perhaps inhibit sleep?
- Are there certain times a day the client should take the medication to promote better sleep?
- Will the client have to sacrifice sexual drive to focus on completing a task?
- How will the medication affect the client's ability to focus on a task?
- How will the effects of focusing benefit them?
- How will the medication affect the client's ability to connect with others?
- Should the client talk to others about their medication use and impact? If so, what could they say and how could they say it?

As appropriate, help the client identify resources that support and/or barriers that prevent their regular and directed use of the medication.

The completion of the Healthy Mind Platter Self-Care Evaluation and resulting conversation could take one or more full sessions. It is important to explore how the client will use this framework as they continue treatment, highlight additional changes to be made alongside medication, and encourage ongoing dialogue with their prescribing health-care provider. At the end of the activity, it is helpful to offer the client time to reflect on the overall process. For example, you can ask, "What has this process been like for you?" Or, "What stands out to you as most useful about this activity?"

FOLLOW-UP

In future sessions, check in with clients about their general medication use and its effect on each area of the Healthy Mind Platter. It can take time for the therapeutic benefits of the medications to fully take effect, and encouraging regular and appropriate use in the early weeks is particularly important. You can encourage clients to create revised Healthy Mind Platter Self-Evaluations based on new areas of awareness (e.g., resources, barriers) and talk about coping strategies to deal with any of the negative effects of the medication on different areas of the Healthy Mind Platter (e.g., sleep, physical time). As clients experience benefits from the medication, as well as the changes to their personal healthy mind platter, it is important to actively consult with the prescribing physician as alterations in dosage might be necessary. For instance, if a client increases naturally producing dopamine by regular exercise and social connection, then their dose of medication might need to be altered. Therefore, ongoing process evaluation is essential.

NEUROSCIENCE IN ACTION

Tiffany was a 29-year-old single-mother with significant life challenges. She worked two demanding jobs, took night classes, and was the primary manager of her daughter's medical issues. She reported having difficulty organizing and keeping track of appointments for herself and her daughter in the midst of her own work schedule. She also reported trouble sleeping and feeling so distracted that she struggled to complete schoolwork. During the intake appointment, she was distracted, fidgety, spoke rapidly, and interrupted often. After some discussion, I made a referral for Tiffany to get an evaluation from a psychiatrist. After about 2 months, she saw a psychiatrist and was diagnosed with ADHD and prescribed Vyvanse.

When Tiffany came to her next appointment after seeing the psychiatrist, we talked about her thoughts and feelings about the diagnosis and the medication. She was able to accurately identify the behaviors that led to the ADHD diagnosis, such as forgetting her personal effects in random places, her inability to keep scheduled appointments, constantly feeling like she was on the go, fidgeting, and rapid, tangential speech. She had questions about Vyvanse, noting that she did not understand how a stimulant would help her hyperactivity. Tiffany had a high literacy level, so we were able to have a conversation about the neuroscience of the drug. She was able to understand that the mechanism of Vyvanse translates into helping her focus, complete activities, and organize her daily life. We also discussed the possibility of misuse that comes with this kind of medication and the risk of building up a tolerance.

We completed a Healthy Mind Platter Self-Care Evaluation before Tiffany started the medication. Thus in the session following her ADHD diagnosis, we revisited it with the discussion tailored toward how the medication could positively and negatively affect the various categories. We explored focus time by factoring in Vyvanse's intended effect of increasing attention. Tiffany hoped to eliminate many of the factors that typically got in her way of focusing and noted that forgetting to take her medication could really affect her ability to improve in this area. Vyvanse is taken once a day, usually in the morning. Tiffany considered potential barriers to her remembering to take her medication. After some thought, Tiffany set two alarms on her cell phone: one as the alarm and one as the backup in case she still forgot.

We also discussed playtime given that she hoped taking the medication would help her get organized be more present for herself and her daughter. Tiffany's daughter often asked her to bake cookies and play games, but Tiffany would say no because she was worried about other tasks she had forgotten about or neglected during the day. For example, Tiffany talked about the time she previously spent looking for items like car keys and homework and how this could be shifted to so she could have more time with her daughter.

Furthermore, we talked about sleep. A common side effect of Vyvanse is trouble sleeping. This side effect was particularly worrisome for Tiffany, as she already had trouble getting enough sleep. We discussed sleep hygiene and the value of a consistent bedtime routine. The Healthy Mind Platter Self-Care Evaluation asks the client to name three ways to incorporate this into daily practice, and Tiffany decided on decreasing screen time 30 minutes before bed, reading a story to her daughter, and writing an entry in her daily journal to wind down.

In our next session, we talked about how she was adjusting to the medication and how the medication was affecting her functioning according to the Healthy Mind Platter categories. Tiffany stated she felt like a new person who could tackle life and "be a good mom" again. This enthusiasm encouraged her to keep taking her medication daily, attend her weekly counseling sessions, and keep her monthly appointments with her psychiatrist. To her surprise, she reported no sleep disturbances and that her sleep was actually more restful. Tiffany attributed her better sleep to feeling less stressed overall and to her attention to other aspects of the Healthy Mind Platter. Although she still struggled with physical time and time in, her playtime and focus time had markedly improved per self-report. We revisited the Healthy Mind Platter on a quarterly basis and used it to revise her treatment plan as needed.

ETHICAL AND MULTICULTURAL CONSIDERATIONS

Many clients present to therapy and indicate they do not want to take medication, and that is why they are seeking counseling as opposed to psychiatry. It is important to respect a client's wishes while at the same time increasing their awareness of all possible options for wellness. It is a delicate balance to provide psychoeducation to dispel any misinformation about medication that may be inhibiting the client from trying it and not letting our own beliefs about medication interfere with the client's wishes.

Access to health care is also a concern that should be considered. Some primary care physicians are willing to prescribe psychopharmaceuticals, and others might opt to refer clients to a psychiatrist and defer prescribing to physicians who specialize in mental health concerns. Many psychiatrists have long waiting lists, and clients could wait months before they are able to get an appointment. In rural communities, the closest prescriber could be hours away. The cost of travel, copays, and the medication itself should also be considered.

Ethically, we must remember that our role as counselors is to refer clients to a prescriber for additional screening and not recommend a specific regimen for a client. We can provide psychoeducation about the drug but should not give advice about how to take the medication, and we should alert the prescriber if the client describes any concerning side effects or if they stop taking it. Although we do not prescribe, we have a responsibility to make sure we are educated about medications, their mechanisms, and the neuroscience of the corresponding behavior change and problematic side effects.

ANCILLARY MATERIALS

http://thebrain.mcgill.ca/

Healthy Mind Platter© Self-Care Evaluation			
Healthy Mind Platter: Self-Care Evaluation	**Sleep Time**	**Physical Time**	**Focus Time**
In which ways do you already focus on this activity?			
What is most likely to get in the way of this activity?			
What are some things you can do to pay more attention to this activity?			
Name three things you can do to incorporate this activity into your daily practice.			
How will doing these things benefit you?			
Which sacrifices will you have to make to do these things daily?			

Healthy Mind Platter: Self-Care Evaluation	Time In	Down Time	Playtime	Connecting Time
In which ways do you already focus on this activity?				
What is most likely to get in the way of this activity?				
What are some things you can do to pay more attention to this activity?				
Name three things you can do to incorporate this activity into your daily practice.				
How will doing these things benefit you?				
Which sacrifices will you have to make to do these things daily?				

PROMOTING THERAPEUTIC CONSCIOUSNESS WITH THE MIRRORING HANDS APPROACH

Richard Hill

Clients seek therapy for a number of reasons. By and large, they feel that "something" is wrong. It may be because of things they feel, or emotions/affects they are experiencing, or things they are doing, or what other people are saying. Although it is helpful that the person is seeking help, they are often not in a good space for problem solving and healing. Facilitating and supporting the client's shift into a conducive therapeutic state is the first step toward effective therapy. It is not unreasonable to suggest that there are three general states: (1) pre-therapeutic, therapeutic, and post-therapeutic. In the practice of Mirroring Hands, first described by Ernest Rossi in the 1970s and developed later in our coauthored material, we suggest these three general states can be described as *states of consciousness* (Hill & Rossi, 2017, p. 28):

- ***A Disrupting Consciousness.*** Where the brain and mind are fractured or disrupted in a protective response to feelings like depression or anxiety or being in the throes of painful trauma. Information and sensations from the inner and outer worlds are interpreted through a mindset that is closed, defensive, resistant, avoidant, and insecure.
- ***A Therapeutic Consciousness.*** Where our psychobiology is receptive and responsive, with a future orientation that is willing to explore novel possibilities. Negative feelings, such as fear, anger, and self-defeatism are calmed or bypassed, whereas positive feelings, such as trust, safety, and positive self-regard are fostered.
- ***An Integrating Consciousness.*** Where the information and sensations from the inner and outer worlds connect and integrate with existing capacities and capabilities in a creative and productive way that promotes personal well-being and social integration. This maintains itself through positive feedback systems.

How, when, and why an individual client moves between these states is different for each client. Shifting consciousness is not achieved by imposing, directing, or even suggesting to the client how they *should* move through these states. For some, it may be necessary, in the first instance, to stabilize the disrupting state by establishing such basics as food, security, and shelter, but for the average client, these conditions are satisfactory, and the therapist is able to stabilize the client by establishing positive rapport, providing a safe therapeutic space, and building the client's confidence in the therapist's capabilities.

Once these necessary foundations are established, it is possible to begin facilitating the client's shift from a disrupting to a therapeutic consciousness. I propose that this can be achieved by activating three fundamental qualities of mind (Hill & Rossi, 2017): (1) focused attention, (2) curiosity, and (3) nascent possibility. Stimulating these qualities creates a change in mental state by affecting the pattern of the flow of energy and information throughout the neural network (Fingelkurts & Fingelkurts, 2017; Siegel, 2016). Changes in mental state are experienced as a change of attitude, feeling, awareness, thought, and/or behavior. These experiences are ideodynamic indicators that something has, indeed, changed. In terms of complex systems, these experiences are emergent properties and qualities from implicit self-organizing processes in response to changes in the neural (and other elements of our biology) functions. These changes range from the pattern of information flow, to the makeup of the neurobiochemical milieu (Jordan et al., 2015; Siegelmann, 2010).

In recent years, there has been a lot of talk about neurochemical balance and imbalance (Belmaker & Agam, 2008). A better understanding is that mental states have a distinctive biochemical makeup because that is how that state is reflected in our neurobiology (Frodl & O'Keane, 2016). In a simple analogy, this is not dissimilar to the makeup of a cup of coffee. If it is sweet with a creamy color, then its "coffee state" will include a distinctive "balance" of sugar and milk. This is not a correct or incorrect balance but simply the qualities and quantities that are necessary for it to be a sweet cup of crème coffee. Altering that "balance" of ingredients in the cup will change the coffee state, which is not inherently correct or incorrect, just a *different* coffee state. It is how those ingredients are changed that is the important question.

Understanding the ways in which we can change the neurobiochemical milieu is vital to facilitating effective therapy. The important message now is that it is possible for external stimuli to create internal neurobiological change, and this change can be noticed as the experience of new feelings, thoughts, and/or behaviors—a new state. This is the essence of mind-to-body healing. When the client shifts into a therapeutic consciousness, their natural, implicit, self-organizing, problem-solving capabilities are engaged (Hill & Rossi, 2017). The qualities of mind that we use to help the client access their natural capabilities and a therapeutic consciousness (focused attention, curiosity, and nascent possibility) are also part of our natural capabilities. They do not need to be forced or directed, just allowed the opportunity to emerge.

FOCUSED ATTENTION

Focused attention is achieved in a variety of ways across a variety of treatment protocols, even though it may not always be directly attributed as such. While establishing rapport, the care and interest that the therapist expresses toward the client can be totally absorbing for the client, who has been struggling to be noticed and cared for. Careful listening focuses on the client's telling of their story. At the same time, it is also possible for the therapist to track nonverbal behaviors, which can be used as windows into internal experiences of the client. Nonverbal behaviors are external behavioral signals of internal neurobiological processes. It is necessary and important to pay close attention to the client in what we describe as *sensitive observation*.

The best support the client can receive from the therapist is a creative responsiveness to indicators that emerge from the client. These indicators may be verbal, somatic, behavioral, or emotional and become elements of feedback in the client's therapeutic system. This feedback will, in turn, enter the therapist's "system" to engage in the natural processes of self-organization to allow the best and most beneficial therapeutic activity to emerge into the therapist's consciousness.

As an example, a client, who had been diagnosed with ADHD, presented to me for anxiety. When I asked her to tell me about her situation, she began a stream of talking that was very convoluted and confusing. After a while, it occurred to me that her jiggling foot would stop jiggling for a few words, a phrase, or even a sentence or two. I found that if I paid closer attention to what she said when her foot was still, I could piece together a cogent message from within her ramblings. When I gave my reflections of what she had said when her foot was still, she was startled that I seemed to have a clearer picture of her situation than she did. From that point, she was able to better *focus her attention* and share with me what she needed to share, as much for me to hear it as to hear it herself. Knowing how to be necessarily sensitive and appropriately responsive may, and can be, difficult, but this is part of what is required to be an effective client-responsive therapist.

CURIOSITY

Our neurobiology, when in a state of curiosity, expresses changes in the neurobiochemical milieu in the same way that all our affective states have a correlating biochemical milieu. The point here being that if you are in a depressed state and you stimulate curiosity, then there will be a change in the neurobiochemical milieu, even if only for a temporary period. Much like the "coffee state" changes when crème is added, the neurobiological milieu changes when curiosity is added. It is the same for anxiety, fear, and anger. Curiosity and fear are mutually exclusive. Fear inhibits curiosity (Barnett & Cowan, 1976; Lester, 1968). The state of fear and the state of curiosity are radically different and in these different affective states, the body and brain have a totally different way of reacting and responding to the world around them in both the outer and inner levels.

Curiosity is probably the most important quality to foster shifts in consciousness. *Curiosity* is a word in two frames of reference. There's the *act* of curiosity—that is, the *doing* of curiosity seeking, wondering what is, looking for the answer playfully, examining the possibilities, and even opening the doors of possibility. There is also just a *state* of curiosity that is more like a *state of being*. Rather than responding to a stimulation that "turns on" curiosity, I suggest it is possible to establish curiosity as a baseline mental state. Rather than being stimulated by something to become interested and curious, it is possible to be in a general state that is open to the potential of interest and curiosity in everything. This is not to suggest that *every single thing* occupies the curious mind. That would be overwhelming and self-defeating. There has been much said about the impossibility of constant happiness, but it may be possible to be more permanently in a state of curiosity, even if it is to wonder why you are not happy all the time. Consider the following question: What is your mood at the start of your day? I suggest that we are better off to start our day *in* a state of curiosity. I suggest this because of what the literature (Gottlieb et al., 2013; Hill & Rossi, 2017; Panksepp, 2010) tells us happens within our biology and particularly our neurobiology when we focus our attention in a curious way.

When we are curious, we are in a "approach" state, which simply means that someone is inclined to move toward things, whereas fear inclines people to move away. To be able to approach or move "toward" something, there needs to be a reduction in fearfulness. A sense of positive anticipation is important to increase interest and expectancy for novel discovery. To be able to notice and appreciate what may be discovered, there needs to be an increase in attention and awareness. It is also very helpful to get a feeling of satisfaction and pleasure as breakthroughs and discoveries are achieved. This acts as an incentive to be curious again. A vital component for the ongoing process of therapy is that curiosity engages interpersonal connection and trust with those people who are part of the experience. All these psychobiological qualities can only be achieved if there is a concomitant change in the neural biochemical balance or, more appropriately, neurobiochemical milieu.

NASCENT POSSIBILITY

Nascent possibility is simply the sense that what is being done can lead to a beneficial outcome—that it is worth pursuing. Again, this aim is achieved in simple ways. The confidence a therapist holds in their own capabilities engenders the client's confidence in a positive outcome. Creating a safe space and establishing trust where there has not been any before can give the client a sense of confident comfort in the sessions to come. Focused attention brings the client into an attentive frame of mind; curiosity encourages exploration and connection to the therapist; nascent possibility opens the client to possibilities.

THE NEUROBIOLOGY OF SHIFTING STATES

Focused attention, curiosity, and nascent possibility are all helpful to shifting states in therapy and can be used separately or in different combinations in response to the client. Each quality has interesting research into the neurobiological changes they create (Ainsworth et al., 2013). Curiosity, however, stimulates a wide range of psycho-neurobiological changes that are well founded in research to produce dramatic changes in the neurobiochemical milieu. Achieving a therapeutic consciousness requires the following beneficial shifts in the quantity and distribution of a comprehensive set of neurotransmitters: an increase in serotonin to reduce fearfulness by calming the amygdala, heightening of our sense of positive anticipation by increasing dopamine in the frontal cortex and mesolimbic region, activating focus and attention by increasing norepinephrine and acetylcholine in the frontal cortex, producing a feeling of reward with endorphins and endokephalins; and engendering a more engaged, cooperative, and interpersonal state by an increase in oxytocin. There are numerous other observed effects of curiosity, and some are yet to be thoroughly researched (Lesch, 2007; Lovheim, 2011; Panksepp, 1986), but we know that these activities require the production of proteins, so curiosity must also be stimulating the necessary gene expression and perhaps altering epigenetic inhibitions that are products of the client's negative experience (Panksepp et al., 1998).

By drawing together a broad selection of single-domain research (see the following), I propose that there is a set of brain regions that act collectively to create the "brain state" of curiosity. They inform various areas of the brain, especially the midbrain and cortex, through the regulation of neurotransmitter production and distribution to create emergent mental states. It is not unusual for brain areas to be considered as acting as collective systems: the limbic area, the basal ganglia, and the hypothalamic pituitary adrenal axis, to name a few. These brain areas act together in a dynamic interplay that is essential in creating the neurobiochemical milieu that is experienced as the mental state. This dynamic interplay is all part of a complex system from which emerges a *state of being* we call *curiosity.*

The research relating to these regions, the neurotransmitters they produce, and the effect on our state of being are described next:

- ***Positive Anticipation.*** Dopaminergic activity from the *substantia nigra/ventral tegmental area* and *nucleus accumbens* (Gruber et al., 2014; Knutson et al.)
- ***Focus and Attention on Issues That Interested Them.*** Norepinephrine from the *locus coereleus* (Aston-Jones & Cohen, 2005) and acetylcholine from the *nucleus basalis* (Buzsaki & Gage, 1989)
- ***Calming of Stress and Hypersensitivity.*** Serotonergic activity from the *raphe nuclei* (Hornung, 2003)
- ***Shifting From Feeling Isolated Toward Trust and Social Engagement.*** Oxytocin receptors in the *paraventricular nucleus* (Yee et al., 2016)
- ***Pleasure and Satisfaction.*** Endogenous endomorphin and endokephalin rewards from the *periaqueductal gray* (Blood & Zatorre, 2001)

These brain regions are found in the upper brain stem and lower midbrain, projecting neurons out into the midbrain and cortex. These brain regions are, collectively, the functional structures of curiosity.

In determining a name, I was attracted to the word *nuntius,* which is Latin for "messenger" or "announcer." The collective name is, therefore, the *nuntius nuclei,* which seems fitting for the brain regions that produce the neurotransmitters that are the messengers that regulate and modulate our mental state—our state of consciousness. The biochemical milieu is a fundamental contributing factor in how various areas of brain function at any given time, not just in curiosity, so the *nuntius nuclei* are relevant when considering a number of mental states, including happiness and love, as well as depression and anxiety.

The *Promoting Therapeutic Consciousness With the Mirroring Hands Approach* activity described next shows how the Mirroring Hands technique (Hill & Rossi, 2017) can be used to foster the psychological qualities (focused attention, curiosity, and nascent possibility) necessary to facilitate a shift in consciousness from the initial disrupting consciousness into a therapeutic and eventual integrated consciousness.

PROCESS OF THE ACTIVITY

The method used to create a therapeutic consciousness as preparation for a therapeutic session of Mirroring Hands is as simple as it is almost universally effective. The fundamentals of attention, curiosity, and nascent possibility can be achieved in all effective therapeutic modalities, although the methods will vary. Mirroring Hands facilitates a therapeutic consciousness by first asking the client to raise their hands in a comfortable position in front, about waist height. The language pattern of Mirroring Hands is one of the keys to avoiding direction and even minimize suggestion by creating a form of invitation for the client to participate in the experience in their own way and to be their own sensitive observer of what they feel and do.

Focused Attention

The client is asked to focus on the hands as if they have never seen them before:

> I wonder if you can look at your hands. I mean, really look at them, carefully, as if you have never looked at those hands quite so carefully and closely before. Notice the different sizes of your fingers and the shape of your palm.

The therapist can participate in the experience with the client by mirroring their hand position and movement to foster the relational importance of the therapeutic experience. Supporting and encouraging words can be shared until there is a shared sense that there is a heightened level of focus and attention on the hands. This is a simple but transformative act that enables focused attention. The way in which any of the techniques in Mirroring Hands are applied varies in relation to the client (i.e., a client-responsive application; Figure 4.10).

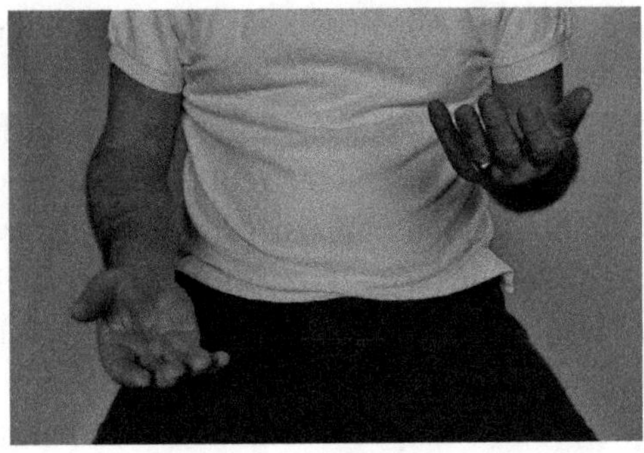
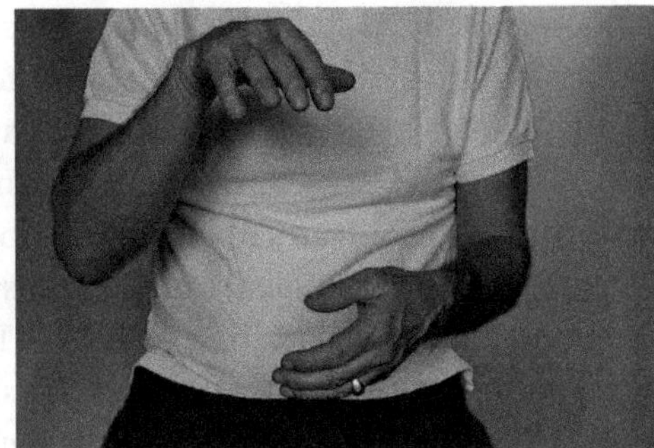

FIGURE 4.10 Example of Mirroring Hands Exercise

Curiosity

The client is encouraged to wonder if there might be some noticeable sensation of difference between the hands. This triggers curiosity about what might be possible:

> I wonder if you can tell me which hand feels a little different? Perhaps cooler, or heavier... or older... or... [other variations can be used in a client-responsive way that might relate to words or feelings they have talked about]? Just allow your conscious mind to become aware of this feeling, as if it is happening all by itself [allow time for the client to engage, test, and play with the experience].

Nascent Possibility

Finally, we ask the client if their hands might give some indication by movement or some other attraction as to which hand wishes to be noticed in this moment. The key is to allow the activity to occur almost as if "all by itself" and not consciously directed:

> Is it possible that you might feel a little movement, or something, in the hand that is... almost all by itself... [wait patiently until one of the hands moves in some way]? Wonderful... yes... that's the hand that feels [whatever the sensation is].... How interesting.

You will notice the proliferation of ellipses to indicate where the therapist does not direct or even suggest what the client should be thinking about. This is one example of "client-responsive language" where the open-ended sentence truly allows the client to be at the center of the experience. If the client notices a movement or feeling that they have not generated consciously, it leaves them with a feeling that they have connected to something else about themselves that is nonconscious and creates a new sense of possibility about what might happen during the Mirroring Hands process.

Now that a "therapeutic consciousness" has been established within the client, and hopefully within the therapist as well, it is both safe and productive to move into an exploration of the client's concerns using the various concepts and components of the Mirroring Hands approach, which is outside of the scope of this text. The approach and techniques are described in detail in the book *The Practitioner's Guide to Mirroring Hands: A Client-Responsive Therapy That Facilitates Natural Problem-Solving and Mind-Body Healing* (Hill & Rossi, 2017).

FOLLOW-UP

The degree to which a client benefits from neuroeducation is entirely based on client responsiveness. Sometimes this knowledge can be of great help, other times not. I have explained the neuroscience of the sensorimotor cortex; the self-organizing nature of complex systems like the brain and other related neural processes when it is beneficial to the client's experience. Usually they ask. I always remind myself that clients are not helped by me proving how clever *I* might be but by being an available and reliable resource for the client as and when needed.

Feedback is an important element of all therapy. The rise of practical forms and questionnaires for feedback, such as feedback-informed treatment scales developed by Scott Miller and others (Prescott et al., 2017), indicates to me that feedback is often not an inclusive aspect of many therapeutic practices. Hence the need to add a retrospective feedback intervention. Mirroring Hands, on the other hand, is a feedback-based therapy. By being client responsive, the therapist is acting in direct response to the client's words, actions, movements, and other ideodynamic behaviors that are both feeding into the ongoing therapeutic process and providing feedback about what has just transpired. The therapist can always "check in" with the client with simple questions or curiosities that give the client the opportunity to inform the therapist of their progress. These invitations seek to respect the client's privacy and minimize interference in their self-organizing therapeutic process. For example, the therapist might ask, "Is there a word or two you would like to share with me or are you content to continue with your own private inner work?" Or, "I can see that something important is happening. Even though I don't know what it is, are you able to continue with this work in your own way or would you like me to...?" In the second example, the sentence is deliberately left incomplete so that the client is free to answer or respond without direction or even suggestion. These are just some examples of how feedback is incorporated as an immediate and ongoing element of the Mirroring Hands process.

NEUROSCIENCE IN ACTION

A recent client, Mary (not her real name), made her resistance to therapy very clear when she told me (paraphrased), "I've had lots of therapy and read everything, so there is probably nothing you can do that would be of any help." She continued to talk about this problem and that problem and this therapist and that therapist, gesturing with the right and then the left hand to highlight the distinction. As her hand gestures became more active and adamant, I used her own implicitly developing activity with her hands. As often happens when entering a Mirroring Hands process, it is triggered by the client's actions and natural behavior. When the therapist is truly client responsive, there is rarely any resistance or discomfort about entering a therapeutic process. We know that the motor cortex and sensory cortex have a large representation for the hands in the brain and so, using this natural neural sensitivity, I remarked, "Wow, look at those hands working so hard to show me the importance of what you are saying!" She was, indeed, able to shift her conscious *focus of attention* rapidly to her hands, so much so that her talking slowed down, and then she stopped talking and just focused on the movement of her hands. This was a unique entry toward her therapeutic consciousness, but she clearly, and rapidly, engaged in the steps of *focused attention* and *curiosity*. She had certainly never experienced anything like that before.

To activate the feeling of *nascent possibility*, I encouraged Mary to be fascinated and somewhat intrigued about her hand movements, as if they may be telling us something more than just highlighting her conversation. While she was closely watching her hands moving and not speaking, I wondered aloud, "It seems like your hands have a mind of their own ... showing you that there is something going on somewhere that you have yet to discover." She furrowed her eyebrows and tilted her head slightly as her attention was even more deeply absorbed into her hands.

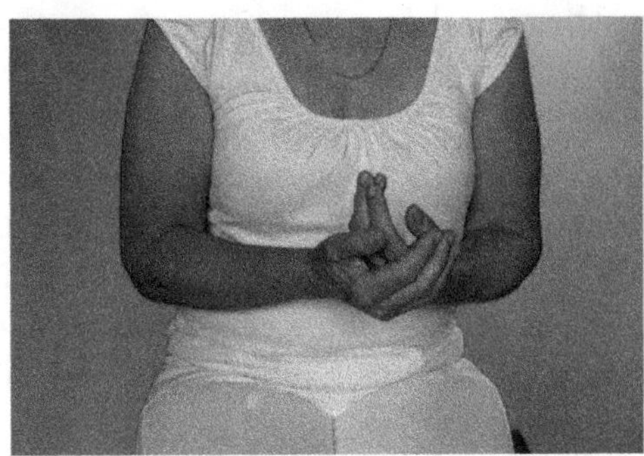

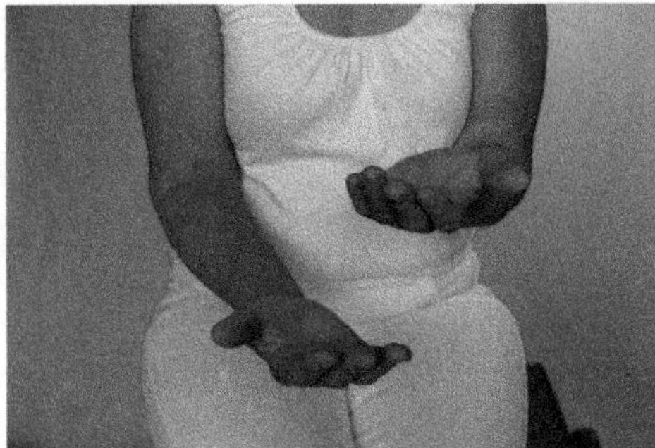

FIGURE 4.11 Client Experimenting With Hand Movements

I continued to facilitate Mary's engagement with her therapeutic consciousness by encouraging her curiosity with statements like the following:

- I wonder what those hands might be helping you discover?
- Will those hands choose to tell their own story?
- I wonder what thoughts might be coming to your mind as we explore this?

These are just examples of the things said during the session, which continued for some 75 minutes before she gave me a natural signal (closing her eyes and taking a deep breath) that she had done all the work she could for the moment.

I asked if she wanted to share a few words with me about her experience. She let out a relaxing sigh and began to explain that the hands came to represent two different "faces" that she showed the world. As the hands moved toward each other and settled over each other, she realized that she had created a protective persona that had become the principle "face" that people saw. In fact, all those other therapists had been trying to solve the problems in her protective persona.

Finally, she understood that she resisted therapy because to lose her protective persona would have left her other persona vulnerable and at risk. Perhaps it was time to let her more desirable and protected self come out into the world. Maybe she was old enough now to be out of the danger she feared in her childhood home, which among other things contributed to the development of the protective persona. Perhaps her protective self could take a well-deserved rest. In the usual manner of closing a Mirroring Hands session, I suggested that she could continue this healing work with herself at appropriate times during the day and in dreams at night.

As a therapist, in the time frame of just one session with a client who was clearly and demonstrably resistant to therapy, and who gave very few details about her past, what kind of genius would I have to be to uncover and unravel her history of childhood abuse and the creation of a protective persona that needed to realize that it was time to relax and let her natural self come forward in the world? The key to the answer is that, fortunately, the client was not dependent on me to resolve her problem or even take her through a process that would reveal her problem. All I needed to do was facilitate her own opening to herself by assisting her into a therapeutic consciousness and then guiding her as she followed her pathways within that moved from her symptoms to a place of enlightenment—without ever really knowing the details of her story. As the therapist, I didn't need to know. Only she did.

ETHICAL AND MULTICULTURAL CONSIDERATIONS

It is in this aspect of cultural and ethical considerations that the Mirroring Hands approach of client responsiveness and the use of curiosity are most beneficial. It is always important to have as much knowledge about anything to do with the human experience. Cultural awareness is a very important part of our ability to be sensitive and suitably responsive. Because the Mirroring Hands approach is not directive and rarely even suggestive but instead focused carefully and sensitively on observing the client and responding accordingly, the therapist is much less likely to make an unintended cultural or ethical error. There is always the potential in a therapeutic situation to cause an enactment, or what is called in psychoanalysis, a countertransference, but being client responsive means that such an error is most likely to be noticed in quick time. That is certainly my experience and that of Ernest Rossi's; collectively, we have over 5 decades of clinical experience with the Mirroring Hands approach.

Creating a unique state of therapeutic consciousness where exploration and discovery are desirable, even when the exploration might be of difficulty and trauma, is an important therapeutic foundation. Focusing attention and holding a sense of possibility for a positive outcome creates the ideal conditions to allow curiosity to embolden a client to look both within and to their growing edge for meaning, purpose, problem solving, and resolution. We can prime our mental state with curiosity to engage our sense of interest and wonder, to seek out what is beneath the obvious and superficially apparent, and to create something new, meaningful, and self-relevant. This is how the therapist has a positive effect on the therapeutic process.

The benefits of shifting the client into a therapeutic consciousness are not restricted to a particular practice, modality, or protocol. Every therapist and every client can use the three elements of focused attention, curiosity, and nascent possibility as a way of stimulating the client's natural problem-solving capabilities. I wonder how *you* might apply the three elements to your preferred style of therapy. Or to particular cultures, sexual orientations, or religious preferences? This is an especially important question when you encounter client resistance or therapeutic stalling or when the therapist finds themselves stuck. The case example of Mary involved the practice of Mirroring Hands, but she may have been equally responsive to another modality if it were underpinned with attention, curiosity, and possibility. Can the blank page of a cognitive behavioral therapy questionnaire be made a fascinating curiosity where the client is interested in what words might be added to the page? Are clients who experience resistance offering the therapist the keys for progress in the words they say, the movements they make, and/or the feelings they express where the therapist needs only to be sensitive and responsive to what the client is offering?

I wonder about these types of questions every time a client walks into the clinic. As Milton Erickson advised Ernest Rossi, "Every psychotherapy encounter is a field experiment" (Hill & Rossi, 2017, p. 205). The therapist does not know what the client will bring into the room, and even though there may be some preparation, the therapist does not know exactly how the therapeutic experience will progress. And so the therapist also needs to be engaged in a therapeutic consciousness to heighten the sensitivity of their observation and allow for the most appropriate and beneficial therapy to emerge.

ANCILLARY MATERIALS

- *The Practitioner's Guide to Mirroring Hands* book
- Richard Hill's website: www.richardhill.com.au
- Ernest Rossi's website: www.ernestrossi.com

WHAT'S HAPPENING IN MY BRAIN? ADDRESSING THE IMPACT OF PROBLEMATIC SUBSTANCE USE ON THE BRAIN THROUGH PSYCHOEDUCATION AND EXPRESSIVE ARTS

Diona Emmanuel and Olivia Bentley

Neuroscience-informed psychoeducation and expressive arts are complementary interventions for addressing problematic substance use. The *What's Happening in My Brain* activity consists of two parts: (1) sharing information related to the impact of problematic substance use on the brain and (2) facilitating a client-driven expressive arts activity illustrating this impact. Psychoeducation can be helpful when working with clients with problematic substance use and is included in many treatment regimens (Chandiramani & Tripathi, 1993; Davis et al., 2002; Fals-Stewart et al., 2006). Ekhtiari et al. (2017) specifically researched the merits of neuroscience-informed psychoeducation for substance use and found evidence to support the idea that understanding the physiological impact of substance use can support clients' sustained behavior changes.

There is flexibility in the application of this activity, making it particularly useful in the field of addiction, as clients are diverse in their paths to recovery. The counselor has the freedom to choose which aspects of neuroscience and addiction are included based on individual client needs and interests. For example, counselors working with adolescents can share that the adolescent's brain is still developing, which affects their decision-making processes; engagement in risky behaviors, such as substance use; and response to substances (Bava et al., 2010; Steinberg, 2008). The prefrontal cortex, the area of the brain that is responsible for managing emotions, assessing situations, and making decisions, continues to develop throughout adolescence and young adulthood (Gogtay et al., 2004). We suggest using an easy-to-understand resource as a guide, such as the National Institute on Drug Abuse's (NIDA) *Drugs, Brains, and Behavior: The Science of Addiction* (NIDA, 2014) or *Neuroscience-Informed Psychoeducation for Addiction Medicine: A Neurocognitive Perspective* (Ekhtiari et al., 2017). NIDA (2014) provides information about the impact of substance use on various areas of the brain and explores changes to the communication system and the overall structure. Ekhtiari et al. (2017) highlights several pertinent neuroscience-informed psychoeducation topics, including neurocognitive risk factors associated with alcohol and substance use disorders, neurocognitive deficits resulting from substance use, and the brain recovery process.

Incorporating expressive arts into talk therapy can deepen engagement and learning, allowing clients to process thoughts and feelings that they may not have words to verbalize (Adedoyin et al., 2014). Expressive arts techniques are developmentally appropriate and illustrate the mind-body connection (Malchiodi, 2005; Zaidel, 2014). The act of creating art can provide new avenues for self-exploration, encourage retention of information, foster new coping skills for self-expression, and help develop greater self-awareness. After the completion of the expressive arts activity, the reflection prompts give clients the opportunity to verbalize some of the thoughts and emotions expressed through the creative process. Although there are no right or wrong answers to the prompts, clients are asked to explore how their brains have been affected by addiction and communicate any thoughts or feelings.

MATERIALS NEEDED

Choose materials based on client needs determined during the initial assessments and discussion of the use of this intervention. Materials we typically use include the following:

- A resource on the neuroscience of substance use (see resources noted earlier)
- A blank sheet of computer paper
- Basic art supplies (crayons, colored pencils, and/or markers)
- Advanced art supplies (optional): paint, pastels, magazines, stickers, glitter, adhesive, and scissors
- Additional neuroscience informational materials (optional): a model of the brain, magnetic resonance imaging of brains affected by substances, or a whiteboard to illustrate brain concepts

PROCESS OF THE ACTIVITY

What's Happening in My Brain can be used in an individual or group setting with adolescents or adults. We recommend using this activity in multiple sessions to infuse relevant neuroeducation topics at various points in the treatment process.

Phase 1: Initial Assessment

One of the first steps in preparing for the activity is getting a sense of how clients perceive the effect of their substance use in a general manner. It is often helpful to first ask about perceived benefits of their substance use and then ask about potential negative aspects. Commonly expressed benefits include help with shutting off their minds, decreasing pain, more fun socializing, and so forth. Commonly identified negative outcomes include loss of family and friends, loss of money, loss of productivity, physical and mental health concerns, criminal consequences, and loss of self. After listing and exploring perceived benefits and negative consequences, you can introduce the impact of addiction on the neurobiology of the brain. You can ask a simple open-ended question, such as, "What do you know about how substances impact the brain?," to get the conversation started. From there, fill in the gaps of information that seem most relevant to the client's situation and interests. Make sure to highlight the potential for the brain to heal as much as you highlight potential damage caused by use. In sharing information, ask the client to reflect on how understanding neuroscience might affect their recovery. Invite clients to deepen their understanding by participating in an activity that includes more information sharing and an expressive arts activity. Once the client consents to this form of treatment, brainstorm specific topics or concepts that are of interest to the client.

Phase 2: Activity

The activity component is divided into three steps: (1) psychoeducation, (2) expressive arts activity, and (3) exploration.

Step 1: Psychoeducation

Begin with a brief introduction and overview of the psychoeducation topic. Introduce handouts or illustrations to help the client visualize the concepts. While sharing information, it is important to check in with clients. You could say, "I realize I am sharing a lot of information with you. What questions or concerns do you have?" The script that follows is an example of information you can share about how substances affect brain structures and functions. You can create additional scripts that focus on a single substance, on how the brain heals, and on other related topics.

PSYCHOEDUCATION "SCRIPT" EXAMPLE

Chronic substance use changes the structure and working patterns of the brain. Drugs affect various areas of the brain, including the brain stem, the limbic system, and the prefrontal cortex. Linking the brain to the spinal cord, the brain stem controls basic bodily functions, including breathing and heart rate. Some drugs can negatively affect breathing, and overdoses can lead to death (NIDA, 2014). Consisting of multiple structures, including the amygdala, hippocampus, thalamus, basal ganglia, and hypothalamus, the limbic system regulates memory, emotions, and behavior (Pascalau et al., 2018). Drug use can affect the basal ganglia because the drug can overactivate the reward circuit of the brain and lead to the feeling of a "high." Substances can take over the limbic system's motivational system, leading a person to hyperfocus on getting more of the drug to feel pleasure. Continuous exposure to substances can lead to a loss of the feeling of pleasure. The prefrontal cortex is significantly affected by substance use. This area of the brain controls decision making, planning, problem solving, and impulse control (NIDA, 2014). Substances interfere with the decision-making process; individuals stop making decisions that are in line with their values or long-term goals.

Substances affect brain communication, which occurs through a network of neurons that pass messages. Neurons are nerve cells that send messages to other neurons. Neurotransmitters are chemical messengers that carry the messages between neurons. Receptors are chemical receivers and provide the site of attachment for the neurotransmitter on the neuron. Transporters are considered to be chemical recyclers because they recycle neurotransmitters. When sending a message, neurons release neurotransmitters into the synapse or space between other neurons. The neurotransmitter moves across this space, attaches to receptors on the next neuron, and the message is then received (NIDA, 2014).

With repeated drug use, neurons and brain circuits are significantly affected. Drugs like marijuana and heroin can imitate natural chemical messengers found in the brain and interfere with the brain's communication system by attaching to neurons and sending abnormal messages. In addition to affecting the type of messages that are sent and received, drugs can also affect the way that information is processed. Drugs like cocaine and methamphetamines can overstimulate the reward center of the brain. Drugs can cause an extremely large number of neurotransmitters to be released from neurons, or they can prevent the neurotransmitters from being recycled. When too many neurotransmitters, such as dopamine, are released, the brain's communication channels are affected, and an individual experiences a high that consists of feelings of excitement, happiness, and pleasure. The brain likes balance, however, so it decreases the number of receptors or produces less of the neurotransmitter. The ability to feel pleasure then decreases and an even larger amount of a drug is needed to experience a high. We call this phenomenon tolerance (NIDA, 2014).

Step 2: Art Activity

Next, transition to the expressive arts component of the activity. Before beginning, it may be helpful to offer the client a break or engage in a mindfulness exercise. Make sure you have enough time left in your session before starting, as clients can take a while to complete their work. When ready, read the following instructional prompt (or a modified version you create) and provide a quiet and safe space for the client to create their work. While the client is working, be present and observe silently.

EXPRESSIVE ARTS INSTRUCTIONS

Based on what you took from the information I just shared, create something that represents what you think is happening in your brain as a result of substance use. You can use colors, shapes/drawings, and/or words to illustrate your brain. There is no right or wrong way to complete this activity.

Step 3: Exploration of Art

Lastly, use reflective prompts to engage the client in an exploration of the art and the interplay of their experience and the psychoeducational material presented in the session. Process questions/prompts include the following:

- Tell me about your artwork/brain.
- What stands out to you?
- How do you feel (after completing the activity/receiving the psychoeducation)?
- What does that feeling look like to you?
- How do you know when you are feeling angry/sad/other?
- What makes you feel that way?
- What makes you feel better?
- What would you call your brain? (or what would you title your artwork?)
- What does this image show you?
- What did you think about the information that was presented?
- What is important to remember about your brain as you recover?
- How do you think your brain will change as you go through treatment?

FOLLOW-UP

This activity is primarily evaluated through informal assessment information gained during observation and follow-up processing. If this activity is used throughout the client's treatment process, you can ask, What has changed since the previous drawing? What has helped with the change? How do you feel about the change?

NEUROSCIENCE IN ACTION

This activity was completed in an individual session with an 18-year-old female who had started treatment two weeks prior. During prior individual sessions, the client asked to learn more about the impact of problematic substance use on her health. I (Diona) provided psychoeducation from the NIDA (2014) guide and asked the client to describe what she knew and learned. Throughout the session, I checked in with the client to see if she had any questions or concerns. The client stated that she did not and was able to summarize key points. She followed the prompt for the expressive arts activity and created an image of what she thought her brain looked like because of her substance use. The client reported that she did not realize how much marijuana and alcohol could truly affect her. The client reported learning a lot about the impact of problematic substance use on her brain and stated that she typically hears about the impact of substance use on her body and relationships. The client reported that she was angry with herself because she had been "damaging" her brain; she said she was ashamed that she had hurt herself in this way. The client and I explored her feelings of anger and shame and discussed ways to address these feelings. The client reported that she wanted to share the information with her family and set a better example.

This activity helped me build rapport with the client, as we were able to work together to explore the impact of substance use on the client's life. The client reported being more open to working with me because I listened to how she had been affected by her use, while also providing psychoeducation. The activity also helped the client actively participate in her treatment. When selecting topics to explore, I was mindful of the fact that the client had just started treatment, so we explored the influence of substance use on the brain. We discussed how substance use affects different structures of the brain, as well as the communication system.

ETHICAL AND MULTICULTURAL CONSIDERATIONS

When selecting information to present, consider the client's developmental age, level of education or literacy, and multicultural identities, which may affect a client's understanding of neuroscience. As much as possible, allow the client to decide which psychoeducational concepts to cover. Counselors should also be aware of their own neuroscience knowledge and be careful not to share incorrect information. Reliance on reputable resources can help avoid misinterpreting or misstating neuroscience concepts.

ANCILLARY MATERIALS

The following are references for the two psychoeducation guides we recommend:

- Ekhtiari, H., Rezapour, T., Aupperle, R. L., & Paulus, M., P. (2017). Neuroscience-informed psychoeducation for addiction medicine: A neurocognitive perspective. In T. Calvey & W.M.U. Daniels (Eds.), *Progress in brain research, volume 235* (pp. 239–264). Academic Press.
- National Institute on Drug Abuse. (2014). *Drugs, brains, and behavior: The science of addiction.* https://www.drugabuse.gov/publications/drugs-brains-behavior-science-addiction/preface

MINDFULNESS

A Vehicle to Pass Through Substance Use Craving and Navigate the Addiction Recovery Course

Reginald W. Holt

Researchers and clinicians have widely acknowledged that cravings are often responsible for many individuals returning to substance use after a period of recovery (Witkiewitz & Bowen, 2010). Even more recently, the *Diagnostic and Statistical Manual of Mental Disorders, 5th Edition* (*DSM-5*; American Psychiatric Association [APA], 2013) includes craving, or a strong desire to use, as a specific diagnostic criterion for substance-related and addictive disorders. Not only does the manual recognize that craving is one symptomatic feature of a substance use disorder (SUD), but it also suggests that the current experience of craving may help gauge the likelihood of an imminent return to use (APA, 2013). The *DSM-5* further emphasizes the pervasiveness of craving by advising that this phenomenon can continue to occur even when an individual no longer meets full diagnostic criteria for a SUD, defined as sustained remission, or 12 months or longer. Taking the aforementioned into consideration, as well as the evidence offered by neurobiological research that craving is associated with substance use, return to use, and recovery (Sinha, 2013), it is essential that clinicians offering treatment for SUDs provide information regarding the etiology, experience, and management of craving.

Cravings have been explained using a variety of theories and paradigms, including conditioning, cognitive, motivational, and psychobiological models (Skinner & Aubin, 2010), and even though the specific neural mechanisms triggering alcohol and drug cravings are complex and possibly best understood by neuroscientists, it is nonetheless important for counselors to support clients as they learn the fundamental aspects of this common experience. At a basic level, the origin of cravings may be best understood in relation to the reward system of the brain. This system, which evolved over time to ensure human survival, is activated in response to natural reinforcers, such as food and sex (Nestler, 2002). A key neurotransmitter that has been specifically implicated in goal-directed behavior and reward is dopamine (Hall & Walker, 2017). When individuals engage in a pleasurable experience, dopamine is released to help the brain remember the event, thus promoting future repetition of behavior and the eventual formation of habits (National Institute on Drug Abuse [NIDA], n.d.). Akin to natural rewards, drugs of addiction induce pleasure; however, they fuel greater surges in dopamine levels, thereby reinforcing the link between ingesting the drugs and the euphoria that follows their use. This chain of events alters neural pathways, which strengthens the drive to automatically pursue and engage in ongoing substance use without intentional thought (NIDA, n.d.). Consequently, the association between memories of past use and exposure to drug-related cues trigger cravings and substance use (Hall & Walker, 2017; Nestler, 2002).

Volkow et al. (2016) offer a more complete paradigm to elucidate the neuroscientific process connected with alcohol and drug-related cravings. The authors described *three stages of addiction*. The first stage is the *binge and intoxication stage* when an addictive substance is ingested, and the person subsequently experiences its pleasurable, rewarding, and euphoric effect. The second stage is the *withdrawal and negative affect stage* in which the pleasurable effect has dissipated, and the person subsequently experiences a negative emotional and/or physical state in the absence of the addictive substance. The third phase is the *preoccupation and anticipation stage* in which the person craves the effect of the addictive substance after a period of abstinence and begins planning or obsessing to obtain it.

During the *binge and intoxication stage,* substance use activates the brain pathways of reward and reinforcement by triggering the release of the neurotransmitter dopamine (Volkow et al.,

2016). Because dopamine is released in anticipation of a reward (i.e., the euphoria caused by drug use), it produces a highly reinforcing effect, and drugs are repeatedly ingested. Recurrent use, however, eventually creates a learning experience where dopamine is now fired in response to the associated environmental stimuli that preceded the actual use of the drug. This pairing of the stimuli with the substance use leads to a conditioned response that triggers drug-related cravings.

Over time, the brain attempts to adapt to ongoing drug use by releasing smaller amounts of dopamine (Volkow et al., 2016). As a result, its reward system becomes less sensitive to drug- and environmental-related stimuli. This decreased dopamine reactivity, combined with the diminished effects or withdrawal of drugs, bring about the amotivation and dysphoria typically seen in an individual with addiction. Other neuroadaptations transpiring in the extended circuitry of the amygdala increase the individual's stress reactivity and the rise of negative emotions. Thus it is in the *withdrawal and negative affect stage* that a person engages in a cycle of addiction by repeatedly using in an attempt to alleviate the emotional, mental, and physical discomforts that are experienced in the aftermath of chronic substance use.

Joint alterations in the brain's reward system and prefrontal regions provide a neurobiological rationale for the impulsive and compulsive behaviors seen in addiction (Volkow, et al., 2016). The same downregulation of dopamine that occurs in the brain's reward pathway also happens in the prefrontal cortex (PFC). The PFC plays a primary role in executive functioning (e.g., abstract thinking, focusing and attending, regulating emotions, anticipating consequences, planning, making decisions, controlling impulses); therefore, when dopamine signaling is impaired in the PFC, the person's ability to resist intense cravings, delay strong impulses, and make healthy choices is likewise impaired. During the *preoccupation and anticipation stage*, altered brain functioning makes it difficult to manage urges despite a desire for sobriety, and once relapse is triggered, the cycle of addiction is maintained.

Although substance use-related cravings are a normal part of the recovery process, attempting to suppress or ignore them is not an ideal way to manage these sometimes intense, yet transitory, experiences. One intervention that has gained considerable attention for its role in craving management and relapse prevention is mindfulness-based meditation. Researchers have proposed that the practice of mindfulness has the potential to help mitigate the cycle of addiction by activating, engaging, and strengthening the brain's executive functioning system (Gallant, 2016), as well as improving emotional regulation by reducing activity in the amygdala while integrating it with the PFC (Doll et al., 2016). A seminal definition of mindfulness is "the awareness that emerges through paying attention on purpose, in the present moment, and nonjudgmentally to the unfolding of experience moment to moment" (Kabat-Zinn, 2003, p. 145). Shapiro and Carlson (2009) further defined mindfulness as a "knowing and experiencing of life as it arises and passes ... a way of relating to all experiences in an open, receptive way ... freedom from grasping and from wanting anything to be different. It simply knows and accepts" (p. 5). Adding in elements of self-kindness and compassion allows clients to create a safe space where they may curiously notice their cravings until the urge to use eventually subsides. With each successful practice, clients can bypass their habitual pattern of immediately satisfying triggers, strengthen their inhibitory responses to urges, and possibly reduce the overall intensity and frequency of cravings in the long term.

Mindfulness has been studied by medical, neurobiological, and behavioral researchers for the past several decades. Its application, especially in clinical settings, has produced promising results for individuals affected by mental and substance use-related problems (Goyal et al., 2014). An objective of mindfulness-based training, especially in the field of addictions counseling, is to help clients develop awareness and nonjudgmental acceptance of thoughts, emotions, and physiological sensations while providing a skill set for managing internal and external triggers (Witkiewitz et al., 2005). In addition, researchers have suggested that mindfulness-based relapse prevention may be effective in reducing cravings (Tapper, 2018), changing the manner in which individuals relate to their experiences (Witkiewitz et al., 2013), inhibiting their craving-related behavioral responses (Tapper, 2018), and even possibly altering the neurobiological changes affiliated with addiction and relapse (Witkiewitz & Lustyk, 2013).

Considering that substance use-related problems are listed among the top-10 major public health problems and concerns in the United States (Centers for Disease Control and Prevention [CDC], 2016), addiction professionals should promote effective treatment models based on scientific advancements in research, which includes understanding the neurobiology underlying addiction and relapse. Although drug cravings often lead to a return to use, their presence does not necessarily indicate that a return to drug use is imminent. When a slip or full-blown return to use does happen, however, it should be received as a commonly occurring experience and processed as a learning opportunity rather than meeting it with reproach and shame (Inaba & Cohen, 2014). In doing so, clients are encouraged that addiction has moved away from being considered a moral defect or character flaw to being recognized as a multifaceted condition that is influenced by neurobiological, developmental, environmental, and genetic factors (U.S. Department of Health and Human Services [HHS], 2016). Not only does this perspective reduce addiction-related stigma and normalize clients' experiences, but it also empowers them with the knowledge and skills needed to initiate and sustain longer term recovery.

The *Mindfulness: A Vehicle to Pass Through Substance Use Craving and Navigate the Addiction Recovery Course* activity offers counselors a strategy to reaffirm to their clients who are diagnosed with SUDs that relapse is influenced by intricate dynamics rather than personal defects or moral failings. This aim is accomplished, in part, by helping clients become familiar with the general neurobiological model of addiction. In addition, offering a mindfulness-based strategy to help manage craving, which includes a focus on self-kindness and compassion, may improve addiction treatment outcomes for clients (especially those who experience feelings of guilt, remorse, and shame related to the consequences of substance use and/or multiple relapses). When all of this is ultimately achieved, addiction-related stigma is defied, clients are empowered, and recovery goals are reinforced.

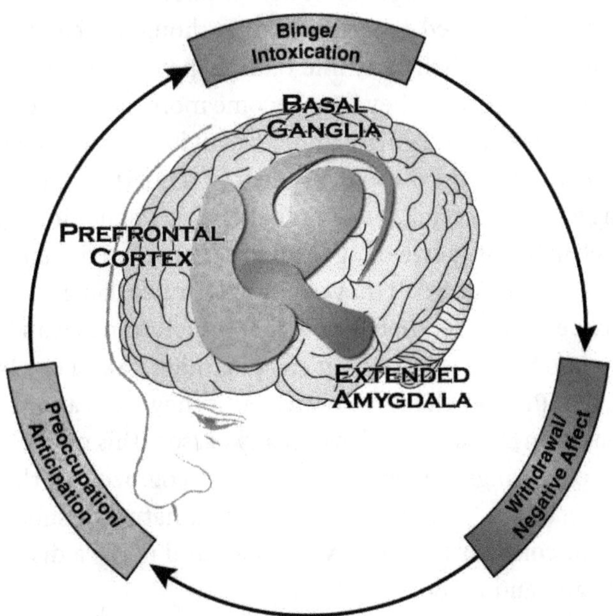

FIGURE 4.12 The Three Stages of the Addiction Cycle and the Brain Regions Associated With Them (HHS, 2016)

MATERIALS NEEDED

- Chairs
- Bell or chime
- Figure 4.12: The Three Stages of the Addiction Cycle and the Brain Regions Associated With Them (HHS, 2016), with *copyright permission or appropriate citation and reference, as applicable
- Whiteboard/markers (optional)

PROCESS OF THE ACTIVITY

This activity may be used in individual or group sessions. The activity begins with the neuroeducation of addiction using the three stages of addiction model (e.g., Volkow et al., 2016) and the neuroeducation of mindfulness. To introduce the neuroeducation of addiction model, you can ask clients to describe their past (or present) experiences with substance-related cravings. This may include how the cravings manifested in response to internal (e.g., thoughts, emotions, physical sensations) or external (e.g., environment, places, people) cues. Clients are encouraged to share how they attempted to manage cravings, if their efforts were successful, and the outcomes following a return to substance use. During this phase of the activity, the counselor should validate clients' experiences and normalize any occurrence of resuming use. This is also an opportunity to integrate a brief discussion on addiction-related stigma while challenging internalized and societal beliefs that promote shame and reinforce ongoing use of alcohol and drugs. The counselor can conclude the introductory part of the activity by providing basic education on the underlying neurobiology of addiction, as well as the experience and role of craving in relapse as previously described.

After offering evidenced-based information regarding the neuroscientific origins of craving, the management of craving, and the overall process of recovery, the counselor can transition to a brief introduction to mindfulness by integrating the information provided earlier and in the rationale section. Clients are then asked to sit comfortably but attentively in a chair with hands in lap and both feet on floor. Eyes may be closed or slightly open while maintaining a soft downward gaze. Inform clients that while they may choose to disengage from this activity at any time should they become uncomfortable, they are encouraged to sit with whatever arises in an effort to become more fully aware and accepting of their lived experiences (e.g., thoughts, feelings, physical sensations).

Begin the activity by ringing a bell or chime (and/or providing a visual cue). Ask clients to direct their attention to their breath so they may become more focused, centered, and grounded. After they have taken a few deep and regulated breaths, invite clients to examine if they are experiencing a craving or urge to use at the present moment (if there is no active craving, ask clients to consider reexperiencing a recent craving that was challenging but not immensely overwhelming). Encourage them to check in by softly sweeping throughout their bodies and noticing if the craving is manifested as a physical sensation. See if they can simply notice, label, and observe any sensation while sitting with the experience. Let them know that if their minds wander at any point during the session, they may acknowledge this without any judgment, take a few breaths to refocus, and then return to the activity. Prompt clients to notice, as if they were a third-party witness to this experience, how the sensation fluctuates and eventually passes. This not only reinforces awareness of the transitory nature of cravings but also helps clients recognize that they can inhibit a behavioral response by learning to "be" with the craving until it naturally subsides. Once the craving is diminished, clients can consider their recovery goals and make a discerning decision that is informed by clarity, insight, and wisdom.

HELPFUL HINT

An acronym that may help guide counselors during the activity, as well as serve clients outside the session, is **PASS**:

Pause (when the experience of a craving or urge occurs)

Acknowledge and **a**llow (the experience to unfold while using the breath to remain steady)

Sit (with the experience as it shifts, changes, and, eventually, subsides)

Select (a wise course of action based on goals and values)

The counselor may continue this activity (or identify a specific focus for a later session) by asking clients to sequentially observe their thoughts, emotions, attitudes and beliefs, and/or behavioral urges while experiencing substance-use cravings. Before ending each session, invite clients to participate in a compassion-based recitation by saying to themselves (either aloud or internally):

May I be kind and compassionate to myself.
May I be patient with myself and my experience.
May I accept my experience as it is in this very moment.
May I be forgiving of myself and my experience.
May I learn and grow from my experience.

The activity ends in a similar manner as it began: returning the attention to the breath, creating a space to become grounded before reintegrating with others in the room, and concluding with the chiming of a bell.

FOLLOW-UP

After the activity, you can have a general discussion (after individual or group session) to review the client's overall experience, obtain feedback regarding skill development, identify successes and barriers throughout the episode, and clarify understanding of the neurobiology of addiction, the role of craving, the process of relapse, and the practice of mindfulness. In addition, a craving rating scale/questionnaire/worksheet relevant to the individual client's substance history may be implemented at baseline and over time to assess changes in the intensity and frequency of cravings and urges to use substances. Examples include the Alcohol Craving Questionnaire (Singleton et al., 1995), Marijuana Craving Questionnaire (Heishman et al., 2001), and Opioid Craving Scale (McHugh et al., 2014).

NEUROSCIENCE IN ACTION

Anne struggled for many years in her attempts to sustain long-term recovery. She had been admitted to and discharged from various levels of care for alcohol use disorder, yet she was never able to abstain from drinking for longer than a few weeks to a month. She previously attempted to control her alcohol use on several occasions by limiting where, when, and how much she drank; however, this approach proved to be routinely unsuccessful, as she always returned to a destructive pattern of drinking. She eventually contacted her counselor and voiced a desire to approach her recovery using an abstinence-based model. She stated her primary reasons for ongoing use was not knowing how to consistently manage her alcohol-related cravings and the subsequent shame she felt after violating her recovery goals. Sometimes the craving would appear in the form of physical sensations and other times as obsessive thoughts or elaborate images. She indicated that they were seemingly overpowering and unbearable, and, consequently, she found herself reacting automatically to find relief from the intensity and discomfort of the cravings. After each use or binge, Anne would experience extreme guilt and shame; she would especially criticize and blame herself for not being a "strong" or "good enough" person.

So that the counselor could have a more accurate understanding of her situation, Anne was asked to provide an actual example to illustrate her personal experience:

During this past summer, Anne's friend invited her to a pool party that many of her former "drinking friends" would be attending. Although she knew there would be alcohol available, Anne had not thought about drinking for the past month and believed she would be able to join her friends without using. After completing her most recent treatment episode, Anne had intentionally kept to herself and was beginning to miss social interactions. When she arrived at the party, it was in full swing, and many people were already feeling the influence of alcohol. Watching her friends triggered an immediate recall of the fun times they had in the past, but because she was attempting to avoid alcohol, she immediately felt uncomfortable and out of place. She initially declined the first few drinks that were offered, but after an hour passed, she began craving the effects of alcohol; she convinced herself that a few "harmless" sips of beer would simply help her relax. Although she drank more beer than initially intended, Anne felt less anxious and more sociable (she had started to forget what is was like to have fun). Before she realized it, she quickly transitioned to mixed drinks. Within hours, she passed out in her friend's guest bedroom after drinking a large but unknown amount of hard liquor (*binge and intoxication stage*). When she returned home the next day, she had a terrible hangover and was consumed with overwhelming guilt and embarrassment. She wondered what was wrong with her. Why wasn't she able to stay sober for more than a few weeks, and why couldn't she just go out with friends without drinking? She criticized herself for being easily led and not trying harder. Maybe these problems only happen to "weak people who make bad choices." She began isolating out of shame and fear and eventually became depressed (*withdrawal and negative affect stage*). All she wanted to do was stay in bed and feel sorry for herself. She compared how she was feeling with how she feels after having a few drinks. She wanted to feel good again and found herself craving alcohol throughout most of the day (*preoccupation and anticipation stage*). The cravings were becoming more frequent and intense; she didn't know if she could bear them. Maybe she should get up and go to the bar. After all, what did she have to lose at this point?

As an intervention within her plan of care, the counselor validated Anne's experiences by informing her that relapse is part of the recovery process, especially for people in the early stages of sobriety, and despite the intensity in which craving manifests, she could be empowered by befriending the experience to realize its impermanence. She was also given information on the neurobiological model of addiction (which disputed her belief that addiction is caused by "weak people who make bad choices"). This newfound knowledge not only challenged the oppressive attitude that Anne had internalized ("I'm beginning to understand that my addiction to alcohol has more to do with my brain than my brawn!") but also strengthened her trust that the counselor would be compassionate and nonjudgmental. In addition, mindfulness-based practices were introduced and incorporated into Anne's treatment plan so that she could ideally acknowledge her craving while simultaneously observing the cognitive, emotional, or mental events that occurred from moment to moment. With ongoing mindfulness practice, she was learning to be more aware of the cues that triggered her cravings, as well as becoming more accepting of her experience as the cravings transpired. She developed an understanding that although her cravings for alcohol may be uncomfortable, they will eventually pass as long as she didn't ignore or feed them. She developed the ability to sit with her unpleasant feelings without having to immediately avoid pain and instantly seek relief. Moreover, she was encouraged to bring a sense of self-kindness and compassion to her overall experience while traveling through it with enhanced mental clarity and increased behavioral control.

Although Anne continued to have alcohol-related cravings, she was able to be with the experience by simply acknowledging and accepting their presence. Over time, her mindfulness practice helped strengthen her executive functioning skills (e.g., self-awareness and self-management) and reduce her sensitivity to stress (e.g., emotional regulation). These newfound traits endowed Anne with an ability to tolerate discomfort, delay impulses, develop mental clarity, and engage in effective problem-solving and decision-making skills, all of which are needed for long-term recovery. And during the infrequent times that she experienced a brief lapse, she was able to meet her disappointment with self-kindness and compassion while reestablishing a recovery program strengthened by greater insight and knowledge.

ETHICAL AND MULTICULTURAL CONSIDERATIONS

Similar to any counseling intervention, mindfulness meditation involves skill building, practice, and commitment, both by the counselor and client. Common concerns about integrating mindfulness meditation into the counseling session revolve around the qualifications of the practitioner (Kostanski & Hassed, 2008) and the possibility of causing harm if unskillfully taught and practiced (Shapiro & Carlson, 2009); therefore, it is highly recommended that counselors only employ mindfulness after having professional training and personal experience practicing, embodying, and teaching mindfulness-based interventions (Pollak, 2013).

Because mindfulness-based interventions are fundamentally connected to Buddhist teachings and contemplative practices, it is important that the concepts and exercises be presented and integrated into health-care practices using a secular approach that is cognizant of language (Pollak, 2013) and inclusive of all client types. Mindfulness-informed or -based counseling practices should be offered in a safe, respectful, and trustworthy environment. Because mindfulness may not appeal to all clients, the counselor should maintain an open mind and remain patient while collaborating with them (Pollak, 2013).

Meditation exercises should be designed around the needs of the individual client and only when deemed clinically appropriate. Special consideration should be given before unsystematically introducing mindfulness to those clients presenting with acute conditions, such as active substance misuse or withdrawal, current psychosis, severe anxiety or depression, and unresolved trauma (Dobkin, et al., 2011).

ANCILLARY MATERIALS

- Bowen, S., Chawla, N., & Marlatt, G. A. (2011). *Mindfulness-based relapse prevention for addictive behaviors: A clinician's guide*. Guilford Press.
- Germer, C., Siegel, R., & Fulton, P. (2013). *Mindfulness and psychotherapy*. (2nd ed.). Guilford Press.
- Volkow, N. D., Koob, G. F., & McLellan, A. T., (2016). Neurobiological advances from the brain disease model of addiction. *New England Journal of Medicine, 374*, 363–371. http://doi.org/10.1056/NEJMra1511480
- Wilson, S. J. (2015). *The Wiley handbook on the cognitive neuroscience of addiction*. John Wiley & Sons.

BUPRENORPHINE IN RECOVERY

Jennifer Reckner

Counselors use a biopsychosocial model of treatment that provides the opportunity to integrate mental health care and physical health care (American Mental Health Counselors Association, 2019). Many therapeutic interventions that counselors use are considered top-down, focusing on cognitive-based regulation of emotions (Gerbarg et al., 2016). Adding bottom-up approaches in a treatment plan can enhance the overall effectiveness of counseling, supporting mind and brain integration and easing symptoms of many common concerns, including anxiety, depression, and post-traumatic stress disorder (Brown, et al., 2013; Gard et al., 2014). Psychopharmacology is considered one type of a bottom-up intervention. The medication affects overall mental functioning by directly targeting certain chemicals, cells, receptors, and/or neurotransmitters in the brain (Kenemans & Kähkönen, 2011).

Medication can be an integral part of treatment for some clients. Buprenorphine is a schedule III semisynthetic opioid with unique pharmacology that is prescribed to treat opioid use disorder (Wesson & Smith, 2010). Buprenorphine acts as a partial agonist at mu opioid receptors and kappa opioid receptors (Escher et al., 2007). Mu opioid receptors are responsible for pain control, mood effects, respiratory depression, and a reduction of gut motility (Wesson & Smith, 2010). Kappa opioid receptor agonists have been shown to block rewards and effects that result from dopamine being released by opioids (Dunn et al., 2018). The medication is considered to be safer than full opioid agonists, such as methadone, because the respiratory depression is minimal, and there are fewer withdrawal symptoms when treatment is stopped (Heit & Gourlay, 2008). Researchers have found that treating opioid use disorder with buprenorphine, also known as medication-assisted recovery, is equal in effectiveness to full opioid agonists, such as methadone. Medication-assisted recovery with buprenorphine has also been shown to reduce illicit opioid use more than a placebo and has a positive effect on HIV/AIDS treatment outcomes (Wesson & Smith, 2010).

Many clinics have full buprenorphine protocols, including consent forms, psychosocial group and individual sessions, urinalysis, and strict follow-up policies with the physician and counselor. The purpose of *Buprenorphine in Recovery* is to explore, within the larger context of a treatment protocol, the neuropsychopharmacology of buprenorphine with clients to promote a greater understanding of their treatment and how it can support their recovery. Specifically, this activity will demonstrate the use of neuroeducation via metaphors illustrating the function of the medication. This approach is intended to start an open dialogue, helping clients visualize their healing journey and the potential risks and benefits of medication-assisted recovery (Kaut & Dickenson, 2007).

MATERIALS NEEDED

- Client handout related to buprenorphine (e.g., SAMHA's The Facts about Buprenorphine for Treatment of Opioid Addiction brochure - file://Users/raissamiller/Downloads/sma14-4442.pdf)

PROCESS OF ACTIVITY

Buprenorphine in Recovery is most commonly used toward the beginning of a client's recovery journey when they are deciding what treatment options are best for them. The steps described next represent a flexible process that counselors can follow when exploring the value and mechanisms of buprenorphine.

Step 1: Introducing Buprenorphine as a Treatment Option

A good starting point with clients is to gauge their perception of the medication and the role it could potentially play in their recovery. For example, you could ask an open-ended question like,

"What is your understanding of buprenorphine?" Once you have some insight into the client's knowledge of the medication, you can work together to fill in the knowledge gaps. It is helpful to initiate a general discussion about the risks and benefits early in the conversation. Some topics to cover include the following:

- The process of going through withdrawal
- The possibility of overdose or misuse
- Potential adverse effects (e.g., nausea, dizziness, headache, insomnia)
- Decreases in the physiological craving to use opioids

One fact I often share is that buprenorphine is unique in that it is a partial mu opioid agonist and can also act as a mu antagonist if taken in conjunction with other opioids, such as heroin, by displacing the heroin in the opioid receptors (Wesson & Smith, 2010). Thus buprenorphine should be started when an individual is as far into withdrawal as possible to avoid triggering severe illness (Heit & Gourlay, 2008; Wesson & Smith, 2010). You can note that these risks are less than that of other full opioid agonists, such as methadone; however, they are still real potential side effects (Wesson & Smith, 2010).

Step 2: Sharing of the Metaphor

Start this step by sharing a broad overview of how buprenorphine affects brain functioning. For example, I often say buprenorphine fits into the same structure in your brain that the drug fits into, therefore possibly tricking your brain into thinking it does not need the drug because something is already there. Then you can use a metaphor to further illustrate how buprenorphine affects the brain, especially in relation to other opioids. In the example that follows, I chose chicken and ice cream, which suited the carnivorous, non-lactose-intolerant American client I was working with at the time. Choosing a food that is nutritious and another that is an indulgent within the client's normal diet and culture is an important consideration.

Step 3: Individualized Treatment Planning

Once clients have a good understanding of the risks and benefits of buprenorphine and have an understanding of how it works in the brain, you can move into a conversation about how use of the medication could potentially fit into the individual's recovery goals. Clients' goals can range from harm reduction aims (e.g., decreasing high risk behaviors, such as needle use that coincide with acquiring infectious diseases or decreasing the risk for accidental overdose) to completely eliminating illicit opiate use.

FOLLOW-UP

I use open-ended questions to get a sense of how the information sharing and discussion facilitation affected the client. For example, I will ask, "How has an expanded knowledge of the medication impacted your recovery?" This question could also provide an opportunity for the client to ask more follow-up questions once they have further processed the information. Formal follow-up for medication management should be done by the prescriber and according to the clinic's protocol.

NEUROSCIENCE IN ACTION

A 40-year-old woman had recently stopped using heroin and was 3 days into recovery when the psychiatrist prescribed her buprenorphine. The clinic nurse had gone through the consent form and protocol with the client and made the appropriate follow-up appointments with medical staff. As the client told me about her experience with the medical team and expectations that were set for her, she voiced confusion over why she was prescribed an opioid to help her stop taking heroin, which is also an opioid. She stated she had heard that it helps many people, and it is a safer drug, but that it did not really make sense to her. The client was able to tell me what the possible risks were of buprenorphine, but she seemed confused about the potential benefits. This questioning led to a conversation about how the brain has natural opiate receptors in the central nervous system, and they appear to be present to help regulate pain in a central system of the body. I shared that although buprenorphine is also an opioid, it functions in a different way than other drugs do.

At this point, I transitioned into the use of a metaphor. I chose to discuss buprenorphine as if it were food. I noted that our bodies need food, and there are different kinds of food we can have, but some food options are more nutritious than others. Heroin could be considered sweets, such as ice cream, and buprenorphine could be considered a healthier food, such as chicken. It is possible to survive without ice cream or chicken, but chicken is a more nutritious, or healthier, option than ice cream. Our bodies will accept both of them because we need nutrition to survive, but one is a better option than the other. Our bodies also need pain control receptors in our brains to function; however, some analgesics have less adverse effects than others. This difference is similar to food.

The client responded by saying, "So heroin is ice cream, and the buprenorphine is chicken!" She said that although she really likes ice cream, chicken fulfills what her body needs in a more efficient way and will lead to healthier long-term outcomes. She indicated that the part that especially stuck with her was that ice cream and heroin have more short-term feelings of satiety and pleasure, but the chicken and buprenorphine have a more long-standing benefits, even if that means less immediate euphoria. She precisely vocalized that she was ready for the long-term well-being of chicken over the short-lived feelings of exhilaration from ice cream. With this increased understanding, she expressed hopefulness about how buprenorphine could help her recovery.

After that discussion, we briefly talked about her daily routine and how she planned to integrate the medication into her schedule. Because she already took other medications daily, she did not feel there were any adjustments for her to work through to be successful. At each session, we checked in on her progress and how she felt she was doing emotionally and physically with the medication. She did not report any problems; however, if she had, we would have talked through her options, and I would have contacted her prescriber with any concerns.

ETHICAL AND MULTICULTURAL CONSIDERATIONS

As counselors, we do not prescribe medication, and thus it is essential to understand our boundaries with medication-assisted recovery. Many treatment centers have protocols that involve the counseling team working together with medical professionals and maintaining open communication, which is crucial for continuity of care and client safety. Because of potential safety concerns with buprenorphine, there is a consent form that should also be signed as part of the protocol. This step should not be taken lightly; the client should be able to understand what they are signing and agree to uphold the expectations that are laid out.

Another ethical consideration is the counselor's attitude toward medication-assisted treatment. Regardless of a counselor's personal stance on psychopharmacology and the pharmaceutical industry, medication-assisted recovery is widespread and efficacious (Kaut, 2011). Counselor attitudes and social stigma about buprenorphine tend to be neutral or negative, especially outside of medication-assisted recovery clinics (Reickmann et al., 2007). Because counselors are often the "gatekeepers" of information about treatment options and referrals given to clients, it is critical that they do not let negative biases against buprenorphine treatment impede a client's chance at recovery (Kaut, 2011; Reickmann et al., 2007).

Access to health care should also be considered when exploring the potential usefulness of buprenorphine with clients. Many psychiatrists have long waiting lists, and clients could wait months before they are able to get an appointment. In rural communities, the closest prescriber could be hours away. This barrier can be especially problematic in medication-assisted recovery because of the number of appointments to see a counselor, attend group therapy, and check in with the physician. Medication-assisted recovery could also affect the client's ability to work because of the time commitment and emotional investment of all of the appointments, which adds a financial component to be considered. Another financial concern could be whether insurance covers the comprehensive treatment program, which is expensive, especially if paid for out of pocket. The cost of travel, copays, and the medication itself can also be quite expensive.

CLOSING THOUGHTS

The purpose of this chapter was to explore basics about the anatomy and physiology throughout the brain. The neuroeducation exercises in this chapter showed ways that clinicians use knowledge of the anatomy and physiology of the brain to inform their interventions, as well as how they brought this information into their sessions. We explored ways to foster compassion, build integration and flexibility, connect horticultural imagery, promote autonomy in the mindful use of medications, and promote therapeutic consciousness. As you reflect on the activities in this chapter, consider the way that you reacted to each activity. Before moving on to the next chapter, consider the following reflection questions:

REFLECTION QUESTIONS

1. What anatomy and physiology concepts do you believe are most relevant to the concerns and healing of your clients?
2. What new ideas do you have about incorporating information about anatomy and physiology into your clinical work?
3. How can you apply principles of anatomy and physiology to your own life to improve your ability to be present and open to clients' experiences?

CREDITS

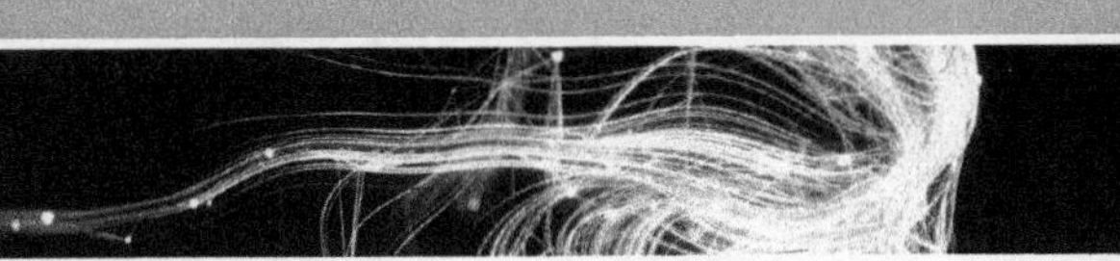

CHAPTER 5

The Autonomic Nervous System

If you want to improve the world, start by making people feel safer.
—Stephen W. Porges

CHAPTER OBJECTIVES

1. Understand the organization and primary functions of the autonomic nervous system.
2. Identify practical strategies to explore clients' responses to stress and threat.
3. Plan useful strategies for the regulation of the autonomic nervous system functioning to promote social engagement.

INTRODUCTION

How is your body feeling as you read this book? If you are comfortable doing so, take a moment to do a quick body scan and notice any internal sensations. Did you notice anything related to your heart rate? Did you experience any perspiration? How did your gut feel? Unless you are in the middle of a stressful period or are feeling unsafe, then you probably did not notice anything out of the ordinary. Safety primes the nervous system for connection, curiosity, and exploration. Human connection also provides a means to regulate and return to a baseline of safety.

This quick body scan taps into your interoception, or the conscious awareness of bodily processes that are generally automatic (Schulz & Vögele, 2015) and governed by complex multidirectional communication systems between the body, brain, mind, and social systems. So far in this book, we have focused on the development, structure, and function of the central nervous system; however, since neuroscience focuses on the study of the entire nervous system, this chapter will focus on the autonomic branch of the peripheral nervous system. The autonomic nervous system (ANS) plays an influential role in the regulation of a variety of bodily processes (e.g., heart rate, blood pressure, temperature).

If you can remember your early science and health classes (do not fret, we will get to memory later in this book), you likely recall learning some basic facts about the ANS.

The ANS is part of the peripheral nervous system that has three main branches: (1) the sympathetic (primarily responsible for normal activation/arousal and the fight or flight response), (2) the parasympathetic (primary responsible for normal rest and restoration and the freeze response), and (3) the enteric (primarily responsible for gastrointestinal functions) (Bear et al., 2007). The enteric branch (which we focus on in Chapter 6) is commonly referred to as the "second brain" given its ability to act autonomously from the other branches, even though they are often influenced by one another, but for this chapter, we will focus on the sympathetic and parasympathetic branches of the ANS (see Figure 5.1).

The ANS plays a role in developing the physiological resources necessary to respond to

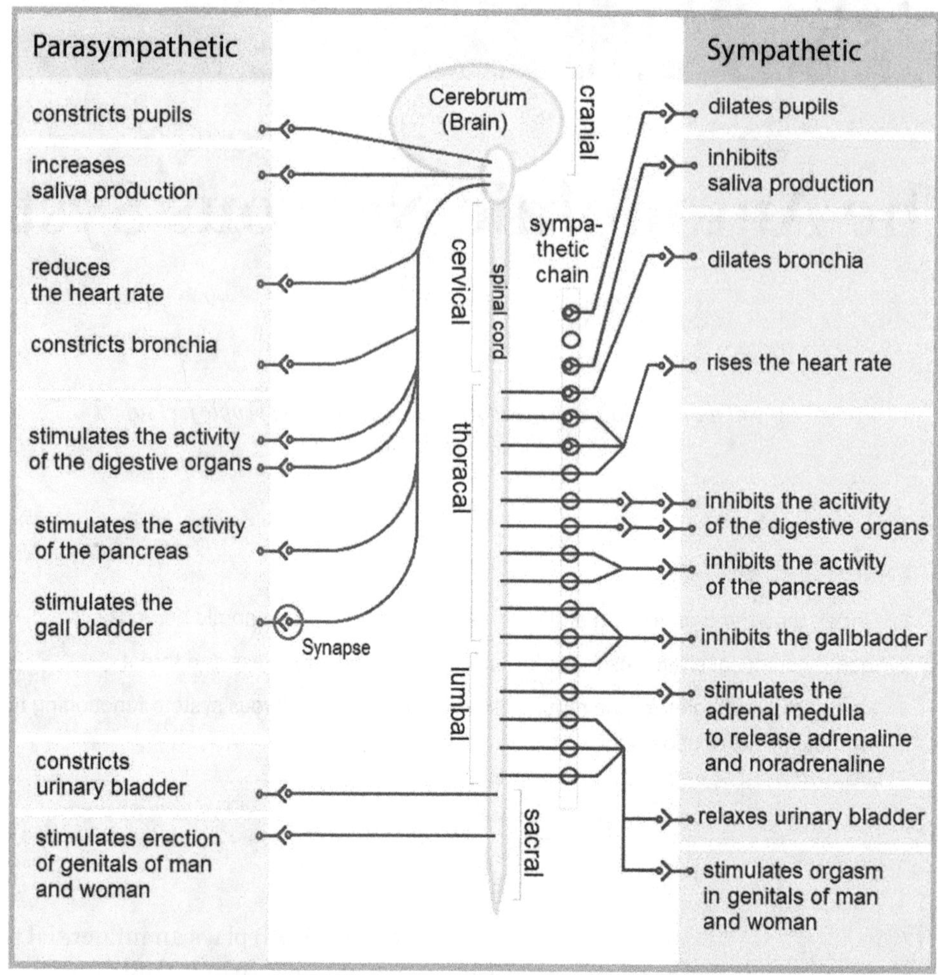

FIGURE 5.1 Impact of Parasympathetic and Sympathetic Divisions of the Autonomic Nervous System

innumerable internal and external stimuli. Many theoretical approaches have emerged to explore the role of the ANS in human functioning and social connection, especially in response to threat and trauma (e.g., Beckes & Coan, 2011; Lohrasbe & Ogden, 2017; Ogden & Minton, 2000; Ogden et al., 2006; Porges, 2011; Schore, 2003a, 2003b; Siegel, 2010a, 2010b; van der Kolk, 1994). Grounded in this body of research, we have created a synthesized model to aid in exploring the role of the ANS in human development to guide your review of the neuroeducation activities in this book (see Figure 5.2).

From interpersonal neurobiology (IPNB) to sensorimotor psychotherapy and polyvagal theory, the ANS is described as a functional system in which "afferent pathways conveying information regarding the visceral organs to the central nervous system and the specific brain structures that interpret the afferent feedback and exert control over the motor output to the visceral organs" (Porges, 2003, p. 505). This process starts in early childhood and is grounded in relationships with early attachment figures and continues to widen or narrow based on confirming or disconfirming experiences throughout life (e.g., Schore, 2003a; Siegel, 2010a, 2010b, 2015; van der Kolk, 1994). Beginning in infancy (perhaps even in utero), we start developing a window of tolerance (WOT) or the range of tolerable ebbs and flows of sympathetic arousal and parasympathetic rest (Lohrasbe & Ogden, 2017; Ogden & Minton, 2000; Siegel, 2010a, 2010b, 2015).

This WOT parallels with what Stephen Porges refers to in polyvagal theory (see Figure 5.3) as the social engagement system (SES), the primary mode of existing in the world when it is perceived as safe (Porges, 2003, 2011, 2017). According to Porges, the ANS has evolved to provide the foundation for emotion, affect, and social behavior. The vagus nerve, the

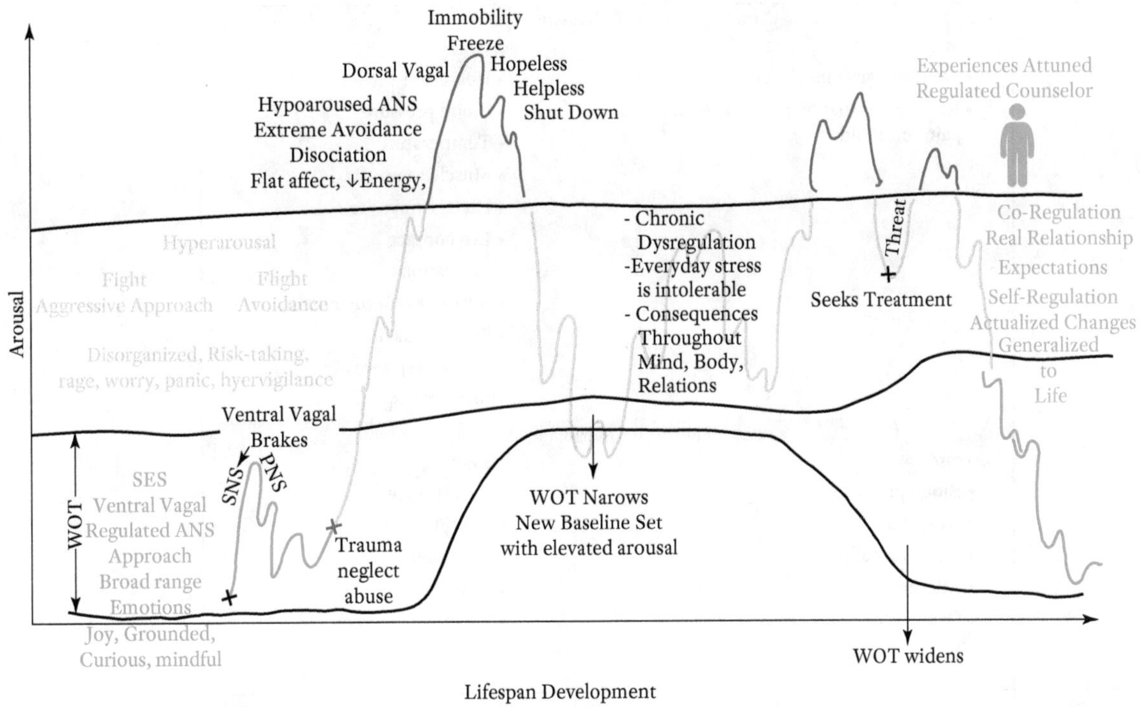

FIGURE 5.2. Synthesized Model of ANS Functioning That Integrates Polyvagal Theory and the Window of Tolerance Model to Guide the Neuroeducation Process Throughout the Therapeutic Encounter

10th cranial nerve, serves as a bridge between the body and brain to increase balance in the ANS and foster social connection to aid in survival (Porges, 2003, 2011, 2017).

When in the SES, the myelinated, evolutionarily newer ventral vagus is essential to increase parasympathetic activity, which applies the brakes to the sympathetic nervous system and promotes social engagement to remain in the WOT (Porges, 2003, 2011, 2017). The ventral vagus applies and lets up on the brakes that modulate the optimal level of arousal needed for certain contexts. People operating in the WOT/SES experience a broad expression of emotions and curiosity, are grounded, and display approach behaviors. If arousal continues, normally when neuroception (the perception of safety) is compromised in times of trauma, abuse, neglect, threat, and other adverse experiences, then the ventral vagus brakes let up and the sympathetic nervous system increases arousal and produces a fight or flight response. This sympathetic activation is evidenced by hyperarousal, hypervigilance, panic, worry, fear, dread, and aggressive approach behaviors (in terms of a fight response) or avoidance behaviors (in times of a flight response). If arousal continues and fight/flight has not been effective, individuals might experience a freeze response or more extreme immobilization, which is attributed to the evolutionarily older, unmyelinated dorsal vagus, to promote survival. This freeze and immobilized response stems from extreme hyperarousal that transitions quickly into dysregulated parasympathetic activation, hypoarousal, and complete shutdown. This response might lead to dissociation, flatness, helplessness/hopelessness, anhedonia, extreme avoidance, isolation, and even preparation for eventual death.

To summarize, it is presumed in polyvagal theory that the baseline level of functioning is social engagement and that individuals, via the SES, initially respond to threat by trying to connect with others to regulate sympathetic activation (imagine when you are startled at a movie and grab the arm of a loved one—see Figure 5.4); however, if social engagement is not effective or the person has never developed a sense of safe, secure attachments, which is common in cases of abuse, neglect, and trauma (imagine your loved one is not there), then they can find themselves in a constant state of hypervigilance and fight or flight (imagine what else can be done when unable to socially engage—see Figure 5.5).

Parasympathetic Nervous System	
Increases	*Decreases*
• Fuel storage & insulin activity • Endorphins that help numb and raise the pain threshold	• Heart rate • Blood pressure • Temperature • Muscle tone • Facial expressions • Eye contact • Intonations • Awareness of the human voice • Social behavior • Sexual responses •Immune response
Sympathetic Nervous System	
Increases	*Decreases*
• Blood pressure • Heart rate • Fuel availability • Adrenaline • Oxygen circulation to vital organs • Blood clotting • Pupil size	• Fuel storage • Insulin activity • Digestion • Salvation • Relational ability • Immune response
Parasympathetic Nervous System	
Increases	*Decreases*
• Digestion • Intestinal motility • Resistance to infection • Immune response • Rest and recuperation • Circulation to nonvital organs • Oxytocin • Ability to relate and connect	• Defensive responses

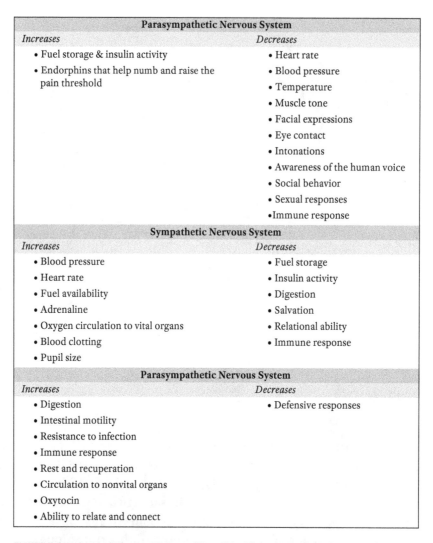

FIGURE 5.3 Polyvagal Theory, ANS, and Possible Clinical Manifestations

If fight or flight is not effective, then the body's last line of defense is to freeze or become completely immobile. This last resort option often takes the form of dissociation and helplessness, and strong defenses are enacted to keep others away and promote safety.

If chronic stress continues and there is no intervention, a new baseline WOT of higher arousal that is narrower in range can develop. In this case, everyday stressors might promote dysregulation, leading to a flurry of challenges that often reflect initial attachment ruptures and trauma that preceded them. This can even lead to individuals experiencing the intimacy of a counseling relationship as a threat, which can impair the ability to develop a sound therapeutic working alliance (Geller & Porges, 2014). However, as we use our microskills to foster a secure base, as we respond to clients' distress in an attuned way that understands and honors the initial necessity of their current reactions (i.e., they needed to fight, flee, and/or immobilize to survive some of the instances in their lives), as we foster synchrony and co-regulation, and as we cocreate new narratives for their experiences, clients can widen their WOT, remain in the SES, and embrace their curiosity in themselves and the world around them.

As with all concepts in this book, this is a simplified description of our natural proclivity toward safety and social engagement to promote survival, how we respond to stress, and how this process can play out in therapeutic encounters. Although many of the concepts in this chapter are theoretical, they provide another framework for understanding the human experience and tailoring interventions, as well as fostering continued research to justify the claims

FIGURE 5.4 Reaching Out for Social Engagement When Startled

FIGURE 5.5 Fleeing When Social Engagement Is Not Possible or Ineffective

and their applied validity. Understanding this process can help enhance our therapeutic stance with clients, conceptualize their reactions and defensiveness, and, ultimately, provide more effective interventions. Exploring these concepts with clients can also aid in their understanding of self, emotions, reactions, and eventual regulatory capacity.

NEUROEDUCATION ACTIVITIES

The five neuroeducation activities in this chapter demonstrate how several clinicians enact the neuro-education process. Using visualization, maps, seesaws, and even streamers, the neuroeducation in this chapter will show you how several clinicians interpret and describe the science of the ANS to capitalize on our innate regulatory processes.

THREE RESPONSES TO PROMOTE SURVIVAL

Yoon Suh Moh and Justin Jacques

The autonomic nervous system (ANS) is complex, and unlike the somatic motor system that selectively innervates and commands skeletal muscle fibers in a relatively fast-paced fashion, the actions of the ANS are typically multiple, widespread, and relatively slow, innervating and exciting smooth muscles (at the root of the hairs, the coats of blood vessels encircling the bronchioles of the lungs), cardiac muscles, and gland cells (the salivary and gastric, the pancreas, and the liver) in the human body without conscious, voluntary control (Bear et al., 2007; Cannon,1963). The sympathetic and parasympathetic divisions work in tandem using distinct pathways in structure and their neurotransmitter systems. The sympathetic nervous system (SNS) tends to promote arousal, especially in times of danger or threats, which can be described as fight or flight, whereas the parasympathetic nervous system (PNS) facilitates digestion, growth, immune responses, energy storage, and a freeze response (Wenner, 2018). In particular, the SNS is organized for the diffuse discharge of nerve impulses, and sympathetic impulses evoke a secretion of adrenaline from the medullary portion of the adrenal glands. These two factors commonly work together as a sympathoadrenal system to produce widespread changes in smooth muscles and glands throughout the organism (Cannon, 1963).

It is critical for counselors to help clients explore their emotional responses to a real or perceived threat and to help clients make meaning out of these experiences. The activation of the SNS is imperative for survival in certain circumstances; however, the chronic activation of the SNS or hypersensitivity to stimuli that signify threat can lead to significant mental health concerns characterized by feelings of anxiety, excessive fear, and related behavioral disturbances (Wenner, 2018). Given the importance of the ANS, we use the *Three Responses to Promote Survival* activity to help clients increase awareness of their neurophysiological responses to real or imagined stimuli through the operation of the ANS and promote healthier regulatory responses through therapeutic techniques (e.g., deep breathing, grounding, or guided meditation).

Research suggests that deep breathing exercises and meditations are effective in reducing anxiety and psychological distress (Chen et al., 2012; Neeru et al., 2015). The increased awareness of the neurophysiological responses is imperative in employing this activity because it is typically a first step of the sequence to promote healthier regulatory responses. Frequently, individuals are unaware of being in a hyperaroused state and react automatically to internal (e.g., chills, or feeling hot, or rapid heart rates) or external (e.g., signals to notify a sense of threats or danger) stimuli. Thus it is essential for counselors to help such individuals gain conscious awareness of their bodily clues and other indicators of fluctuations in their ANS. This increased awareness can help them gain an enhanced sense of control for their responses and consciously choose to move toward regulation. To help promote healthier regulatory responses, the clinical interventions such as deep breathing or guided meditation can be employed in session or between sessions. The *Three Responses to Promote Survival* activity will show one way that we help clients capitalize on awareness and regulation.

MATERIALS NEEDED

- A hard copy of a figure of the chemical and anatomical organization of the sympathetic and parasympathetic divisions of the ANS (Example in Figure 5.6)
- Interactive 3D brain model (such as BrainFacts; http://www.brainfacts.org/3D-Brain#intro=false&focus=Brain-limbic_system-hypothalamus; Figure 5.7)

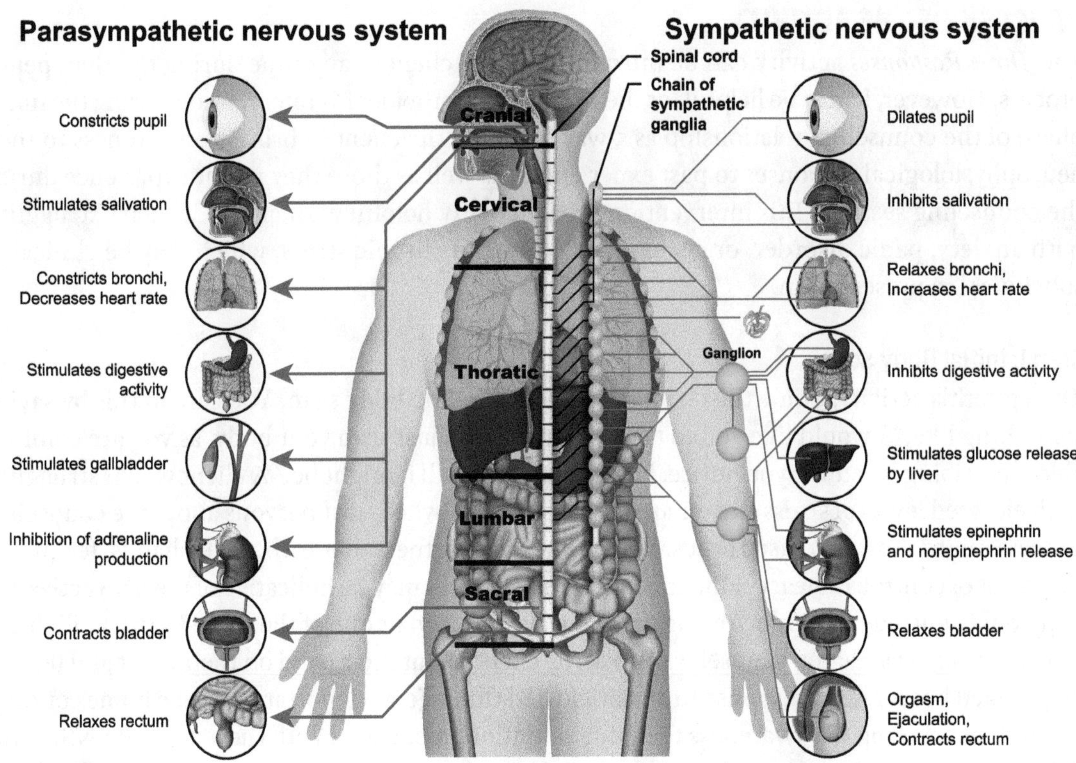

FIGURE 5.6 The Chemical and Anatomical Organization of the Sympathetic and Parasympathetic Divisions of the ANS (Bear et al., 2016)

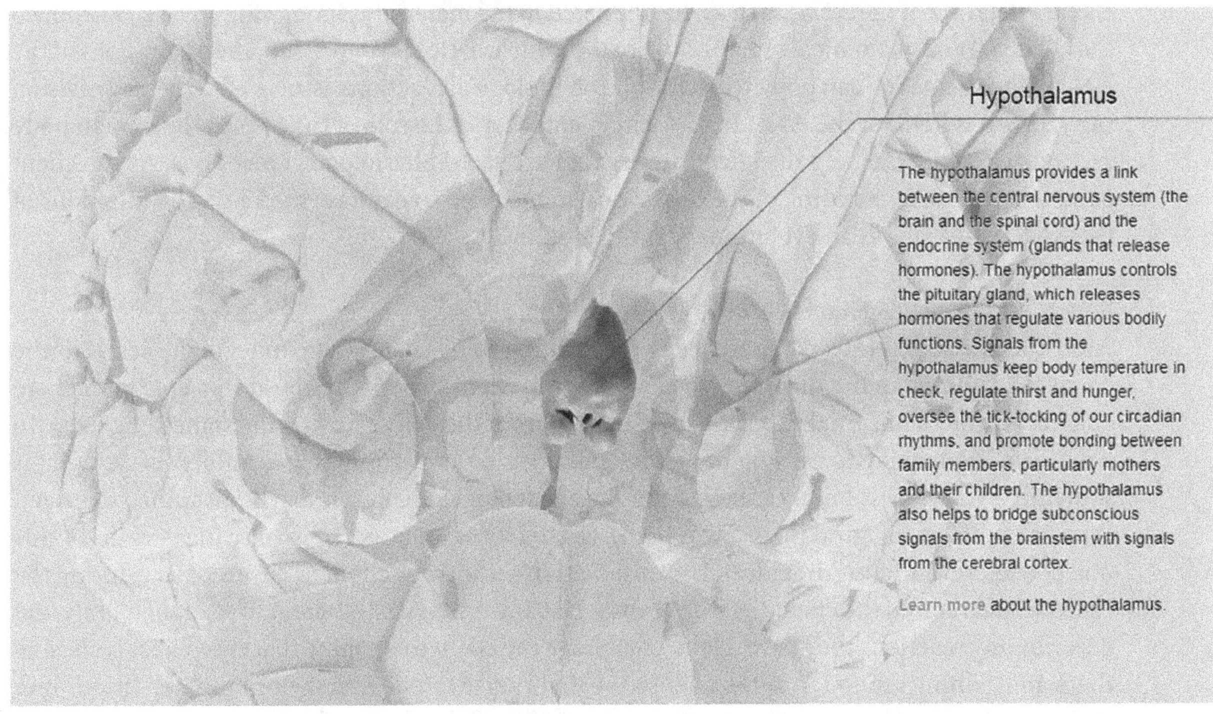

FIGURE 5.7 Map of Nervous System Response. Example of Interactive Map on Brainfacts.org

PROCESS OF THE ACTIVITY

The *Three Responses* activity can be introduced to the client at any time during the therapeutic process. However, it may be helpful for the counselor to provide this intervention during the initial phase of the counseling relationship as a way of aiding the client in bringing awareness to their neurophysiological responses to past experiences, as well as those they might experience during the counseling session. This intervention is particularly helpful with clients who are struggling with anxiety, panic disorder, or generalized acute and chronic stress, which may be clinical or subclinical in presentation.

Step 1: Initial Body Scan

To begin this activity, guide the client in taking a baseline body scan. You can do this by saying something like, "I would like you to take a moment and just scan your body, as you are comfortable, describing whatever you notice, however big or small it might be." A client who is struggling with elevated levels of stress and/or anxiety or someone who is just nervous about the counseling process might show increased arousal in the form of shortness of breath, shaky hands, feelings of being out of control, or heart palpitations. These responses may be indicative of the SNS activation that could continue to produce a normal defensive reaction or one of the three Fs (fight, flight, or freeze). In such cases, the counselor can ask the client to put their hand on their chest and feel the heightened heart rate in response to an anticipated threat (e.g., deportation to the home country) as a way of bringing the awareness to bodily sensations associated with the activated SNS. If you have not already done so, introduce self-regulation techniques (e.g., breath work, grounding) that can be used if they need to reduce their arousal in the next phases of the activity to remain safe.

Step 2: Introduction to ANS and Processing Concepts

Using a diagram of the ANS, such as the one listed in the materials section (Figure 5.6), introduce the chemical and anatomical organization of the sympathetic and parasympathetic divisions of the ANS to the client. You can point to each of the physiological reactions associated with each division (i.e., SNS and PNS) of the ANS. In particular, emphasize the role of the SNS in the human body as a survival skill and help the client understand activated physiological reactions. As the client gains a better understanding of the SNS, you can move on to explore, in-depth, the functions of the ANS in humans as an evolutionary survival skill.

Step 3: Introduce Imaginal Exposure

After the client develops competence in performing body scans and connects the scans to the concepts explored in the diagram, you can help the client experience these concepts in the here and now through imaginal exposure. Begin this part of the activity by saying something like, "In a moment, I am going to ask you to picture and imagine something that is mildly scary. What is something you view as mildly scary?" After the client names an object, maybe an animal or insect, then ask them to imagine themselves being chased by an enlarged, fast-moving version of this object (e.g., seven-foot-tall spider). Use observation skills throughout to ensure safety during the exercise and remind the client that they can stop at any time. Ask the client to scan their body and describe any reactions they have. Next, encourage the client to imagine that this object is chasing them and gaining ground. Ask the client to again bring awareness to their bodily sensations into the scene they are imagining, noticing any attempts to fight, flee, or freeze.

Step 4: Secondary Body Scan to Connect Physiological Experiences During Exposure to Concepts Reviewed

After the imaginal exposure, encourage the client to reflect on the experience. Ask the client to describe what they noticed during this exercise. The client may describe physiological reactions (e.g., pupil dilation, high heart rates, chills or feeling hot, or dry mouth) indicative of one of the three responses that increased as the object gained ground, but others might have trouble with this type of exposure and report very little at all. In this case, continue to promote a positive tone and ask the client to reflect on other experiences in their life that have promoted such arousal. Encourage clients to connect their experience to the concepts in the diagram. Consider using the diagram as a guide to help the client explore and make meaning of this experience while thinking about how this could be useful in future experiences that they have.

In the same session, it is important for you to help the client regain a sense of safety through an activity, such as deep breathing or guided meditation. After completing a safety-orienting activity, encourage the client to reflect on how the experience relates to the core concepts of the ANS. You can also use the handout to assist the client in increasing their understanding of general physiological reactions (e.g., pupil contraction, simulated salvation, or slower heartbeats) in association with parasympathetic activation.

Step 5: Connect to the Reason for Counseling, Past Events, and Future Plans

As the client demonstrates engagement and self-competencies, you can hypothesize with the client about how their cluster of presenting symptoms, as well as other past events, may relate to the ANS. The counselor will encourage the client to use the handout or create their own drawing about how their functioning relates, or does not, to the concepts related to the three Fs, as well as the ANS functioning. With practice, the client can develop agency and awareness related to their ANS functioning, presenting symptoms, and future goals.

FOLLOW-UP

The *Three Responses* intervention can be evaluated informally through process feedback and/or formally with a measure, such as the Session Rating Scale (Duncan et al., 2003). For instance, the counselor may ask the client, "What was it like for you to practice this exercise today?" It can be helpful to revisit the ANS concepts during the processing of the SRS. For instance, revisiting their physiological experiences as they evaluate the session (e.g., what did you notice about yourself as we talked about our session today?) or using their ratings to reinforce gains in the session or adjust interventions moving forward can promote collaboration and personalize treatment.

NEUROSCIENCE IN ACTION

Rosemary was a 21-year-old who identified as a transgender, heterosexual Latina with asylum to live in the United States. Born in Bolivia, Rosemary immigrated to the United States at the age of 10 with her parents and a sister. Rosemary's parents were deported to Bolivia 3 years ago, while she and her sister remained in the United States. Rosemary appeared to have a tough time building trust with males and subsequently developing and maintaining intimate romantic relationships. Rosemary reported that she was sexually abused several times as a child by a former neighbor in her home country. She did not recall exact details of what had happened to her when these traumatic incidents occurred.

As a highly intellectual female, Rosemary was articulate and outspoken, and she embraced social justice and the rights of individuals, including those affiliated with the lesbian, gay, bisexual, transgender, queer, intersex community. Rosemary was a Deferred Action for Childhood Arrivals recipient. However, she had just heard the dreadful news of a possible discontinuation of the program in the next couple of weeks. This incident contributed to a surge of seemingly uncontrollable anxiety and worry running through her body. Rosemary felt her heart beating rapidly and tremors in her hands. She presented at her individual counseling session with enlarged pupils and difficulty breathing. Rosemary eventually burst into tears as she told the counselor about the news that she had heard. The following dialogue shows how the *Three Responses* activity was used in this session.

Counselor: Rosemary, I'm sorry to hear the dreadful news. How do you feel?

Rosemary: It is awful. I am so frightened. What if I were kicked out of the U.S.? I cannot even think of going back to Bolivia. I would be treated like a stranger.

Counselor: It is frightening for you to think about, and I want to encourage you to feel what you are feeling in a manner that is safe for you. Can I please invite you to bring your awareness to see how your body is experiencing this dreadful event?

Rosemary: I guess that is fine with me.

Counselor: Okay. I see your hands in tremor. How does that feel for you?

Rosemary: Oh, it is like my hands are going out of control.

Counselor: Can you place your hand on your heart? How does your heart feel?

Rosemary: It is running so fast. I feel like I can even hear my heart palpitations.

Counselor: Thank you for trying it, Rosemary. Would it be a good time for us to explore more about what is driving all this? [client nods yes]. Do you mind if I come and sit next to you for this activity? [client nods yes]. Let's look at this picture [Figure 5.6] together, and I will introduce some basic brain-related concepts that may be helpful in reducing your current distress. These ideas relate to the three Fs: fight, flight, or freeze of the ANS, which we talked about last session and may be activated right at this moment. In addition, I want to know what concepts resonate with you so we can expand on the ideas.

Rosemary: OK.

Counselor: [Counselor proceeds to explore the handout in simple, understandable terms while sitting next to the client.] Do you have any questions about what we have reviewed?

Rosemary: No, not at the moment. These brain-related ideas seem to make sense right now, but I may have further questions later.

Counselor: That sounds good! Please ask for further clarification if you need. I want to take some more time to talk further about the function of the ANS in humans as an adaptive survival skill and why at times in modern human history it can be disadvantageous.

Rosemary: Tell me more.

Counselor: Well, briefly, our ANS, and specifically our SNS, was very helpful for responding to threats in our environment and triggering our flight, flight, or freeze response. An example would be seeing a lion in the jungle. It was very advantageous to either fight, flee, or freeze for survival. However, as humans have evolved, we begin to see "lions" in everyday situations that might not actually be life-threatening. So, it is important that we learn how to regulate our SNS and utilize our PNS by employing skills like mindfulness to mitigate less helpful stress responses. What are your thoughts?

Rosemary: Wow! I haven't thought about it. Very interesting!

Counselor: Terrific! Can we shift gears and try a simple exercise? [Counselor moves back to her chair across from the client.]

Rosemary: Sure.

Counselor: Can I please invite you a second time to bring awareness to your body and see how it is experiencing something distressing?

Rosemary: Yes! Please.

Counselor: I want you to think about an object that you distinctly dislike . . . something that brings about some discomfort, just enough to notice.

Rosemary: I really don't like spiders. They make my skin crawl.

Counselor: Perfect! This next activity may cause you some discomfort. Your body may react to the imagined image of spiders in ways that you don't like. While you are practicing the activity with me, I want to invite you to bring your awareness of your bodily sensations to your imaginary scene. Know that you can stop at any point.

Rosemary: What do you mean by bodily sensations?

Counselor: Good question! Rosemary, do you recall when you came in for the session today that I asked you to place your hand on your heart to feel it? That is an example of bringing your awareness to your bodily sensations. Can you bring your awareness to the movement of your abdominal areas while you are practicing this activity with me [alternatively, you can focus on other indicators of peripheral activation such as heart rate or skin temperature]?

Rosemary: Yeah, I think I can do it.

Counselor: Great! Now, I would like you to have a spider in your imagination. It is a seven-foot-tall spider, the largest you have ever seen. You are being chased by that fast-moving spider, and it is gaining on you.

Rosemary: Yuck! That sounds awful.

Counselor: Can you keep your awareness to the movement of your abdominal areas while you're having that spider in your imagination? How about your heart rate? How do your hands and arms feel?

Rosemary: Oh my goodness! I feel my heart is beating out of my chest.

Counselor: [After a moment or two, the counselor moves back over with the client's permission and sits next to her with the handout. Counselor then points to the SNS in the diagram.] What you're experiencing is a typical physiological reaction of the activated SNS in response to your perceived threat. Particularly, it is a flight reaction; your body is automatically reacting to the imagined threat. It may sound strange, but it is a healthy reaction.

Rosemary: [Client seems amazed by this new knowledge.]

Counselor: As you can see, when your SNS is triggered, it then significantly impacts your heart rate by speeding it up and also creating a stress response. [The counselor uses her finger to trace the pathways of acetylcholine and then norepinephrine to the heart for the client to see.] Did you experience any other reactions in your body?

Rosemary: I started to experience a little dry mouth.

Counselor: That is also another aspect of the activation of the SNS where that activation signals to your salivary glands to inhibit salivation. [Counselor again points and traces the pathways from the brain to the salivary gland for the client to see.] What are your thoughts?

Rosemary: It is all new to me, but mostly I think I get it. Once the SNS is triggered, and I experience a stress response, what can I do to calm myself down?

Counselor: I am glad you asked! I was about to show you a simple tool that can help when you feel triggered like you may feel now. Can I show you a quick breathing exercise?

Rosemary: That'd be great!

Counselor: I will have you sit in a comfortable position and with your eyes closed if comfortable and begin to breathe in your nose and out your mouth. I typically recommend breathing in for a four count, then holding, then releasing for a six to eight count. As you notice your mind starts to wander, bring your thoughts back to your breath. In addition, focus on breathing with your stomach and not as much of your lungs. Let's give it a try.

Rosemary: Sure.

Counselor: I will put on some soft music and will have you do your breathing for three minutes. I will let you know when we are done [you can adjust the length of the breathwork depending on the client].

Rosemary: Great!

Counselor: Begin! [Counselor puts on some soft music and client participates in the breathing exercise for 3 minutes.] Alright, you can open your eyes and stop the exercise. How did you experience the exercise and, more importantly, how do you feel?

Rosemary: I feel much better; my heart rate has slowed, and my dry mouth has completely gone away.

Counselor: [Counselor gestures and with permission from the client sits next to the client so they can both look at the handout with the ANS image.] What you are experiencing now is your parasympathetic nervous system (PNS) coming online to mitigate the stress response [the counselor again uses her finger to trace the pathways of the acetylcholine neurons to the heart and salivary glands for the client to see]. As you can see in this image, the PNS through the pathway of neurons slows the heartbeat and stimulates saliva production, which brings the body back into a more homeostatic state. You should feel a sense of safety and calm. Any questions regarding how this works?

Rosemary: Not at this time! I can't believe that works so fast and effectively. I am just amazed! So, if I'm getting this right, I can guess why my body responded so strongly to my fear around anticipated deportation. It sounds like my brain interprets that as a threat to my life.

Counselor: Yes! You are getting it! In our last ten minutes, I also wanted to hypothesize with you regarding the role of your life events and how your current symptoms relate to your ANS.

Rosemary: That would be helpful. I think that there are two events that really impact me and my stress response and triggers anxiety. My immigration to the U.S. and the struggles I had with covert racism and the possibility of deportation.

Counselor: That is really insightful! Tell me how that relates to your ANS and particularly your SNS if you had to guess.

Rosemary: When I think about what I had to go through, I sometimes feel difficult emotions. When this occurs, I start to feel anxious, and I am guessing it triggers a stress response.

Counselor: Could be! Say more.

Rosemary: I often have the same reaction that brought me in today, but I now feel like I have a few tools to help slow the fight, flight, or freeze response and calm my SNS. It feels very empowering to know what I can do!

Counselor: That is good to hear! The good news is that there are other similar techniques that will replicate the breathing exercise you practiced with me in session today. Research has shown that mindfulness, which is defined as a state achieved by focusing one's awareness on the present moment nonjudgmentally, while calmly acknowledging and accepting one's feelings, thoughts, and bodily sensations is helpful in calming the sympathetic portion of the ANS and activating the parasympathetic nervous system.

Rosemary: I have heard of mindfulness; my friend uses the app *Headspace* [https://www.headspace.com/] to achieve this state you are talking about. He tells me it is helpful.

Counselor: I agree! How do you feel about expanding on this learning between sessions as well?

Rosemary: That would be good!

Counselor: I want you to take this handout with you today and have you look through it further. If you feel that you are having another stress response to the recent political events, I want you to identify further awareness of your physiological reactions using the SNS portion of the image. In addition, use our breathing exercise to be mindful of how and where you experience your SNS being calmed while your PNS is activated. I will check in with you next week about your progress.

Rosemary: OK, I will give it a try.

Through the *Three Responses* activity implemented in session, Rosemary experienced three important outcomes: (1) she learned about the automatic functions of the ANS with emphasis on the activation of the SNS in session using her anecdotal experience of having a fear of spiders arisen from using the guided imagery in session; (2) she brought awareness to her physiological reactions to an anticipated stimulus or stress using the knowledge learned; and (3) she activated the parasympathetic division of the ANS using a mindfulness exercise (e.g., 3-minute breathing exercise) guided by the counselor in session.

ETHICAL AND MULTICULTURAL CONSIDERATIONS

As with all therapeutic interventions, one must be competent in the basic neuroscience concepts being reviewed and ensure that one has the adequate training and education to integrate those concepts in a therapeutic encounter. In addition, it is important to monitor safety when any form of exposure is being implemented. As we saw with Rosemary, it is also essential to be mindful of the various multicultural factors that influence the development and functioning of the ANS.

RELATIONSHIP STREAMERS AND THE AUTONOMIC NERVOUS SYSTEM

Gina Martin and Carol Seehusen

At the beginning of this chapter, the editors described the functioning of the ANS related to Stephen Porges's polyvagal theory (2011). We believe these concepts are vital to the therapeutic process. In addition, historical and modern perspectives on attachment theory aid in the understanding of how we regulate ANS functioning for optimal human development. This activity incorporates both of these concepts.

Traumatic experiences pose a significant threat to survival and affect the functioning of the ANS, resulting in a variety of physical and psychological symptoms (Williamson et al., 2015). Sensory information resembling the traumatic experience can trigger a traumatic response throughout the ANS, even when actual threats are not present, leading to a heightened baseline in physiological responses, such as fight or flight (Dale et al., 2018).

Early childhood trauma, especially when related to a caregiver, poses significant challenges to the development of the ANS and the regulatory mechanisms of the vagus nerve (e.g., Schore, 2001a, 2001b, 2003; Siegel, 2010b, 2015; van der Kolk, 1994). Therefore, it is important to explore the effect of early attachments on the development of autonomic and vagal regulation.

Influenced by the seminal work of Mary Ainsworth (1991) and John Bowlby (1982), attachment theory describes an individual's early childhood interpersonal interactions (Figure 5.8). Many configurations of attachment styles exist. As can be seen in Figure 5.8, anxiety runs on the horizontal axis as a spectrum from low to high anxiety. On the vertical axis, avoidance runs on a spectrum from low to high avoidance. If anxiety remains fairly low and avoidance also remains low, secure attachments can be formed. This secure attachment could be described as one in which the caregiver responds appropriately and promptly to an infant's cries for comfort, ultimately leading to low anxiety for the infant. The infant can trust that the caregiver will respond to their needs. If both anxiety and avoidance are high (avoidance meaning the caregivers' response to the infant), then a fearful-avoidant attachment style may be seen. In this attachment style, the caregiver likely did not respond appropriately or promptly to the infant's cries for comfort. Therefore, the infant has high anxiety surrounding getting their needs met and develops a fearful response to the caregiver, ultimately making the infant avoid interaction with that caregiver.

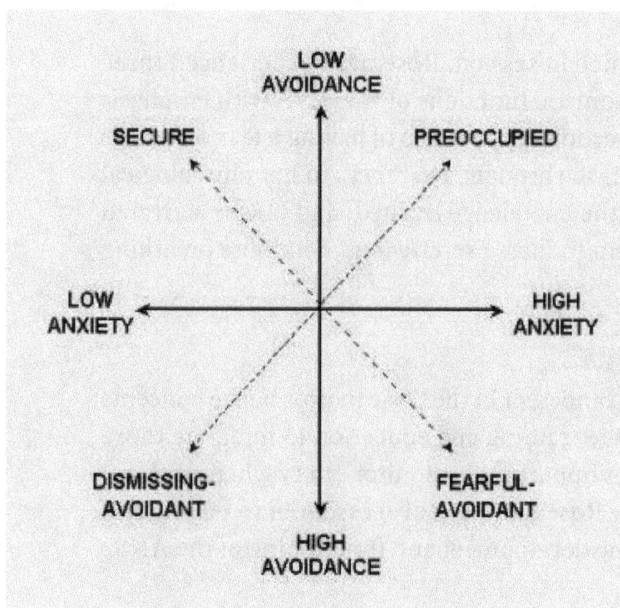

FIGURE 5.8 Axis of Attachment Styles

Neuroscience researchers have provided evidence linking the quality of individuals' attachments with how individuals respond to external stimuli (Choi et al., 2018; Geller & Porges, 2014). With infants, researchers have shown that an empathic caregiver's response to the infant is an important piece within a complex cycle of attachment (Schore, 2005). Schore and Schore (2008) outline how Bowlby's attachment theory has actually shifted to a theory of regulation, including concepts such as affective body processes, interpersonal interaction and regulation, brain maturation, stress, and unconscious relationship interactions. Foundational to this modern attachment theory is that communication or social engagement (as labeled in polyvagal theory) is crucial for brain development. More specifically, this brain development is involved in emotion processing, regulation of stress, and self-regulation (Schore, 1994). Schore (2001a, 2001b) notes that within therapeutic contexts, an empathic therapist can help develop emotional and affect regulation in clients effectively via unconscious transference and countertransference.

According to Schore and Schore (2008), for caregivers to form secure attachments with infants, they must be aware and attuned to the infant's psychobiological states—or those arousal states linked with the ANS. This allows the caregiver to attend to verbal and nonverbal interaction from the infant and reinforces secure attachment. The more the caregiver is able to do this through social engagement, the easier it is for the infant to regulate itself during periods of disengagement from the caregiver (Schore & Schore, 2008). On the other side, if an infant is presented with behaviors of insecure attachments (distress, fear, etc.), then the infant's development will be affected negatively. This includes psychological and neurological development (Watt, 2003). Attachment styles and their unique patterns of attaching, or relating, are synonymous with different ANS responses and elements of polyvagal theory (Geller & Porges, 2014).

Characteristics of secure attachment parallel with the SES, as described in polyvagal theory. The caregiver has responded to the child's needs, and there is appropriate attunement (Bowlby, 1982), leading the child to experience the world and relationships as safe. Behavioral patterns in anxious attachment seem to parallel the internal patterns of SNS activation. The child learns that the caregiver can be a source of safety or a source of hostility, and they begin to be anxious around the caregiver. This puts the SNS into a state of constantly anticipating risk, as the child does not know what to expect from the primary caregiver. Finally, there is the ambivalent pattern, which parallels the dorsal branch's freeze response. In these cases, the child recognizes that the primary caregiver responds perpetually with hostility, anger, or another unsafe reaction or withdrawals altogether, which in turn makes the child shut down (freeze) because that relationship is not safe (Bowlby, 1982). Flores and Porges (2017) assert that the process of integrating the vagus nerve into social interactions is a subconscious process that is programmed biologically. When danger is sensed, and prior methods of regulation and safety-promotion are not successful, the ANS moves toward immobilization or the system shutting down to protect itself (Flores & Porges, 2017).

Depending on these early childhood interactions, the ANS is primed to respond in certain ways as described earlier. According to Porges (2011), the ANS can either restrict social engagement or enable social engagement depending on the levels of oxytocin in the blood. Oxytocin is an enzyme that enables self-soothing and bonding between primary caregiver and infant. When the individual feels safe, or oxytocin levels are normal, the ANS is in a state of social engagement (Flores & Porges, 2017).

For example (Figure 5.9), imagine an infant reaches out to their caregiver for comfort (reaching out is social engagement, which is the infant's first attempt). The caregiver responds by ignoring the infant. The SNS is then mobilized, eliciting a fight or flight response (which occurs after social engagement fails) from the infant (e.g., a crying tantrum) to get the desired comfort from the caregiver. Again, the caregiver ignores the infant's cries. Having been further ignored, this response from the caregiver forces the infant into the freeze state (the final state), where the infant lies motionless. If this garners the attention of the caregiver, then the person may learn that withdrawing or immobilizing themselves is an effective means to get their needs met. As the infant grows up, intimate relationships may be viewed as a threat, which can activate similar fight and flight responses, and without adequate regulation strategies, as an adult, the person may enact previously learned responses (i.e., withdrawing) to future relationships, leading to interpersonal difficulties. However, if new, significant relationships, perhaps in counseling, are met with attunement and positive social engagement, then the prior responses may be modified, and the individual can build the capacity to

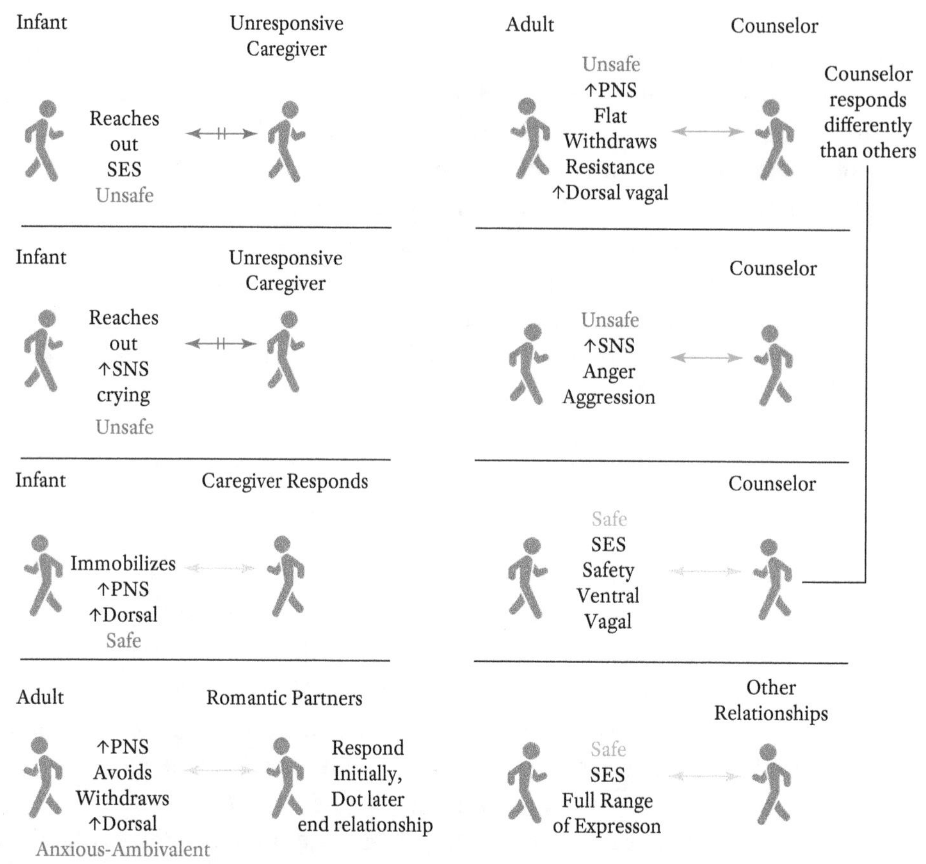

FIGURE 5.9 ANS and Vagal Responses to Early Attachment Figures, Counselors, and Other Relationships

form a secure, positive relationship. Eventually, the fight, flight, and freeze responses that interfere with their desired outcomes can be replaced with positive social engagement.

Theorists believe that attachment styles are constant throughout the life span if there are no interventions, or corrective emotional experiences, to shift how individuals relate to others (Bowlby, 1982; Simpson et al., 2007). This *Relationship Streamer* activity is an intervention that helps raise awareness of ANS functioning and shifts the focus internally, helping the individual understand what is happening and how to change it. This simple, visual, and experiential method provides added opportunities to process these reactions with the client to develop insight into how significant relationships in their life may affect their physical and mental health. Thank you to Drs. Cynthia Yesko and Ashley Anne who introduced a similar activity in Gina's graduate coursework that was adapted into the *Relationship Streamers* activity reviewed next.

MATERIALS NEEDED

- Three differently colored streamers: red, yellow, and green.

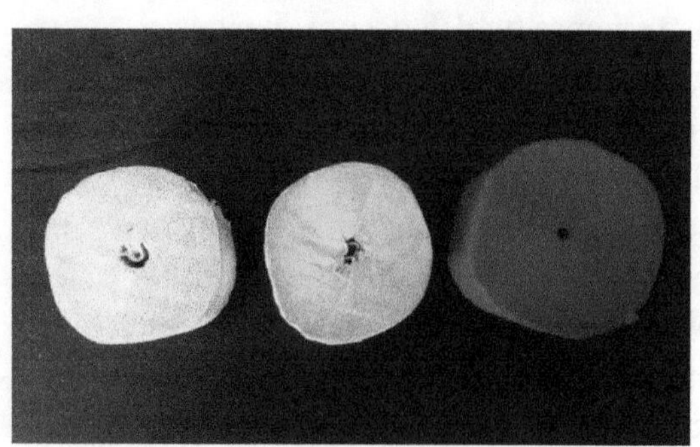

FIGURE 5.10 Example of Three Colored Streamers Aligning With Social Engagement (Green), Fight/Flight (Yellow), and Immobility (Red)

PROCESS OF THE ACTIVITY

The purpose of the *Relationship Streamers* activity is to help clients explore three ways of responding to external stimuli (social engagement, fight/flight, immobility) through the visualization of three colored streamers (Figure 5.10): green (social engagement), yellow (fight/flight), and red (immobility), as well as how these modes of responding develop and function within the context of interpersonal relationships.

This activity can be used at any point in treatment with a wide range of client concerns (e.g., interpersonal struggles, personality disorders, trauma) after a strong therapeutic alliance is established to provide the secure base needed for processing past relational patterns and ANS functioning. In addition, knowledge of clients' existing coping frameworks is essential to assist the client in regulating any undesirable reactions that could emerge during the activity. It is also beneficial to have a conversation about physical touch, as the therapist will be assisting the client in wrapping themselves in streamers. This conversation will include safety checks throughout the activity and provide the client with ways to navigate any discomfort (e.g., can rip the streamers off if it becomes overwhelming).

Step 1: Introduce the Colored Streamers

To begin the *Relationship Streamers* activity, you will first introduce the colored streamers, as well as what they stand for. For instance, you could say,

> Each colored streamer represents a way that we respond to a perceived threat. Green represents social engagement, which is the way we actively engage with others positively in response to our needs. Yellow represents hyperarousal, which is a feeling of needing to flee or fight within an interaction. And red represents hypoarousal, which is our freeze response or shutting down. Which way do you typically find yourself responding?

Depending on the stage of counseling and the client's engagement with the actual science of these concepts, you can go into more or less detail about the functioning of the ANS and polyvagal theory.

Step 2: Identify a Significant Attachment Figure and Their Primary Mode of Response

Identify a significant attachment figure in the client's life who will be used for the rest of the activity. This attachment figure could be someone in the client's current life or from their past, depending on their readiness and insight. You will explore the themes in the attachment figures' primary mode of response and then indicate that you, the therapist, will be representing this attachment figure for the duration of the activity. This often invites transference (i.e., client directing feelings or emotions from other relationships to the counselor) into the room, so you will want to be mindful of the potential effect of transference and countertransference throughout the activity. A possible adaptation to the activity to help with transference issues is to use an empty chair as the significant attachment figure.

Step 3: Attach the Streamers to Attachment Figure

After identifying the primary mode of response for the attachment figure, wrap yourself or the chair in the appropriately colored streamer. For example, if the attachment figure's primary mode of response was withdrawal, then you would use the red streamer.

Step 4: Attach the Streamers to the Client

Encourage the client to wrap themselves in the same streamer that is connected to the attachment figure. You will explore how the attachment figure's primary mode of response can influence and transfer into the client's own mode of response later in life.

Step 5: Attach the Streamers to Other Relationships

Encourage the client to connect the streamer to another object in the room representing future relationships in their life. For example, if there is a current relationship that applies, then another chair could be used to represent that relationship. You will then explore how that primary mode of response to the attachment figure can also be transferred to other important relationships in their lives, including the therapeutic relationship with the counselor, even when those relationships are to new, healthier attachment figures.

Step 6: Remove the Old Streamers

After the client has connected how attachment patterns and the polyvagal theory can be applied to previous relationships, explore what they would like to do to the current streamers as a representation of how they would like to enhance new attachments and modes of responding in the future. Some clients might like to rip the old streamers off and throw them away or keep them as a reminder. This can be a liberating experience for many clients.

Step 7: Create New Streamers

After the client set goals for how they would like to develop new attachments and modes of responding, encourage them to connect the information regarding the ANS and polyvagal theory to explore how they can create new streamers, new attachments, and new ways of responding.

Step 8: Process the Experience

Help the client explore their experiences during the exercise, perhaps their new understanding, or awareness, of how these attachments and modes of responses have affected them throughout their life. Highlight how our ANS is often co-regulated with those around us. For instance, being around others, including the counselor, who tend to respond with social engagement can promote co-regulation and social engagement in the client.

You can repeat this activity as necessary using other attachment figures and future relationships throughout the client's life. You can also use the counselor as an attachment figure to assess the way the client perceives and responds to the therapeutic relationship. Attention should be given to aid the client in making meaning throughout and collaboratively making plans for how the client wishes to respond moving forward. In all things, ethically follow the client's lead as they make meaning of this experience in their own unique way.

FOLLOW-UP

This activity is primarily evaluated using informal processing and observation. The activity will be effective if the client is able to identify the different states (social engagement, hyperarousal, and hypoarousal) in themselves after engaging in this activity. It would also be beneficial to check for client enjoyment and whether they believed they gained something from this exercise. Some examples of questions to ask include the following:

> How did you feel that exercise went for you? What were some things that became apparent to you? What are some things you learned about yourself and how you relate or respond to others given the social context? How could you incorporate this new knowledge into your interactions with others?

Follow-up with clients is important to see if their awareness of how they interact and respond in relationships has been raised, making it more apparent to them and facilitating positive changes in relationships. After a session has passed, it might be useful to refer to this activity and ask,

> How has your awareness increased in social settings? Have there been any changes in your interpersonal relationships?

NEUROSCIENCE IN ACTION

This case study demonstrates how Gina used the *Relationship Streamer* activity with a client we will refer to as John, a 17-year-old man struggling with romantic relationships. The client described his difficulty as, "I just shut down when they [the women] want to talk about emotions or feelings." John had five significant relationships with young women, and they all resulted in him "shutting down" when emotions became deeper and more involved, leading to his inability to engage in or sustain the relationship. During the biopsychosocial assessment, John described his mother as "unpredictable, mentally unstable, and generally absent," so he would often withdraw from her. Gina noticed that they were struggling to build rapport and suspected John may be working primarily from a hypoaroused shutdown system because of how John's mother attached to him as an infant. Gina decided to use the *Relationship Streamer* activity to explore early attachments and their effect on his current ANS functioning and romantic relationships.

Gina began by giving a description of what each colored streamer signified: green (social engagement), yellow (hyperarousal), and red (hypoarousal). Gina gave an example of how John would cry out for attention when younger and how his mother would not respond. After identifying the mother as the attachment figure and the primary response of hypoarousal and withdrawal (red streamer), John indicated his comfort with using the streamers, and Gina representing the role of the mother for the exercise. Gina connected the red streamer to herself, representing John's mother, and then to John while summarizing his experiences with his mother's withdrawal from him as a child. This allowed Gina to show John how his mother transferred her level of engagement or lack of engagement and hypoarousal to him (see Figure 5.11).

FIGURE 5.11 Immobility/Hypoarousal From Mother Transferred to Client

The next step was to explore how that red streamer, or level of hypoarousal, projected onto John's future romantic relationships. Romantic relationships posed a threat to John because they required a level of intimacy that he has not yet experienced, leading to his own withdrawal and hypoarousal toward future romantic partners. Gina used an empty chair to represent a romantic partner later in John's life. Gina attached the red streamer to the empty chair and discussed how the red streamer (still wrapped around John and herself from earlier as the mother figure) was how he was attaching or responding to new romantic partners. This aided John in visualizing how levels of hypoarousal transfer to other people and reinforced his new knowledge about the ANS. During the discussion, John gained a new understanding, or awareness, of how this was affecting his responses to his romantic partners. He was able to see that when he responds by shutting down, which is how he learned to respond to his mother, it was leading to the end of his relationships.

Once John gained insight, he decided that he wanted to rip the red streamer off, breaking the old attachment bond to his mother. After doing so, Gina helped John explore how he could change these patterns. While collaboratively discussing and brainstorming other possible responses to his romantic partners with John, Gina wrapped a green streamer around the two of them (see Figure 5.12).

FIGURE 5.12 Building Social Engagement With Counseling

Once wrapped in the green streamer, Gina discussed how heightening social engagement would begin to chip away at the red streamers and began tearing the red streamers away. This reinforced the idea that John was in control and that it was possible to change the outcome. In addition, over time, he was able to see how this hypoarousal response became a pattern in his romantic relationships, friendships, and even in session with Gina. They were then able to focus his therapy on identifying, developing, practicing, and strengthening alternative responses to lead to more positive outcomes and interpersonal relationships.

ETHICAL AND MULTICULTURAL CONSIDERATIONS

In cases of severe trauma and somatic pain, it may be ill-advised to use an activity that involves wrapping the client with streamers, which could promote a sense of being trapped or without autonomy. Clinicians should always approach this activity with caution and a strong clinical acumen for the client's level of trauma and/or physical pain. To address these concerns, drawings or play figures could be used as the focus of the exercise. This activity could also be difficult with very young children who may not have the developmental ability to understand the process or have difficulty paying attention for more than short spans of time. As with any therapeutic intervention, collaboration and discussion with the client should occur prior to the activity beginning.

ANCILLARY MATERIALS

Here are some other resources about polyvagal theory that we have found helpful:

- Wagner, D. (2016, June). *Polyvagal theory in practice.* https://ct.counseling.org/2016/06/polyvagal-theory-practice/
- NICABM (2011, June 30). *The polyvagal theory and PTSD with Stephen Porges* [Video]. YouTube. https://www.youtube.com/watch?v=8RKC3Ga6shs

"MAPPING" NERVOUS SYSTEM RESPONSES

Finding a Path to Feeling Better

Dee Wagner

As discussed earlier in this chapter, Stephen Porges's (2011) book *The Polyvagal Theory: Neurophysiological Foundations of Emotions, Attachment, Communication, Self-Regulation* presents his polyvagal theory about the two major branches of the vagus nerve: the dorsal (in the back—like a dorsal fin) and ventral branches (in the front). The vagus serves the parasympathetic system—the calming part of the ANS. The vagus' two major branches each calm the body, but in different ways. The dorsal branch creates a more dissociative kind of calm, while the ventral branch creates the more playful, restful, and rational kind of calm that invites day-to-day self-care. Knowing about the functions of the vagus nerve helps counselors intentionally select interventions that help clients engage the ventral branch of the vagus nerve, thus promoting regulation.

Polyvagal theory "maps" three circuits of nervous system functioning—social engagement, fight/flight, and shutdown—helping us see that our sympathetic and parasympathetic systems have much more complicated interactions than we had pictured in the past. Cells, molecules, hormones, networks, and nerves—to name a few—work together to help us navigate the world using these maps. Our social engagement system (SES) is our baseline system that provides us with an active mobile state of sympathetic arousal that does not progress into a fight/flight response, what Porges calls *play/dance* and Taylor (2012) refers to as *tend and befriend.* As counselors know, attending to relationships is an active task. Our SES also creates a restful state of parasympathetic activation that does not progress to a shutdown response, which has been referred to as *rest and digest.* Porges decided on the name *social engagement* for this multifaceted system because it involves anatomy that is used during social encounters, such as middle ear muscles, facial muscles, and the larynx—which creates vocal patterning. SES functioning develops during social interactions in early childhood, and once the anatomical functioning is trained, it offers self-regulation when we are alone and even during challenging social encounters that might tempt a fight/flight response.

Fight/flight mobility results from other biological interactions that are different from day-to-day sympathetic activation. Day-to-day sympathetic mobility can be quickly calmed by the ventral vagus nerve while fight/flight arousal cannot. When facing life-threatening danger, the body first moves from social engagement into fight/flight but then may add shutdown, along with fight/flight creating what has been called the *freeze* response. When there is a sense of hopelessness, shutdown manifests in the disembodied sensation that some clients describe as depression.

Trauma expert Peter Levine studied animals for years to understand human trauma responses. Along with contributor Ann Frederick, Levine described the biological burst of fight/flight that occurs when we awake from the dissociative calm of shutdown in his first book *Waking the Tiger* (Levine & Frederick, 1997). If we do not then discharge the leftover fight/fight energy out of the body—*shake it off* as the expression goes—and thereby return to the safety of the SES, then we are stuck in a trauma response. Conversely, remaining in states of immobility for prolonged periods can lead to disease and eventually death (Karr-Morse, & Wiley, 2012).

As discussed earlier in this chapter, attachment theory extends the discussion related to the development of the ANS and parallels with polyvagal theory. Secure attachment aligns with social engagement—and ventral vagus system—whereas insecure attachment aligns with both fight/flight and shutdown. Insecure attachment styles that include anxiety are associated with the fight/flight response. Insecure attachment styles that include an overly independent coping strategy are associated with the shutdown response (Shaver & Mikulincer, 2007). People surviving

MATERIALS NEEDED

- The Hierarchy of Nervous System Response handout (Figure 5.13)
- A way to tactically follow the map (e.g., a finger, marker)

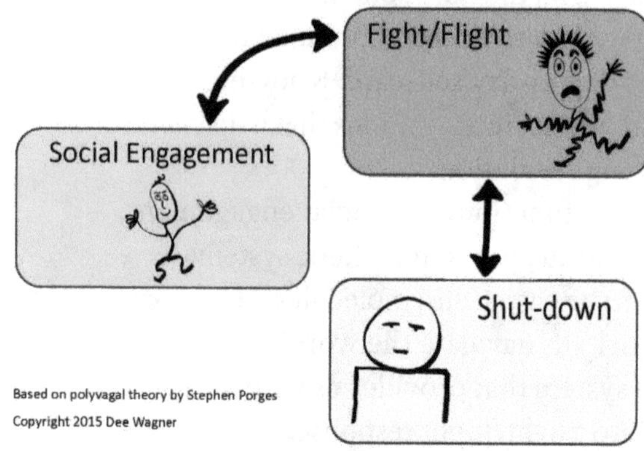

FIGURE 5.13 The Hierarchy of Nervous System Responses Handout

in degrees of shutdown use dissociation to avoid the fight/flight that gets stirred by the uncertainty inherent in relationships (Wagner, 2015a, 2015b).

Over my years of using polyvagal theory with clients, I have developed this *Mapping Nervous System Responses* activity to help people see the hierarchy of the human nervous system response as we now understand it in light of Porges's discoveries. I scribbled many versions of this "map" in my efforts to help clients understand the sensations they were describing. The arrows got added to show the path to the ANS functioning they were seeking. Over the years, the "map" evolved into a specific diagram that has been such a highly effective tool that I decided to have it professionally rendered. My clients and other counselors I have shared it with have also found similar benefits, and I am happy to share it with you in this book.

PROCESS OF THE ACTIVITY

After performing an assessment, the *Mapping Nervous System Responses* activity can be used at many phases of the counseling process. Rather than a step-by-step process, this map provides a shared language to co-construct a narrative of past functioning, as well as a model to foster future behavioral changes desired by the client. Regardless of how you are using this activity, it is useful to first introduce the map and its characters to the client. The counselor can point to the map and say something like the following:

> New science helps us recognize that our bodies have different ways of functioning depending on whether we sense we are safe [points to SES]... or we have a sense of some sort of life-threatening danger [points to fight/flight and shutdown characters and the line between them with the two arrowheads].

I usually ask clients to select the character with whom they resonate most. I have had clients immediately point to the fight/flight character or the shutdown character saying, "That's me." Sometimes one partner in a couple's session will point to two of the characters, suggesting to their mate, "I'm like this, and you're like this, right?" Several clients have piped up with statements like, "Everyone tells me to stop being so sensitive," and I have helped them appreciate the fact that sensitive people notice possible life-threatening danger quickly. Some clients begin to talk more generally about issues leading to chronic danger, such as climate change and driving fast vehicles. With most clients, we often discuss how we can maintain a feeling of life-threatening danger from unresolved past events, as well as how we move in and out of these response states.

In this case, it is useful to elaborate on how fight/flight can move us out of SES functioning with something like the following:

> "Lots of people have heard of the response we call fight/flight," pointing at the character made up of sharp zigzag lines. Counselors can name, "If we are facing life-threatening danger, our bodies shoot off a chemical cocktail that can create superhuman functioning to help us fight

off a predator or flee danger. Using fight/flight responses, people have been known to lift a car off a person trapped under it."

After elaborating on fight/flight responses, I generally point to the shutdown character with the absence of affect and continue:

> If our fight/flight response does not succeed in getting us to safety, our bodies are designed to go into a state called shutdown. We leave our bodies. This is called dissociation, and we all experience it to varying degrees. When we go on autopilot at work, that's a form of dissociation. Shutdown is a way to survive when we feel trapped in a situation that seems life-threatening. Maintaining a job only to make a living can feel so life-threatening that we use shutdown to robotically go through the motions.

Inviting the processing of these ideas, it is helpful to ask questions such as the following: *Can you think of times when you have reached out for social engagement? Can you think of times you are aware of feeling fight/flight? Are you aware of ever being in a shutdown response?*

As we integrate the shared language of the "map" throughout counseling, it is essential to listen actively and follow our clients' leads, reflecting to them the emotional energy we sense when they communicate with us. The "map" helps filter clients' experiences and grounds this exploration. I will offer a few other examples of how you can use the "map" in your work.

For clients who experience types of dissociation/depression, counselors can name it as follows:

> We can hang out in shutdown for quite a long time, but it can create disease. Shutdown can feel robotic, zombie-like, foggy, disoriented, or out-of-body. Eventually, shutdown accompanies death and even makes death seem less painful.

After processing aspects of shutdown that clients may wish to name, the counselor can begin to follow the arrow back up to fight/flight, stating,

> "When/if we sense a way out of the trapped-feeling situation that sent us into shutdown, our bodies are designed to shoot back into fight/flight." Helping clients feel in their bodies how we wake up from shutdown by going into fight/flight illuminates and normalizes the sensation. "Think about the sudden anxiousness you feel if you're driving on autopilot, and you realize your device that is giving you directions shuts off, and you panic thinking about how lost you'd be without it directing you."
>
> For clients who experience a lot of anxiety, counselors can add the following:
>
> We can keep shooting off fight/flight chemistry, creating adrenaline rushes even to the point of mania [circling the finger around and around on top of the zigzag character] until we exhaust ourselves and move back down into shutdown. Our bodies are designed to move back and forth and back and forth [moving finger on arrow between fight/flight and shutdown] until we find safety—social engagement system functioning.

As with all counseling, it is important to tailor the journey to each client's unique experience. When clients find situations that may trigger unbearable fight/flight, counselors will want to help them move small amounts of flight/flight chemistry through the body. Focusing on one distressing aspect at a time can titrate fight/flight discharge, allowing space to work the chemistry through the body and spend time in SES functioning before focusing on another aspect.

The safety of the therapeutic relationship provides a means of regulating fight, flight, and shutdown responses to aid clients as they shift to the SES. As clients are ready to step back down from flight/flight to SES functioning, counselors can get out the "map," point to the curvy character and clarify functions:

> We function in the social engagement system when we feel safe enough to engage with others. When we are over on the other side here [pointing up and down along the arrow between fight/flight and shutdown], we move into a more every-person-out-for-themselves kind of place. As you and I spend time together in our counseling journey, you may feel safer to move back over here [following arrow from the fight/flight character to the social engagement character] where we can be playfully competitive and creative. Where we can sense when we're tired and hungry.

As counselors, we know that finding a sense of safety involves validation for having needed to use nervous system responses designed for life-threatening danger. The vulnerability invited by the counseling relationship can trigger fight/flight and possibly shutdown. Counselors who pronounce the relationship as safe (e.g., "This is a safe space for you to share whatever you want.") may miss important relational cues. Inquiring about the degree of safety each client may feel in the counseling relationship (e.g., "How does it feel to share with another person?) invites clients to risk waking up from dissociative patterns they may have developed to prevent confrontation. When clients risk challenging their counselors, we can use the "map" to indicate the courage shown in stirring fight/flight by risking conflict and the path back to social engagement that occurred as we wrestle our way to satisfactory agreement and collaboration in the therapeutic process.

FOLLOW-UP

The "map" of nervous system functioning is an ongoing tool, which can be used throughout the counseling process. To evaluate the effectiveness of its use, note the client's body language. If the client's eyebrows furrow, chances are your explanation of one of the characters feels too complicated. If the client gets irritated, perhaps wanting to brush the map aside, that indicates a need to check in with the client: "What are you feeling in your body as you look at this 'map?'" Offer small pieces of information while looking for body language that suggests resonance before proceeding with additional clinical insight. As you share the science, if the client's head is nodding, that is a sign that the "map" is serving as a mirror helping the client recognize themselves.

As you and your clients discover each other's unique movement, whether it involves frequent loss of SES functioning and flying into fight/flight or anxious efforts to move out of shutdown through fight/flight and back into SES functioning, you will recognize the effectiveness of the "map" by clients' starting to use the descriptors fight/flight, shutdown, and even SES biology as part of how they talk about managing the sensations they feel in their bodies. This generalization of therapeutic gains into their actual lives is a great sign of effectiveness.

NEUROSCIENCE IN ACTION

I shared the "map" with a client I will call Chris—mid-forties, the youngest of three children who grew up in a home with parents with substance use disorders. Chris was the child who picked up the empty beer cans the morning after his parents' parties. When I explained how we come out of shutdown with a dose of fight/flight, Chris's head starting nodding. With a finger pointing at the curvy character in the social engagement box, Chris exclaimed,

> When I drink, it brings me here, but then [Chris's finger moved slowly up to the zigzag character and down to the affect-less character] it gets awful, and I end up back here.

Several sessions later, Chris asked me to get the "map" back out. Pointing a finger at the affect-less character of shutdown, Chris said, *"Drinking actually gets me here. I'm pretending to be this one [pointing at the curvy character] ...but I'm really here [pointing at affect-less character]. ...Every time I feel myself headed here [sliding finger up toward the zigzag character] ... I drink again. It's awful."* We sat with that truth reverberating in the room for a while. At the next session, I found out that Chris went to an Alcoholics Anonymous (AA) meeting. We talked about past stints of sobriety using AA. Chris asked for a copy of the "map" saying, *"When I was in that meeting, I thought about Curvy Guy—I felt like Curvy Guy... for a minute."*

In that session, we talked about the words *social engagement* that define the nervous system functioning that invites social interaction. To Chris, sharing in AA meetings felt scary. Sharing vulnerable information and having others accept the words and the feelings felt like everything Chris had longed for growing up. We talked about how childhood interaction can train SES functioning, but if over the generations, the kinds of parent/child interactions that train that kind of functioning happen less and less, counseling and 12-step work offer ways to undo old patterns and create new ones.

Chris felt anxious talking about interactions from childhood, and after using a body movement exercise that involved pushing into a sofa to help transition through fight/flight into SES functioning, Chris said, *"After the AA meeting, this person—this kind person—who had told this really moving story earlier in the meeting was talking to me and must have seen something in my eyes. The way this person looked back at me—was—it was like a hug. It felt like being hugged. And I felt like Curvy Guy, like I said, for a minute."*

In 12-step work, the Serenity Prayer offers a lovely way to appreciate polyvagal theory, so in the course of our work with the "map," Chris and I used phrases from the prayer to measure movement toward greater resiliency, self-regulation, and, therefore, true recovery. The "map" helped Chris recognize efforts to force a solution that might result in fight/flight. At those times, we invited the serenity that allows an acceptance of things that cannot be changed. When there were actions Chris could take to change aspects of difficult situations, we invited the kind of courage that is available using the SES's day-to-day mobility rather than fight/flight. Over time, Chris displayed increased wisdom to know the difference between that day-to-day mobility and fight/flight. The Serenity Prayer, alongside the "map," served as an anchor for our work and Chris's life.

SERENITY PRAYER

God, grant me the serenity to accept the things I cannot change, the courage to change the things I can, and the wisdom to know the difference.

ETHICAL AND MULTICULTURAL CONSIDERATIONS

Should a client have a visual impairment, I suggest describing the map. Because I used to draw the map for each client, I can imagine making a version of the map for a visually impaired client using cloth squares that have quite different textures. For instance, the social engagement square might be velvet, fight/flight might be wool, and shutdown might be satin. When the client felt comfortable, the counselor could invite the client to guide a finger from section to section through verbal instructions or hand-to-hand touch.

ANCILLARY MATERIALS

Miller, R. (Producer). (2018, January 17). *Polyvagal theory applied: Moving from fight or flight to social engagement for sustainable living* [Audio podcast]. The Thoughtful Counselor. https://wp.me/p7R6fn-je

BALANCING YOUR SEESAW

Using Animation and Metaphors to Explore How Chronic Stress Affects the Brain and Body

Whitney McLaughlin

Chronic stress is a common experience that can take a psychophysiological toll on the brain, mind, body, and relationships (Juster et al., 2010). For this activity, chronic stress is defined as the persistent imbalance between an individual's perceived demands and perceived resources (Lazarus & Folkman, 1984). Chronic stress occurs when external and/or internal demands continually exceed the individual's perceived ability to cope.

External/Environmental Demands	Internal Demands
• Everyday responsibilities that are neglected or poorly managed (e.g., work tasks, household chores, parenting challenges) • Exposure to traumatic events (e.g., natural disaster, violent neighborhood, witnessing domestic violence) • Experiences of overt or covert prejudice and discrimination • Relationship conflict • Poverty • Loss • Coping with chronic illness or pain	• Personal goals and expectations • Perceptions of thoughts and feelings (e.g., "I shouldn't feel this way." Or, "I cannot handle this challenge.") • Fatigue • Insufficient nutrition

(American Psychological Association, 2013b)

Researchers have found that chronic stress can alter brain structures and impair brain functioning (Radley et al., 2015). For example, individuals who experience chronic stress show differences in executive functioning, associated primarily with the prefrontal cortex (Arnsten, 2009; Arnsten et al., 2015). Alterations in corticosteroid receptors in the limbic system, which are critical to stress responsiveness and behavioral adaptation, have also been linked to chronic stress (Alt et al., 2010; Finsterwald & Alberini, 2014; Gadek-Michalska et al., 2013). Researchers have also observed that chronic stress can result in shrinkage of the hippocampus and enlargement of the amygdala (Cacciaglia et al., 2017; Diamond et al., 1994; Hanson et al., 2015; Sapolsky, 2000; Vyas et al., 2002).

Other scholars have focused on the role of the hypothalamus pituitary adrenal axis (HPA axis) in response to stress and the ways that chronic activation can affect the immune system and neural functioning (Maniam et al., 2014). In a review of the effects of stress on neuroendocrine, autonomic, and behavioral processes, researchers (Radley et al., 2015) highlighted the adaptive nature of the stress response. Specifically, they found that neurophysiological networks that mediate biological processes involved in adaptive coping also consisted of targets of the effects of repeated stress exposure that develop into maladaptive coping. One theory that has emerged from this focus is the idea of allostatic load (McEwen, 1998; McEwen & Morrison, 2013).

The allostatic load is defined as the cumulative effects or "costs" on the brain and body because of chronic stress exposure (McEwen, 1998). This repeated exposure results in overactivity or inactivity of physiological systems involved in coping and adaptation. Research on allostatic load is sparse, but researchers have found that the structure and function of social relationships are associated with allostatic load (Brooks et al., 2014). However, there is a lack of research on psychosocial interventions (e.g., self-regulation, optimism, social support, and social integration) geared toward altering allostatic load (Wiley et al., 2017). Without intervention, increased allostatic load may also shrink the WOT and promote sympathetic dysregulation.

Interestingly, researchers have found that perception of stress (i.e., stress mindset) can have more adverse effects on the brain and body than the stressful event itself, specifically in the medial prefrontal cortex (Treadway et al., 2013) and the hippocampus (Zimmerman et al., 2016). Researchers have also linked perceived stress to cortisol reactivity in response to recent stressors (Crum et al., 2013). Lastly, recent research has demonstrated the effect of perception of stress on physiological responses (i.e., neuroendocrine outcomes) to challenging and threatening stressors (Crum et al., 2017).

The purpose of the *Balancing Your Seesaw* activity is to initiate discussions about neuroscience and stress, specifically related to clients' allostatic loads. Using a "seesaw" image (see page 168–169 1: What's Your Load) to illustrate the balance or imbalance of allostatic load, these discussions are intended to enhance self-understanding and insight to motivate change. When feasible, clients can focus on changing behaviors that contribute to their experiences of stress and developing positive coping skills (e.g., reframing, relaxation techniques). When decreasing stressors is less feasible, clients can explore the concept of stress mindset. This approach is outside the scope of this activity, but I encourage readers to learn more by visiting the Stanford Mind and Body Lab (https://mbl.stanford.edu/).

MATERIALS NEEDED

- A desktop computer or mobile device (cell phone, iPad, laptop, etc.) with access to the Internet
- TED-Ed video (https://ed.ted.com/lessons/how-stress-affects-your-brain-madhumita-murgia)
- The What's Your Load? worksheet
- Pen or pencil

PROCESS OF THE ACTIVITY

Step 1. To begin this activity, introduce the general topic of stress by asking clients for their definitions and/or thoughts related to the topic. Example prompts include the following: *What does the word stress mean to you? What comes to mind when you hear the word stress?* Next, share with clients that there is a mind-body connection with stress. Note that some stress can be positive (e.g., eustress—job interview, starting a new business venture) but that too much and chronic stress can be negative (e.g., distress—conflictual relationships, exposure to neighborhood violence). I recommend providing clients with examples of each, connecting these concepts to elements of the client's biopsychosocial history when possible. From there, you can share that when stress is experienced continuously over an extended period (e.g., chronic stress), it can become problematic for the brain and body.

Step 2. Introduce the video (https://ed.ted.com/lessons/how-stress-affects-your-brain-madhumita-murgia; Figure 5.14) and view it with the client. Observe the client's body language while watching the video and use process questions (e.g., "How did you feel while watching the video?" "What sense do you make of the information?") and observational immediacy (e.g., "I noticed you were rubbing your hands while watching the video.") to get a sense of how the client is taking in the information.

Potential TED-Ed Video to Explore the Effects of Chronic Stress on the Brain

How Stress Affects Your Brain
TED-Ed, 2015
Watch at: **https://ed.ted.com/lessons/how-stress-affects-your-brain-madhumita-murgia**

Step 3. The next step of the activity includes introducing the concept of allostatic load via the What's Your Load? worksheet. Define allostatic load as the "wear and tear on the body" that builds up as an individual is exposed to repeated or chronic stress. Help clients identify their past, present, and/or anticipated stressors and their response (i.e., inputs). Then talk with the client about how stress and their response to it affects their mind and body (i.e., outputs).

Step 4. The final phase of the activity is helping clients modify their allostatic load. Primarily, clients can adopt one or two strategies: (1) eliminating and/or reducing exposure to stress or (2) developing and engaging in positive coping. Positive coping could include shifts in the perception of stress and/or changes in behavior. A variety of cognitive and behavioral interventions (e.g., evaluating stress mindset, reframing, problem solving, mindfulness, behavior activation) can help clients achieve these goals. Biofeedback strategies can also be used to help regulate physiological responses that may interfere with decision making or enacting changes.

FOLLOW-UP

This activity can be evaluated both informally and formally. Examples of informal evaluation include asking open-ended questions, such as the following: *How did you feel while participating in this activity? What did you like best about this activity? What did you like least? What have you learned about yourself that you didn't already know before engaging in this activity?* Examples of formal evaluation tools include measures of pre- and post-symptomology (e.g., Outcome Rating Scale) or measures of allostatic load (e.g., biological testing of cortisol secretion, cardiovascular activity, and hemoglobin levels).

NEUROSCIENCE IN ACTION

Kayla was a 20-year-old Caucasian American woman in her junior year at a large public university in a southeastern city. She initially sought counseling because of relationship issues. However, she also reported that she had academic, financial, and personal demands that had become very taxing on her physically and emotionally. Kayla started failing two classes because she had difficulty managing her full-time course load. She was in jeopardy of losing a scholarship at the end of the semester. She also expressed difficulty paying for her educational and living expenses because she came from a single-parent home with limited financial resources and was working part time and earning minimum wage. In addition, Kayla was involved in several extracurricular activities and held a leadership position in two student organizations. These demands put a strain on Kayla and her relationship, and she was fearful that it would lead to a breakup. Kayla shared that the past 6 months had been exceedingly difficult, and she "always felt tense and anxious." She reported that she had lost 10 pounds in the last 2 months. She also reported having sleeping problems. After rapport building and treatment planning, the *Balancing Your Seesaw* activity was used with Kayla in the fourth counseling session to help her explore how chronic stress can impact her psychophysiological health.

Clinician: Kayla, what comes to mind when you hear the word "stress"?

Kayla: I don't like stress, but it's common when you're in college. For me, when I hear the word stress, I think of being overwhelmed. I feel stressed when I have too much on my plate that I can't handle. I get very overwhelmed, and I've been feeling like that every day for the past few months.

Clinician: It sounds like you view stress as something to be avoided.

Kayla: Yes, I don't like being under a lot of stress.

Clinician: Stress definitely has a negative connotation and part of that has to do with how it impacts our mind and body. There are stressors like being in an abusive relationship that can lead to negative stress or distress, and there are other stressors such as a job interview that can lead to positive stress, which is called eustress.

Kayla: That makes sense. I can see how there can be good and bad stress.

Clinician: In either case, when someone experiences a stressful event, there is a mind-body connection. When stressful events become too extreme or intense and last too long, it can take a toll on the brain and the body. It sounds like the stress you've had has been going on for quite some time. I have a short animated video that shows how too much stress can impact the mind and body. Would you like to watch it?

Kayla: Yes, I've been stressed for too long. I'd like to see the video.

[Watches the animated TED-Ed video (https://ed.ted.com/lessons/how-stress-affects-your-brain-madhumita-murgia)].

Clinician: How did you feel while watching the video?

Kayla: I got worried because I didn't realize how much stress can impact my brain. I'd heard about cortisol before, but I didn't know exactly what it does. I don't remember the part of the brain that's responsible for learning, but I've been having difficulty concentrating in my classes. I feel like I'm constantly worrying about my money problems and possibly losing my scholarship.

Clinician: It sounds like there were some things from the video that resonated with you. It also seems like your stress has really been impacting you both inside and outside the classroom.

Kayla: Yes, it's like I can't escape it.

Clinician: It's even been preventing you from committing things to memory which is one of the main functions of the part of your brain called the hippocampus. This affects your ability to learn, which can put further stress on you.

Kayla: Yes. I feel very tense. It's like I hold the stress in my body.

Clinician: Do you feel that way right now?

Kayla: Yes.

Clinician: That's where the mind-body connection comes from. When we experience stress, cortisol, and other hormones are activated to help our bodies respond. That's where our "fight or flight" response comes from. Although necessary at times, when we have too many stress hormones building up, it can hurt rather than help our body.

Kayla: Then maybe that's why I've been feeling this way. It's like I'm on alert all the time, which makes it harder for me to sleep and concentrate in class.

Clinician: Absolutely! It's like you've been in overdrive the past few months.

Kayla was very receptive to the neuroeducation provided in the video, and processing questions like the ones mentioned earlier were used to further help Kayla make connections between her stressors and their effect on her brain and body. Next, I introduced the What's Your Load? worksheet:

Clinician: Our minds and bodies are like seesaws. When we're balanced, we are well, and we can perform at an optimal level of functioning. However, when both sides of our seesaw are weighed down, it puts a strain on us and makes it harder to function. What do you think about that idea?

Kayla: That makes sense, but it seems too hard for me to get balanced with everything that's going on.

Clinician: Let's take a closer look at everything. I have a worksheet called What's Your Load? that I believe may be helpful to you. I use the term "load" to refer to your allostatic load. Have you ever heard of that before?

Kayla: No. What does that mean?

Clinician: Allostatic load is just a fancy way of saying that "wear and tear on the body" builds up over time because of stress. This can happen because inside the brain, the HPA axis (one of our stress response systems) keeps signaling that something is stressful. When this happens, stress hormones like cortisol and adrenaline can be released over and over again. Over time, this can make it harder to respond to something stressful because your body has been "on alert" for too long. Based on what you've shared with me, your load seems to be very strained right now.

Kayla: Yes, it is. I'm not really sure how to make it better.

Clinician: [Gives client the worksheet.] We can use this worksheet to help you identify your stressors, how you've responded, and, ultimately, how it's impacting you mentally, physically, emotionally, and even socially. We can also use this What's Your Load Worksheet to see if there are changes that you could make to help your load more manageable. How does that sound?

Kayla: It sounds like it can be helpful.

During this part of the activity, Kayla wrote down her stressors and determined which ones could be eliminated and which ones she could reduce her exposure to (see completed worksheet). She identified behaviors she had engaged in (e.g., alcohol use, sedentary activities) that exacerbated her symptoms. By the end of the session, Kayla developed two goals: (a) participate in a yoga class once a week on campus and (b) reduce her screen time before bed by 1 hour.

At her seventh counseling session, Kayla reported that she was feeling less tense and that she attended and enjoyed yoga class because that was her "one hour of me time." She also reported that she fell asleep sooner and stayed asleep longer, even though she still was not getting the amount of sleep that she wanted (i.e., 8–9 hours per night). Overall, she increased the average amount of sleep she was getting on weeknights from 4–5 hours to 6 hours each night. Kayla also reported that she was eating more regularly, and she felt that her academic and financial stress were more manageable because she had connected with helpful resources on campus. Although Kayla shared that she felt progress was made in several areas of her personal life, she continued to report difficulties in her romantic relationship.

Overall, this activity had a positive effect on the therapeutic relationship. The initial discussion and ensuing reduction in stress-related symptomology seemed to strengthen the working alliance. Although the client's relationship problems were still a concern, she now had more energy and focus to devote to working on her relationship.

ETHICAL AND MULTICULTURAL CONSIDERATIONS

This activity is designed primarily for adolescents and adults with typical developmental capabilities. Modifications in language and presentation style would need to be made for children and individuals with developmental disabilities. This activity would not be appropriate for clients who are in crisis and/or lacking basic needs. In that case, stabilization would be the first priority. Lastly, I caution using this activity with clients who are experiencing chronic stressors for which they have no ability to significantly affect (e.g., terminally ill family member). Highlighting the way that their stressors are harming them can increase the toll of their situation. In such cases, it is better to focus on helping clients access internal and external resources and make meaning from their experiences.

There are relevant multicultural considerations for using this activity with diverse clients, particularly clients from historically marginalized populations. It is important to emphasize the psychophysiological impact of sexism, racism, ableism, heterosexism, and other forms of oppression on clients who have been marginalized and discriminated against. Microaggressions can be a form of traumatic stress, and their effect on the brain and body must be considered when working with marginalized clients (Sue, 2010). Nadal (2018) coined the term *microaggressive trauma* to refer to the "excessive and continuous exposure to subtle discrimination (both interpersonal and systemic) and the subsequent symptoms that develop or persist as a result" (p. 13). Subtle and systemic forms of discrimination can automatically increase a marginalized client's allostatic load without any observable events because they are so persistent and pervasive in society. Therefore, counselors must explore their own cultural identity development, establish therapeutic rapport, and create a sense of safety for clients when facilitating this activity. Lastly, cultural and socioeconomic factors must be taken into consideration when using the worksheet to help clients identify health behaviors for stress management and health promotion.

What's Your Load?

The *allostatic load* is "the wear and tear on the body" that builds up as an individual is exposed to repeated or chronic stress. When too much stress is put on the brain and the body, it becomes overloaded—like a seesaw that is under strain and may eventually break.

Write down a list of stressors and identify your response to those stressors by circling the behaviors in the "My Response" column. Then, on the right side of the page, circle any symptoms you have experienced in response to stress. There is space at the bottom of each column for write-in responses. You can use the questions that follow to guide you.

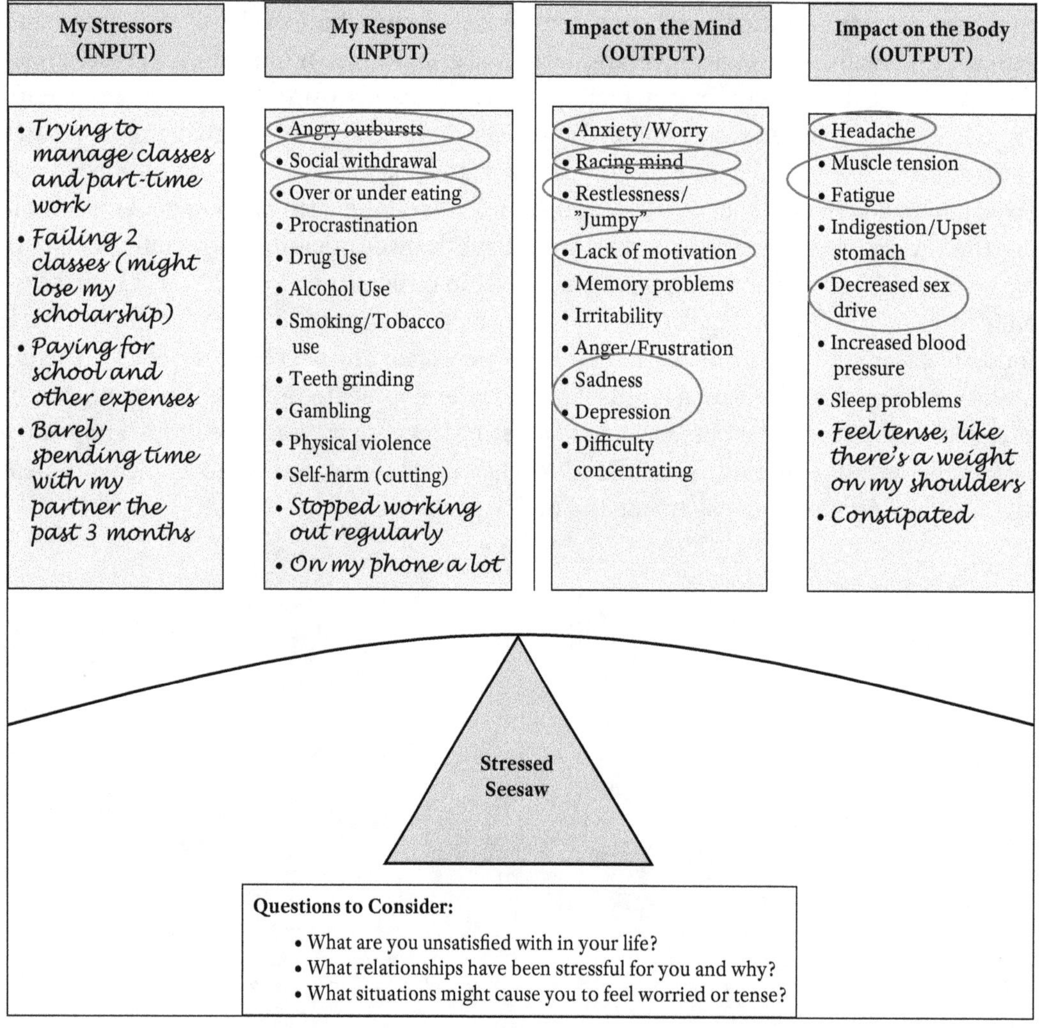

Reduce Your Load

To decrease your *load* and have a more "balanced seesaw," it is important to do the following:

- Eliminate as many stressors as possible
- Reduce exposure to the remaining stressors
- Counteract stress with de-stressing activities (develop positive coping behaviors)

From the list of "My Stressors" on the previous page, write down how you can either eliminate or limit your exposure to the stressors in your life. Next, circle coping skills that you would like to engage in more from the "My Response" column (you can also add activities to the list). On the right, list positive results you would like to experience in your mind and body. You can use the questions that follow to guide you.

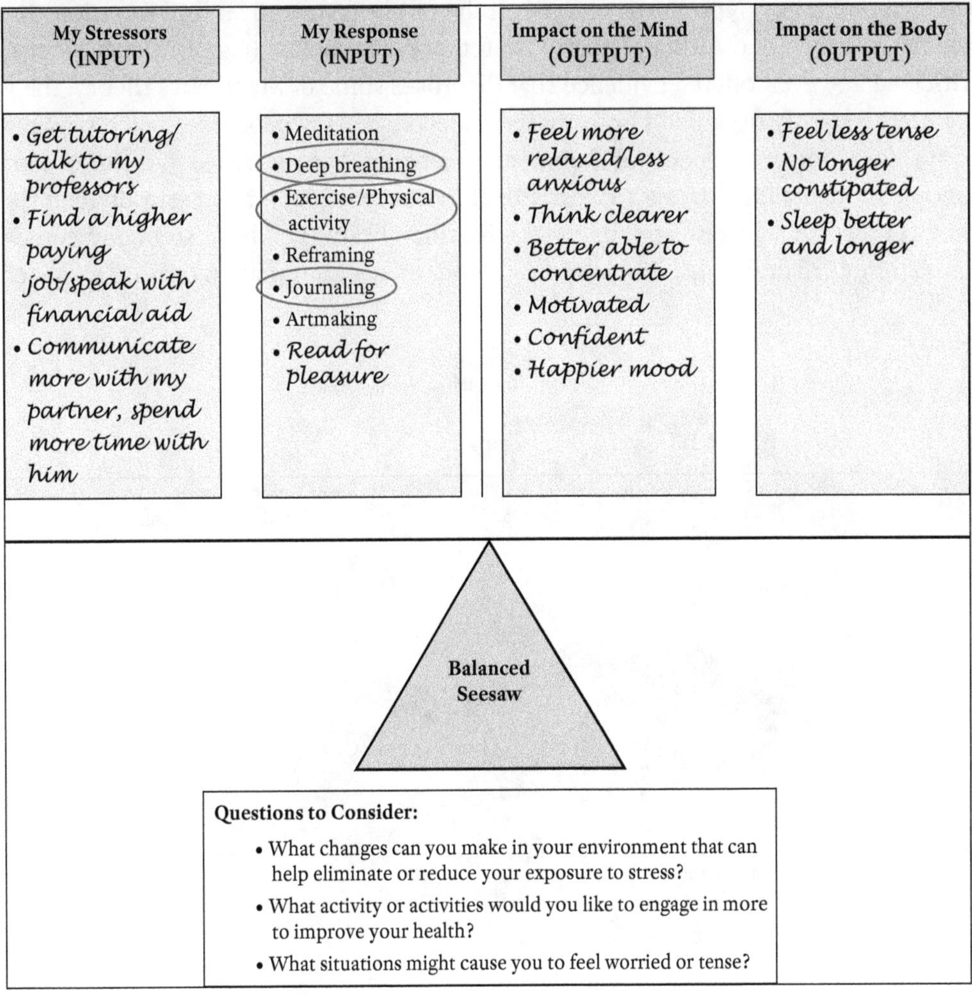

My Stressors (INPUT)
My Response (INPUT)
Impact on the Mind (OUTPUT)
Impact on the Body (OUTPUT)
• Get tutoring/ talk to my professors
• Find a higher paying job/speak with financial aid
• Communicate more with my partner, spend more time with him
• Meditation
• Deep breathing
• Exercise/Physical activity
• Reframing
• Journaling
• Artmaking
• Read for pleasure
• Feel more relaxed/less anxious
• Think clearer
• Better able to concentrate
• Motivated
• Confident
• Happier mood
• Feel less tense
• No longer constipated
• Sleep better and longer
Balanced Seesaw
Questions to Consider:
• What changes can you make in your environment that can help eliminate or reduce your exposure to stress?
• What activity or activities would you like to engage in more to improve your health?
• What situations might cause you to feel worried or tense?

BRAIN WORK

Doris D'Hooghe

The developmental process of brain structures and regions provides additional insight into the functioning of the autonomic nervous system (ANS). Paul MacLean (MacLean, 1990) coined the term "triune brain," hypothesizing a hierarchy of brain structures and functions based on evolutionary development. Although many contemporary scholars (e.g., Butler & Hodos, 2005) have criticized and even offered evidence that disproves some of MacLean's theory, the general idea of a hierarchically organized brain based on evolutionary processes, each part playing a dominant role in different aspects of human experiencing, has remained a useful construct for many people in mental health (e.g., Wiest, 2012; Panksepp, 2011). MacLean divided the brain into three (Figure 5.14) interrelated parts: the reptilian brain (i.e., brainstem and cerebellum), the paleomammalian brain (i.e., limbic system), and the neomammalian brain (i.e., neocortex).

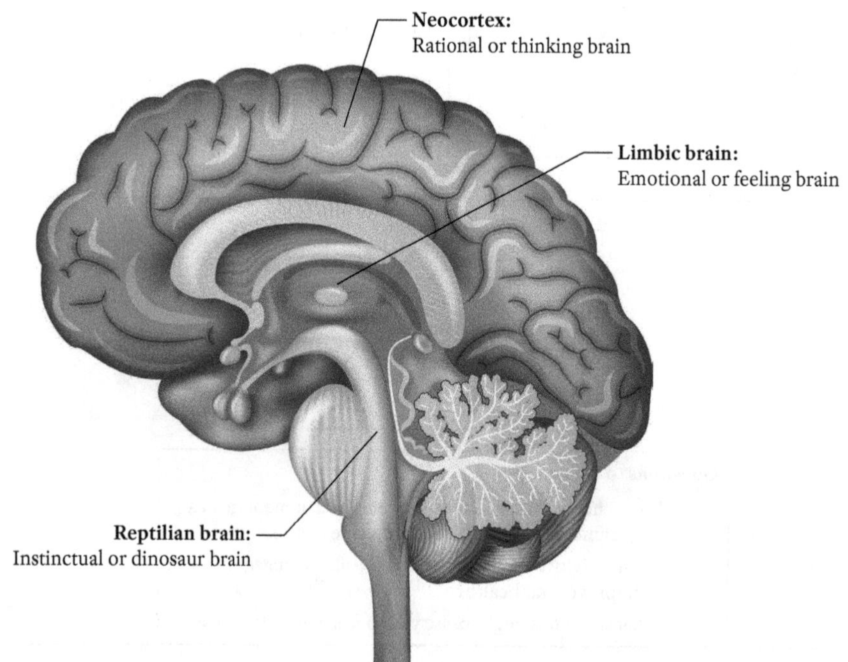

FIGURE 5.14 Paul MacLean's Theory of the Triune Brain

The reptilian brain consists of the brain stem and the cerebellum. The brain stem houses the vital control centers for basic survival, including all regulatory functions (heartbeat, breathing, swallowing, etc.). The reptilian brain also includes rudimentary actions/behaviors that increase survival and maintenance of the species, such as simple, primary aggression, courtship/mating behaviors, and territorial defense (Rustin, 2013). The limbic system, a group of interconnected structures found underneath the cerebral cortex, includes the amygdala (which plays a role in processing fear, safety, danger, attachment, early memory, emotional experience, implicit memory) and the hippocampus (explicit memory, working with cerebral cortex; Montgomery, 2013). The amygdala is considered the "alarm center" of the brain. When the amygdala perceives danger, it activates a cascade of responses within the ANS. Stress hormones, such as adrenaline, are released in the blood and prepare the body for "flight" or "fight" (heightened sympathetic nervous system

[SNS] activity). When a threat is overwhelming and the sympathetic activity peaks, as in trauma, the parasympathetic nervous system (PNS) kicks in, shutting the SNS down, and we freeze (PNS activity). Finally, the neocortex, the latest developing part of the triune brain, is the largest part of the brain in humans. It is the part responsible for high-level functions, such as speaking, reasoning, writing, decision making, consciousness, and judgment (Rustin, 2013). When individuals perceive danger, the reptilian part of the brain takes charge and is predominant in functioning. This often results in actions that occur before thinking, sometimes leading to undesirable consequences. When individuals perceive safety, the brain works in a more integrated manner, with more energy available to the limbic system and neocortex functioning. This leads to more intentional, regulated decisions to be made about how to respond to one's environment.

The goal of the *Brain Work* activity is to increase awareness of the hierarchical functioning of the brain and the automatic nature of the ANS to help clients explore their experiences and gain insight about the survival mechanisms of fight, flight, and freeze. Individuals can begin to see their reactive responses in a new light, which in turn lessens self-blame. This knowledge can also help clients become more aware of bodily changes and begin naming potential triggers. Individuals can learn to tune in to their bodies and regulate their ANS before the stress response gets too strong, thus limiting automatic responses that have caused problems in their past.

MATERIALS NEEDED

- Pictures illustrating the brain model, fight/flight/freeze, and brain plasticity
- Computer, tablet, or phone with Internet access to watch YouTube video: https://www.youtube.com/watch?v=iHg9KXhJf5M

YouTube Video Illustrating the Immobilized Response

WATCH: Mouse Play Dead—Real Life Tom and Jerry

Love Your Animals!, 2017

Watch at: **https://www.youtube.com/watch?v=iHg9KXhJf5M**

PROCESS OF THE ACTIVITY

An underlying principle of *Brain Work* is the value of connecting with clients in a genuine and authentic manner. There is a lot of sharing, laughing, and having fun together. In these interactions, children experience an attuned and regulated therapist who enhances their social engagement system, resulting in a multitude of bodily sensations and emotions. *Brain Work* is designed for children ages 6 to 12 years with a history of developmental trauma and grounded in the three phases of trauma treatment: (1) stabilization, (2) trauma confrontation, and (3) integration (Herman, 1992). This activity takes place during the stabilization phase of the treatment.

Step 1

This first step of this activity is exploring the hierarchical organization of the brain highlighted in MacLean's triune brain theory. Use images (Figure 5.15a) or other experiential means to talk about the parts of the brain. Dan Siegel's hand model of the brain is one such experiential approach (Figure 5.15b). I might say something like this:

> The brain has three parts: brain stem, limbic system, and neocortex. [Point to the lowest part of the brain.] This part is called the reptilian brain; it includes the brain stem and cerebellum. This part of your brain is really important for basic survival—it is responsible for your heart beating, for your breathing, making you sweat when it is hot in the summer, and turning you cold when it freezes during winter. [Point to the limbic system, noting the amygdale specifically.] This is the limbic system. An important part of your brain in this region is the amygdala. The amygdala is like a danger detector. It is like a guard dog that is warning you of danger. The dog reacts

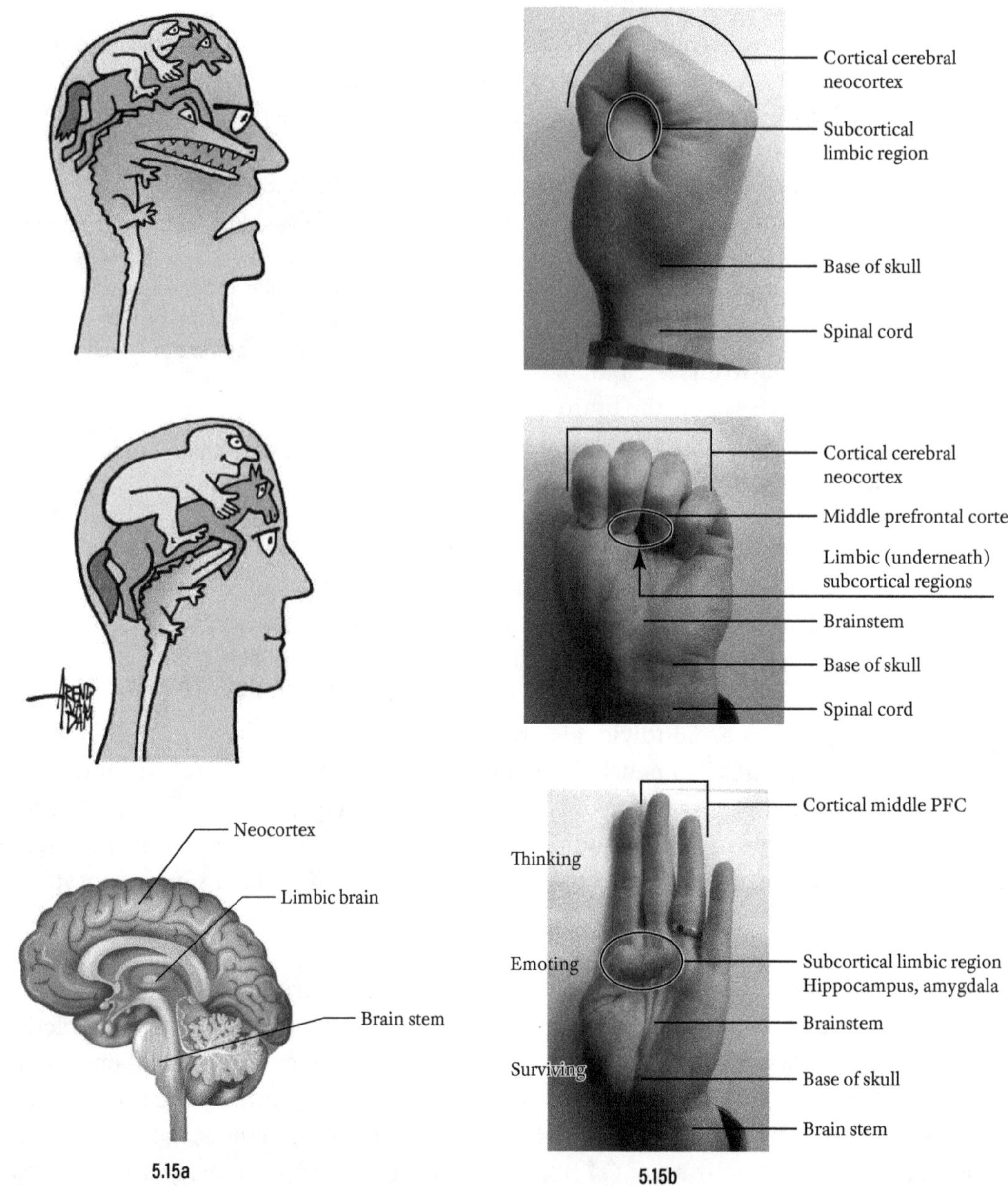

FIGURE 5.15 Dan Siegel's Hand Model of the Brain Aligns With Paul MacLean's Theory of the Triune Brain.

Figure 5.15a A Creative Rendering of Paul MacLean's Triune Brain Theory
Creative renderings, analogies, and metaphors can be extremely useful. For instance, some clients will connect with language such as "your crocodile is under attack" after an act of aggression more than "the subcortical regions of your brain are overactive." In these figures, we see three images used to represent the components of MacLean's triune brain: crocodile (reptilian brain), horse (paleomammalian brain), and human (neomammalian). As seen in the image on the left, all three components are relatively the same size, representing regulated functioning and communication between all levels. On the right, the crocodile has taken over, shrinking the horse and human. This represents the activation and potential overactivation of the survival centers in response to some threat, thus limiting the connection and functioning of the higher order sections of the brain. Notwithstanding the value of these renderings, it is important to acknowledge the complex interactions and connectedness throughout the brain. In fact, these are not necessarily three separate brains but rather three portions of the brain that are interconnected with the rest of the nervous system throughout the body. Each portion, section, and structure of the brain may be more active in certain human processes, but this does not negate the role of other portions, sections, and structures in that same process.

Figure 5.15b Dan Siegel's Handy Brain Anatomy Model
The Handy Brain Anatomy Model provides an easily accessible tactile and visual image to use in any setting. In this model, you can clearly see the bottom-up and top-down connections that foster neural integration as well as what happens when our cognitive regions disconnect from our emotional regions. We encourage you to trace your hand and practice labeling the brain regions, structures, and functions as you build your competency level.

amazingly fast and starts a stress response in the body like shouting, hitting, or withdrawing from your friends. The amygdala's job is to keep you safe. [Point to the neocortex.] This is the neocortex. This is the part of the brain that allows us to talk to our friends, pay attention in class, and plan a surprise party for your parents or friends.

Step 2

After describing the parts of the brain, introduce the ANS. You can ask the child an open-ended question, such as, "What do you think animals do when they are scared?" Highlight the possibilities of fight, flight, and freeze. Note that humans have similar ways of responding. I find the YouTube video *WATCH: Mouse Play Dead—Real Life Tom and Jerry* (https://www.youtube.com/watch?v=iHg9KXhJf5M) as a great illustration of the freeze response. Follow up with a reflection question, something like, "Have you ever felt like that mouse?" Explore how the mouse might feel and how they responded. Using an external projection of the child's experience (such as a mouse) usually creates enough distance for the client to safely explore their past experiences with threatening situations. Process ways that the client might have felt and responded similarly to the external projection with a specific focus on naming various fight, flight, and freeze responses.

Step 3

The last step of this activity involves collaborating with the client to explore ways that they can generalize their experiences in the session to their everyday life. For instance, you can ask something like, "What will you take away from our time together? Yes, we have learned about three parts of our brain and three ways that we all tend to respond to things in our environment. Do you think this will be useful to you moving forward? How so?" Sometimes clients will create unique images and names for the fight, flight, and freeze response as they begin generalizing to their life outside of sessions. Continue to build this shared metaphor, as it can supply language to previously unconscious material that promotes neural integration, thus aiding in future regulatory capacity.

FOLLOW-UP

As you close the session, ensure social engagement to promote curiosity and play together. During this time, you can use open-ended questions to explore what meaning the child took from the experience. Example reflection questions include the following: "What are you thinking now about your experience?" Or, "What do you think about what we just talked about?" In the following sessions, you can refer to the video and discussion and ask questions such as, "What do you remember about ...?" or "Have you noticed anything different in your thoughts, feelings, or behaviors since our last session?" You can make note of the new language clients use to make meaning out of their past, present, and future experiences.

NEUROSCIENCE IN ACTION

This case relates to an 8-year-old boy who was suffering from severe sleeping problems after witnessing a violent incident between his parents. The session began with an exploration of the triune brain:

> **Therapist:** The brain has three parts. The brain stem, here at the bottom, helps survival. Animals also have this. If they are in danger, then this part of the brain becomes active. This means that the animals are receiving signals from the brain to take action to escape the danger. *If* there is a threat and fear, a sort of alarm sounds in the brain's limbic system. This is where the amygdala is located. It acts as a kind of guard dog. It warns you of danger and sends signals to

other parts of the brain so that your body can act to counter the danger. And here we see the cortex, responsible for reasoning, thinking logically. You can call it the "smart" brain that helps you remember what happened in your life and how to do all kinds of things, such as playing an instrument, walking, riding a bicycle, and so on. What is an animal's first reaction if he feels scared and threatened?

Child: Escape.

Therapist: Exactly. And what if he can't escape?

Child: Fight, bite, attack.

Therapist: That's right. And then there is another mechanism that isn't active. What would an animal do if it could neither escape nor fight?

Child: Make itself small and roll up in a ball.

Therapist: Absolutely. We call this freezing or playing dead. People do the same thing. Do you recognize one of these three when you feel in danger or scared?

Child: I either run away or I fight.

Therapist: Those are your reactions when you feel threatened, and that is because your alarm goes off telling you to run away or fight.

Child: Then the brain is a sort of factory that is still starting up when you are young *[the client created his own language through metaphor to make meaning of his experience]*. As you get older, more and more workers join, and the factory grows bigger. Once you are an adult, the factory is complete, with many workers. And in my factory, you can find a "fear" department with lots of employees.

After processing the factory metaphor and connecting it to his current life experiences, I showed a video of the mouse playing dead to explain the freeze response. The child and I were sitting next to each other on the floor in the therapy room watching the video. I explored the specific features of the freeze reaction with the child while watching the mouse's behavior on the video. After the video stopped, I asked the child about experiences of this kind in his personal life.

Therapist: Have you ever felt like that?

Child: Yes, when Daddy hurt Mummy, then I didn't dare to move and only listened to what Daddy was shouting.

Therapist: Did you feel something in your body while you were in bed?

Child: I had a weird feeling in my belly; it felt like butterflies, and I was shaking all over my body. My heart said "boom."

Therapist: These bodily sensations are telling you that you are afraid. Your "fear department" *[used client's metaphor/language to connect neuroeducation]* in your brain is warning you of danger.

Child: I'm concerned about Mummy. I think she has a lot of stress. At night, when I am in my bed, I hear them arguing.

Therapist: [*Maintained regular eye contact with the child]* Mummy is also receiving help to learn how to manage her stress. And together, you and I, we are going to learn a lot of things that will help you sleep at night. We are going to teach the "fear department" in your brain, to work when it needs to and take a break when it does not.

Child: Yes! The workers are exhausted and need a break!

The child silently listened and nodded yes while his body was relaxing. I asked the child if he wanted a drink or treat. After this nourishment, he smiled at me and suggested playing a game. We played a card game together using face-to-face interaction, with a lot of eye contact and laughter to promote social engagement. During this time, we continued to explore the meaning he was making, as well as how he planned to incorporate his growing *workforce* to accomplish the things that were most important to him.

ETHICAL AND MULTICULTURAL CONSIDERATIONS

It is important to take into account that a child's response to trauma highly depends on the culture in which they grow up. Thus recognizing and understanding the cultural differences in the way children perceive and interpret their traumatic experiences is necessary. Specifically, counselors should build in culturally appropriate communication (e.g., some cultures have a sensitivity to nonverbal communication).

In addition, it is important to be aware of cultural variations in the expression of emotions and distress and how the therapist's view on healing may differ from the family's view. Be sure that the family's view on healing is integrated into therapy. Further, value each child as an individual with their own rights and respect the relationship of the child with their parents, family, and community they live in. Respect the privacy of children in how you use the gained personal information and provide information that is important for the children. The therapeutic relationship can be used for trust building and functions as a tool to restore safety in the child and family. Offer protection where necessary and optimize growth and healing through tailored therapy. Tailored therapy considers the individual circumstances, needs, developmental stage, and age of children when designing a treatment plan. Work within the family system to enhance emotional and social support. In work with children, the availability and presence of the therapist is a basic requirement for change and healing.

CLOSING THOUGHTS

The purpose of this chapter was to introduce a framework to guide your use of neuroeducation related to the ANS in your work. Although these considerations are important, it is crucial to remain flexible during the neuroeducation process. In the spirit of flexibility, the activities in this chapter showed unique ways that similar concepts were applied to clinical scenarios. As you read this chapter, you probably started to see some parallels and even carryover with other chapters. This is evidence of the beautiful interconnectedness of our nervous system. Remember the principles outlined in this chapter as you continue to think about how they apply across chapters and clinical scenarios. Before moving on to the next chapter, take a moment to reflect on the following questions:

REFLECTION QUESTIONS

1. How has your view of the ANS changed while reviewing this chapter?
2. In what ways will you incorporate these activities into your work?
3. What personal meaning has this chapter had in your life?

CREDITS

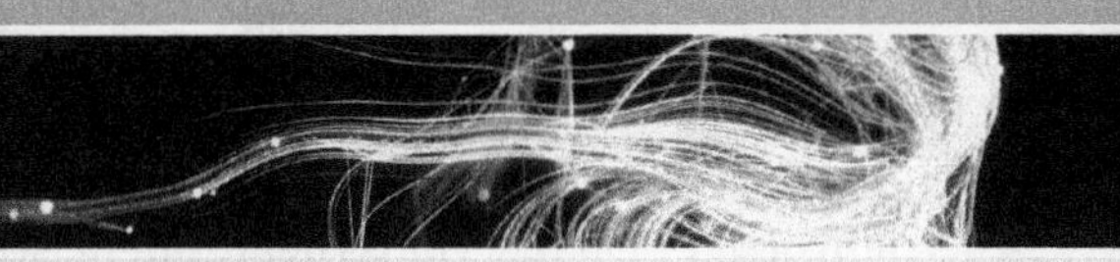

CHAPTER 6

The Embodied Brain Systems

All disease begins in the gut

—Hippocrates

> **CHAPTER OBJECTIVES**
>
> 1. Understand the key components of the microbiota-gut-brain-environment axis.
> 2. Understand the key components of body-based interventions.
> 3. Identify strategies to incorporate body-based interventions that support nervous system regulation.

INTRODUCTION

Earlier in the book, we encouraged you to complete a quick body scan, focusing on signs of sympathetic and parasympathetic nervous system activation. Now, we would like you to turn your attention back into your body and down to your stomach. How does your gut feel? Do you ever have gut instincts? Do you act on your gut? Do you ever get butterflies in your stomach? Do you ever feel heartache? Does your body tend to react with a rush of energy or hold in tension? How does activity in the mind and brain influence the body, and how does the body influence the brain and mind?

Last chapter, we talked about how the nervous system extends into the body. When people think of the "brain" and functions associated with the brain (e.g., thoughts, feelings), they often think of the skull brain. In reality, however, thoughts and feelings are often affected by systems outside of the skull brain. In this manner, the brain actually extends into the body—specifically into the heart and gut (Soosalu et al., 2019)—a phenomenon we refer to as the embodied brain. Historical debates about the connection of mind, brain, and body go back to the 17th century, when Renée Descartes (1644/1984) popularized a dualistic perspective that the mind and body are separate entities—an idea that has permeated and persisted in much of Western culture (Schore, 2012). This mindset has led to the belief that human functioning can be evaluated as all mental or all physical rather than embracing the complex interactions between body and mind.

Human functioning can also extend beyond the mind, brain, and body, encompassing the influence of social and spiritual frames of existence. Although it may still be useful at times to search and identify discrete influencers of distress, increasingly mental health-care providers are recognizing the complex interactions of body, mind, spirit, brain, and environment, which broadens the options for therapeutic intervention. Increasingly, neuroscience research is providing evidence that processes and systems below the neck (i.e., not just the "skull brain") have a significant effect on functions previously thought to reside primarily in the head. For example, we now believe that trauma memories can be stored in the body, influencing perceptions, bodily impulses, and affective states. Diet and other factors can influence the health of the gastrointestinal tract, which can then affect mood and cognitive processing. Experiences of the body (such as movement and pain) generate neurochemical reactions that influence thoughts and feelings. Ultimately, it is important for mental health professionals to understand that the body, through various streams, provides important information to the skull brain that then influences mental activity (and vice versa). This information-sharing loop is not generally experienced in conscious awareness, and yet it often guides and directs important aspects of mental life.

EVIDENCE FOR MIND-BRAIN-BODY-ENVIRONMENT CONNECTIONS

Despite tendencies to reduce human functioning into a mind-body duality, the nature of human functioning is increasingly understood as complex and integrated. Recent research paradigms give evidence for this trend. The National Institute of Mental Health and its Research Domain Criteria (NIMH, n.d.) provide a research framework that focuses on the full spectrum of the human experience, from the pathological to the well, which is measured across seven units of analysis: (1) genes, (2) molecules, (3) cells, (4) circuits, (5) physiology, (6) behavior, and (7) self-report and incorporates developmental and environmental influences (Beeson et al., 2019). This integrated approach shows a clear connection between the internal and external world, as well as the interconnectedness of mind, brain, and body across several levels.

The Greek physician Hippocrates is credited with a more specific and direct statement about this integration and its influence on pathology: "All disease begins in the gut" (Sandoval-Motta et al., 2017). Research focusing on the microbiota-gut-brain axis has exploded over the past decade. Although much of this research has been conducted on animals, some human studies have been conducted, and initial evidence suggests a significant influence of the microbiota-gut-brain axis in neurodevelopment, behavior, cognition, and disease progression (e.g., Borre et al., 2014; Chrobak et al., 2016; Desbonnet et al., 2014; Foster et al., 2016; Herpertz-Dahlmann et al., 2017; Liang et al., 2018a; Liang et al., 2018b; Lyon, 2018; Mayer, 2011; Oana et al., 2018; Ochoa-Repáraz & Kasper, 2018; Parashar & Udayabanu, 2016; Vuong et al., 2017). The "axis" nomenclature itself demonstrates the interconnectedness of various systems, structures, and functions in human beings. Liang et al. (2018b) provide a comprehensive review of the existing body of literature related to the microbiota-gut-brain axis and advocate for gut-brain psychology, a discipline focusing on the relationship between the mind and the gut brain.

At a macrolevel, human beings are a collective superorganism composed of many microorganisms (Liang et al., 2018a; Liang et al., 2018b). The microbiome is "the ecological community of commensal, symbiotic, and pathogenic microoganisms" (Ochoa-Repáraz & Kasper, 2018, p. 1). At a microlevel, specific organs have specific microbiota (e.g., bacteria, viruses, fungi), and the intestinal or gut microbiota are considered the most important given that they outnumber the total number of human cells by 10:1 (Sandoval-Motta et al., 2017). The gut, sometimes referred to as the second brain (Gershon, 1998) or gut brain, includes a somewhat independent nervous system, the enteric nervous system, which is connected to the brain and helps regulate neurotransmission, behavior, and cognition similar to the way the skull brain does. This brain-gut axis describes the bidirectional communication network between the brain and the gut that takes place via various nerve (e.g., neurotransmission), endocrine (e.g., hypothalamus pituitary adrenal [HPA] axis), and immune pathways (e.g., inflammation) (Liang et al., 2018a; Liang et al., 2018b). The gut microbiota creates the foundation for the functioning of the gut-brain axis that completes the integrated microbiota-gut-brain axis that has been shown to influence brain development, emotion, cognition, and behavior leading to optimal health or mental disorders (Liang et al., 2018a; Liang et al., 2018b). In an attempt to synthesize this literature, let's take a look at Figure 6.1.

Beginning in utero, the gut microbiota starts developing and is influenced by prenatal care and genetics. The gut microbiota continues to develop across the life span, alongside the rest of the nervous system. The gut microbiota is influenced by a number of factors, including delivery method (e.g., cesarean section vs. vaginal birth), diet (e.g., high fiber vs. meats), lifestyle (e.g., working indoors vs. outdoors), health care and hygiene (e.g., oversterilization), other environmental exposures and newer therapeutic interventions (e.g.,

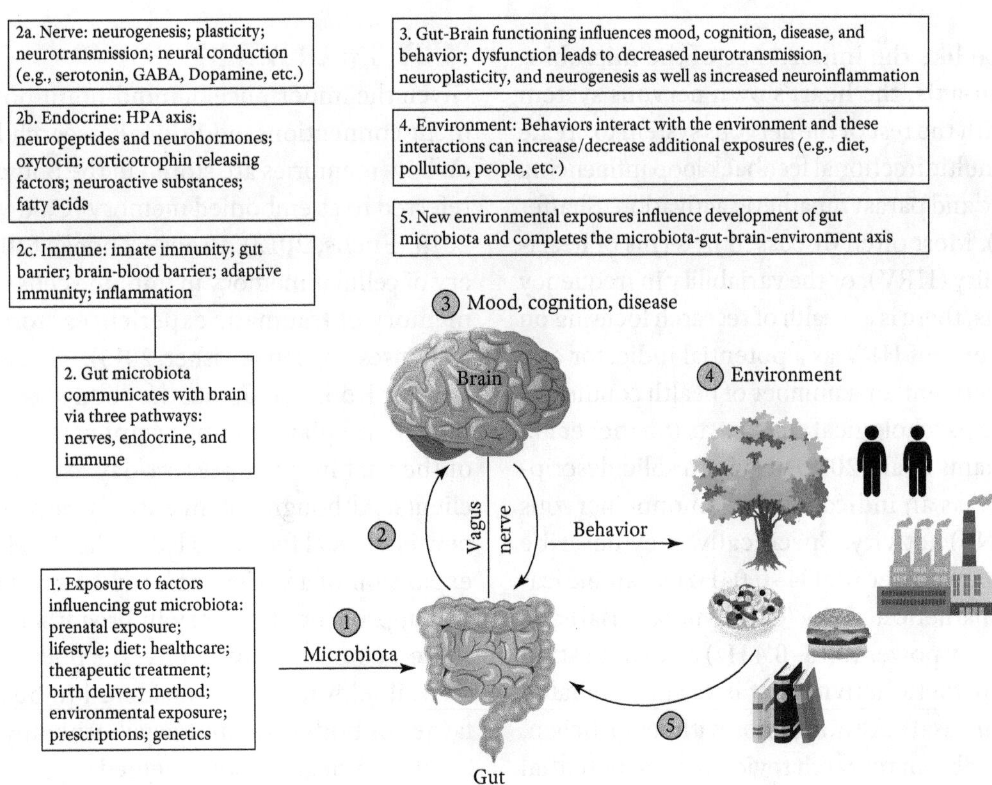
2a. Nerve: neurogenesis; plasticity; neurotransmission; neural conduction (e.g., serotonin, GABA, Dopamine, etc.)
2b. Endocrine: HPA axis; neuropeptides and neurohormones; oxytocin; corticotrophin releasing factors; neuroactive substances; fatty acids
2c. Immune: innate immunity; gut barrier; brain-blood barrier; adaptive immunity; inflammation
3. Gut-Brain functioning influences mood, cognition, disease, and behavior; dysfunction leads to decreased neurotransmission, neuroplasticity, and neurogenesis as well as increased neuroinflammation
4. Environment: Behaviors interact with the environment and these interactions can increase/decrease additional exposures (e.g., diet, pollution, people, etc.)
5. New environmental exposures influence development of gut microbiota and completes the microbiota-gut-brain-environment axis
2. Gut microbiota communicates with brain via three pathways: nerves, endocrine, and immune
1. Exposure to factors influencing gut microbiota: prenatal exposure; lifestyle; diet; healthcare; therapeutic treatment; birth delivery method; environmental exposure; prescriptions; genetics
3 Mood, cognition, disease
Brain
4 Environment
2
Vagus nerve
Behavior
1
Microbiota
5
Gut

FIGURE 6.1 Pathways in the Microbiota-Gut-Brain-Environment Axis

fecal microbiota transplantation). This composition of gut microbiota influences the functioning of the gut-brain axis via three pathways: (1) nerves (neurogenesis, neurotransmission, and neural conduction), (2) endocrine (neuroendocrine, neuropeptides, neurohormones, and neuroactive substances), and (3) immune (permeability in the gut and blood-brain barrier, innate immunity, and inflammation). If balanced, then these pathways communicate to the brain and the brain back to the gut to improve neurogenesis, neuroplasticity, mood, and cognition and promote prosocial behavioral interaction with the environment. If there is dysfunction in the microbiota, then this could lead to increased inflammation and neurodegeneration, as well as pervasive stress-responsive behaviors in the environment (e.g., fight/flight/freeze). This interaction with the environment creates a complete cycle of mind-brain-body-environment connection. It is important to remember that this cycle is multidirectional, and changes in one can influence change in another.

An understanding of the microbiota-gut-brain axis is only as important as the guidance it provides to treatment. Liang et al. (2018b) review several microbiota interventions that show promise for human intervention, including fecal microbiota transplantation, probiotics, prebiotics, and diet. Although the body of literature is relatively new and promulgated with animal models, the initial findings and innovative translations provide optimism for another potential mechanism of disease and wellness progression. Although we don't know which comes first—does the microbiota cause the brain disorder or does the brain disorder cause the microbiota dysfunction—the complex intricacies in the microbiota-gut-brain axis provide interesting options for alternative interventions for a myriad of mental disorders and other medical conditions. Neuroeducation focusing on this axis could provide an alternative conceptualization of the client's experience that motivates therapeutic lifestyle changes.

Moving up from the gut, another "little brain" (Armour, 2008, p. 165) has been said to exist on the heart, further elucidating the idea of an embodied brain. Much like the importance of the microbiota-gut-brain-axis, the heart's own nervous system connects with the rest of the nervous system to create a complex multidirectional feedback loop influencing sympathetic and parasympathetic activation (Shaffer et al., 2014). Most often discussed in terms of heart-rate variability (HRV), or the variability in frequency of heartbeats, there is a wealth of research focusing on the importance of HRV as a potential indicator and target of treatment for a number of health conditions and positive psychological constructs (Shaffer et al., 2014). Williams et al. (2019) provide a solid description of HRV as an indicator of autonomic nervous system (ANS) activity. Specifically, they describe low frequency power (0.004–0.04Hz) as an indication of sympathetic activity (e.g., hyperarousal) and high frequency power (0.15–0.4 Hz) as an indication of parasympathetic activity that is vagally mediated (e.g., hypoarousal). Although not without criticism, there is a wealth of research reviewing the potential of HRV both as a marker for various conditions and a target for intervention (e.g., Faurholt-Jepsen et al., 2017). As the research continues to evolve, the heart's "little brain," as well as the heart-brain axis, continues to justify the need for a more comprehensive view of the brain that extends from the skull into the rest of the body (see Figure 6.2).

BODY-BASED INTERVENTIONS

Given the importance of mind-brain-body-environment connections, additional research has focused on how memories are stored in the body, commonly referred to as embodied memory (Caldwell & Koch, 2018; Fuchs, 2012). From Kandel's (2006) discovery of cellular memory in immune cells to embodied memory of traumatic experiences stored as bodily responses (Ogden & Fisher, 2015), it is clear, as Bessel Van der Kolk stated, that the "body keeps the score" (2014) and plays an important role in the seepage of the past into the present-day experiences of our clients. Although not an entirely new concept, this new empirical focus has led to the development and expansion of a variety of body-based interventions and approaches that vary in breadth and scope but share a common philosophy: the body comes first.

Wilhelm Reich is considered to be the "grandfather of body-oriented psychotherapy" (Fernald, 2000). The field of body-oriented psychotherapy, also commonly referred to as somatic psychotherapy, has evolved to include the creation of two professional associations: the European Association for Body Psychotherapy (EABP), http://www.eabp.org/, and the United States Association for Body Psychotherapy (USABP), https://usabp.org/. The EABP published competencies to guide the practice of body

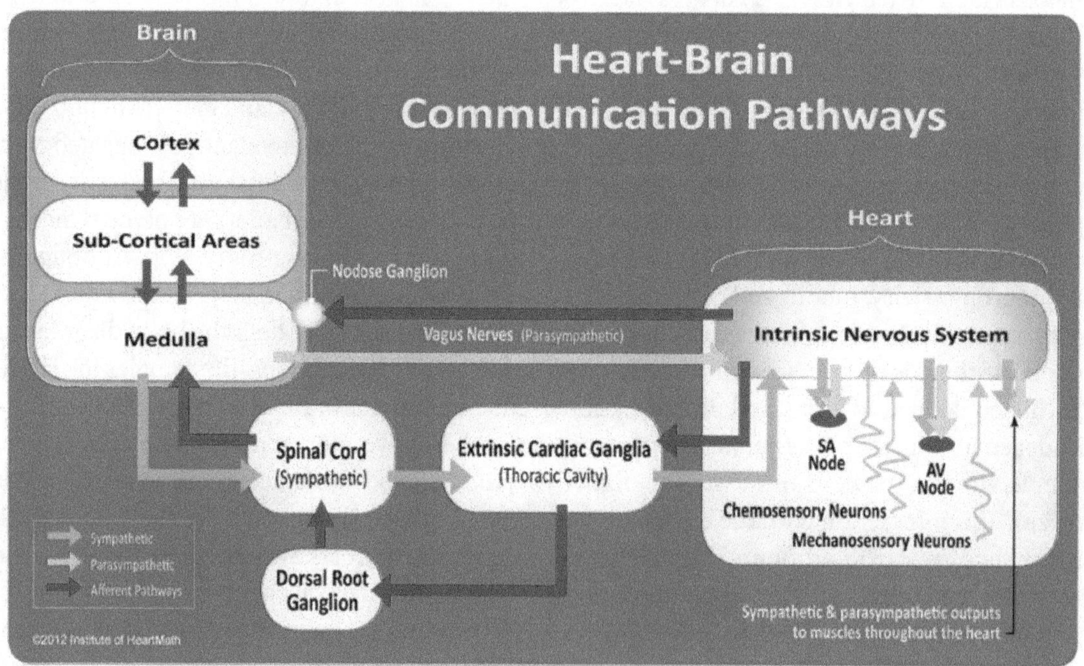

FIGURE 6.2 Heart-Brain Communication Pathways

psychotherapy, defined as a "distinct branch of psychotherapy, with roots in psychoanalysis and the work of Wilhelm Reich specifically" (Boening et al., 2012, p. 4). These competencies do well to separate body psychotherapy from other body-based approaches (e.g., craniosacral therapy) given the emphasis on psychological factors and the effect of unconscious drives and the therapeutic relationship.

Although there are many forms and degrees of body-based interventions, we will use this term broadly to describe a family of approaches that focus on the primacy of somatic experiences as a precursor to verbal interventions traditional in talk therapy. Although a complete review of this family is outside of the scope of this book, we will discuss a few approaches as an example of how somatic interventions can be incorporated into counseling and psychotherapy that will serve as a preface to the neuroeducation activities in this chapter.

Caldwell and Koch (2018) describe the Moving Cycle approach to body-oriented psychotherapy that capitalizes on the playing out of embodied cognition first, prior to creating verbal meaning of the body experience. The Moving Cycle includes a four-step process: (1) awareness of the tendency for the body to react in certain ways while suspending judgment of those actions, (2) connecting this "physical free association" (p. 247) to the themes in psychotherapy that are being attended to, (3) appreciating the past and moving through the embodied memory into the present, and (4) taking action to rehearse the bodily reactions that are desired in future relationships and situations. In essence, the body talks through the experience first and then the cognitive, perceptual dimension makes meaning of that experience.

Sensorimotor psychotherapy (SP) "is a body inclusive approach advancing the notion that beneath conscious verbal narratives lies a rich somatic narrative ripe with information to guide solutions for resolving both the present moment experiences of dysregulation and the historical origins of current challenges" (Lohrasbe & Ogden, 2017, p. 575). Created by Pat Ogden and many colleagues (e.g., Ogden et al., 2006) over the past 2 decades, SP is grounded in various theories of attachment and its relation to arousal dysregulation throughout the ANS. Grounded in the modulation model (Ogden et al., 2006), SP uses the window of tolerance (Siegel, 1999) to explore the optimal zone of functioning between hyper- and hypoarousal. SP focuses on the need to regulate the arousal first through somatic resourcing (e.g., sensual experiencing, breathing, reducing heart rate, eye gaze, movement, touch) and the creation of embodied agency, before verbal processing. They even discuss that anchoring any stimulus, such as music, in physical experience through the five senses can create an embodied regulation that is a precursor for any verbal processing.

Somatic experiencing (SE), created by Peter Levine (2010), is a body-based therapy that posits the inner physical experiences are carriers of traumatic memory. SE aims to create awareness, invite the physical discharge through tolerance of traumatic energy that was incomplete during the initial traumatic events, and monitor and downregulate through positive memories, self-regulation, and pleasant sensations. SE has produced large effect sizes in at least one randomized control trial (Brom et al., 2017).

Although there are many other approaches that incorporate various degrees of physical movement, we hope this sampling provides a glimpse into the common thread of emerging neuroscience in psychotherapy that expands the view of the mind and brain into a complex interaction throughout the body, extending into the environment so that it is hard to separate one from the other. Even though the literature and some of the activities in this chapter will refer to multiple "brains," it is essential to remember that the nervous system is highly integrated. Some individuals might say the brain and body are two parts of one whole and, even further, that the brain, body, mind, and environment are multiple parts of one larger ecosystem influencing human experiences.

NEUROEDUCATION ACTIVITIES

The entries in this chapter demonstrate how several clinicians infuse the complex interrelationships of mind-brain-body-environment into the neuroeducation process. You will see seven activities that help clients increase their focus on body awareness, find relief and liberation from their chronic pain, use movement and exercise to self-regulate and enhance the therapeutic connection, and even use their bodies to aid in career decisions.

REVEALING THE HIDDEN

Imaginal Exposure and Neurophysiological Activation

Thomas A. Field

As an organ, the brain is intricately connected to the body (Kandel et al., 2012). Brain activity is often associated with physiological activity, and vice versa. We sometimes forget this connection in mental health and have detached the brain from the body. This disconnection is evident in models of mental illness that focus entirely on brain function and in neuroscience literature that tends to narrowly focus on isolating brain regions associated with functions such as visual perception (parietal lobe of cortex) or threat detection (amygdala in subcortex). This tendency to distinguish the functions of the brain from the body is also evident in counseling and psychotherapy practices that tend to emphasize the importance of changing rational conscious cognitions while neglecting associated physiological activation.

Historically, this brain-body divide stems from a European philosophy known as dualism. This branch of philosophy was especially connected with the 17th-century philosopher René Descartes who associated self-identity with the mind alone (rather than mind-body). In his book *The Biological Mind* (2018), Alan Jasanoff theorized that this ongoing dualistic divide between brain and body has been perpetuated by the *cerebral mystique*, a term used for explaining our fascination with the brain. Jasanoff (2018) criticized our naïve hope that human behavior can be understood through our knowledge of the brain, thus the reason we place such emphasis on brain function. Jasanoff argued that while it is useful to understand the varying functions of the brain, it is crucial to remember that regions of the brain work in concert with other regions and work in concert with different parts of the body. For example, the hypothalamus and the pituitary gland send messages to the adrenal cortex and medulla to release corticotropic hormones associated with the stress response. When cortisol is overproduced, it can cause inflammatory responses in the enteric nervous system (i.e., the gut). If cortisol is thus secreted at a chronically high level, it results in chronic inflammation. During chronic inflammation, proinflammatory cytokines are eventually overproduced. This process then affects the central nervous system, as cytokines can cross the blood-brain barrier, where they overstimulate and degrade neurons in the brain. Reducing the stress response can therefore have an eventual effect on protecting brain function. To summarize, the brain does not function in isolation.

Individuals often have gaps in knowledge about the interrelationship between the brain and body. For example, clients are often perplexed at why their physical health is affected by stress. They often do not have a basic understanding of the functioning of the autonomic division of the peripheral nervous system and its effect on neurophysiological activation during threat detection and stress response (Kandel et al., 2012). Further, some clients may want simplified conceptualizations of their mental disorders as forms of brain disorder alone (e.g., neurotransmitter deficits) and wonder why a medication cannot fully treat a complex neurophysiological condition, such as traumatic stress. For these reasons, it can be useful to help individuals explore the interdependent relationship between the brain and body.

In the *Revealing the Hidden* activity, I specifically use interoceptive exposure to help participants connect the importance of brain and body functioning through a felt sense experience. Interoceptive exposure has been proposed as a transdiagnostic intervention and change strategy that helps to reduce anxiety, helps clients understand and develop

MATERIALS NEEDED

No materials are needed for this activity.

acceptance of physiological symptoms (Boswell et al., 2013), and has been piloted with post-traumatic stress symptoms (Wald & Taylor, 2007).

PROCESS OF THE ACTIVITY

The *Revealing the Hidden* activity can be used in an individual or group setting. As a caution, this activity can be triggering for some people, and clinical judgment must be exercised to maintain safety. The activity asks participants to consider sharing a private secret with others, which commonly includes experiences of trauma. I recommend giving a trigger warning before the activity to grant participants full autonomy in whether to participate.

Step 1: Introducing the Activity

Begin the activity by explaining to participants that the following exercise has the objective of helping people experience the connection between the brain and body. Share that the activity might bring up emotional responses and discomfort. Allow participants to choose whether to participate or even to leave the room if they would prefer.

Step 2: Interoceptive Exposure Prompts

After giving a pause, ask participants to close their eyes and pay attention to sensations in their bodies. Ask participants to continue this awareness during and after the ensuing prompt. Pause again and ask participants to imagine telling the person next to them a personal secret, something they have not told many people before or perhaps have never told anyone else before. Prompt participants again to notice sensations in their bodies. Pause for 15–20 seconds and then ask participants to open their eyes and come back to the present moment. In my clinical experience, the cue of imagining talking to a peer about a deeply held secret often engenders a physiological response labeled as fear and shame.

Step 3: Processing the Experience

After the exercise has ended, process participants' experiences. First, acknowledge that this was a challenging exercise for some people and express gratitude for participants' willingness and courage to try out the exercise. Next, provide support and relief to participants by explaining that they will not actually be required to share the personal secret with the person next to them, as the exercise was a mere simulation. Here is an example of how to acknowledge and clarify the exercise:

> Before we process what came up for you, I want to first acknowledge that this can be a difficult exercise for some people. I respect your courage to try out the exercise. The exercise is a simulation, and you will not be asked to actually share the secret you were considering earlier.

Second, ask for volunteers to share what they noticed happening in their bodies. After each response, reflect back what the participant has said to demonstrate that you value their sharing and understand their experience (to some extent). Continue until everyone who wants to share has had an opportunity to do so. It is not unusual for participants to have a variety of responses to the exercise. Some participants will experience visceral sympathetic activation (i.e., stress response) such as sweating, heart racing, inhibited gut functioning (e.g., "butterflies" in the stomach), and muscle tension, among others. I typically provide a brief statement that helps participants understand these responses (e.g., "For some of us, our brains detected threat, and our bodies responded accordingly to prepare for action to mitigate the threat."). Others will share cognitive processes, such as wanting to ignore or avoid the prompt or noticing they are more comfortable with revealing information than they had imagined they would be. Still others will share emotional responses, such as feelings of anger.

Step 4: Review Major Takeaways

At the conclusion of processing with the group, review the major findings of the exercise. Generally, you will find that individuals share their experiences of physiological arousal from being given a

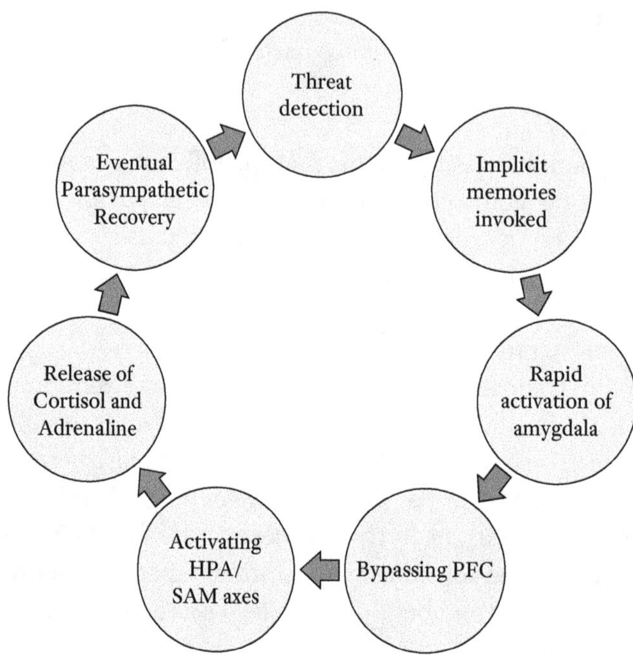

FIGURE 6.3 Brain-Body Stress Response to Threat Detection

challenging cognitive task. Emphasize that the brain and body are deeply interconnected. During this phase, a graphic can be helpful for describing the related functioning of the brain and body during threat detection. See Figure 6.3 for an example image that I use.

During my explanation of parasympathetic recovery, I often introduce the importance of diaphragmatic breathing to assist clients with returning to a homeostatic baseline after sympathetic activation and may include a brief training on a diaphragmatic breathing model (e.g., four-square deep breathing). I quick internet search will provide various resources on four-square deep breathing and other breathwork that you can evaluate for use with this activity. I typically also add that clients experience the same reactions when asked to reveal deeply personal information to their counselors. This often gives clients a window for understanding why it can be challenging to self-disclose deeply held secrets with their counselors because of marked physiological responses and feelings of shame associated with closely held secrets. Lastly, and perhaps most important, I share with clients that such activation in response to threat is normal, to be expected (i.e., predictable), and that they need not experience secondary shame regarding their bodies' response to disclosing a secret associated with shame and embarrassment.

FOLLOW-UP

General questions can be used to inquire about the usefulness of the activity within the context of each individual's concerns and treatment process. Examples of such questions include the following:

"How does this exercise relate to your experiences in life?" Or, "What sense do you make of this information?" In future sessions, you can refer back to the exercise with a shared vocabulary to interpret and discuss ongoing client concerns.

NEUROSCIENCE IN ACTION

During a group counseling session, I introduced and facilitated the *Revealing the Hidden* activity with a group of adolescents. The group topic was the role of shame in the treatment of post-traumatic stress. The activity was geared toward helping participants become aware of the importance of brain-body connectivity as a step toward understanding why some adolescents can have difficulties with disclosure in interpersonal situations. During the exercise, I mentioned that adolescents experience the physiological manifestations of emotions, such as shame, which can prompt action. In the case of shame, people tend to shut down and avoid interpersonal contact as a means of self-protection from potential rejection. The underlying cognition here is typically "if people found out what happened to me, they would reject me." The adolescents responded well to the exercise and shared vulnerable emotions, such as feeling scared, paranoid, and yet open to the experience. We normalized these feelings and helped each other understand that such responses were normal and expected. I then introduced some breathing techniques for parasympathetic recovery. The group session closed on a positive note, and future sessions revealed the clients' ability to notice their tendency to self-protect with appreciation rather than shame; they affirmed this appreciation came from knowing the physiological reasons for this reaction.

ETHICAL AND MULTICULTURAL CONSIDERATIONS

Because this activity is likely to generate some degree of physiological activation for participants and could be potentially upsetting, providing a trigger warning beforehand seems important. Participants should be aware of the potential for upset and be reminded of their ability to make an autonomous choice about whether to participate in the activity. From a multicultural perspective, it is likely that participants from some cultures will be more familiar with the connection between the brain and body. Exploring how cultural background informs their degree of connection between mind-body can be a valuable experience in itself.

LIBERATING PEOPLE IN PAIN WITH PAIN NEUROSCIENCE EDUCATION

Adriaan Louw and Jessie Podolak

Pain is a normal human experience, and without the ability to experience pain, people would not survive (Gifford, 2014; Moseley, 2007). Living in constant pain, however, is not normal (Butler & Moseley, 2003; McMahon & Koltzenburg, 2005). Approximately 25.3 million adults in the United States are suffering from daily chronic pain, and of those, 10.5 million individuals state they have a lot of pain every day (Institute of Medicine, 2011). For people living in pain, it is common to experience profound alterations in day-to-day function, quality of life, mood, social connection, community involvement, and financial security (Smith et al., 2001).

Understandably, people in pain seek relief. Medication is a common method of treatment. Americans, constituting only 5% of the world's population, consume 80% of the global opioid supply and 99% of the global hydrocodone supply (Manchikanti et al., 2010), and the Centers for Disease Control reports that prescription opioids cause 3 times more annual fatalities than heroin and cocaine combined (Patrick et al., 2016). In addition to medication, other common interventions offered to patients in pain include injections, surgeries, passive modalities and a host of alternative therapies, such as acupuncture, chiropractic care, and nutritional supplements. Patients often get stuck in endless quests for explanations and solutions to their pain. A cycle of hypermedicalization, excessive health-care utilization, and patient disability, depression, and dissatisfaction ultimately result in more pain (Vlaeyen et al., 2016).

One emerging strategy to help people experience less pain and disability is to educate patients on the biology and physiology of their pain experience (Moseley, 2002). This intervention is called pain neuroscience education (PNE; Louw et al., 2011; Moseley et al., 2004; Nijs & Van Houdenhove, 2009). Traditional patient education related to pain relies on various anatomical, biomechanical, or pathoanatomical models to help people in pain understand why they hurt (Louw & Butler, 2011; Nijs et al., 2013). These models tend to connect the health of tissues to pain, yet it is well documented that the health of tissues and pain do not necessarily correlate (Haldeman, 1990; Kjaer et al., 2005; Spielmann et al., 1999).

To examine this idea further, consider Figure 6.4, which depicts three different scenarios: First (6.4a), the traditional model that equates the health of tissue with pain is shown. The more the tissue is affected, the more pain is experienced. Although this process does certainly occur (i.e., often a grade I ankle sprain hurts a little bit, while a grade III ankle sprain hurts a great deal), it is also well documented that there are many different situations in which people have significant issues with their tissue, yet experience little to no pain (Figure 6.4b). Commercial fishermen, farmers, rodeo clowns, cowboys, and demolition derby drivers all sustain tissue injury with subsequent "damage," yet often report little or no pain. Lastly, many patients present with significant pain, yet they recall no specific injury, and many of their medical tests and imaging studies fail to find any significant tissue issues (Figure 6.4c). This scenario includes patients with diagnostic labels of fibromyalgia, low back pain, chronic fatigue syndrome, complex regional pain syndrome, etc. *In short, a person can have pain that is proportionate to the amount of tissue pathology/injury present, but they can also have severe pain with no injury/damage, and they can have zero pain but have significant tissue pathology. Injured tissue doesn't have to hurt; conversely, you don't need damaged tissue to suffer from pain.*

Another example of the tissue damage/pain discrepancy is as follows: 40% of individuals over the age of 40 demonstrate disc bulges in the lumbar spine on magnetic resonance imaging (MRI) scans, yet report no pain or disability (Kjaer et al., 2005). Clearly, injured tissue doesn't have to hurt, but traditional models suggest otherwise. Traditional models also fall short of being able to

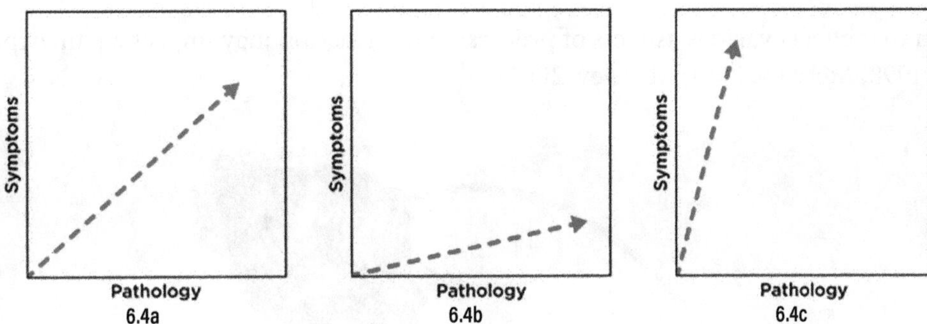

FIGURE 6.4 The Dichotomy of Tissue Health and a Pain Experience. Adapted from Haldeman (1990). Pathology = Actual Tissue Damage; Symptoms = Reported Pain

explain persistent pain, spreading pain, allodynia, pain in absence of injury or disease, immune responses, or stress biology (Moseley, 2007). Furthermore, these commonly used biomedical models have been associated with inducing fear, anxiety, and faulty beliefs, which all contribute to an increased pain experience (Louw et al., 2014; Sloan & Walsh, 2010).

In contrast to traditional models, PNE is an educational strategy used by health-care providers that focuses on teaching people in pain more about the biological and physiological processes involved in their pain experience (Meeus et al., 2010; Moseley, 2002; Moseley et al., 2004). PNE helps demystify the pain/tissue-problem dichotomy and helps patients understand that tissue injury and pain are not synonymous and that because of neuroplasticity, human beings have the potential to feel, move, and function better, even in the presence of less-than-perfect tissue (Louw et al., 2016). PNE fosters hope.

HISTORY AND EVIDENCE

One of the first documented uses of neuroscience education for pain came from zoologist turned physical therapist Louis Gifford at the International Association on the Study of Pain conference in Austria in 1999 (Gifford & Muncey, 1999). Gifford suggested that people in pain are interested in learning more about pain versus learning about anatomy. Gifford proposed the mature organism model, which describes pain in terms of input processes, processing issues, and output mechanisms (Figure 6.5; Gifford, 1998). For example, injury to tissue (i.e., motor vehicle collision) occurs, but this is only one aspect of the pain experience. This tissue damage occurs in an environment, which may further modulate the pain experience (i.e., increased stress, fear, and anxiety). This information/input (tissue injury and environmental factors), however, needs to be processed and interpreted by the brain. For this process to occur, our various senses, including a network of sensory nerves, send information to the spinal cord with the intent of informing the brain. It is now well understood that various peripheral and central nervous system processes further influence the pain experience, including ion channel expression, immune responses, neuroplastic changes in the dorsal horn, central endogenous mechanisms, and so forth. At this point, the tissue and environmental information, once again, are subject to various peripheral and central nervous system processes that may increase or decrease the pain experience (i.e., neural facilitation and inhibition, respectively). All this information is then processed by the brain (pain neuromatrix). The information about the motor vehicle collision is then further influenced by various personal and past experiences. Ultimately, the brain assesses the level of threat, and if enough threat is perceived, a response is warranted. Responses include pain, motor control, changes in immune and endocrine function, and so forth. In essence, pain is an output (response) of the brain, occurring after the brain has interpreted the information available to it and concluded that the present threat warrants action to protect the individual. It is thus argued that if pain is an output of the brain, then education that affects various aspects of processing information may impact a pain experience (Gifford, 1998; Melzack, 2001; Moseley, 2007).

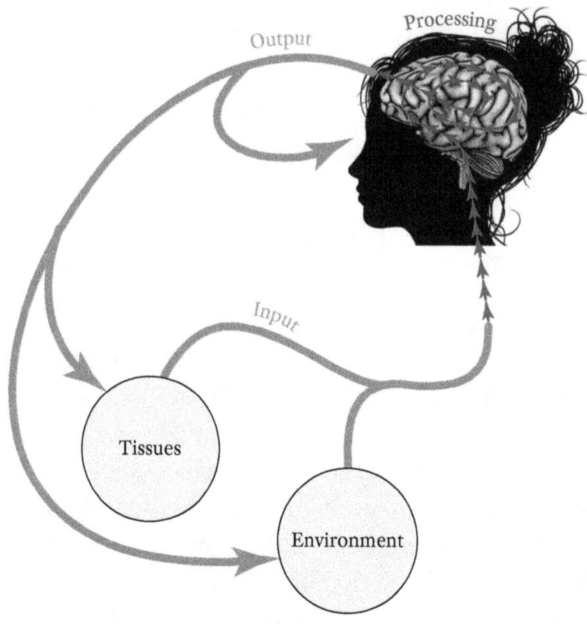

FIGURE 6.5 The Mature Organism Model. Adapted From Gifford (1998)

Since 1999 and subsequently through the evidence-based medicine revolution, various scientists have explored the efficacy of PNE, culminating in a number of randomized controlled trials and systematic reviews (Louw et al., 2011; Louw et al., 2014; Meeus et al., 2010; Moseley, 2002; Moseley, 2004; Moseley et al., 2004; Ryan et al., 2010; Van Oosterwijck et al., 2011). Current evidence provides strong support for PNE to positively influence pain ratings, dysfunctions, fear avoidance, pain catastrophization, limitations in movement, pain knowledge and health-care utilization (Louw et al., 2011; Louw et al., 2016). Evidence suggests that when implementing PNE, the numbers needed to treat (NNT) for improving pain are 3:1 and 2:1 for improving function (Moseley, 2002). In contrast, the current "gold-standard" medication for pain (membrane stabilizers and/or antidepressants) has an NNT of 7:1 (Moore et al., 2011; Moore et al., 2015). This means that treatment with PNE would require treatment of only two to three patients to prevent an undesirable outcome, whereas the "gold-standard" pain medication would require treatment of seven patients to prevent an undesirable outcome.

FOUNDATIONAL CONCEPTS

There are several biological, physiological, and psychological foundational concepts that deserve attention when describing PNE: the pain neuromatrix, central sensitization and hyperalgesia, and biopsychosocial influences on sensitization (Louw et al., 2018).

Pain Neuromatrix

World-renowned researcher and psychologist Ronald Melzack, PhD, proposed the neuromatrix as a theoretical framework by which to understand the production of pain in the late 1990s (Melzack, 2001). Melzack's theory suggested that multiple parts of the brain and spinal cord work together in response to input from the body and/or the environment to create a pain experience (Melzack,

2001). The emergence of the functional MRI has subsequently allowed researchers to observe brain activity in patients experiencing pain, and indeed, a characteristic pattern has emerged in which multiple areas of the brain engage to process sensory input (Flor, 2000). These areas of the brain, including the premotor/motor cortex, cingulate cortex, prefrontal cortex, amygdala, sensory cortex, hypothalamus/thalamus, cerebellum, hippocampus, and brain stem, are not specifically designated as "pain centers." Rather, the brain employs these areas, which have their own unique functions, to analyze the input to determine the level of danger and necessity of pain to protect an individual from threat (Flor, 2000; Melzack, 2001). The "neuromatrix of pain" offers a reasonable explanation for why individuals experiencing chronic pain often find themselves with impairments in many areas of life, such as memory loss, decreased coordination, lack of motivation, struggles with problem-solving skills, and problems with focus, concentration, and autonomic regulation (Louw et al., 2018). These and other areas are "enslaved" by the pain experience, rendering them unable to perform their usual functions at normal capacity.

Central Sensitization

Central sensitization is another cornerstone of PNE. Central sensitization is the process by which injuries in the periphery can lead to neuroplastic and immune changes in the spinal cord and brain, culminating in ongoing symptoms, even after the initial tissue insult or injury has healed (Nijs et al., 2011; Nijs et al., 2013). The chronification of symptoms involves a shift in processing patterns centrally through mechanisms such as cell death in the dorsal horn of the spinal cord, loss of inhibition via endogenous mechanisms, and cortical reorganization in the brain itself (Woolf, 2011). The immune system is highly involved in this process, with glial cells and inflammatory chemicals contributing to changes in the blood-brain and blood-spinal-cord barriers, which pave the way for sensitization (Beggs et al., 2010). In addition to persistent pain long after the normal tissue healing time frame has passed, many non-injury-specific painful conditions, such as fibromyalgia, nonspecific chronic low back pain, chronic fatigue syndrome, and irritable bowel syndrome, demonstrate features of central sensitization and respond favorably to PNE (Louw et al., 2016).

Biopsychosocial Influences

Lastly, biopsychosocial influences on sensitization should be considered in relation to delivering PNE. The environment plays a key role in the pain experience, and it is estimated that injuries occurring in a stressful environment are far more likely to develop into chronic pain conditions (Sterling et al., 2006; Walton et al., 2009). Frequent stressors in a patient's environment, regardless of the intensity of the stressor, yield accompanying biochemical stress responses, including the activation of the sympathetic nervous system and, ultimately, the release of adrenaline and cortisol. Corticotropic hormones, which are key in mobilizing energy stores for repeated or perpetual "fight, flight, or freeze," render tissues themselves sore, achy, fatigued, and sensitive, thereby contributing to chronic pain (Louw et al., 2018). In addition, cortisol has multiple undesirable effects on brain health, including mood changes, impaired memory, focus, and motivation. All the consequences of stress affect the pain experience and can be addressed via PNE as practitioners help patients see the connection between stress and pain and guide patients through various activities that promote autonomic regulation and relaxation responses.

MATERIALS NEEDED

- Dry erase board and markers can often be implemented, allowing the clinician to draw a sensitive alarm, for example
- Pen and paper
- Prepared booklets and patient workbooks
- There are other products on the market, such as full-color cards and electronic slide presentations, which depict several metaphors and stories, enhancing patient learning
- Many clinicians also make their own workbooks using three-ring binders, pictures, and drawings they have found helpful throughout their ongoing education regarding pain science

PROCESS OF THE ACTIVITY

The PNE process requires an empathetic and attentive health-care practitioner with a deep understanding of the neuroscience of pain. Although patients may only need to know "the tip of the iceberg" when it comes to concepts such as cortical reorganization or hyperalgesia, clinicians must understand the underlying mechanisms and be prepared to answer questions, offer multiple explanations for concepts, and apply pain knowledge to an individual's unique clinical presentation (Louw et al., 2018). Topics covered in PNE typically include complex biological issues, such as ion channel expression, inhibition and facilitation, hyperalgesia, and endogenous analgesia (Louw et al., 2013). However, these concepts are presented to patients in easily understandable formats, using metaphors, stories, analogies, and drawn images, with care taken during explanations to provide a safe and optimistic tone (Louw et al., 2016). A clinician's words and ability to connect with their patients are foundations in the PNE toolbox, but other tools are employed as well. As noted earlier, supplies used often include a whiteboard and markers for hand drawings, prepared pictures or workbooks, and computer or tablet applications for interactive visual aids to promote learning (Louw et al., 2016).

PNE is typically delivered in a one-on-one educational format, although there is emerging evidence for its application in groups and via telehealth (Louw, 2014; Moseley, 2003). The intervention is most often implemented for patients who have diagnoses of chronic pain (i.e., central sensitization/nociplastic pain) for which traditional techniques have proven ineffective (Louw et al., 2016). PNE may have limited efficacy for people who have difficulty learning new concepts, such as those with cognitive deficits, brain injuries, or dementia. Other challenges include language and cultural barriers, which may limit the ability of the clinician to communicate the message accurately. However, it has been shown that students as young as fifth grade can learn many of the key concepts taught in PNE (Louw, Podolak et al., 2018), and some of the principles of PNE transcend most barriers, such as the importance of the therapeutic alliance, trust, and hope.

In physical therapy, for example, PNE is typically initiated once a skillful interview and thorough physical examination have been completed and the practicing clinician is confident that the pain the patient is experiencing is not indicative of any sinister underlying disease state (i.e., red flags have been ruled out). For example, the patient does not fall into risk categories regarding their age, prior history of cancer, family history, nor unexplained significant weight loss, the presence of which would necessitate a referral to the physician to rule out malignancy. If adequate time is available, PNE can be delivered at the patient's first visit or in subsequent visits (Louw et al., 2016). Clinicians often explain one facet of pain on the first visit and then delve more deeply into other aspects of pain in subsequent visits, parceling and pacing the education to avoid overwhelming a patient with too much information at one time (Louw et al., 2016).

Skilled providers of PNE involve the patient in the educational process, asking frequent questions to confirm understanding and engagement (i.e., "Does this make sense?" Or, "How do you see your pain in light of what we just talked about?"). Concepts of motivational interviewing are often employed, and providers are encouraged to avoid lecturing; rather, they should engage the patient in a dialogue about how pain works and, specifically, how *their* pain works and potential solutions. This type of interaction facilitates the therapeutic alliance by fostering trust and patient empowerment versus a paternalistic and/or "fix me" interaction between the clinician and patient.

A clinical dialogue may look something like this:

Clinician: "Has anyone explained to you why you hurt?"

Patient: "Well, the doctor told me it's because I have degeneration in my spine."

Clinician: "I understand that the images they took of your back show some age-related changes, and I'm wondering if we could talk a bit about how pain works. Quite frequently, we see these types of changes in folks who actually report no pain, and sometimes we see people with beautiful X-rays, yet they have 10/10 pain. So, pain and tissue problems aren't always the same thing, and after evaluating you just now, I believe it is possible for you to become one of those folks with some positive X-ray findings yet no pain."

Patient: "Really? I don't see how that's possible."

Clinician: "Well, would you mind if I explained it to you?"

The body's nervous system is then metaphorically described as an alarm system (Louw, 2013; Louw et al, 2015; Louw et al., 2016). The patient is made aware of the sheer vastness and complexity of the nervous system:

> There are more than 400 individual nerves that combined make more than 45 miles of nerves within your body, and they all are connected like a network of roads. These nerves continuously carry information about the state of your body. An example of normal pain/alarm system process occurs when you step on a nail. When you step on a nail, the alarm system ramps up, sends a message to the brain to get your attention so you can act to protect yourself: you take the nail out, get a tetanus shot, and bandage the foot. Once the appropriate action has taken place, the alarm gradually calms down, ready to warn you of another nail in the future. Does this make sense? Have you ever stepped on a nail? *(Figure 6.6)*

Note that the tone remains conversational and continually involves the patient.

The message communicated is that pain is a normal biophysiological process and occurs in every human being. The general example (nail in the foot) is then applied to the patient's clinical presentation (e.g., low back pain) with further explanation in nonthreatening language that they likely hurt some tissues when they had an injury or surgery, and these tissues are or have gone through a normal healing process over time:

> The nerves in the area, working like an alarm system, also ramped up (like the foot example) telling you to go seek treatment and care from a health-care provider, which is why you are here.

The alarm story is used to convey the message that pain may not necessarily be a true reflection of the health of one's tissues but includes various complex biologically driven processes (as opposed to psychologically driven), and it may help patients reconceptualize their pain experience

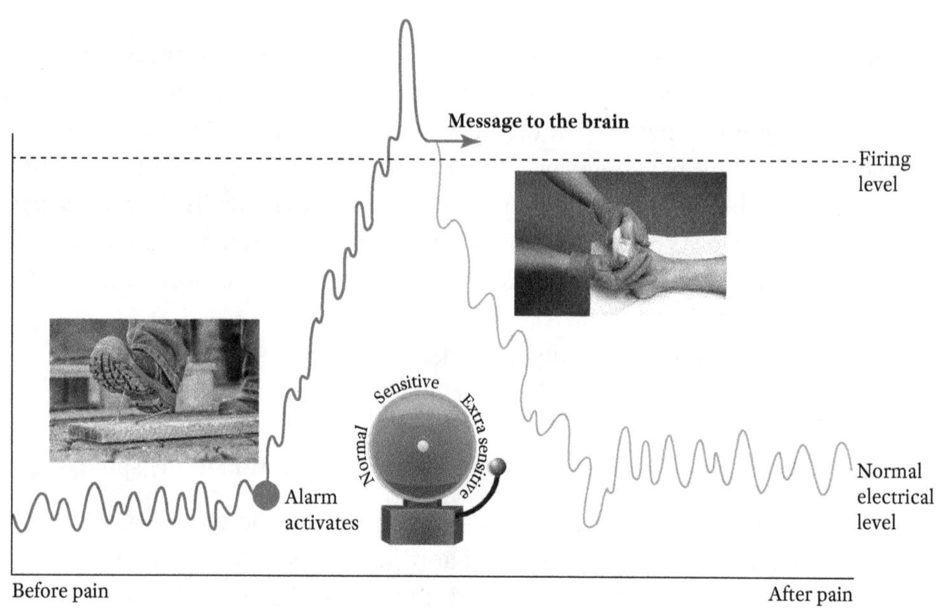

FIGURE 6.6 Metaphorical Alarm System Responding to a Nail Injury (Louw, 2013)

(Gifford, 1998; Moseley, 2007; Nijs et al., 2013) and avoid patients falling into the mindset of "*you think my pain is in my head.*"

The educational story continues with information regarding the fact that in approximately one in four people, the alarm system does not calm down after ramping up but stays extrasensitive, in line with current pain epidemiology (Goldberg & McGee, 2011; Johannes et al., 2010). The extrasensitive alarm system (as opposed to ongoing tissue damage) is a big reason why they are still experiencing pain. Before the onset of this pain, the alarm system had lots of space (tolerance) for activities, but since becoming extrasensitive, there is less tolerance (Figure 6.7; Louw et al., 2013). Now, after only 5 minutes of walking, for example, the alarm system goes off. This metaphor of nerve sensitization gives the patient a different paradigm about why they still hurt (Louw et al., 2013). It provides a framework for the therapist to discuss the issues surrounding

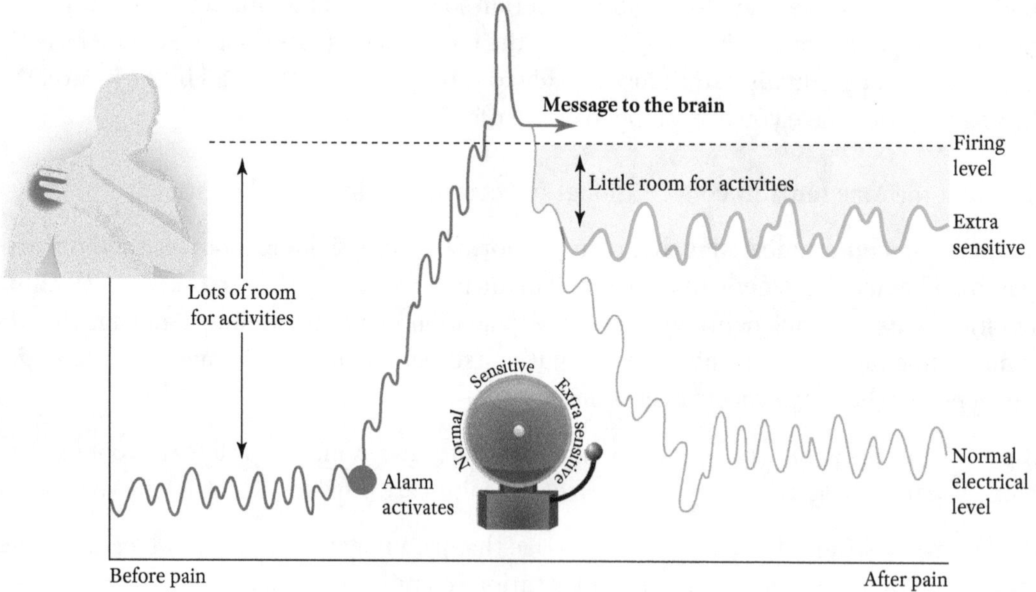

FIGURE 6.7 A Sensitized Alarm System After a Pain Experience, Severely Limiting Function (Louw, 2013)

the injury that have likely caused the alarm system to remain extrasensitive (yellow flags), such as failed treatments, stress and anxiety, different explanations about the constant pain, and lost hope (Kendall et al., 1998).

Next, the clinician and patient devise a treatment plan together, appealing to techniques that the patient is interested in and expects to be effective, thereby leveraging patient expectation, autonomy and self-efficacy. The purpose of the treatment plan is to calm down the extrasensitive alarm system, and the clinician fosters hope in the patient by emphasizing that the nervous system is, indeed, changeable. Additional treatment options include further PNE, aerobic exercise, meditation, relaxation, graded exposure, pacing of activities, manual therapy, diaphragmatic breathing, goal setting, sleep hygiene, and more (Figure 6.8; Louw et al., 2015; Moseley, 2004; Nijs et al., 2011; Young, 2007). Please note, the example used here, a sensitized alarm system, is specific to a biological process of central sensitization. Various metaphors can be used to educate patients on different aspects of pain, including psychosocial stressors (Louw et al., 2018). Some metaphors include comparing the pain experience to being stuck in an endless traffic roundabout or having a situation as simple as receiving a bill that needs to be paid igniting the same stress response that occurs when a lion walks into the room.

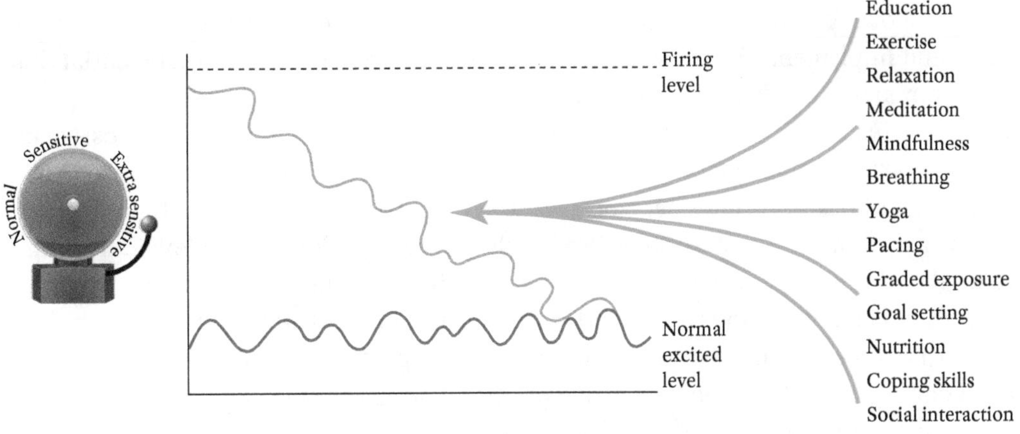

FIGURE 6.8 Various Strategies Aimed at Reducing Sensitization of the Nervous System (Louw, 2013)

The prevailing research in PNE indicates that knowing how pain works in and of itself is not adequate to yield substantial pain relief for many individuals. The idea of "turning down the alarm system" requires a multimodal approach, with movement being a key component in terms of behavior change to facilitate function. It is, therefore, optimal for many patients to receive PNE within a multidisciplinary setting in which all team members have a current understanding of how pain works so that the message can be reinforced and a variety of treatment modalities can be implemented to improve movement, function, autonomic regulation, and goal achievement (Louw et al., 2016; Louw et al., 2018). Furthermore, given the complexity of chronic pain and the influence of various psychosocial factors involved in the pain experience, the provision of mental health services is often a critical element in a multidisciplinary approach to patient care. This recommendation is especially true for the more complex cases. Given the current pain epidemic and the limited resources available, including a relative scarcity of mental health providers knowledgeable in pain science, it can be argued that patients should be screened for psychosocial risk factors (i.e., depression, pain catastrophization, fear avoidance) and referred according to their risk category. For example, a patient with a tissue-based injury (i.e., knee surgery) with some level of fear avoidance can likely be helped by a rehabilitation specialist, such as a physical therapist with a true working knowledge of the biopsychosocial model. If, however, this patient displays additional psychosocial issues and meets/exceeds various cutoff thresholds (i.e., Zung Depression Scales), then they would benefit significantly from the addition of a mental health professional.

FOLLOW-UP

Success with PNE is best measured via a patient's function. If pain is the primary outcome, many patients will remain frustrated, as some degree of pain may well persist in the majority of patients who undergo PNE (Louw et al., 2014). However, when patients' attention is brought to their functional capacity (i.e., their ability to engage in life *despite the pain*), outcomes and patient satisfaction improve (Louw et al., 2014; Louw et al., 2016). In addition, careful goal setting and monitoring personalizes the rehabilitation experience and assists in maximizing a patient's motivation to continue to do the hard work of behavior change, which is often involved in one's treatment plan. Pain is normal and suffering is not. We like to say, "Know pain—know gain."

NEUROSCIENCE IN ACTION

Note: The following is an abbreviated composite case study. The exam, assessment, clinical decision making, and implementation surrounding PNE is far more complex and substantial than what can be summarized in a brief vignette such as this.

Patient. Tina is a 47-year-old female referred to physical therapy with a diagnosis of low back pain. She reports that her symptoms started 18 months ago when she was moving some furniture in her mother's house. She rates her pain as 3/10 at best, 8/10 at worst, and 6/10 on average on the numeric pain rating scale. She scores 38% on the Oswestry Disability Index, indicating a moderate level of disability, and a 36 on the Fear and Behavior Belief Questionnaire Work Subscale (FABQw), indicating a high level of work-related fear. She has had to switch to part-time hours at her job as a teacher's aide because of her pain and reports sitting on the low chairs at school, lifting, bending, and sitting too long in one position also aggravate her symptoms. She is starting to notice pain spreading into her right leg and is worried that she may have developed a problem with her hip. She has had X-rays at her chiropractor's office and has been told she has arthritic changes in her spine and that her sacroiliac joints are "bad."

Physical Exam. Tina has a mild loss of trunk flexion active range of motion (AROM) and moderately decreased extension AROM in standing. Her balance is normal, but transfers to and from sitting, standing, and supine are guarded. Her neurologic exam, including reflex testing, myotome testing, sensory testing, and subjective screening for red flags are all within normal limits. She is diffusely tender to light touch palpation on the spinous processes and surrounding soft tissue from T6 through L5, as well as over her sacrum and sacroiliac joints (SI) and across her iliac crests. Accurate testing of her segmental spinal mobility is limited by tenderness and guarding. Her muscle tone throughout the lumbar paraspinals is increased, and overall, she appears very cautious with all movement. Tina's slump test is positive bilaterally, and her straight leg raise elicits her recent symptom of right leg pain at 50 degrees, indicating neural tension in her lower extremities, right > left. Range of motion, strength, and special tests for the hips are unremarkable.

Assessment. Tina's subjective report and exam findings lead her therapist to suspect that Tina's symptoms are primarily the result of central sensitization. Her symptoms have lasted longer than the usual tissue healing time; she demonstrates diffuse tenderness and allodynia; her Fear Avoidance Belief Questionnaire (FABQ) and Oswestry Disability Index (ODI) scores are elevated; she notes significant impact on her work and personal life. While she has some right leg pain, it does not follow a cutaneous or dermatomal distribution. The therapist's clinical decision-making skills lead him to ask Tina two more questions to "peel back the layers" before beginning treatment.

Additional Questions. Tina's therapist asks her, "Can you tell me a little bit more about what was going on in your life in general when your symptoms arose?" Tina reflects for a moment and reports, "It was actually a really difficult time. We were moving my mom into a memory care facility and dealing with packing up her house, getting it ready to sell, and dealing with the legal aspects of that. I was lifting one of her favorite end tables when I felt the muscle pull. I know that's when I ruined my back." The therapist makes a mental note of the patient's strong association between the act of lifting the table and her current symptoms. The phrase "ruined my back" causes the therapist to suspect catastrophization. The therapist then asks, "What concerns you the most about the symptoms you are currently experiencing?" At this point, Tina becomes tearful and states, "What concerns me the most is that the pain hasn't calmed down, and it's been 18 months. My doctor says nothing is wrong with me, my chiropractor keeps adjusting my SI joint, and my massage therapist keeps working on my muscles, but she says they always tighten back up between every visit. I'm worried this is my new normal, and I don't see how it's ever going to get any better. And now, with my hip hurting. ... I just don't know where this is going to go, and I'm only 47."

Intervention. The therapist hands Tina a tissue, gives her a moment to compose herself, and then says, "Tina, before we get to some of the physical aspects of your treatment, I think it's important that we both start out on the same page when it comes to understanding your back pain. Would it be okay with you if we talked a little bit about how pain works? I know you've heard a lot about your muscles and joints and such from the other providers you have seen, but I would like to do something a bit different and explain to you how pain works. Would that be okay with you?" Somewhat perplexed, but reassured by her therapist's warm and kind tone, as well as his thorough interview and exam, she agrees.

At this point, the therapist introduces the sensitive alarm story, described previously. He uses colored cards to engage Tina's sense of vision, as well as the description of how and why we experience pain when we step on a nail. The therapist reiterates that Tina's exam findings do not suggest serious spinal pathology and normalizes her pain by noting that in 25% of people, the alarm system ramps up and never calms all the way back down. The therapist engages the patient throughout the encounter, asking questions like, "Can you think of some reasons why your alarm system may have stayed up here on high alert?" Tina connects the stress of the situation in which her injury occurred, as well as the subsequent season of family strain, to the development and persistence of her pain. The therapist validates that the mechanical act of lifting an end table awkwardly most certainly could have resulted in a tissue injury but strongly affirms that tissue heals. He reassures her that there is nothing in his testing to suggest her muscles and joints have not properly healed; rather, his exam points to an alarm system that has remained vigilant. He uses exam findings, such as her positive slump test and diffuse tenderness, as evidence for this conclusion.

Patient Response. The patient, while viewing the picture of the alarm system shown earlier, begins to nod in understanding. When the therapist points out "room for activities" in the space between the wiggling line and firing threshold before injury and then that space after injury, an "ah-ha moment" occurs, and the patient says, "That is it! That is my life, right there. I have been buzzing up here ever since that day and have never been able to get my system to calm back down. That's why I can't stand those little chairs at work anymore, but they never used to bother me before." The therapist picks up on the patient's relief and excitement and seizes the opportunity to build hope.

The Plan. The therapist states, "That's exactly right, Tina. And the cool thing is that once you understand this aspect of pain, the possibilities to re-calibrate your system open up! What we need to do now is stop focusing so much on the joints and muscles; rather, we need to reign in that vigilant nervous system. The nervous system is so amazing. It's changeable and moldable, and it can, with the right information and plan, calm back down to where it used to be. There are a few things that are key to this, including understanding how pain works, setting meaningful goals, getting moving with some gentle aerobic activity, and getting enough sleep. From there, you can also choose from a whole host of additional treatments that have been shown to calm the nervous system: for example, mindfulness, breathing exercises, and grading your activity back to your desired level. Here is a list of treatments that we know can help. Are there any that intrigue you?"

From here, the patient and physical therapist work together to sketch out goals and a plan. Over the next 6 weeks, the patient is seen one time per week. More in-depth PNE is provided, including information on how stress modulates pain, how ion channel sensitivity can change for the better or the worse, and how to integrate graded exposure to desired activities. These lessons are provided in short stories, using colored flash cards to enhance the learning experience. Again, active engagement in the educational process is emphasized, with PNE occurring as a two-way conversation versus a lecture, and with the patient completing short homework assignments to assure understanding of concepts. The practice of "PNE Plus" is implemented, meaning that in addition to PNE, proven techniques to promote endogenous pain relief are employed, including establishing good sleep hygiene, deep breathing exercises, mindfulness, and humor. The patient embraces increased physical activity and an individualized exercise program to restore movement to her spine, learning that she no longer needs to guard and protect it; rather, "motion is lotion" and helps improve symptoms.

Outcome. At the end of six visits, the patient demonstrates normal trunk AROM in all directions, has a straight leg raise of 75 degrees bilaterally, and scores 12% on the ODI and 6 on the FABQ work subscale, indicating low disability and low fear. She is in the process of attempting to increase her work hours and notes that her average pain is 2/10. She understands that fluctuations in symptom intensity are to be expected, as pain can act as a barometer of life. She is pleased with her outcome and states she feels ready to "graduate" from physical therapy but hopes her therapist will keep her chart open for a couple of months, just in case she needs a "booster" session once she is out on her own. Her therapist agrees to this plan, as he is fully aware that patients with chronic pain can often benefit from a tethered approach to the discontinuation of therapy. Tina does, in fact, call 1 month later for an additional visit, having experienced a flare-up in symptoms. Here, Tina and the therapist review her "Back First Aid" plan, review and modify her physical therapy exercises, and reestablish her sleep hygiene program, which had fallen off the rails, to promote maximal well-being. Following this visit, the patient emails the therapist 3 months later with a short note of thanks: "All is going very well. I think of you every time I sit in those low chairs at work ... sore, but safe! I think you can go ahead and close out my chart if you need to. I'm going to be okay."

ETHICAL AND MULTICULTURAL CONSIDERATIONS

Ethical considerations when performing PNE primarily surround professionalism and courtesy between health-care providers. Many health-care providers are still firmly entrenched in a biomedical model, and the pain neuroscience-informed practitioner must tread carefully to avoid disparaging language when answering patient questions, such as, "Why are you the first one to explain this to me? All the other people I saw just wanted to make money off of my insurance." Undermining another professional and/or calling others' motives into question must be avoided. In addition, the health-care provider performing PNE must be confident that the patient's pain is, indeed, related to the concepts described rather than signaling a more sinister condition. A thorough evaluation to rule out red flags is essential prior to commencing PNE.

Cultural variables, such as age, gender, and race, must be considered in the construction of metaphors and ways that PNE is communicated. Cultural variables and religious beliefs can influence the way that inputs (e.g., motor vehicle accidences) are processed ("the accident was a punishment from God"). These variables can also influence outputs. For example, many cultures, such as Asian and Scandinavian, are stoic when it comes to pain expression, while others, such as Mediterranean or Hispanic, tend to be more expressive. These are generalizations, but it is important for health-care providers who perform PNE to understand the communication style and belief systems of their patients. Language barriers may also pose a challenge, necessitating the use of an interpreter. In this scenario, it would be helpful to assure that the interpreter has a solid understanding of how pain works so they can communicate PNE accurately and in a personally meaningful way for the patient.

Overall, empathy and a deep understanding of the neuroscience of pain is key to the ethical practice of PNE. Clinicians need to know enough about the neuroscience of pain to be able to respond to client's questions and individualize metaphors to bring the concepts to life. Clinicians should be mindful of their scope of practice and level of competence before infusing PNE in their practice. In addition, PNE begins with a complete biopsychosocial assessment to identify the appropriateness of the client for intervention. This assessment might also identify additional referrals for ancillary services to build into the treatment plan.

ANCILLARY MATERIALS

Textbooks, such as *Pain Neuroscience Education*; educational booklets, such as *Why Do I Hurt* and *Whiplash: An Alarming Message from Your Nerves*; posters; workbooks, such as the *Why Do I Hurt Workbook*; and visual aids for clinic use, such as the Why You Hurt: Pain Neuroscience Education System, are often reported as highly useful tools by health-care providers using PNE routinely in the clinic setting. These can be found at www.optp.com.

HAPPY BODY, HAPPY BRAIN

Physical Exercise for Mental Health and Wellness

Michele Kerulis and Daniel Wilsea

Exercise is a powerful tool people can use to heal their minds and bodies (American Counseling Association [ACA], n.d.). The American College of Sports Medicine ([ACSM], 2018) defines exercise as "a subset of physical activity performed for the purpose of improving or maintaining physical fitness" (p. 2). Exercise is a subset of physical activity in which the activities are planned, purposeful, structured, and repetitive (Caspersen et al., 1985) that is integral in both the prevention and treatment of many medical conditions (ACSM, 2018). Exercise contributes to both short-term and long-term positive physical health functioning by reducing blood pressure, increasing cardiorespiratory fitness, and fostering weight loss and disease prevention (Deslandes et al., 2009; Hatfield, 2012; Mikkelsen et al., 2017).

In addition to the well-known physical benefits of exercise, exercise has been linked with improvements in psychological well-being (Leith, 2010). Matta Mello Portugal et al. (2013) examined literature related to exercise and neurobiology and found that a regular exercise routine can have a positive effect on common mental health symptoms, including anxiety and depression. Exercise creates a distraction from depressive and anxiety symptoms and increases self-efficacy as a result of mastery and successful performances (Mikkelsen et al., 2017). Furthermore, exercise is thought to increase serotonergic and adrenergic levels in the brain, accounting for similar traits as selective serotonin reuptake inhibitor (SSRI) antidepressants (Deslandes et al., 2009; Mikkelsen et al., 2017).

The "feel better" effect, defined as "a decrease in state anxiety, an increase in perceived vigor, or a general improvement in various mood states" (Ekkekakis & Acevedo, 2006, p. 91) has been researched extensively in sport and exercise psychology literature. Leith (2010) presented a plethora of exercise research that was conducted with both clinical and nonclinical populations, and the benefits were remarkable. Leith described the potential mechanisms of change related to exercise and mental health: the endorphin hypothesis, the monoamine hypothesis, and the thermogenic hypothesis.

The endorphin hypothesis, which some people know as the "runner's high," links the psychological benefits of exercise with the release of endorphins and other peptides that are responsible for emotion regulation. Endorphins are known as feel-good chemicals and help people have desirable emotional experiences (Hatfield, 1991; Leith, 2010). The monoamine hypothesis refers to the association between improved affect and exercise related to changes in brain monoamines, such as serotonin, dopamine, and norepinephrine, which are linked to anxiety and depression. In theory, when these chemicals are regulated through exercise, people can experience enhanced moods and alleviation of anxiety and depression symptoms (Leith, 2010; Meeusuen, 2006). The thermogenic hypothesis suggests that exercise induces a similar body response as fighting viruses and bacteria, raising core body temperature and releasing pyrogens and leucocytes that are linked to physical healing (Hong & Mills, 2006; Leith, 2010).

Kita (2014) continued the neurobiology of exercise and mental health discussion by explaining the positive neuroplasticity that develops as a result of physical exercise. Exercise-induced neurogenesis affects stress response and emotional regulation, which have both been associated with improved mental health (Hand et al., 2006). Further, exercise requires executive function activity and the ability to manage both gross and fine motor skills, which are very important aspects of brain health, especially in older age (Acevedo & Ekkekakis, 2006).

The purpose of the *Happy Body, Happy Brain* activity is to provide an intentional framework for integrating exercise into a mental health treatment plan. Neuroscience information is shared as a means to support clients' understanding of the importance of exercise on mental well-being and enhance overall motivation for starting and continuing an exercise routine. Clinicians can use the Exercise for Mental Health and Wellness Worksheet as a tool in implementing the neuroeducation activity.

MATERIALS NEEDED

- The Exercise for Mental Health and Wellness Worksheet
- A computer or mobile device with Internet access can be useful during the brainstorming process and for viewing Dr. Wendy Suzuki's TED Talk, *The Brain Changing Benefits of Exercise*: https://www.ted.com/talks/wendy_suzuki_the_brain_changing_benefits_of_exercise?language=en

PROCESS OF THE ACTIVITY

The *Happy Body, Happy Brain* activity can be used with clients at any fitness level who are interested in using exercise as a tool to achieve and maintain wellness. Encourage clients to receive medical clearance from a physician prior to beginning their exercise program (ACSM, n.d.a–d). We use principles of motivational interviewing in each step of the activity, from eliciting clients' own reasons for exercise to supporting sustained change through intentional planning (Lambie, 2016; Sjoling et al., 2011).

Step 1: Discuss Interest in and Motivation to Exercise

Begin this activity by asking clients about their motivations for including exercise as an aspect of their treatment plans. Often, individuals are not aware of the neuroscience research supporting exercise, so this is a good time to share basic information about how exercise can improve brain health and psychological well-being as a means of additional motivation. We like to share in a general way about the mind-body connection, the short-term and long-term cognitive benefits of exercise, and how exercise can positively affect mood and motivation. Much of the information cited in the introductory section of this activity is the type of information we share with clients. You can also invite your clients to watch Dr. Wendy Suzuki's TED talk titled *The Brain Changing Effects of Exercise* in which she describes her clinical neuroscience research related to exercise, as well as her own lived experience.

Step 2: Complete the Exercise for Mental Health and Wellness Worksheet

Once clients articulate their motivations and endorse a genuine desire to include exercise in their daily lives, you can use the Exercise for Mental Health and Wellness Worksheet as a guide for goal setting and maintenance support. The worksheet can help clients break down exercise goals into manageable steps and helps with planning ways to overcome potential barriers to reaching their goals. You can begin by helping the client brainstorm the types of exercise they might enjoy. Internet searches can be helpful during this point of planning to help clients locate nearby facilities and fitness professionals. Then proceed with setting specific goals. A framework you may want to use in facilitating goal setting is the specific, measurable, achievable, reasonable/realistic/rewarding, and time-oriented (SMART) philosophy (ACSM, 2018). For example, clients who experience depressive symptoms can set a SMART goal to perform aerobic exercise (specific) for 30 minutes (measurable) at vigorous intensity (achievable; eight to nine rate of perceived exertion; ACSM,

2018) two times per week (reasonable) for one month (time limited). The more specific the goals, the more likely clients are to achieve their goals (Weinberg & Butt, 2005).

Once exercise goals are selected, ask clients to list at least three barriers to achieving their exercise goals and ask them to identify a solution for each identified barrier. This will help clients think ahead and create ways to maintain their exercise plans. Common barriers include childcare, work schedule, perceived lack of time, or low motivation. The next step is to talk with clients about how they feel as they complete the worksheet. Help them process feelings related to this exercise and discuss how they hope to feel once they have 1 month of exercise successfully completed.

Step 3: Review and Revise

In subsequent sessions, ask clients how their plan is going. Ask what was successful about the plan and what they would like to change or do differently moving forward. The Exercise for Mental Health and Wellness Worksheet can be used on an ongoing basis and is designed to help clients create an attainable plan for exercise with the goal of enhancing their overall mental health and wellness.

FOLLOW-UP

We recommend formally reviewing the Exercise for Mental Health and Wellness Worksheet with clients every 4 weeks (ACSM, 2018) and processing clients' subjective perceptions of improved mental health symptoms and feelings of success related to their exercise goals. Help clients understand that new habits take time to adopt and encourage them to continue adhering to their self-developed exercise plans. Exercise changes do not occur overnight or in a vacuum. Time is a key factor in gauging the success of symptom reduction. Clients might like incorporating a variety of activities into their exercise plans as they learn how to navigate the world of physical health and mental wellness.

NEUROSCIENCE IN ACTION

Katie is a 24-year-old who had symptoms of depression related to developmental transition issues. She is a new professional and questioned her abilities in her career. She reported having a career mentor whom she described as "awesome" who helped Katie navigate her job. Katie admitted to having low motivation to engage in social activities with her friends and feeling lethargic on weekends. Katie said, "I want to feel like my old self," signifying her past ability to manage her mood and move through challenges with confidence. She said she used to be on a rowing team and believed that exercise could help improve her outlook and overall mood. Six months ago, Katie was prescribed SSRIs to manage her depression. Dr. Kerulis talked with Katie about the monoamine hypothesis and how exercise has been shown to be beneficial to clients who use SSRIs (Mikkelsen et al., 2017) to decrease symptoms related to depression. Katie was interested in learning more about how her physical activities could affect her brain and her moods, so she searched the Internet to learn more and watched Dr. Suzuki's TED talk.

After discussing the effect of exercise on the brain, Katie and Dr. Kerulis created an overall mental health and wellness goal to experience a positive mood (subjectively defined) four out of seven days a week. She was interested in learning something new, so her exercise goal was to take two to three 60-minute stand-up paddle boarding (SUP) classes a week (at least two during the week and one on weekends). Katie's identified barriers were (1) low motivation, (2) potential weather conditions resulting in canceled classes, and (3) unpleasant mood. Her solutions to the barriers were (1) reconstruct her thoughts; (2) use indoor equipment, such as a rowing machine or go to other group fitness classes if the SUP class is canceled because of weather; and (3) recall past successes. Katie said that she felt uncertain about her ability to commit to her goals and was disappointed in herself that motivation and depressive symptoms had interfered with her happiness. She stated that she hoped to feel successful, proud of herself for fulfilling a commitment, and more willing to socialize at the 4-week review period.

At the time of the review, Katie had, in fact, achieved her goals. She enjoyed the social aspect of her SUP classes and experienced confidence in her new exercise skills. She stated that she told a friend about her goals who helped her remain accountable. Katie also said that, even though she still has work to do with her career transition, her increased confidence seemed to have an effect on her ability to perceive life situations differently, which also helped her regulate her mood. One thing Katie wanted to change in her revised exercise goals included incorporating a variety of new exercise lessons, such as tennis, swimming, and martial arts. Katie felt like her recommitment to a non-work-related goal helped her gain confidence in a new skill, which led her to believe she could be successful in her new career and helped her change her thought process, resulting in increased motivation. Additionally, Katie used the neuroscience of exercise as an anchor when finding herself drifting away from her goals.

ETHICAL AND MULTICULTURAL CONSIDERATIONS

As with any practice, it is essential to adhere to codes of ethics and practice within our scope of competence and knowledge, as well as show the utmost respect for cultural diversity. It is recommended that clinicians develop professional relationships with physicians, kinesiologists, fitness facilities, and certified personal trainers to learn more about the physiological aspects of exercise. It is important to note that access to exercise resources is not equal among different populations and that low cost and free services are available in some communities (Brown & Stanforth, 2017; Hongu et al., 2014; Houlihan, 2008; Langton & King, 2018; Reger-Nash et al., 2011). We encourage people to begin by literally taking just a few steps to build motivation. Increasing daily movement, such as taking the stairs instead of the elevator, parking farther away from stores than usual, and taking short daily walks, is a free way to increase exercise in daily life. Increasing exercise can be as simple as going outside or to the local park where clients can be encouraged to use the exercise "equipment," both natural and human-made. For example, park benches can be used for squats, step-ups, incline push-ups, and triceps dips. Open spaces or grass are ideal for walking lunges, plank walkouts, inchworms, and sprint intervals. When it comes to exercise and the outdoors, the mind and creativity are sometimes the only tools that are required. Clinicians should also be aware of exercise options for people of all abilities and become familiar with organizations developed to assist people who have a variety of needs.

Exercise for Mental Health and Wellness Worksheet

Dr. Michele Kerulis, LCPC, CMHC, and Dan Wilsea, M.A., ACSM CPT

Regular exercise has been linked to physical fitness and mental health and wellness. This worksheet will help you develop an exercise plan with your specific goals in mind.

My Mental Health and Wellness Goal: Set a measurable mental health and wellness goal.

My Exercise Goal: Create a goal related to exercise. ____________________

Type of exercise: ____________________

Duration: ____________________

Frequency: ____________________

Time Frame: ____________________

Potential Roadblock: ____________ **Solution:** ____________

Potential Roadblock: ____________ **Solution:** ____________

Potential Roadblock: ____________ **Solution:** ____________

How I feel today while I think about creating my mental health, wellness, and exercise goals:

____

How I hope to feel at the review date: ____________________

What I learned while working toward my mental health, wellness, and exercise goals:

____

What was helpful during this review period: ____________________

What I will do differently during the next review period: ____________________

Review date:

THE PHYSICALLY ACTIVE BRAIN

Saba Aqel

Toxic stress is known to exacerbate mental and physical health concerns (Aqel et al., 2017). Toxic stress can also have detrimental effects on brain health, especially during childhood when the brain and body undergo critical periods in development (Anda et al., 2006). The Adverse Childhood Experiences (ACE) scoring system, which has been combined with epidemiological and neurobiological studies to detect correlations between ACEs and physical and mental health comorbidity (Merrick et al., 2017), is one way to assess exposure to toxic stress during childhood (Anda et al., 2006). Researchers have demonstrated a "dose-dependent" response, indicating that as the ACEs increase, so too do comorbidity and disease severity.

Stress is a natural automatic response intended to prepare the body for a perceived threat (American Psychological Association [APA], 2013b). Although the body's threat response system is complex, our current understanding involves the notion that when the amygdala interprets a stimulus as potentially threatening, it alerts the hypothalamus, which initiates a signaling cascade through the hypothalamic pituitary adrenal (HPA) axis, resulting in the fight-or-flight response (Harvard Health Publishing [HHP], 2018). More specifically, the hypothalamus signals the body to release corticotropin-releasing hormone, resulting in the pituitary gland releasing adrenocorticotropic hormone, which then triggers the adrenal glands to release cortisol (HHP, 2018; Sapolsky, 2000). Toxic stress can cause constant activation of the threat response system. Over time, this hyper-activation of the body's threat response system can lead to high blood pressure, diabetes, cardiovascular complications, weakened immune system, depression, anxiety, neurobiological changes, and cognitive impairments (Anda et al., 2006; Stults-Kolehmainen & Sinha, 2013).

One potential avenue for helping clients protect against the negative effect of adverse experiences is by encouraging physical activity. Low-intensity physical activity has been repeatedly shown to lower cortisol levels in the body, thus helping to reduce the body's stress response (Vilaça-Alves et al., 2018). Physical activity also increases endorphins and neurotransmission, which helps reduce fatigue, improve poor motivation, balance mood swings, and ease muscle cramps, aches, and pains (Cadman, 2018). Aqel et al. (2017) found that physical activity was beneficial in ameliorating disease through decreasing levels of inflammatory proteins, increasing levels of anti-inflammatory proteins, and reducing the presence of autoantibodies in the body. Aqel et al. (2017) concluded that the incorporation of regular moderate physical activity, defined as equivalent to a 45-minute fast walk, 4 or more days a week, may be beneficial in symptom reduction of chronic mental and physical illnesses. Additional studies have shown the benefits of physical activity in improving the overall quality of life, health outcomes, sleep, and mood (Olex & Olex, 2018). In fact, physical activity has been shown to be as effective as medication and cognitive behavioral therapy in reducing the symptoms of major depressive disorder (Swan & Hyland, 2012). In addition, physical activity has the ability to regulate the HPA axis, leading to antidepressive effects (Budde et al., 2018).

Beginning and/or maintaining a physical activity regimen is not always easy. In fact, individuals struggling with mental health disorders, including chronic depression, are often sedentary and lack motivation to engage in physical activity (Olex & Olex, 2018). Craft and Perna (2004) suggested introducing physical activity education as part of treatment plans, starting with 20 minutes/day, 3 days/week. The researchers found that this amount of exercise is sufficient for reducing depressive symptoms. Key elements of success in supporting clients beginning exercise routines include starting with low-intensity physical activity, helping clients keep a physical activity log, encouraging social support, and discussing perceived barriers (Craft & Perna, 2004).

Furthermore, using interventions to reinforce the reward system is a helpful way to promote and sustain behavioral change. Forming a new habit involves an intricate neurological process that includes three important aspects of habit formation: (1) the cue, (2) the action, and (3) the reward (Dolan & Dayan, 2013). Habits form following the neural coding of goal-directed actions in the dorsal lateral striatum and are modulated by an endogenous cannabinoid-based system that acts by reducing the flow of information to the orbitofrontal cortex (Gremel et al., 2016). The cue involves a reminder to engage in the action (e.g., calendar reminder, Post-it Notes, visual reminders), the action is the activity (e.g., waking, lifting weights, going to a dance class), and the reward (e.g., drinking favorite shake or eating favorite meal following physical activity). Although physical activity has many long-term benefits (e.g., weight loss, improved cognition), they are generally not evident quickly enough to reinforce the action as a habit.

The purpose of the *Physically Active Brain* activity is to share with clients neuroscience-based information related to chronic stress, behavior change, and physical activity in an effort to enhance motivation to engage in exercise. Increasing engagement in exercise will then support improvements in mental health functioning.

MATERIALS NEEDED

- Handouts illustrating the benefits of physical activity, the detriments of toxic stress, and the basics of the habit formation system (Figure 6.9, 6.10, and 6.11)
- The Fatigue Assessment Scale (FAS; Michielsen et al., 2003) https://pure.uvt.nl/ws/portalfiles/portal/510406/psychometric.pdf
- Additional optional materials:
    - The Rosenberg Self-Esteem Scale (Rosenberg, 1965)
    - The Subjective Exercise Experiences Scale (Meauley & Courneya, 1994)

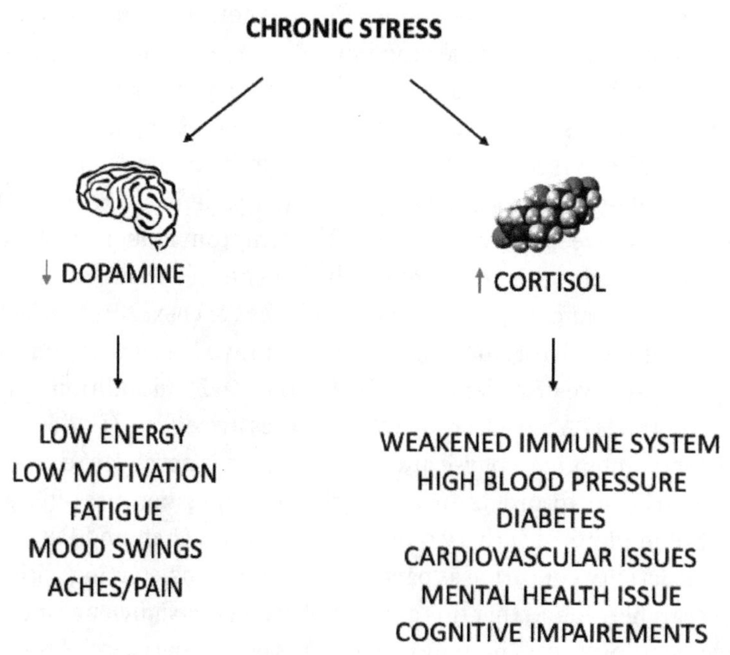

FIGURE 6.9 Effects of Chronic Stress on Dopamine and Cortisol

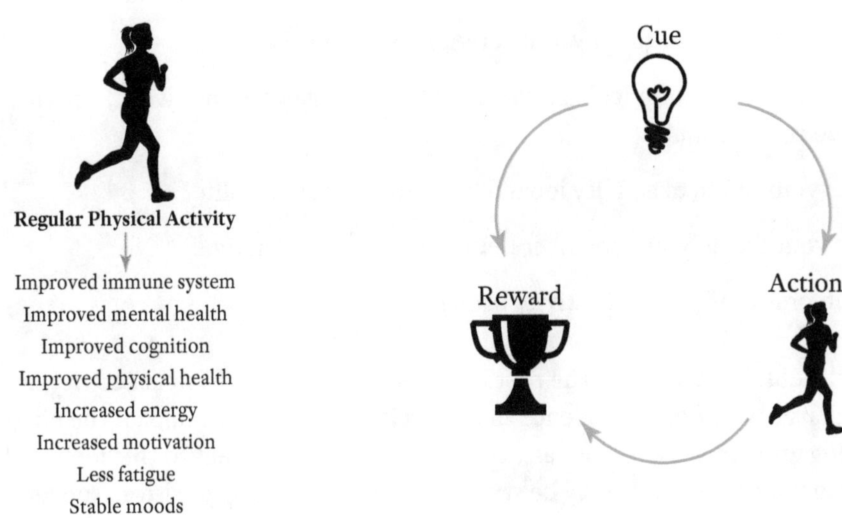

FIGURE 6.10 Benefits of Regular Physical Activity

FIGURE 6.11 Habit Formation System

PROCESS OF THE ACTIVITY

The following image provides a visual flow of the activity process.

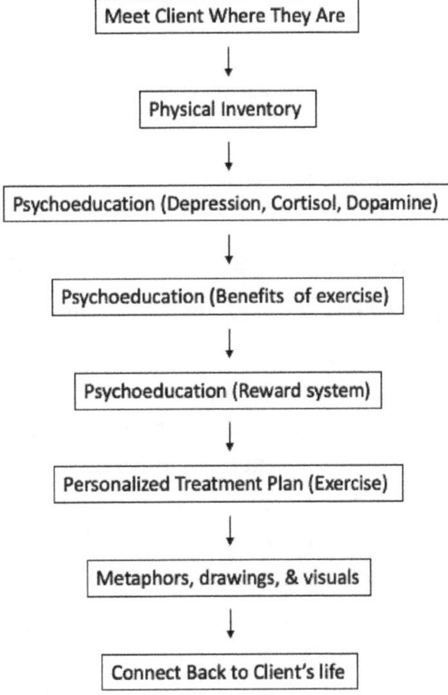

Step 1: Meet Clients Where They Are

Begin by assessing the client's willingness to engage in physical activity and their level of current physical activity (e.g., frequency, duration, intensity). Empathically connect with clients by validating their experiences that may contribute to their lack of physical activity (e.g., fatigue, social anxiety at the gym, low energy, lack of motivation). Ask questions like the following:

- What is your current physical and/or mental motivation to engage in physical activity?
- Where does your desire for physical activity come from?
- What is your current physical activity level (e.g., transportation, work, activities around the home, and recreational)?
- What has your physical activity looked like throughout your life?
- When in your life do you remember being the most/least active?
- What outcomes has physical activity brought to you?

It can be helpful to fully explore the past benefits and costs of physical activity and lock-in any emotional charge with positive valence that exercise has produced (e.g., if the client shares feeling happy engaging in yoga in the past, the counselor can connect to this feeling during future discussions in which the client may be struggling to imagine any positive aspects of exercise) of physical activity.

Before pursuing additional physical activity, you will also need to ensure that the client is physically capable of engaging in physical activity.

- "Do you have any preexisting health conditions that may prevent you from engaging in physical activity?" **Ensure and prioritize safety with the client, including whether they require clearance from their physician before engaging in physical activity.

Step 2: Physical Inventory

Explore some of the more rewarding and pleasure-inducing activities in the client's life:

- "What brings you joy?"
- "What physical activities bring you the most pleasure?"
- "What hobbies get you moving?"
- "In what way can you incorporate physical activity into your hobbies?"

If the client exhibits low motivation and/or fatigue (refer to the handout and FAS), validate their experience by empathically discussing the neuroscience of fatigue to help the client feel understood and supported. Example statements and/or questions include the following: "You're walking around like you're carrying weights all the time, just walking can feel like a task." "How often does it feel like you're carrying around weights?" "How much weight are you carrying around today?" You can provide encouragement by noting that physical activity can help reduce low motivation and fatigue. A metaphor of weightlifting can also be useful in these circumstances (e.g., all weights feel heavy and hard to lift in the beginning, and with increasing repetition, you build the capacity to carry the weights with less burden and more benefit).

Step 3: Depression, Cortisol, and Dopamine Psychoeducation

Share with clients that low dopamine and high chronic levels of cortisol are strongly linked to depression and other mental health disorders. Using Figure 6.9, share with clients that chronic toxic stress leads to higher levels of the stress hormone cortisol floating around in the body and lower levels of dopamine in the brain.

Step 4: Physical Activity Psychoeducation

Share with clients that physical activity is highly effective in improving cognition, mood, and sleep, as well as reducing symptoms of anxiety and depression. You can inform clients that physical activity has been shown to be as effective as antidepressants and cognitive behavioral therapy in improving depressive and anxiety symptoms. Refer to Figure 6.10 for a full list of benefits and be sure to add to this list with information from clients' past experiences. When referring to the information shared earlier, note that daily low to moderate physical activity is highly effective in decreasing levels of cortisol and increasing levels of dopamine in the body. At this point, it is important to broaden the view of physical activity. Clients, and sometimes counselors, have a narrow view of physical activity related to going to a gym; however, going to a gym is just one example of physical activity, so you will want to explore as many options to increase physical activity as possible.

Step 5: Reward System and Habit Formation

In addition to sharing about the benefits of exercise, it can be useful to provide clients with information that helps support their development of a positive exercise habit. Using Figure 6.11, briefly describe the reward system and its role in habit formation. Note the importance of daily (or near daily) physical activity to effectively form the habit. Also emphasize the importance of the client rewarding themselves with something they love immediately following the completion of a workout. You can say something like "treating yourself after the workout can make you more likely to engage in physical activity the next day."

Step 6: Treatment Plan

The next step is incorporating physical activity into a client's treatment plan. A good place to start if the client has no regular physical activity in their lives is low-intensity activity for 20 minutes, 3 days per week. An emphasis should be placed on frequency first and then duration. Once clients have achieved relative success in frequency and duration, you can work on increasing their intensity. As part of the treatment planning process, encourage clients to keep a physical activity log and to seek social support. It is also important for you to facilitate a conversation about perceived barriers and work with clients to develop plans for overcoming those barriers.

Step 7: Metaphor

Once the treatment plan has been established, you can use a metaphor to help seal the client's understanding. One metaphor I use related to stress is that of a wound. You can say, "Think of stress as a wound. A wound needs to be disinfected, covered, and taken care of. You might use medicines (e.g., an antibiotic) to help with the healing. Physical activity is like medicine for stress. Along with other important ways of caring for yourself, physical activity can help heal some of the negative aspects of toxic stress." I recommended using a metaphor that fits the client's life experiences and culture as much as possible. You may even consider asking the client to come up with their own metaphor.

Step 8: Connect Back to the Client's Life

The final step is creating a unique and personal conclusive summary statement that ties all the information together for the client. For example, you might say, "You have done yoga in the past, and that has made you happy. You do not have the resources to join a yoga class after the financial and career hardships you have experienced this year, and it sounds like doing yoga in your home using free online videos will be feasible and attainable in helping you feel happy and healthy more often." It is also useful to encourage further reading about optimal exercise times, types, and so forth.

FOLLOW-UP

In subsequent sessions with the client, administer the FAS and review their physical activity logs together for accountability. Discuss the client's thoughts and feelings surrounding the process, highlight improvements, and adjust the treatment plan to work through setbacks. Some of the potential outcomes to highlight include improved FAS scores and improved mental health (anxiety/depression) via self-report. In addition, discuss perceived barriers and difficulties the client may be experiencing. Common barriers include the difficulty of starting a new routine (e.g., time), lack of social support, negative self-talk, and so forth.

NEUROSCIENCE IN ACTION

The abbreviated dialogue below represents my (Saba) work with a 23-year-old male client. He came to counseling endorsing symptoms of depression (e.g., low motivation, fatigue, lack of interest in activities he used to enjoy, and so forth). I decided to introduce the *Physically Active Brain* after initial sessions that focused on assessment and relationship building. This activity was intended to support his overall treatment plan aimed at improving mood and motivation.

Counselor: I am thinking it might be helpful to spend some time today talking about physical activity and mental health. How would you feel about that?"

Client: Okay.

Counselor: Let's start with talking about your current activity levels. What is your day-to-day activity like right now?

Client: Sure. I used to walk my dog regularly, really my parents' dog, but I do not do that anymore. I have no motivation to do it. I go to college Monday-Wednesday and on Thursday-Sunday I work. On campus, I usually walk to and from my car to class which is about a 10-minute walk, and most of the day I am sitting down. At work, I am on my feet most of the time, I work behind the register, and I help restock the shelves on a regular basis. That takes a lot of effort.

Counselor: It sounds like you have quite a bit of activity in your life. What is the frequency and duration of activity at work?

Client: Usually, I'm on my feet for 8 hours and restocking the shelves takes a couple of hours, like 2 hours, and that usually happens once or twice a week.

Counselor: Okay, that is helpful. What other physical activity is in your life?

Client: None really.

Counselor: What did your physical activity look like growing up?

Client: I used to be a normally active kid. Then in middle school, I gained some weight. I started to work out a lot in high school, I used to lift weights. I became really healthy and toned. That was really nice. Then when I went away for college, that is when everything spiraled, you know.

Counselor: Yes, you were experiencing some real struggles with your mental health.

Client: Exactly, I started drinking a lot and, you know, I was hospitalized twice, dropped out, and came back here.

Counselor: That is right, do you remember the floating metaphor we often use in here? The one where you feel like you are floating without momentum or direction when your mental health is exacerbated, and how we are working to create momentum and direction in therapy?

Client: Yes, I remember.

Counselor: The point behind incorporating physical activity into your daily life is to work toward building up that momentum to move in your desired direction.

Client: That sounds great, and that is what I am looking for.

Counselor: Right, how do you feel and think about physical activity today?

Client: I think that it is harder to do, because of my low motivation and commitment, but I would love to have some form of it in my life like we discussed before.

Counselor: Right, you are currently floating without movement. You want to have some level of physical activity, and I understand that the main purpose behind that is to feel healthier overall.

Client: Yes, that's right.

Counselor: Now that I am aware of your current level of physical activity, let us explore activities that you can engage in.

Client: Sure, I used to love walking my dog, those walks are so relaxing, but I can't find the motivation to do that nowadays.

Counselor: I hear you; it is hard for you to gather up that energy to walk your dog when it barely gets you through your day.

Client: Exactly. I want to do it, but it is hard

Counselor: There is a fatigue assessment scale that I would like to administer regularly to track your baseline fatigue and changes in those levels

Client: Sure, that sounds good.

I administered the FAS, which identified that the client was experiencing high levels of fatigue.

Counselor: I would like to discuss this handout with you before we move to a plan that best suits you, would that be okay?

Client: Definitely

Counselor: I can see that fatigue is a regular struggle for you. Typically, when individuals actively struggle with depression, they often experience fatigue as a symptom. There could be many reasons for this, and one possible contributing factor could be less production of dopamine. Less dopamine means that you find yourself walking around as if you were carrying weights on your wrist and ankles. Getting out of bed or walking may feel like a task. The good news is that for many people, physical activity helps increase dopamine and decrease feelings of fatigue.

Client: Yes, that sounds about right. I remember how good I felt when I used to work out and I miss that feeling.

Counselor: It sounds like you have a pretty good recollection and understanding of the benefits of regular physical activity. Although the weight of depression sometimes feels like too much for you, lifting actual weights in the past perhaps helped you feel lighter and move throughout the world with less hinderance and more joy.

Client: Yes, that time was definitely one of the happiest times of my life. I never thought physical and emotional weight like that before.

We continued to process the client's language related to physical and emotional weight and then reviewed Figure 6.9 to explore the potential impact of chronic or constant stress related to dopamine levels, low energy levels, low motivation, fatigue, mood swings, aches, and pains.

Client: Wow, that sounds so familiar to my life.

Counselor: Seems like you connected to that description...additionally it leads to increased cortisol levels which in turn weakens the immune system and increases blood pressure, which can cause diabetes, cardiovascular issues, additional mental health issues, and cognitive impairments. Luckily, there is a vast body of clinical research that shows daily low to moderate physical activity is highly effective in increasing dopamine levels and decreasing cortisol levels.

Client: That sounds great.

I reviewed Figure 6.10 to talk about the potential benefits of physical activity.

Client: I have always known that exercise is good for me, but it never really got through. It sounds really effective, and this is motivating me. Lifting the physical weight can lighten the emotional weight.

Counselor: Glad to hear. It is a successful therapeutic tool to improve mental health symptoms and quality of life. In fact, some studies have shown that it is as effective as antidepressants and cognitive-behavior therapy in improving symptoms of anxiety and depression.

Client: I did not know that.

Counselor: Yes. I know that motivation is an issue, and so, I would like to discuss habit formation and integrating that into this activity.

Client: That sounds good.

I reviewed the reward system (Figure 6.11) to help the client normalize the change process and begin thinking about strategies to enhance his change process.

Client: That sounds great, I can add a daily reminder in my phone, and after the exercise, I can grab a shake or play video games.

Counselor: That sounds rewarding for you. The plan is shaping up already. You might even remind yourself of your previous phrase: Lifting the physical weight can lighten the emotional weight. To determine the daily activity, could you tell me more about your highly enjoyable daily activity or hobby, one that involves physical activity?

Client: I really love walking the dog every day. I enjoyed doing that in the past, and the walks always helped me clear my mind, plus, I love our dog. I don't mind taking jogs with the dog too, if I can motivate myself to do it.

Counselor: It sounds like walking your dog is an activity that has a lot of benefits for you. How could you build that into your daily routine?

Client: Hmm, I am so busy, but I think I could start by adding reminders to walk my dog, would 3 times a week, for about 10-15 minutes, work?

Counselor: If that works for you, we can start there with low intensity and work our way up from there. I believe that it will be important for us to start small and work our way up. Does that sound feasible?

Client: Yes, very.

Counselor: Great. How do you feel about incorporating this into your daily journaling?

Client: I don't mind.

Counselor: Once you are finished journaling like you normally would, write out your activity for the day.

Client: That sounds good.

I then summarized our discussion so far to ensure goal consensus and process any assets or barriers that came up.

Client: Sounds good, I am excited to try this. It doesn't sound too bad at all and being held accountable with you and my journal will motivate me more so.

Counselor: I am hearing that this is within your ability. It also sounds like connecting it to your well-being and approaching it with a positive perspective has given you a renewed excitement for incorporating physical activity into your life.

Client: Exactly, I really want to improve my mental and physical health. I want to be able to walk up the stairs without losing my breath given I am in my twenties.

Counselor: You want to feel your youth and enjoy the health benefits that may accompany it.

MULTICULTURAL AND ETHICAL IMPLICATIONS

It is important to take into account clients' ability status, socioeconomic status, and mental health conditions, as well as use a holistic approach. It is important to meet the client where they are and to use preexisting resources and practices to incorporate a physically active lifestyle. For example, clients may not be able to afford a gym membership or have access to transportation to go to a gym, so it will be necessary to focus on increasing physical activity in ways that the client can access (e.g., parking farther away from the store).

PROMOTING PSYCHOLOGICAL WELL-BEING THROUGH BODY MOVEMENT AWARENESS EXERCISES

Mohiuddin Ahmed and Charles M. Boisvert

The cerebellum, which sits below the cerebrum in the human brain, is primarily responsible for associated movements in one's physical and social environment and often referred to as the "adaptive controller" (Barlow, 2009, p. ix), given its key evolutionary role in human development. As humans differentiated from primates and other living beings on the evolutionary ladder by the development of the neocortex, the cerebrum became increasingly prominent in influencing thinking, reasoning, memory, attention, problem solving, symbolic and creative thinking, and emotional regulation, along with language and social development, which are now primarily associated with higher cognitive functions (Teffler & Schmendefein, 2011). Recent research, however, has ascribed cognitive functions to the cerebellum and identified it as an important site in promoting one's adaptive thinking and behaving and thus aiding and supplementing traditional higher order cognitive functions historically reserved for the cerebrum (Barlow, 2002; Gallese & Lakoff, 2005; Gordon, 2007; Koziol et al., 2012; Paul, 2016; Rapoport et al., 2000). Therefore, using movement as an intervention capitalizes on the adaptive control of the cerebellum to promote therapeutic gains.

Movement is important, and human beings spend a great deal of time in varied motoric activities and goal-directed behaviors across the life span. Play activities provide opportunities to engage in specific types of movements that prepare us for survival and adulthood adaptation. Various cultures and species value play to promote adaptive skills acquisition by requiring one to pay attention to the current activity and immediate physical and social surroundings while following a set of social rules and evaluating risks to self and others with whom we are in intimate physical contact (Ahmed, 2018; Bartenieff & Lewis, 2002).

Engaging in play also requires us to concentrate on a task, work toward a goal, engage in trial and error learning, and handle frustration and obstacles. More importantly, play- and movement-related activities help us identify our own boundaries and respect the boundaries of others as we navigate the social and physical environment. All of these are important skills to acquire for social and physical adaptations as one matures into adulthood and continues to advance in years. Awareness of one's body movement, as well as the body movements of others, and anticipatory vigilance provide one with a sense of one's identity and boundary awareness and are essential to effectively navigating one's social and physical world (Ahmed, 2018; Ahmed & Boisvert, 2013; Boisvert & Ahmed, 2018).

As living human beings, our bodies are always in some form of motion, whether in rest or activity, reflecting the social and physical world, where people and objects are always moving. Successful adaptation to our environment requires us to continuously navigate our physical body with people around us in our immediate social and physical environment, all of which involve awareness of boundaries as we are moving and anticipating our movements and the movements of others while in the process remaining engaged in goal-directed activities.

In our social interactions, respecting physical boundaries and an awareness of our proximity to each other without intruding on each other's space is necessary for successful adaptation to the physical and social world. As such, in our caring, loving, and play interactions where physical contact with others may be more intimate and necessary, we still need to display a keen awareness of and respect for our boundaries and the boundaries of others, some of which may be mandated by social and cultural mores. Aggressive behavior and abuse, on the other hand, can be viewed as examples of boundary violations and intrusions into the personal physical and social space of another. Even in conversation with others, we need to maintain some degree of awareness of both physical and psychological boundaries by respecting others' privacy and being careful to avoid a degree of intrusion or probing that would make others uncomfortable.

Body movement awareness (BMA) is implicitly operating as we move around in our physical and social environment and make adaptive responses to various people and situations in our life space. Some benefits of the BMA exercises include the following:

1. ***Training in Mindfulness.*** The exercises promote awareness of being in the present, affirming one's awareness of being alive in the moment, and acknowledging the value of trying to do one's best to be "present" in the immediate living moment (Ahmed, 2018; Brown & Ryan, 2003; Brown et al., 2007)

2. ***Training in Attention Control.*** The exercises promote paying attention, developing concentration, following directions, and learning how to adhere to rule-governed behavior in various social situations (Ahmed, 2018; Bogels et al., 2008; Boisvert & Ahmed, 2018; Hedlund et al., 2013; McNevin et al., 2000).

3. ***Training in Self-Control.*** The exercises promote self-control by teaching clients to control certain body movements. Developing a greater degree of self-control can enable clients to potentially reduce aggression toward others or other boundary violations, including the destruction of property or similar at-risk behaviors (Ahmed, 2018; Boisvert & Ahmed, 2018; McNevin et al., 2000; Ogden & Fisher, 2015).

4. ***Training in Goal Attainment.*** The exercises promote goal attainment by teaching clients how to set a goal and complete the steps necessary to achieve the goal. Therapists can explain how a simple BMA exercise can enable one to achieve a goal by following specific steps and how this goal-setting process is relevant to one's learning in school, work, play, and social settings (Gallahue & Donnelly, 2003; McNevin et al., 2000).

5. ***Training in Relaxation.*** The exercises promote relaxation practice and enable clients to experience an enhanced sense of well-being in the moment. Clients also learn how the relaxation exercises can serve as a redirection strategy to ward off negative feelings and thoughts or disrupt ongoing engagement in such (Ahmed, 2018; Boisvert & Ahmed, 2018; Smith, 2005).

Given the importance of movement to our adaptive survival and its relation to brain development and functioning, we created several BMA exercises to promote psychological well-being. Drawing from our years of clinical experience in working with children, adolescents, adults, and geriatric psychiatric clients, we believe these BMA exercises can be used as adjunctive exercises to the counseling and psychotherapy process to promote psychological well-being (Ahmed, 2018; Ahmed & Boisvert, 2013).

MATERIALS NEEDED

Most of the BMA exercises can be demonstrated in an ordinary therapy office. We recommend creating client tracking and staff feedback forms to guide the interventions and gather outcome data.

PROCESS OF THE ACTIVITY

In demonstrating the exercises, clinicians discuss the rationale for the exercises drawing from biological and psychosocial perspectives involving brain-behavior interactions and how they affect our psychological and social learning and our adaptation to the physical and social world. Before presenting any of the BMA exercises, the clinician can review the rationale for the exercises as follows, specifically using any of the six BMA exercises as part of the counseling process:

> I am going to ask you do some simple body movement exercises that can be performed by using your ability to move in ways without feeling any particular discomfort. The purpose of this exercise is to develop intentional awareness of the movement of your body, stimulating the part of your brain that controls movement and to maximize your sense of being aware in the present moment and being aware of your immediate physical and social surroundings.

Clinicians are welcome to present brief clarification on how awareness of one's body movement experience is important by asking questions, such as, "How do we know we are alive in this world?" Follow-up with citing examples from the importance of play activities and our constant awareness of regulating our movements in our physical and social environment to avoid undue and inappropriate contact that could be harmful to ourselves or others. Clinicians can also improvise on the variation of the exercises, as well as the explanations they choose to provide based on their assessment of their clients' needs.

Each of the six versions of BMA can be done separately or sequentially depending on clients' needs, receptivity to the exercises, and counseling goals. Versions 1 and 2 are ideal for adult clients. Version 3 is best for geriatric clients or clients who are bedridden. Versions 4 and 5 can be used with children and adolescents, and Version 6 can be used with clients who have boundary violation challenges, such as aggression. Clinicians are encouraged to modify and creatively adapt any of the versions or add new variation of the BMA exercise as they are appropriate to serve their counseling service needs.

Version 1—The Relaxing Skier

This exercise consists of standing up with the feet shoulders' width apart, knees slightly bent (like a skiing position), and pressure applied on the heels. The firm grounding of the feet gives one a sense of connecting one's body to the earth. This skiing position is maintained while moving both hands slowly up and down in a rhythmic fashion, with the elbows descending first, all in a constant motion, akin to a tai chi exercise.

The client is instructed to raise their hands with the palms up and elbows slightly bent when inhaling through the open mouth and to lower their hands with palms down and elbows slightly bent while exhaling through the nose with a closed mouth. The exercise is performed to a specified count, such as 10–15 repetitions, to maximize concentration and attention and sustain a keen awareness of anticipatory movements (see Ahmed & Boisvert, 2013, pp. 36–38; Boisvert & Ahmed, 2018, p. 314).

Version 2—One-Hand Movement

The client is instructed to maintain a "skiing posture" with slightly bent knees and their arm and hands stretched out. This time, the client is instructed to move only one hand up and down without stopping and to watch the moving hand. The client then does the same exercise with the other hand. This exercise may also be accompanied by the breathing exercise of inhaling and exhaling for a count of 10.

Version 3—Clapping Hands

The client is instructed to maintain a "skiing posture" with slightly bent knees and their arm and hands stretched out; however, this can also be accomplished by simply laying down, especially for clients who are limited in movement. This time, they simulate a slow clapping motion, never touching their hands, but keeping their hands moving (i.e., never touching their hands and never stopping their hand movement during the exercise). The client withdraws or retracts their hands just before they touch and continues the exercise for 10 repetitions in a rhythmic motion coordinated with breathing in through the nose with a closed mouth and exhaling through the open mouth.

Version 4—Erect Stance

The client is instructed to stand erect in a "robot-like manner" or to sit still and slowly perform a breathing exercise to a count of 10 or 15 without making it noticeable to anybody except to the client. The exercise may be useful to practice for younger clients in a classroom or other social situations where they need to remind themselves to pay attention to the teacher's instructions and to avoid becoming restless or engaging in daydreaming.

Version 5—Ball Catching

The client is instructed to take 10 steps slowly and face the wall while remaining still. The client is then instructed to turn around to catch the ball when they hear their name being called. The client then throws the ball back to the counselor. The counselor and client complete three to five repetitions of the exercise. Then the client is instructed to initiate the same exercise with the counselor, who will now be walking to the wall. The client and counselor complete three to five repetitions of the exercise. In this exercise, the client and counselor take turns in their role play to provide the client with the opportunity to practice both adhering to and initiating instructions. We will describe a case study with this activity in more detail next where we have included a handout to help guide your implementation.

Version 6—Partner Matching

The client partners with the therapist, and together, they try to simulate each other's hand and body movements. Each takes a turn initiating a certain hand movement or motion while the other partner tries simultaneously to mimic and follow the movement by keeping their hands close to their partner's hands but not touching and moving "in step" with the path of the partner's hand movements. Once the movement is complete, the other partner takes the lead role in initiating a movement. The exercise can continue until each participant has had a chance to initiate four to five movements. This exercise can be used to discuss impulse control, maintaining boundaries, and increasing awareness of the physical space that exists between oneself and another. This can also promote movement synchrony, brain coupling, and co-regulation with the counselor.

Each BMA exercise is brief (1–5 minutes) and can be easily integrated as an adjunct intervention in a variety of individual and group counseling formats. We have used each version with different client populations (children to elderly clients) in a variety of treatment settings: outpatient clinics, special education programs, residential programs, psychiatric inpatient settings, and nursing home settings (Ahmed & Boisvert, 2013, Boisvert & Ahmed, 2018). The BMA exercises can also be used to prepare or prime clients at the beginning of therapy sessions to optimize clients' receptivity to counseling and/or at the end of sessions to conclude therapy on a positive and productive note. In addition to practicing these exercises as part of the counseling process, clients can also be instructed to practice them in between counseling sessions to promote relaxation and to use the exercises as a positive redirection strategy to ward off unwanted feelings and thoughts. The counselor can provide the client with specific guidance as to what, when, and how often they should practice the exercises given their specific needs and goals.

FOLLOW-UP

The BMA exercises can be evaluated by clinicians in the following ways:

1. Observing clients' readiness to engage in such activities by noting their level of adherence to instructions, completion of the exercises, and observation of their attention skills, nonverbal behaviors, and body movements, which may indicate the level of relaxation the client may be demonstrating.
2. Asking feedback questions immediately after the completion of an exercise (e.g., "What did you notice as we completed that exercise?"). These questions can elicit information on how the client perceives the potential benefits of the exercises, such as enabling the client to focus more on the present, achieve a goal, and minimize preoccupation with worrisome or distressing thoughts. Discussing the perceived benefits of the exercises can also help clients integrate their understanding and knowledge of the information that the therapist shared about the nature of the exercises. As such, this feedback process helps to elicit the client's understanding and internalization of the therapeutic dialogue—an important process in all therapy and counseling sessions. The clinician can reinforce, paraphrase, or expand on any comment the client makes while giving feedback to support how the clinician conceptualizes the potential benefits of these exercises.
3. Using a written self-assessment feedback questionnaire to assess how the exercises may contribute to a client's enhanced well-being and improved relaxation.
4. Asking members, specifically in group counseling, to use a whiteboard or easel to communicate their understanding of the exercises and provide feedback about the benefits of the various BMA exercises can facilitate group discussion about the value of the exercises in promoting relaxation and self-awareness.

NEUROSCIENCE IN ACTION

Elizabeth was an adult client in an inpatient psychiatric facility with a diagnosis of mild-to-moderate cognitive disability and schizophrenia. She exhibited behavioral outbursts associated with hyperactivity and difficulty staying focused and often repeated requests and demands, such as "When can I go home?" The hospital staff members were having considerable difficulty managing Elizabeth's repeated "demands" despite their efforts to provide explanations as to why they could not comply with her requests. The client also had persistent difficulty in complying with routine care, which necessitated a referral to behavioral counseling and consultation from the staff psychologist.

This client was not considered appropriate for traditional talk therapy because of her limited ability to process verbal instruction (i.e., mild cognitive limitations) and because of her persistent behavioral problems despite prior counseling and medication treatment. The therapist, having experienced some degree of success in engaging "challenging" clinical populations in counseling (Boisvert & Ahmed, 2018, pp. 169–194), agreed to provide individual sessions primarily using BMA exercises. In addition to teaching and practicing one of the simplest elements of the BMA exercises involving standing and practicing deep breathing, as illustrated in Version 1 and Version 2, the therapist also used Version 5—ball catching. Given the client's current state of functioning, there was not much verbal explanation given. In addition, the client was not required to take turns in playing the counselor's role to give instruction.

This client responded well to the role-play demonstration and the cues provided by the therapist. She actively participated in both the deep breathing exercise and the ball catching exercise. The client was seen for a total of six sessions. The staff reported improved compliance with nursing care. However, it was not clear how much benefit this exercise had on her functioning, as her mood also became somewhat more stabilized through a medication adjustment, and the client was shortly discharged to a community placement. The important issue to note is that the client was reported to be somewhat more compliant in following the routine ward activities and was transferred to a community residential facility soon after. The exercises provided the client with training in learning how to pay attention, waiting for one's turn, developing anticipatory movement awareness, and developing general compliance in following social rules. Practicing these skills seemed to promote her adherence to rules during community outings and eventually secured her placement in a community residential program.

ETHICAL AND MULTICULTURAL CONSIDERATIONS

Before starting any BMA exercise, the current medical record should be reviewed and necessary referrals made to ensure medical appropriateness for the BMA exercises. All BMA versions can be modified to accommodate the needs of various clients, including people of all ability levels and health statuses. The instructions can be modified to ensure that clients do not perform any movements that are stressful or difficult because of their personal movement restrictions. These exercises are not a substitute for physical therapy exercises, where the goal is the restoration of physical functions that are lost or impaired. BMA exercises are not designed to repair, rehabilitate, or strengthen any aspect of physical functioning, as are the goals of physical therapy and rehabilitation, but rather to promote awareness of the client's current ability to move any of their body parts within their comfort zone without encountering any stress or discomfort.

The exercises are tailored to each client's individual range of motion, physical capabilities, interests, and degree of comfort. It is important to emphasize that there is no demand or request to engage in any movement exercise beyond the individual client's comfort level. Clients from diverse backgrounds should respond well to the exercises given the universal nature of movement and its role in our everyday lives.

POWER OF PUSH

Dee Wagner

In *The Meaning of Movement: Developmental and Clinical Perspectives of the Kestenberg Movement Profile* (Amighi et al., 1999), we learn of the work of child psychologist Janet Kestenberg Amighi. With her colleagues, she observed children's movements and identified important early childhood rhythms, half of which were referred to as *fighting* rhythms. The *fighting* rhythms play an important role in how children establish themselves as independent beings. Dance and movement therapists theorize that the way caregivers respond to a child's expression of the *fighting* rhythms affects ventral vagus nerve development and activation (Wagner & Hurst, 2018).

Polyvagal theory (Porges, 2011) identifies the importance of the ventral branch of the vagus nerve in determining the role of the dorsal vagus. When the ventral branch is engaged, the dorsal branch—which effects the body below the diaphragm—is free to promote functional digestion and reparative rest. When the ventral branch of the vagus is not engaged, the dorsal branch creates a dissociative kind of calm that compromises digestion and rest. When we can be playfully present in our bellies, we are signaling a sense of safety that invites ventral vagus nerve engagement (Porges, 2011).

From tai chi to yoga and even sports, the belly plays an important role in movement. Scientists are discovering the power of our "belly brains" to communicate with the brains in our skulls (Carabotti et al., 2015). For instance, our belly brain might communicate safety or threat to the skull brain, creating a complex neurochemical feedback loop to guide movement toward or away from various stimuli. We engage our core as we send energy out into our heads and our limbs. If we think of the spine extending like another limb out of the torso, our bodies look like starfish. We train the movements that create our posture and gestures in our first embodiment moves as we send energy out from the core, pushing our "starfish" limbs—including our heads—into our primary caregivers. This movement first happens in the womb, and after birth, as we push into the arms of whoever holds us. Functional embodiment comes from the core up through the spine—out the head, arms, and legs (Olsen & McHose, 1991). Embodiment that supports resiliency is strengthened in these interactions with our primary caregivers (Porges & Carter, 2016). Amighi and colleagues (1999) help us understand how the dances they call the *fighting* rhythms help us recognize ourselves as separate beings.

As we wrestle with containers like the womb, swaddling, and other types of holding facilitated by our caregivers, we can discover the kind of core embodiment that invites the ventral vagus nerve engagement of social engagement system functioning (Wagner & Hurst, 2018). When signals are able to travel freely up from the gut, we are more capable of sensing when situations are truly dangerous (Porges, 2011). Offering our clients an experience of pushing out with their hands from an upright seated position can get them in touch with the core of their body.

Bonnie Bainbridge Cohen talks about the starfish image and navel radiation as she invites movement that pushes out from the core (Amighi et al., 1999). An upright seated push can help clients find their "starfish" center because legs are bent, encouraging grounding through the sits bones—the bones that hurt when you ride a horse or bicycle too long. Grounding through the sits bones can help the legs feel free to react should there be danger. We understand from the trauma work of Peter Levine that freeing our legs helps us find and remain in the social engagement system because we do not feel trapped (Levine & Frederick, 1997; Levine et al., 2015).

When core energy begins to move from the arms into the hands, the body's enteric nervous system can feel freer to communicate with the head brain (Wagner, 2017; Wagner & Hurst, 2018) through ventral vagus nerve engagement and gut bacteria (Carabotti et al., 2015; Klarer et al.,

2014). Given the importance of movement in the connection of the belly brain and head brain, I created the *Power of Push* activity as a body-awareness exercise. By inviting an exploration of the emotional power inherent in a pushing move, pushing hands forward toward an important person of authority, we can help clients gain more nuanced awareness for navigating their environment and relationships (Amighi et al., 1999).

MATERIALS NEEDED

To complete this activity, you will need a portable chair and a blanket as options for therapist support and for times when clients express verbal and/or display nonverbal aversion to hand-to-hand touch.

PROCESS OF THE ACTIVITY

As counselors, we are trained to notice nonverbal cues such as posture, gestures and perhaps vocal patterning. Our training may not have invited us to notice how those nonverbal cues relate to our clients' awareness of their literal core self. When we notice these nonverbal cues, we can reflect what is being seen and heard, naming the possibility of some inner conflict—some cognitive dissonance. After this processing, it is an opportune time to introduce the *Power of Push* activity as a body-awareness experiment. Naming the activity as an experiment invites frequent pauses for observation and questioning during the exploration of sensations that arise. Rich insights can be made around topics such as boundaries, belonging, freedom of expression, right to personal space, and consent protocols.

Offering an Experiment

The *Power of Push* is best introduced tentatively as an experiment with several steps and possibly several *push* experiences. The first step suggests the possibility of the experiment. The counselor might say, "As I watch you wrestle with the issue you are telling me about, I feel an urge to invite you into an experiment. Your energy seems intense, and I keep imaging it might feel good to you to experience what I call the *Power of Push*." As counselors suggest the experiment, it is good for them to sit up on their sits bones and hold their hands out in front as if pushing into a wall that rises up from their laps out about where their knees are so their elbows do not straighten completely (see Figure 6.12). Seeing the counselor in this position helps the client picture what might happen. Counselors can explain, "When we push into something, we find ourselves," and ask, "What's it like to hear me describe the feeling many people have when they push with their hands? This awareness of self—of finding yourself?"

FIGURE 6.12 Demonstration of the Push Position

Conversations around the idea of being "too pushy" might occur. Counselors can offer, "Pushing can help us feel centered and grounded—confident we can manage our lives—handle things that happen." Perhaps adding, "The word *manage* comes from the Latin word *manus*, which means hands." After suggesting the general idea of pushing, counselors can discuss what clients might push into, which depends on the comfort level of the counselor and the client. I often invite clients to push their hands into my hands while I kneel in front of them (see Figure 6.13)—as they sit on the sofa—but I am a dance therapist and feel comfortable kneeling. Sometimes I sit beside clients on the sofa (see Figure 6.14). This positioning requires a twisting of the torso and shifting of the hips such that one knee is bent in toward the back of the sofa to bring our hands together. The hip shifting can invite greater awareness of sitting up on sits bones in preparation for the *Push* experience. Counselors can put a portable chair in front of the client and then sit in the chair for hand-to-hand push. Also, it is possible to turn the back of the chair (see Figure 6.15)—the taller part—toward the client for the client to push into the chair back. If clients are pushing into the back of a portable chair, counselors will want to anchor the chair with their bodies or some other weight.

FIGURE 6.13 Hand-to-Hand Kneeling Push

FIGURE 6.14 Hand-to-Hand, Side-by-Side Push

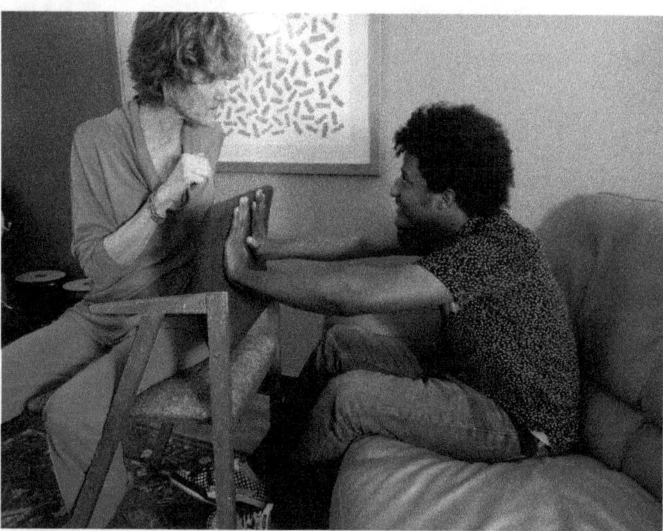

FIGURE 6.15 Hand-to-Chair Push

Processing Body Awareness

If and when clients feel up for the experiment, counselors either place themselves or the portable chair in front of wherever clients are sitting and invite them to push their hands into the counselors' hands or into the back of the chair. If the chair is being used, the therapist can ask, "What's it like to picture yourself pushing into the back of this chair that I am sitting on ... kinda sorta facing you?" If the client says something like, "silly"—as clients often do—the therapist can share that *Push* plays an important role in childhood developmental movements. When we explore sensations that begin in our belly—which we use to lift our hands to push forward—we may experience some feelings left over from childhood. A similar questioning can happen when the therapist gets in place for hand-to-hand push, "What's it like to see my hands here inviting you to push your hands into mine?" Therapists can become more and more mindful of all the many points within the *Push* experiment where pausing to invite awareness might be useful.

While a client is pushing, the counselor can ask, "Do you feel you?" If the answer is *no*, the counselor can invite a firmer push by saying, "Would it feel okay to try pushing a little harder?" If the counselor does not feel strong enough to provide adequate resistance for a client's push, perhaps switching to the chair back can provide the surface needed. If the client has an experience of feeling the core self, the counselor can ask, "What's it like to find you?" and "Where in your body do you feel you?"

Clients might also have experiences in parts of their bodies other than their core that can be further processed. A client might say something like, "I feel myself in my shoulders" rather than saying they feel themselves in their belly or core in the first *Push* experience. The counselor and client can process this body awareness. If a client is more aware of their shoulders than their core, counselors can explore ways the client may feel some hyper-responsibility suggested in the expression *shouldering adversity*. If the client is more aware of their arms, counselors can talk about how the word *arm* also means *weapon* and inquire about the possibility that the client is perhaps trying to protect themselves in some aspect of their life. With more awareness of the legs than the core, conversations could explore issues related to support. Whenever clients talk about neck pain, this offers an opportunity to explore what aspect of their lives feels like *a pain in the neck*. Of course, you will also want to ensure regular medical consultation to encourage proper treatment of any other medical problems that might exist.

The urge to shove can show up during an exploration of *Push* for those of us who have survived through types of disembodiment. If a client's first exploration of the possibility of a *Push* experience indicates an urge to shove, then the counselor can name what is called a high five as a type of *Push*. Counselors can inquire about how it might feel to imagine experiencing the short burst of *Push* that would occur if the counselor clapped one palm into one of the client's palms in what can be a customary way to celebrate accomplishment. If the idea sounds doable, then the counselor and client can do one or more mindful high fives. The high-five connection is a version of the first of the fighting rhythms identified by Kestenberg—the biting/snapping rhythm. The fact that it is forceful and brief can help it feel less threatening than the two-handed *Push*. A high five can offer belly awareness because of the quick lifting of the arms in preparation for the clap of the high-five connection, which begins with an arm-swinging motion that originates in the core. The high-five connection can become a double-handed "high five" and eventually lead to more comfort with the two-handed experiment of *Push*.

Invitation of the Belly-Brain/Head-Brain Connection

Whether or not clients feel their core self in the first *Push* experience, counselors can talk about the growing scientific validation of the importance of our "belly brains." Counselors can invite the belly-brain/head-brain connection through guiding awareness by saying, "Scientists suggest that our intuitive sensing comes from our belly brains. We have lots of nerves in our intestines, and they send messages up our spines to our head brains. As you think about your 'belly brain' connecting with your head brain, are there places in your body that feel like the information is getting kinked up?"

To invite a second experience of *Push* that perhaps encourages more core awareness, counselors can say, "When you push, it could help you connect your belly brain and your head brain. When we're struggling with something like what you were talking about before we tried the first *Push*, we can get caught up thinking we've got to figure something out in our head brains alone, and we can tense up in our necks or shoulders and cut communication off between our belly brain and our head brain. We could try a second *Push*, and we could invite you to focus on your belly this time. How's that sound?"

If the client is up for another *Push* with belly focus, the counselor can set up for the *Push* and during the *Push* say, "As you push and feel your arms and legs and hopefully whole body—as you think about your belly brain connecting with your head brain—are there any places that you feel your body cutting off the belly-to-head connection?" If there is awareness of blocking connection, then the counselor can ask, "Is there any movement you could play with that might help you find a more flowing sense of connection between your belly and your head?" The counselor might add, "As you push and move around to get more connected to your gut thoughts, does it help you feel like you have more space and time to work out the issues you were wrestling with earlier?" Counselors might ask, "Do you feel more present in your body?" And if the answer is yes, add, "How might this feeling of presence in your body help you find your path as you wrestle with this issue?"

If a client is a bodybuilder, they may have overly developed external abdominal musculature that pulls the pelvis into a tucked-tail position, even when the client is standing. If we notice this about a client, an experiment with *Push* could invite a discussion of body armor. For instance, a counselor might ask, "Do you feel the ability to hold the world at arm's length long enough to check in with yourself and get a read on what you might need in a particular moment?" When our arms feel free to move forward and pause an interaction in which we are engaged, we feel less of a need to hold our bellies rigid. Our belly brains have more freedom to function and send messages to our head brains.

FOLLOW-UP

After clients have explored some of the sensations they feel when they push into the palms of their counselor or into a chair back, processing the *Push* experience can continue for many sessions. Counselors and clients can discuss times when *Push* is useful, as well as when it is not. Using our *Push* to stand our ground tends to be deemed useful. Hands moving into the *Push* position as part of boundary setting—accompanying words requesting space—is often an example of appropriate self-care. That gesture might accompany a statement like, "Let me stop you for a moment please. I am not feeling so good. Let's come back to this discussion soon. Right now, I need to take a break." Being a "pushover" can lead to negative self-talk and, ultimately, dissociative survival patterns. Counselors and clients can redo the body-awareness exploration that the *Power of Push* provides, inviting greater mindfulness each time.

NEUROSCIENCE IN ACTION

Mason (parent) and Sam (13 years old, oldest of two siblings in a one-parent home) came in to see me because Sam was being defiant in ways that seemed out of character, according to Mason. Mason reported that Sam's teachers said things were fine at school, but at home, Sam's challenging behavior felt out of control to Mason. I explained to them that my usual goal with families is to invite the kids to help me help their parents help them, to which Sam smiled.

After Mason gave me several examples of recent dialogue between the two, Sam quickly sat up, speaking and gesturing in percussive ways. Mason cut Sam off with explanations about why Sam's behavior was clearly irrational. I asked if I might interrupt, and when they nodded their agreement, I explained that scientists have new understanding of nervous system functioning that helps us appreciate ways we interact with each other. I asked if they would be willing to try an experiment in which they each took a turn pushing into my hands, so they could experience what I call the *Power of Push*. They were both surprised but nodded curiously.

I first knelt before Sam with my palms out and said, "If it feels okay to try this, push your hands into my hands." Eagerly, Sam pushed. I said, "Can you feel you?" and Sam nodded. I said, "If you push really hard, you can feel all the way down to your feet." Sam pushed harder, nodded again, and then sighed. I moved over to Mason and said, "You wanna try it?" Mason more reluctantly reached out, touching my palms but not yet pushing. I invited, "Can you push into my hands and notice what you feel in your core?" Mason pushed in a measured sort of way. "Can you feel you?" I asked, and Mason nodded slowly.

As I moved back to my chair, I asked them, "What was it like to watch each other do that?" Sam quickly looked to Mason who remained silent. Sam looked away and got very still. I ventured, "Could you feel how pushing into someone else increases your awareness of yourself?" Sam remained still but Mason nodded slowly, so I continued, "Us therapists know that sometimes when people fight—especially kids with their parents—the fighting is less about the topic and more about energetic fighting dances—more about discovering who you are—learning to 'trust your gut' as they say. Does this make any sense?" Sam snuck a peek at Mason, who looked shaken. I asked Mason if there were any boundaries that had previously existed for Sam but had shifted recently. Mason said yes—boundaries shifted because Sam had become a teenager.

The concrete experience of the *Power of Push* elicited conversations over many sessions related to Mason's own sense of self at 13. After some time of hearing appropriate pieces of what Mason's life was like at 13, Sam began to understand why this *parental figure* seemed to have no gut sense of how to parent a teenager. The lack of core strength in Mason as Sam was turning into a teen had originally scared Sam. Feeling shakiness in Mason had increased Sam's urge to be pushy, and the increased pushiness in Sam had—in turn—increased the shakiness in Mason.

We only revisited the *Power of Push* exercise a couple of other times over the year we worked together off and on, but the felt experience of the *Power of Push* was always part of our discussions. Often, I invited Mason and Sam to see if they could sense what they felt in their bellies. Sometimes, when I invited them to tune in to their cores, I suggested that they think about all the nerves in their belly brains and how those nerves connect with their head brains to see if they noticed any places where the information might seem blocked.

The first time I suggested they notice any belly-to-head communication flow blockages, Sam immediately flipped sideways, pushing into the sofa arm. Mason looked uncomfortable. With families, I often invite the parent to try letting the child push into their hands, but because Mason was so easily triggered by Sam's *Push* moves, I had not offered this option to them. When Sam pushed into the sofa arm, I asked him, "How's it feel to push?"

He turned back forward saying, "Good."

I responded, "Yay for you for letting your body do what it wanted to do," and then to Mason I said, "Wanna offer Sam a high five?"

Mason let out a quick laugh and held up a hand, which Sam gladly and soundly slapped, exclaiming "Yeah!"

After this session, high fives became the move that ended every session. One-handed high fives evolved into two-handed high fives. In the later part of our work, the end-of-the-session two-handed high fives were from Mason to Sam and from me to each of them with an accompanying, "Go team!"

ETHICAL AND MULTICULTURAL CONSIDERATIONS

Before using this activity, it is good for counselors to seek out a colleague or another partner to explore the *Power of Push* personally. Counselors can explore *Push* in each variation so that they are prepared for various client needs and responses. If they do the exploration with a colleague, they can process their experiences together. Once counselors have experienced each *Push* themselves, then they can begin to incorporate each variation with their clients and build confidence with each administration.

When *Push* is involved, touch can feel less threatening than it does with touch that is offered for comfort, such as patting or hugging. However, all touch should be discussed before it happens to give clients an opportunity to express discomfort, and consent should always be obtained. Palm-to-palm touch is part of the agreed-upon greeting when offering a handshake, so the skin-to-skin touch that happens when doing palm-to-palm pushing may feel fine to clients, but if a client seems uncomfortable, a blanket can be draped over the counselor's hands so that skin-to-skin touch is not necessary. Pushing into a helping professional's hands more closely replicates the child/caregiver differentiating dances identified by Kestenberg and colleagues than pushing into a chair back, but both increase awareness of the core self.

Clients whose hands are not capable of pushing with palms can benefit from pushing fists and/or pushing with arms. Counselors can sit beside clients and invite pushing an arm out to the side. The counselor's hand or a pillow or blanket can provide the resistance for the client's *Push* of an elbow away from the torso out to the side. In all exploration of touch in counseling, be sure to explore the cultural definition of touch in general and as it pertains to the therapeutic encounter.

FOLLOW YOUR GUT

A Body-Mind Approach to Enhanced Career Decision Making

Christian D. Chan and Timothy J. Hakenewerth

Decision making is a highly relevant issue within career development modalities and practices (Amir et al., 2008; Niles & Harris-Bowlsbey, 2017; Tinsley, 1992), necessitating the ability to integrate in-depth counseling skills, culturally responsive practices, and career domains (Gysbers et al., 2014). Despite the prioritization of career and vocational wellness as an influential factor tied to indicators of mental health (Dieringer et al., 2017; Pisarik et al., 2017), scholarly literature has not historically linked neuroscience with career development. Several career theories and models, such as the cognitive information processing (CIP) approach and social cognitive career theory (SCCT), address this concern by focusing the tenets of their theories on executive processing and specific steps in the decision-making process (Lent et al., 1994; Reardon et al., 2011). Holland's theory involves static classifications of occupations, which is useful as a foundation (Niles & Harris-Bowlsbey, 2017). In isolation, however, the theoretical framework does not necessarily offer holistic perspectives generated by integrative frameworks and approaches, especially with fluidity shaped by contextual factors and plasticity emphasized by neuroscience. Combined with Holland's theory, CIP and SCCT operate as highly integrative frameworks and approaches instituting multiple contextual factors to wellness, future-oriented narratives, and client awareness (Bullock-Yowell et al., 2011), which ultimately inform career decision-making processes. Taking both approaches into account bridges the necessary gaps among career development, wellness, neuroscience, and counseling. Notably, both counselors and clients focusing on career concerns may overlook contextual factors connecting their awareness of barriers and opportunities facilitating client growth and wellness. Counselors may strengthen their services by assisting clients in gaining awareness and agency in their exploration of career pathways and decision-making processes.

Current research in neuroscience supports the somatic-marker hypothesis (Naqvi et al., 2006). This hypothesis posits that emotions are connected to decision making and felt through physiological states. When considering different options with uncertain consequences, the body experiences these states, which help an individual make a propitious choice. By exploring this hypothesis and eliciting greater mindful body awareness, clients may be more attuned with how they feel and how to adaptively react to these physiological states (Bingaman, 2011). With greater awareness, clients may be more comfortable making decisions and maintaining greater synchronicity between cognition and their physiological states during this process. This approach is central to the body-mind connection by illustrating the communication operating between the physiological signals of the body and the distinct complex processing and cognitive signals involved in the brain (Goss, 2016). Captured in this connection, the body and mind communicate primarily to bridge holistic aspects and integration of the whole body while assisting clients with increased empathy, connection, and compassion (Coutinho et al., 2014; Oliveira-Silva & Gonçalves, 2011). Integrating the body-mind connection more holistically, clients can capitalize on heightened awareness to produce more informed career decisions. Although research and scholarship connecting career choice are scant, career choice and decision making do not solely rely on cognitive aspects. Career choice can also be contingent on the mind communicating with the body. This perspective is representative of clients who might have more awareness of their bodies and somatic responses to a particular task or work environment. With awareness of this body response, clients may be able to use this stimulus as a prompt for cognitive reflection on health and goodness of fit in a work environment. In contrast, clients without this awareness of their body responses may continue in a work environment that adversely affects their health.

Given the importance of mind-body awareness in decision making, we created the *Follow Your Gut* activity to illustrate a holistic application of Holland's theory. Holland's theory relies heavily on the typology of RIASEC (i.e., realistic, investigative, artistic, social, enterprising, conventional) or Holland codes (Niles & Harris-Bowlsbey, 2017). The lack of neuroscience literature and career development scholarship fused together prompts this idea of using awareness to aid career exploration and choice.

FIGURE 6.16 Example Picture for Enterprising Holland Code Type

MATERIALS NEEDED

To use this activity, counselors will need the following: (a) 18 photos of work and career with three photos reserved for each Holland code type, (b) paper, and (c) pen. The photos (see Figure 6.16 for an example of the enterprising Holland code type) will prompt messages that mediate the decision-making process in critical thinking and envisioning of career pathways. The pen and paper will assist the client in noting which associations emerge within their body on a specific worker or career image. The client can use this tool to jot down feelings and responses occurring within their body to coincide with the specific images connected to specific careers.

PROCESS OF THE ACTIVITY

The *Follow Your Gut* activity requires a strong therapeutic relationship. This connection will help build the trust necessary for gaining comprehensive information about relationships, experiences, or moments influencing clients' perspectives on career or connection with their bodies. After fostering the initial therapeutic relationship and gaining a complete biopsychosocial history, the activity progresses as follows:

- Introduce the idea of the body-mind connection by helping the client reflect on moments when they noticed specific feelings in their body. Perhaps, the counselor can walk the client through a body scan as an example to help them attune to how they have previously observed their body and their connection to their body during certain experiences in their life.

- Explore the meaning of career in the lives of the client: "When I say the word 'career,' what does it mean to you?" "When I say the word 'work,' what does it mean to you?" "What are some differences you see between career and work in your own life?" "When we talk about work, what physical reactions seem to happen? If anything, how does your body react?"
- Elaborate on the activity for the client to gain permission for both counselor and client to participate in the activity: "Are you okay with trying this activity with me?"
- Offer/provide the client with pen and paper.
- Share with the client that you will be showing 18 pictures. Ask the client to use their pen and paper to take notes and observe sensations occurring within their body. Alternatively, you can provide the client with an outline of a body to write notes on or to color their sensations with art supplies for specific body parts. The client might notice their heart beating faster, they sweat more, they bristle at certain photos, or their body temperature goes up or down. Example: "I am going to show you around 18 photos. As you look at each picture, notice sensations in your body, such as feeling sweaty or hot. Also notice any internal sensations, such as your heart fluttering or that 'gut feeling.'"
- Show the client each photo in a randomized order. The images serve as a stimulus to activate implicit meaning systems and preconscious physiological responses. Spend no more than 10 seconds with each photo.
- Once you finish, provide the client with a few minutes to organize their reflections or sit with their observations.
- Discuss the meaning of the activity with the client. Returning to the body scan might be helpful to prompt the client. Other example questions for reflection include the following: "What kind of thoughts, feelings, and bodily responses did you include in response to the photos?" "How would you describe your body reacting to the photos?" "How did you notice your body responding in the course of the activity?"
- To prompt more responses concerning decision making with career choices, you can ask the client the following questions: "If those sensations could speak about a career, what would they be saying?" "Given what you felt about those images, how might they be influencing your thoughts about your career?" "If those sensations could speak about specific jobs or careers in the photos, what would they say?" "How do you think these reactions are helping/hindering your career decisions?"

FOLLOW-UP

Because a major focus of the activity emphasizes awareness, counselors can benefit from integrating reflective questions:

- "As we complete the activity, what are your initial reflections? Did your body react to certain images? What images did you gravitate to the most? What did you feel connected to the most?"
- "Since the last time we participated in the activity, have you noticed anything change? How have you noticed your body responding?"

If feasible, a heart-rate variability (HRV) device may be useful in determining HRV in response to certain stimuli or images. HRV devices can be worn on the chest, wrist, finger, and/or ear.

NEUROSCIENCE IN ACTION

Janet (pseudonym) was a Latinx, cisgender, heterosexual, able-bodied woman with Bolivian heritage seeking counseling services in response to a recent breakup and prior marital issues. I (Christian) was her first counselor in an outpatient setting at a community agency since she had never sought counseling services in any setting. Throughout the course of five counseling meetings, it became apparent that she was experiencing dissatisfaction with her current position of employment as the front desk receptionist at a doctor's office. She was considering a career change but felt somewhat unsure about her direction and wary of going to career centers or taking examinations in regard to her career choices. Her recent breakup with a boyfriend and prior marital issues prompted her "change of heart": she wanted to follow more closely with what her heart wanted. She also spoke heavily of her body responding in certain ways when she was beginning to be tearful or when she spoke about her career—namely, some sadness she could feel in certain parts of her body. Janet enjoyed speaking with me as the counselor about her current career concerns because of a feeling that I could understand her experiences more so than someone at a career center. As the counselor, I felt, by the seventh weekly meeting with Janet, that she might be open to participating in a creative activity, given the rapport I built with her over nearly 2 months of consistent sessions.

After I explained the activity to her, Janet expressed excitement for creative activities involved in counseling. I handed her a pen and paper with the explanation that I would show 18 photos of different types of careers and asked her to take note of any sensations felt in her body similar to her prior descriptions. I asked her to focus on how her body might be responding rather than her thoughts about them since I would flash through each photo for no more than 10 seconds. After showing her all 18 photos, I gave her a few minutes before transitioning into processing and reflection. Janet described that her heart felt specifically different when she noticed women in the pictures using the creative arts (artistic) and building their own businesses (enterprising). She explained that her heart started beating faster in response to those photos, but, concurrently, she felt more "grounded" when viewing the specific images. Over the next 2 weeks, I asked her to reflect on her body responses as she thought about both images and, subsequently, career possibilities. I explored the connection between body responses and our thought processes that reflect choices. Two weeks later, I asked her if any of her responses had changed. In her response, Janet illustrated that she felt more confident to take on this career change and wanted this change to be part of her counseling plan. Janet later expressed that she began conducting research on new job opportunities and shared them during counseling sessions. Although we continued to work on a variety of other concerns in counseling, Janet eventually switched into an upper management position within a graphic design company.

ETHICAL AND MULTICULTURAL CONSIDERATIONS

It is necessary to ground this activity with complete social, cultural, and contextual information about clients' presenting concerns. Counselors will need to institute a comprehensive process of determining how mental health, wellness, and career concerns might be interconnected. Referring to the activity, specific images may trigger certain experiences for clients. Some experiences may be traumatic or elicit significant emotional reactions. Counselors can assess for client readiness with such an activity.

Similarly, counselors can consider the culturally responsive nature aimed toward unifying career knowledge domains, career development practices, and mental health. Counselors can serve as culture brokers by noting the differences in mental health practices in a wide array of cultural contexts, especially common norms of mental health. Although clients might have a physiological response toward their own culturally informed lens regarding specific career and mental health experiences, clients may not have a preexisting framework for understanding services associated with mental health. When using this activity, counselors should also be intentional about the images used by establishing a relationship with the client and gaining more context as to the salience and interpretation of specific careers. Counselors can heavily consider the presence of the photos to ensure they are relatable and representative to the client (e.g., having multiple career photos of women to remain conscious of representation for services with a female client). Thus counselors can heavily consider the importance of discussing the meaning of the body-mind connection, the manner in which the client is accessing the construct, and the brokering of career interpretations and pathways.

ANCILLARY MATERIALS

The following items can serve as ancillary materials for counselors wishing to implement this activity, especially if they need ideas for images associated with specific careers:

- For photos, we also recommend visiting links for free photo use and stock photos (e.g., www.unsplash.com).
- Bureau of Labor Statistics. (2018). *Occupational outlook handbook*. https://www.bls.gov/ooh/
- Gottfredson, G. D., & Holland, J. L. (1996). *Dictionary of Holland occupational codes*. Psychological Assessment Resources, Inc.
- Holland, J. L. (1997). *Making vocational choices: A theory of vocational personalities and work environments* (3rd ed.). Psychological Assessment Resources, Inc.
- O*Net. (n.d.). *O*NET online*. https://www.onetonline.org/

CLOSING THOUGHTS

The purpose of this chapter was to explore how the brain extends into the body and how awareness of and intervention with the embodied brain can promote therapeutic gains. From pain to exercise, awareness, and direct movement, the neuroeducation exercises in this chapter showed ways that clinicians capitalized on the brain-body-mind-environment connection to bring about health and wellness. As you reflect on the activities in this chapter, continue to think through the complex interactions of the brain throughout the entire body. Before moving on to the next chapter, consider the following reflection questions:

REFLECTION QUESTIONS

1. How does your gut affect your thoughts, feelings, and behaviors?
2. How might you help clients to apply these concepts in their lives?
3. Which of the neuroeducation activities did you like the most? How might you incorporate the activity into your clinical work?

CREDITS

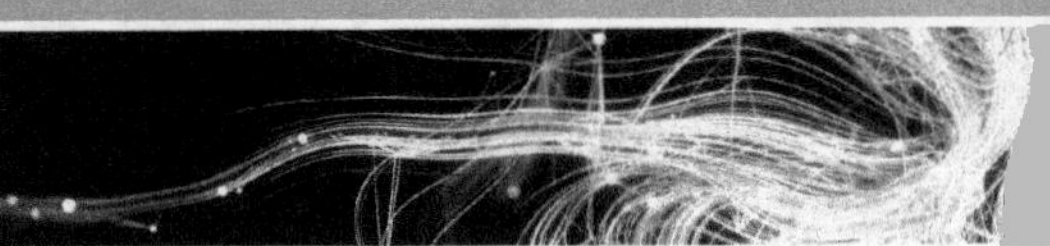

CHAPTER 7

The Social-Emotional Brain Systems

Human brains assume proximity to their predictable social environments. When proximity is maintained or reestablished, the brain is simply less vigilant for potential threats, because it is embedded within the social environment to which it is adapted.

—Lane Beckes and James A. Coan

CHAPTER OBJECTIVES

1. Identify neuroscience-informed theories of emotions and emotion regulation.
2. Discuss the role social connection plays in emotion regulation.
3. Apply neuroeducation of emotions and emotion regulation to clinical work.

INTRODUCTION

Think about the last person you talked to in your office or work setting. What struggles did they share? What areas of their lives did they most want to improve? Odds are their struggles and goals related in some way to emotions. They either wanted to experience less of one emotion, more of another emotion, or change behavioral outcomes related to an emotion (e.g., stop yelling when feeling anxious or exercise more despite feeling unmotivated). In fact, many serious mental health concerns (e.g., suicidal behaviors, addiction) are increasingly conceptualized in part as problems of inadequate emotion regulation skills (Bryan et al., 2013; Hormes et al., 2014). Emotion regulation is also deeply rooted in individual's relationship history and current social environment (Beckes & Coan, 2011). Our nervous systems rely on human connection to help regulate emotions, and when they are not available, our brains and bodies have to work much harder to regulate arousal. Helping clients understand and modify emotions is at the heart of our work as mental health professionals (see Figure 7.1). Having a neuroscience-informed understanding of emotions can help support and guide this important work.

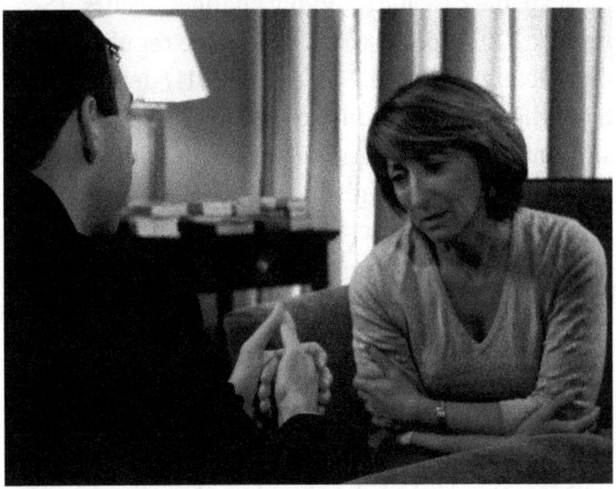

FIGURE 7.1 Emotion-Focused Work in Therapy

Unfortunately, a unified and easy to understand neuroscience-informed definition of emotion does not yet exist (Clark-Polner et al., 2016). Scientists and scholars vary greatly in their understanding and study of human emotion (Scarantino, 2016). For readers interested in a deep dive into the science of emotions, also called affective neuroscience, the academic text *Handbook of Emotions* (4th ed.) offers a comprehensive and impeccably referenced source. We will briefly introduce two leading contemporary theories of emotion that can serve as templates for viewing the neuroeducation activities offered in this chapter.

Clark-Polner et al. (2016) identified two broad theories of emotion: classical theories and construction theories. The classical view "posits that individual emotions have diagnostic psychological and neurobiological features, in which there should be relatively (if any) variation across instances" (p. 153). Scarantino (2016) reviewed one popular classical theory: the basic theory of emotions. This theory, made popular by researchers such as Paul Ekman, Robert Levenson, and Jaak Panksepp, emphasizes the existence of discrete emotional categories (e.g., anger, surprise, happiness, sadness) that have evolved to support our navigation of life tasks (i.e., activities that move us toward pleasure and away from pain). According to this theory, basic emotions are universal and have distinct physical signatures in the body (e.g., anger is associated with a particular facial expression, autonomic nervous system response, and specific physiology). Once a basic emotion is triggered, "an inescapable cascade of bodily changes occurs" (Scarantino, 2016, p. 21) that can only be regulated, not completely inhibited. Panksepp (2011) defended the basic theory of emotions perspective, citing evidence supporting the evolutionary stratification of brain functions and highlighting the existence of primary-process affect across human and animal species. Damasio and Carvalho (2013) further argued for an evolutionary and body-based perspective on emotions, emphasizing the automatic physiological reactions we have that help us move toward homeostasis and the mental experiences (i.e., feelings) we generate related to those body states. Research and theories that include being able to "read" (either by a person or by artificial intelligence technology) emotions by looking at a person's facial expressions (Figure 7.2) and/or identifying and intervening with specific physiological systems in relationship to particular emotions are likely operating from a basic theory of emotions assumption.

FIGURE 7.2 Reading Facial Expressions

Constructionist theorists argue, however, that "emotion categories are unlikely to have distinct and innate physical correlates within the brain that are replicable across different contexts" (Clark-Polner et al., 2016, p. 153). These theorists point out that parts of the brain commonly implicated in emotional experiences (e.g., amygdala, basil ganglia, ventral striatum, orbitofrontal cortex) are involved in a wide range of emotions and active in nonemotional tasks (Clark-Polner et al., 2016). Lisa Feldman Barrett's theory of constructed emotion is one empirically supported constructionist theory (Barrett, 2017; Barrett et al., 2016; Siegel et al., 2018). Barrett (2017) defined emotions as "meaning ... they explain your interoceptive changes and corresponding affective feelings, in relation to the situation ... they are a prescription for action" (p. 126). Barrett (2017) argued that there are no generalizable objective biological signatures of emotion and instead emphasized that emotions are best examined and understood within individuals' unique contextual lives. Barrett asserted that although emotions are often experienced as uncontrollable impulses, they are, in fact, constructed mental models that can be modified. Research and theories that emphasize understanding individuals' unique meaning making related to emotions and/or focus on cognitive control of emotional experiences are likely grounded in constructionist theories.

Some researchers focus more on theories of emotion generation, delineating emotions as products of either top-down or bottom-up processes (Figure 7.3; McRae et al., 2012; Silvers & Moreira., 2019).

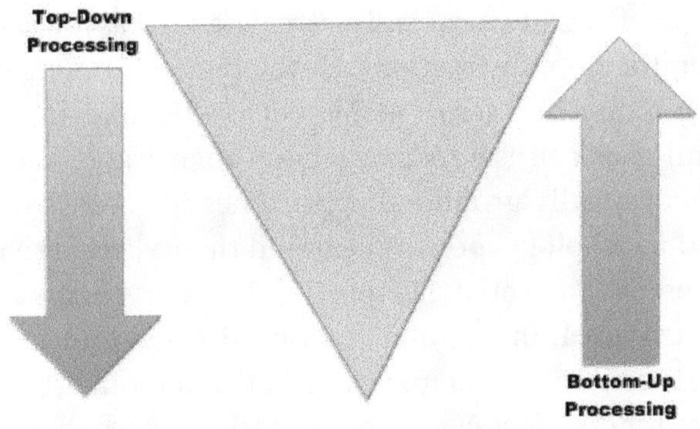

FIGURE 7.3 Top-Down, Bottom-Up Processing

Top-down emotion generation generally refers to more cognitive-oriented processes, such as "the elicitation of emotion by the activation of appraisals that a situation is relevant to an individual's goals" (McRae et al., 2012, p. 254). For example, an individual may experience disappointment at receiving a "B" on a paper because earning "As" is an important family value and will help them get into medical school, a long-term goal. Bottom-up emotion generation is more so outside of conscious awareness and is thought to be related to a stimulus that has evolutionary biological significance, such as the fear that is elicited at the sight of a snake. Bottom-up emotion generation and regulation may also be related to individuals' general states of well-being (i.e., basal states).

Regardless of one's adherence to the theories discussed earlier, or a different theory altogether, interest in regulating emotions is a paramount clinical concern. Silvers and Moreira (2019) define emotion regulation as "the use of conscious or unconscious processes that change the nature, intensity or duration of one's emotions" (p. 35). This definition implies that emotion regulation can be implicit (and likely affect more bottom-up emotion generation) or explicit (targeting emotion generated from more top-down processes; McRae et al., 2012). Individuals' abilities to regulate emotion tends to improve naturally over the course of development, aligning with brain changes, most notably strengthened connections between the prefrontal systems and the amygdala (Martin & Ochsner, 2016). However, experiences of trauma, substance use, and exposure to other adverse experiences can inhibit this natural developmental progression, leading to children, adolescents, and adults with underdeveloped neural circuitry to support regulation. Fostering individuals' capacity to regulate emotions can take various forms in counseling.

First and foremost, individuals must attend to the basic biological needs of adequate sleep, sufficient nutrition, and physical activity (Epel et al., 2016). These factors contribute to individuals' baseline emotional states, appraisal of stimuli, and neurobiological processes and brain systems needed to flexibly respond to emotionally provocative experiences. This reality is likely not new to anyone; the colloquial term "hangry" and the familiarity of being irritable or sensitive after a bad night's sleep are evidence of the widespread intuitive first-person knowledge and experience of the effect of biological needs on emotion regulation capacity. The influence of environmental and societal conditions (e.g., poverty, racism, mass shootings, natural disasters) that contribute to individuals' perceived and/or actual distress can also strain individuals' regulation capacity (Raio et al., 2013). Higher levels of stress, both chronic and acute, impede individuals' ability to activate cognitive control strategies to regulate emotion.

Further, one must acknowledge and attend to the role relationships and connections play in both the development and maintenance of a regulated emotional life. Individuals' emotion regulation capacity is greatly influenced by relational experiences in early childhood and beyond (Martin & Ochsner, 2016). Often, individuals' regulation strategies reflect patterns modeled to them by early caregivers and are clues to a person's unmet needs or desires. Greenberg (2007) espoused a view of emotion regulation that emphasizes "how people synthesize adaptive responses to the world rather than how they control dysregulated responses" (p. 415). He noted that this view of emotion might require more implicit experiential learning (e.g., properties of relationships in which all emotions are acknowledged, validated, and understood in terms of their adaptive function) versus explicit conceptual learning (e.g., teaching skills to regulate disruptive or unwanted emotions). The implicit view of emotion regulation is connected to a contemporary neuroscience-informed theory called social baseline theory. According to social baseline theorists Beckes and Coan (2011), social proximity with trusted others downregulates the brain's vigilance system (i.e., emotional self-regulation). Coan et al. (2006) first identified this neurological phenomenon in a functional magnetic resonance imaging–based hand-holding experiment with married couples. To the surprise of the researchers, the women who were getting electric shocks showed less activation in neural systems associated with regulation when holding the hand of their spouses. The better the quality of the marriage, the less activation of the threat response circuitry. Caring connection, the researchers proposed, is the "baseline" condition for which the brain has adapted and best functions, and when in connection with a trusted other, the brain does not have to work as hard (i.e., activate the threat response system) to regulate (see Figure 7.4).

FIGURE 7.4 Connection

Linking back to Greenberg (2007), "the provision of a safe, validating, supportive, and empathic environment is the first level of intervention that helps soothe and regulate automatically generated underregulated distress" (p. 416). Offering clients this implicitly regulatory type of relationship and helping them develop similar capacities outside of therapy is paramount in any neuroscience-informed approach to counseling.

Finally, there is supporting evidence for some cognitive approaches to emotion regulation (Etkin et al., 2015). The major themes of these approaches include (1) awareness of emotional experience, (2) accurate identification of emotion, and (3) engagement in some type of cognitive control strategy (e.g., reappraisal, suppression, distraction). Developing awareness is a common aim across many therapeutic modalities, and thus counselors can rely on their established theoretically grounded approaches (e.g., individual psychology, person-centered theory, cognitive therapy, existential therapy, Gestalt theory) for work in this area. In addition, various forms of mindfulness activities (e.g., mindfulness meditation, breath awareness practices, yoga, tai chi) and body-based therapies, such as those covered in Chapter 6, offer guided, structured ways to develop greater awareness of bodily states and associated emotions. Evidence suggests that such awareness practices can grow the parts of the brain (e.g., prefrontal regions) and strengthen connections (e.g., prefrontal regions to the amygdala) that are most active in top-down regulation (Siegel, 2009).

Once a person becomes aware of their emotions, it can be helpful to label them accurately (Kashdan et al., 2015; Starr et al., 2019). Kashdan and colleagues (2015) discussed the value of emotion differentiation, also sometimes referred to as emotional granularity, noting that individuals who can label their emotional experiences with a high degree of specificity tend to experience less distress and are able to regulate in more healthy and effective ways. Starr and colleagues (2019) found supporting empirical evidence for this idea, discovering a correlation between adolescents' abilities to differentiate negative emotion and depression in response to stress. The researchers stated that "affect labeling reduces emotional reactivity and bolsters emotion regulation strategies, which may protect against development of depression" (p. 9; see Figure 7.5). Relatedly, Dan Siegel (2010a) popularized the phrase "name it to tame it," which is a helpful way to remember the concept of emotion differentiation.

The third theme relates to strategies that promote regulation through cognitive control. The parts of the brain most implicated in the use of cognitive top-down management of emotion include the dorsolateral prefrontal cortex, the posterior parietal cortex, dorsomedial prefrontal cortex, the ventromedial prefrontal cortex, and the ventrolateral prefrontal cortex (Silvers & Moreira 2019). Silvers and Moreira (2019) noted that interactions between these regions and the amygdala support reappraisal techniques in

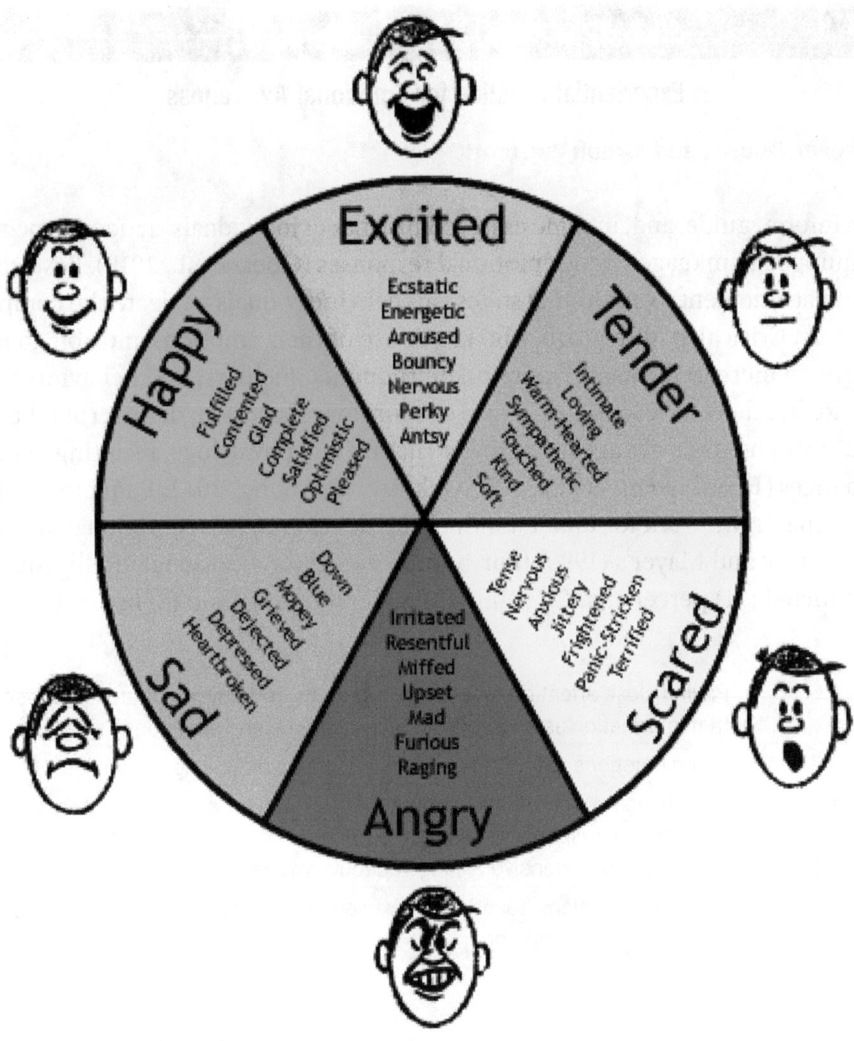

FIGURE 7.5 Affect Labeling

particular. Reappraisal (Figure 7.6), intentionally modifying one's thoughts about an emotionally stimulating situation or event, has been one of the most studied cognitive control methods (Etkin et al., 2015). Other methods of explicit regulation include emotional distancing, distraction, and suppression.

NEUROEDUCATION ACTIVITIES

This chapter includes six neuroeducation activities that relate to the social and emotional brain. You will note the underlying assumptions of both classical and constructionist views of emotion and various strategies linked to implicit and explicit emotion regulation.

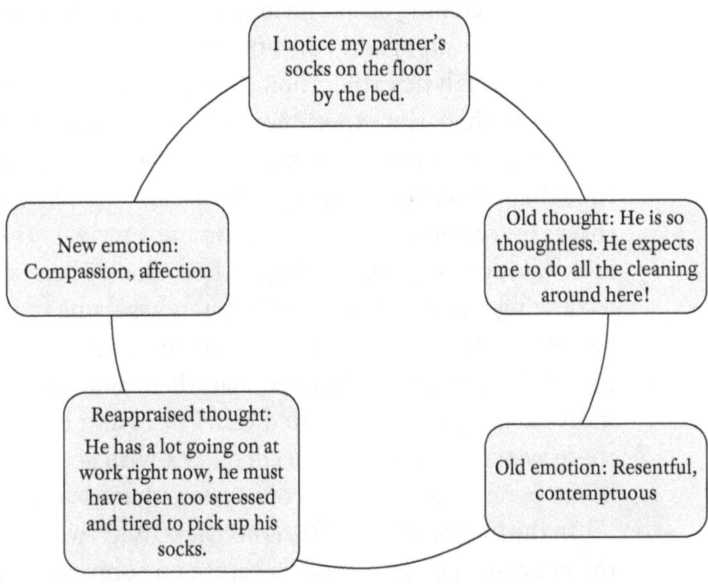

FIGURE 7.6 Example of Reappraisal

COMPASSIONATE DISCERNMENT

An Experiential Practice for Emotional Awareness

Elizabeth A. Keller-Dupree and Jordan Westcott

Emotions can inform, guide, and, in some cases, commandeer individuals' actions, especially when they feel ill equipped to manage strong emotional responses (Goetz et al., 2010). Fostering a sense of curiosity and attunement to emotional states can help individuals navigate the complexities of lived experiences. Critically, individuals who are aware of their emotions and able to label them accurately have an increased capacity to regulate thoughts, feelings, and behaviors (Salovey & Mayer, 1990). Researchers have found empirical support for this notion, discovering that cognitive and emotional awareness can change the brain's structure and physiology, resulting in meaningful behavioral changes (Felmingham et al., 2007; Makinson & Young, 2012; Paquette et al., 2003).

One conceptual framework for understanding the development of emotional awareness and regulation is Salovey and Mayer's (1990) four-branch model for emotional intelligence (EI). The four branches include (1) perceiving, (2) using, (3) understanding, and (4) managing emotions.

Perceiving	Paying close attention to feelings, thoughts, and physical states and then using that information as an appraisal of self, others, and situations.
Using	Using emotions to facilitate logical and creative thinking processes.
Understanding	Identifying how emotions connect to relationships, appreciating the complexity of emotional responses, valuing the nuances of emotional differentiation, and developing an extensive feeling vocabulary to relay emotional experiences.
Managing	Choosing emotions based on their usefulness, leading to improved intra- and interpersonal functioning.

Each branch informs the function of the next (Mayer et al., 2008). Although some individuals have a greater starting point for EI abilities based on genetic makeup and early life experiences, research on neuroplasticity overwhelmingly supports the idea that new experiences continually shape a developing brain, including the ability to develop EI (Goleman, 2011).

A second important concept related to emotional awareness and regulation is compassion. In a meta-analytic exploration of compassion's evolutionary underpinnings, Goetz et al. (2010) explained that "the experience of emotion is thought to serve as an internal signaling device, providing information about events in the environment and guiding the individual's patterns of thought and action in appropriate fashion" (p. 361). The brain is adaptively hardwired for quick threat detection and action to promote survival. This largely automatic processing can lead to faulty assumptions and unhelpful behaviors. There are significant benefits in the modern world to slowing down and more deliberately assessing the emotions that are influencing thoughts and behaviors. Taking a compassion-oriented approach to emotional awareness may be particularly useful. Goetz et al. (2010) noted that when compassion is engaged through an experiential process, individuals report decelerated heart rates and increased respiratory sinus arrhythmia. Both of these systemic processes are correlated with activation of the vagus nerve, a critical component of the parasympathetic nervous system that has evolved to support caretaking and attachment.

In the *Compassionate Discernment* activity, we built upon Salovey and Mayer's model of EI and the neuroscience-informed literature on compassion to offer individuals a reflective experiential approach to accurate self-appraisal and effective regulation of affective states. Compassion is a caring posturing to the self and others; discernment is an acumen for distinction. Together, the activity title colloquially means to care enough about oneself to find the right words to relay his/her experience accurately.

MATERIALS NEEDED

- Feelings wheel or
- Smart device (phone, tablet, etc.)

PROCESS OF THE ACTIVITY

The *Compassionate Discernment* activity is designed for clients ages 10 and older. The activity is useful for clients who revisit emotion-based stories in counseling but struggle to identify the feeling word(s) associated with the story. It is also useful for clients who overuse an underdescriptive or inaccurate feeling word. Feelings are not inherently right or wrong/good or bad, but sometimes clients can struggle to correctly identify their feelings so that they can be useful in motivating or providing insight into the client's life. The following steps outline the *Compassionate Discernment* process.

Step 1. Defining and discussing compassionate discernment. The first step of the neuroeducation activity is to introduce the idea of compassionate discernment to the client. An example explanation is as follows:

Compassionate discernment is a fancy way of saying "I care about myself enough to find the right word to explain my feelings." It is important that we "find the right word" when we are explaining our experience because our words have a lot of power and influence on our thoughts, feelings, and behaviors. Every time we have an experience, our brain connects that experience with how we talk to ourselves about that experience. This develops a neural pathway in the brain. If we mislabel our feelings, we, in essence, create an inaccurate neural pathway. In neuroscience talk, we need to name it to tame it.

Step 2. Practicing compassionate discernment using a real-life scenario. The second step involves supporting the client in applying the compassionate discernment concept to one of their real-life situations, for example, saying the following:

> I am wondering if you would be open to practicing a Compassionate Discernment exercise with me right now. Doing so may also open your mind and heart to the choices you make about how you wish to respond to that situation. Are you interested in trying it out?

If the client consents, we will then ask them to consider a recent real-life situation in which they felt an emotional response. Using a technology-medium (e.g., smartphone, computer, tablet) with access to the Internet, we instruct the client to open a blank Internet browser page and access the dictionary page through a search engine (e.g., Google, Bing, Yahoo, etc.). Next, we ask them to enter a feeling word tied to the emotion-provoking situation. Some clients may experience difficulty identifying a feeling word, and in such cases, we encourage the client to foster a compassionate approach to curiosity and exploration by stating, "It's okay to hold a feeling word very loosely. Feel free to use really tentative language like 'maybe I was feeling ... '" If necessary, a feeling wheel or feeling chart could also be used to facilitate the word selection (see Figure 7.7; Roberts, 2019). The client will then type a feeling word associated with the story. For example, if the client stated that being overlooked for a promotion led him to feel "angry," then he would type "angry" into the dictionary search field. This step parallels the perceiving branch in the four-branch EI model (Salovey & Mayer, 1990).

We then ask the client to read the definition of the feeling word and decide if that explanation captures their lived experience, representing the understanding emotions branch of the EI model. If the definition does not resonate with the client, we encourage them to consider synonyms to that feeling word (e.g., irritated, mad, annoyed, cross, vexed). We ask the client to click the hyperlink to synonyms that more accurately reflect their experience of the event, with each search involving reading the definition, considering the accuracy of the description, and viewing synonyms to the word for a more discerning choice. This step represents the using emotions branch of the EI model in which the client expands the feeling vocabulary and attunement to their emotional experience. This experiential walk-through continues until the client confirms the word choice that they believe most accurately conveys their emotional experience.

FOLLOW-UP

Following the experiential walk-through, we facilitate a debriefing using the following questions:

- How did your final word differ from your original word?
- How do you notice these two words differently in your body?
- Now that you have accurately described your feeling, what do you want to do with it, if anything?

We often encourage the client to practice *Compassionate Discernment* with multiple situations to enhance familiarity with the experiential technique, thus building efficacy. Across sessions, we assess the effectiveness of a client's use of the *Compassionate Discernment* activity by noticing changes, improvements, or deepening of the client's affective vocabulary and emotion regulation capacity. We particularly attend to the client's emotional hastiness (reactivity) versus affective processing (deliberate, contemplative exploration of affective states) as a metric for EI improvements.

NEUROSCIENCE IN ACTION

I (Elizabeth) used *Compassionate Discernment* with Client J, a 16-year-old female seeking therapy for self-harm behaviors. In session, she often discussed her conflict with her parents and with peers at school. I introduced her to *Compassionate Discernment* as a means to improve her emotional awareness and affective regulation related to those situations. I first defined compassionate discernment (as noted earlier) and then invited J to practice together. The following transcript reflects our engagement in the *Compassionate Discernment* process.

Counselor: J, I know that last week we talked about how several life situations were creating some strong feelings for you—feelings that felt nearly unmanageable. I mentioned at the end of the session that this week we could use our time together to learn about and practice an in-the-moment experience to help with naming and understanding those strong feelings. Are you interested in trying out that activity today?

J: Sure.

Counselor: Okay, the activity is called *Compassionate Discernment.* It sounds like a big title, but really, it simply means that you care about yourself enough to find the right word for what you are feeling. Compassion means to care. Discernment means to choose. So, to practice *Compassionate Discernment,* let's begin with this question. What is a recent situation in which you had a "big feeling," something that occurred within the past week?

J: Well, I had a huge fight with my parents last week and ended up losing my phone privileges.

Counselor: Okay, talk me through the fight—what happened?

J: Well, they came up to me and accused me of texting cuss words to my friends and planning to get booze. Of course, I denied it, but, apparently, they had some way of seeing my actual text messages. So, then they were mad at me for lying. The whole thing got bad real fast. My parents were yelling at me and saying how disappointed they were with me. And then they took my phone away for a week.

Counselor: Sounds like a hard situation for you. Thank you for sharing it with me. I can think of a lot of feelings associated with that fight. If you had to identify a feeling word that you think captures that experience with your parents, what feeling word would you choose? You felt ____ (what)?

J: I don't know.

Counselor: It's okay not to know the exact word or the right word. Maybe start with a very tentative stance ... like maybe I felt ____ (what). If you use that stem "maybe I felt," what feelings word might you choose?

J: Umm ... maybe I felt mad.

Counselor: Ok. So, maybe you felt mad in that moment. Here is where we compassionately discern. I'm going to hand you my smartphone, and I want you to pull up an open browser page. Type in the word "mad" and hit enter. You see the word "mad" on your screen?

J: Yes.

Counselor: Great. Now read the definition. Does that definition match your feeling in the moment with your parents? Is that the right word?

J: Um.... Kind of.

Counselor: Alright. That word kind of captures what you were feeling. Close, but not quite. Now I want you to look at the words that are hyperlinked in blue. Do you see them?

J: Yes.

Counselor: Can you read aloud a couple of those words?

J: Sure. Like, angry, furious, and irate. Is that what you mean?

Counselor: Yes. Those are synonyms. They are like the word "mad" but are slightly different. Take a couple minutes and click on a couple of those hyperlinks. Read the definition and see if those words more accurately capture the "big feeling" you had with your parents during that fight.

J: [Client searches through the words angry, furious, irate, and enraged]. I can't find a word that gets it.

Counselor: That's okay. That's exactly the point of this activity. If we are building a story around our feelings in a hard situation, we want to make sure we are accurately labeling that feeling word.

J: Maybe I didn't feel mad. Maybe I felt hurt.

Counselor: Ok then. Let's start over. Go back to the original browser screen and type in the word "hurt." Then do the same steps—read the definition, consider the hyperlinked blue synonyms, and try to find the right word to describe the "big feelings" of that fight.

J: [Client searches through the words injure, damage, wound, upset, sadness, sorry].

Counselor: Can you talk me through what you are reading and considering?

J: Yep. I clicked on "upset," and it was close but not really big enough. I went to "unnerved" because it was on the screen. It was closer. Then I saw "disheartened." That's the word. I felt disheartened."

Counselor: Okay J. Read the definition out loud. Disheartened means what?

J: To cause someone to lose determination or confidence.

Counselor: You felt disheartened because of the conflict with your parents.

J: Yes. I often feel disheartened. I lose confidence because they lose confidence in me.

Counselor: What an incredibly challenging feeling to have with your parents. J, what is it like to finally be able to label that experience?

J: Weird because I wouldn't have known that word. But it's the right word. It's more than mad. It's different than mad. It's like upset, but it's bigger than upset.

Counselor: It's clarifying. It showed you a different more accurate feeling.

J: You know, I never really feel angry, so I don't know why I started with the word "mad." I never get mad. I usually just leave the situation altogether.

Counselor: You withdraw when you hurt. You retreat when you feel disheartened. You feel discouraged in those moments. It makes me wonder; we have talked a lot about your conflict with friends. Is this the same pattern you have with your peers—not just with your family?

J: Yep. I just check out.

Outside of the therapy room, the client was invited to practice *Compassionate Discernment* with a minimum of one other "big feeling" situation between the upcoming therapy sessions. In the next session, the client's *Compassionate Discernment* experience was debriefed with the therapist, leading to a discussion about how the brain and body experience these affective moments.

Counselor: I'm excited to see that when you have used *Compassionate Discernment* this week, you have been able to better identify what you have been feeling. Here is why that process is so important. Our emotions are like signals that alert us to what is happening within us and within the world around us. When we compassionately and patiently hold curiosity about what we are experiencing, it slows down our brain and body. Instead of reacting—like shutting down—we get curious about our feelings, thus slowing our reactive process. As we slow down, we physically calm our mind and body, allowing us to better label our experience, use it, understand it, and, ultimately, determine a value-congruent action for how we wish to proceed behaviorally. Over time, as we deliberately engage in this emotional awareness and regulation process, we initiate a rerouting of our own brain connections, allowing us to respond and behave differently in "big feeling" situations.

Client J seemed to appreciate the information about the mind and body, particularly acknowledging how much she likes the slow down part. Over time, she became more fluent in her emotional vocabulary and began to better manage her emotions. She was not as overwhelmed by "big feelings," and she became better able to voice her experience in the moment. She used *Compassionate Discernment* both on her smartphone and, sometimes, in a physical journal. At first, her emotional inquiry began with exaggerated tentative language (for example, "I think maybe I just might be feeling," or "Perhaps, in that moment, I was feeling..."). The added tentative tone and posture allowed the client to "not know" and just "be curious" about the feeling. This orientation to the activity helped the client embrace self-compassion and feel safe to try feeling words when she was accustomed to the default statement of "I don't know."

Two years after beginning therapy, Client J came to a therapy session with a screenshot of a word image. The discussion unfolded as follows:

J: I have a new word to show you.

Counselor: A word? A *Compassionate Discernment* word?

J: Yep! [Turning the phone to the counselor]. Have you heard of this one?

Counselor: Nope. I'm not sure I can even pronounce it. What is it, and what does it mean?

J: The word is "sophrosyne," an ancient Greek concept for soundness of mind and well-balanced qualities, such as moderation, self-control, and temperance. This word reflects my goals for daily living.

Counselor: That sounds like a worthwhile goal if I have ever heard of one. Thanks for showing it to me! I want to hear all about this—how you found this word, what it personally means to you, and how you intend to practice it.

This session demonstrated that when clients integrate this activity into practice, *Compassionate Discernment* can be used not only for "big feelings" associated with "negative" experiences but also for "positive" ones.

ETHICAL AND MULTICULTURAL CONSIDERATIONS

A primary ethical concern relates to client autonomy. Counselors can feel pulled to identify an emotion word for the client; however, it is very important that clients choose and are affirmed in their choice. An additional consideration is the client's primary language. This exercise may be especially difficult to complete with clients who are not fluent in the primary language that the counselor speaks. Similarly, clients' use of cultural dialect may affect the utility of this exercise, as there may not be dictionary definitions or synonyms available. Counselors should also be aware that clients from diverse backgrounds, including different socioeconomic backgrounds, may have difficulty using complex emotional language. Relatedly, those with cognitive or developmental delays/disabilities may encounter similar struggles. For these situations, alternative tools (such as the feeling wheel depicted in Figure 7.7) may be necessary to provide full benefit to all clients. Lastly, counselors should attend to clients' access to the required technology (e.g., a smartphone, a computer), as some clients may lack access to resources needed to practice the activity on their own.

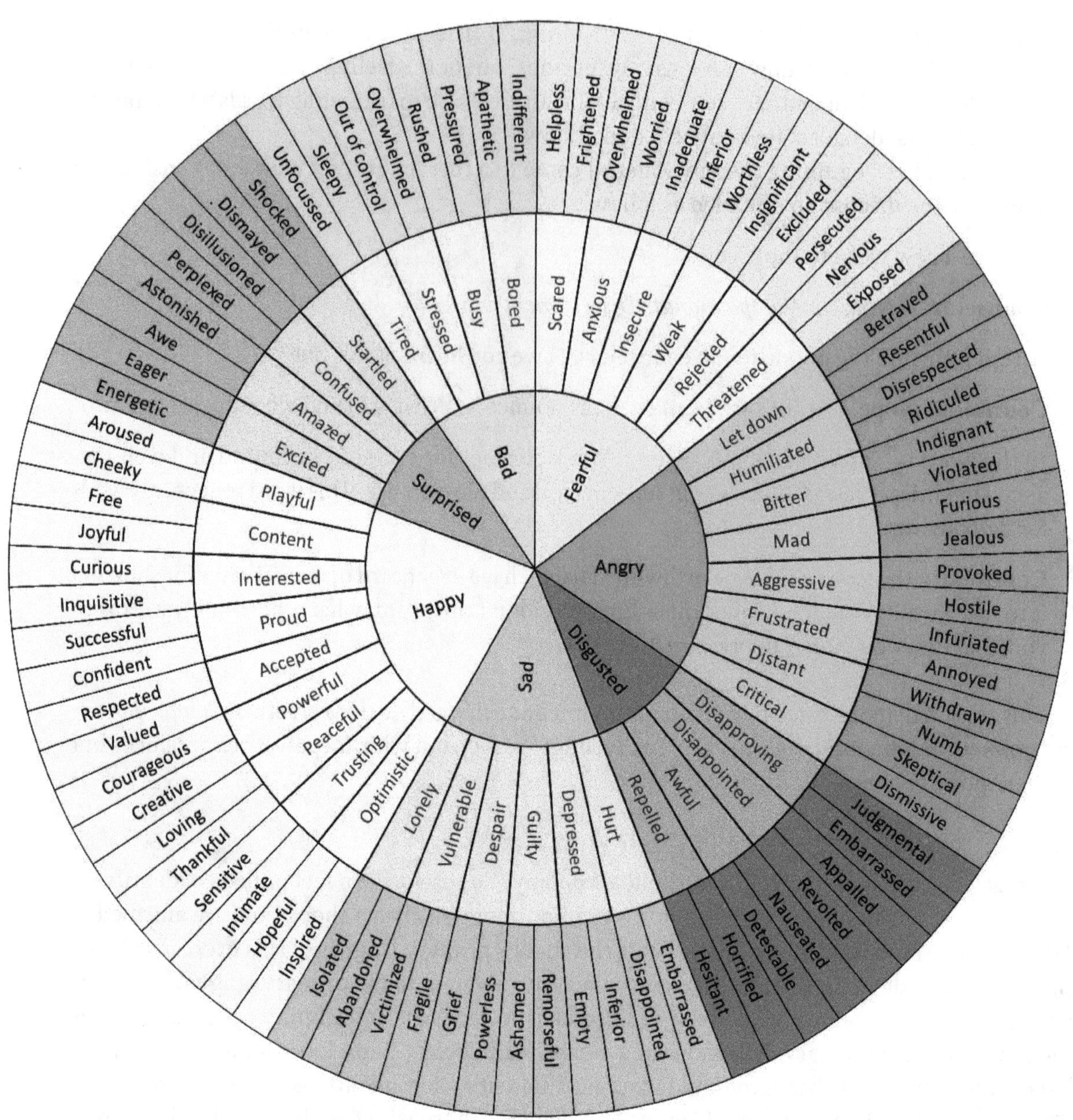

FIGURE 7.7 Feeling Wheel

BOTTOM-UP NEUROMODULATION

Calming From Below

Gary G. Gintner

Anxiety and depressive disorders are highly comorbid in adolescence and portend increased suicide risk, adult psychopathology, and adverse health outcomes in later life (Birmaher et al., 2002). Current evidence-based treatments, such as cognitive behavioral therapy are often effective in the short term, but show poorer long-term efficacy, with relapse rates as high as 50% within 2 years (March & Vitiello, 2009; Renna et al., 2017). One hypothesis for this long-term treatment failure is the idea that these treatments often target disorder-specific symptoms rather than underlying neurobiological mechanisms that produce them.

The Research Domain Criteria (RDoC) initiative sponsored by the National Institute of Mental Health ([NIMH]; Cuthbert & Insel, 2013) offers an alternative approach to traditional models of research and treatment. In contrast to the traditional descriptive system of classifying discreet disorders, RDoC assumes that there are a set of neurobiological systems that have evolved to meet environmental demands. Six general systems have been proposed: (1) negative valence systems to deal with threat and loss; (2) positive valence systems to seek out opportunity and reward; (3) cognitive systems responsible for attention, perception, language, memory, and cognitive control; (4) systems for social processes, such as attachment, social communication, and understanding of self and others; (5) arousal and regulatory systems responsible for homeostatic regulation, alertness, sleep, appetite, and related processes; (6) and sensorimotor systems focusing on motoric behavior, agency, and habits (see Yager & Feinstein, 2016).

Research Domain Criteria: **https://www.nimh.nih.gov/research/research-funded-by-nimh/rdoc/constructs/rdoc-matrix.shtml**

A major charge of the RDoC initiative is to understand how these systems function across the full spectrum of experience, from the well to the unwell, to develop more precise diagnostic and treatment procedures for discrete clinical manifestations. For instance, instead of studying major depressive disorder (MDD), the RDoC-informed researcher might focus on a more discrete feature of MDD, such as the construct of "sustained threat" within the negative valence system. Research would inform our understanding of how this sustained threat, and its parallel sustained safety, comes to be, which could guide more precise interventions.

Within this framework, anxiety and depressive disorders are primarily seen as dysregulation in brain circuits serving the negative valence system (McKay & Tolin, 2017). The negative valence system and associated emotions are designed to assess and respond to acute threat (fear), potential threat (anxiety), or loss (sadness and depression). The relevant brain circuits include those involved with our fight/flight/freeze response and are primarily mediated by structures in the limbic system and frontal lobes. The amygdala, in particular, is an area in the limbic system that plays a role in assessing, tagging, and initiating responses to emotionally charged stimuli that may pose a threat or danger. Frontal and higher cortical areas, dominant in executive functioning, help to modulate, direct, and dampen limbic responses (Canbeyli, 2013). Both the amygdala and frontal areas can affect the regulation of metabolic systems through their joint connection to the vagus nerve. Developmentally, lower brain areas, including limbic structures, mature earlier than higher order cortical areas. Consequently, children and adolescents may be more prone to emotional reactivity and impulsivity and more challenged in containing emotional responses via top-down cortical means (Blom et al., 2014; Lebowitz et al., 2018).

Individuals with anxiety and depressive disorders often have hyperactive amygdala activity (i.e., high sensitivity to detecting threat, even when there is no actual danger) and impaired prefrontal control (Lebowitz et al., 2018). These factors, in turn, decrease vagal input or afference to the central nervous system, resulting in an enhanced sympathetic tone (Canbeyli, 2013). Heightened reactivity is also associated with increased self-referential thinking and attentional bias toward threat and loss stimuli. Early adversity and trauma appear to increase amygdala volume and reactivity and blunt the development of frontal control mechanisms (Blom et al., 2014; Canbeyli, 2013). In contrast, parental nurturance, especially early in life, appears to optimize the balance of frontal and limbic control (Lebowitz et al., 2018).

Two general approaches have been considered for addressing problems in the negative valence system. Top-down approaches try to engage higher frontal areas through activities such as self-talk, disputing, cognitive restructuring, problem solving, and guided imagery. Bottom-up strategies, on the other hand, aim to stimulate inhibitory vagal control by providing calming sensory and motor inputs to the vagus nerve (Canbeyli, 2013). This approach has a dampening effect on limbic hyperactivity and enhances frontal modulation. Various bottom-up interventions have been studied, including light exposure, auditory stimulation (e.g., calming music), diaphragmatic breathing, physical exercise, and yoga (see Canbeyli, 2013, for a review). In treatment studies, diaphragmatic breathing and yoga movements are often implemented in combination to amplify vagal afference (Allen et al., 2018; Balasubramaniam et al., 2013; Blom et al., 2014; Cabral et al., 2011; Streeter et al., 2012; Woolery et al., 2004).

Treatment protocols generally begin with bottom-up interventions, as they are easier to implement, provide more immediate symptom relief, and serve as a platform for more complex top-down techniques (Blom et al., 2014; Renna et al., 2017). As an example of an RDoC application, Blom and colleagues (2014) developed a 12-session program for adolescents experiencing depression and anxiety symptoms. Treatment targets included decreasing limbic hyperactivity and increasing interoceptive awareness. The progressive protocol begins with bottom-up strategies to enhance vagal tone. Participants were taught diaphragmatic breathing first and were then shown how to use yoga movements that incorporate the breath. With this foundation, subsequent modules use more top-down strategies, such as labeling and communicating emotions, cognitive restructuring, and creating goals in line with personal values. Findings showed that participants found the program very acceptable and measures of somatic complaints, anxiety, and depression significantly improved (Blom et al., 2017).

The following activity is adapted from the protocol of Blom et al. (2017). The *Bottom-Up Neuromodulation* activity is a sensorimotor intervention intended to support enhanced vagal input to calm limbic hyperactivity.

MATERIALS NEEDED

- Diaphragmatic breathing video (see Riehl, 2018, in "Ancillary Materials")
- Pictures of different yoga-like movements (you can also draw or demonstrate)
- Yoga floor mat for floor exercises (optional)

PROCESS OF THE ACTIVITY

This activity has been used as part of the overall treatment protocol for adolescents, as well as for adults, with a range of anxiety disorders and/or depression. *Bottom-Up Neuromodulation* has three phases: (1) education, (2) diaphragmatic breathing, and (3) yoga-like movement exercises. As much as possible, use language that aligns with adolescents' desire for increased autonomy and control. For example, the diaphragmatic breathing, yoga movements, and interoceptive awareness exercises are framed as ways that the adolescent can start to "pull their own strings" by dialing down the stress system and tuning up the safety/relaxation system (i.e., vagal-parasympathetic enhancement).

Step 1: Initial Neuroeducation

The education component includes a discussion of the brain and the role of the limbic system's "danger detection system" and the frontal "brake and steering system." An example of how I might engage in this type of education is provided in the case study that follows. It is important to be developmentally and diversity sensitive in the way the material is presented and processed in terms of language, life examples, and collaborative style. For example, the client's own life situations can be used to illustrate key points.

Step 2: Diaphragmatic Breathing

Begin breath training by asking clients to lie down and put one hand on the chest and one on the stomach. Instruct them to take deep breaths into the stomach and exhale slowly as a way of "massaging" the vagus nerve. Ask them to breathe in through their nose and breathe out through their mouth using the following count:

Breathe in 2-3-4

Breathe out 2-3-4-5-6

The rationale here is that inhalation stimulates the sympathetic system and raises the heart rate, while the extended exhalation decreases the heart rate and engages more parasympathetic and vagal activation (see Riehl, 2018, for a video demonstration). Once this basic breathing technique is mastered, you can expand the exercise to include instructions to now inhale and exhale through the nose, paying attention to the sensation of coolness with inhalation and warmth with exhalation. This activity introduces clients to sensory awareness that can facilitate calmness and focus on the present. Diaphragmatic breathing is framed as a skill that improves with practice. As such, an important step in skill acquisition is to collaboratively identify a regular time and place to practice daily for about 10 minutes.

Step 3: Movement Exercises

Next, you can introduce movement as another way to calm the mind. In my experience, traditional sitting yoga and the use of mats are not well accepted among teens, especially males. Instead, this protocol starts with movements of the neck (back, forth, and side to side and then shifts to standing exercises that involve bends and stretches. The following are the four basic positions (see Figures 7.8–7.11) that are applicable for beginners with figures included to illustrate the position. In the "Ancillary Materials" section, I include web links to videos and training information for those unfamiliar with the poses listed. I have found these videos to be more helpful for teaching than static pictures, as they capture the essential role of smooth movement in forming these positions. The positions can be done in this order (see Ansari & Lark, 1999):

Mountain Position. Stand facing forward with legs together, feet facing forward and touching, arms down along your sides; then smoothly move arms above the head, placing palms together with fingers pointing up.

FIGURE 7.8 Mountain Position

Forward Bend Position. With hands in the air, bend all the way forward and try to touch your toes; exhale at the end.

FIGURE 7.9 Forward Bend Position

Repeat the mountain and forward bend movements together three times in a row.

Return to mountain position.

Star Position. Extend arms straight out to each side and spread legs 3 feet apart, hold for five breaths.

FIGURE 7.10 Star Position

Side Bends. Move the right foot to a 90-degree angle, place the right hand on the right thigh and stretch your left arm over your head so that you bend sideways.

FIGURE 7.11 Side Bend Position

Repeat the side bend on the other side.

Repeat the star position and side bends in one smooth motion.

End in mountain position with 10 breath cycles.

Throughout the process, instruct clients to focus on the sensation of moving smoothly throughout each part of the exercise. Again, a daily practice schedule should be discussed in which they practice the movements for 5 minutes at three different times of the day. Other types of sensory stimulation, such as music, can be added to breathing and moving.

These activities provide multimodal sensorimotor stimulation, which has been shown to be more powerful than single modality stimulation. Later, more top-down interventions, such as self-instruction, cognitive restructuring, and problem solving can be introduced that build on these more fundamental bottom-up skills.

FOLLOW-UP

Evaluation includes initial screening measures, measures of symptom improvement, and state measures. The American Psychiatric Association (2013, n.d.) provides a set of symptom measures that are free to download (see https://www.psychiatry.org/psychiatrists/practice/dsm/educational-resources/assessment-measures). The DSM-5 Self-Rated Level 1 Cross-Cutting Measure-Child Age 11–17 is a 25-item measure of symptoms from major diagnostic categories. This tool helps initially screen for conditions not appropriate for this exercise (e.g., active suicidal thoughts) and guides the selection of further diagnostic and outcome measures. For the activity, depression and anxiety measures could include The Patient Health Questionnaire-9, Modified for Adolescence (PHQ-9A) and the DSM-5 Level 2 Anxiety Measure-Child Age 11–17. Both measures are administered at the beginning of treatment and then periodically afterward to assess progress.

Prior to and after an activity like abdominal breathing or yoga movements, clients are asked to do a three-point check of their thoughts, body sensations and behaviors in the moment. They rate their subjective units of distress (SUDS; 1 = low and 10 = high) before and immediately after the activity. The following questions can help to process the exercise:

What went well with the exercise?

What did you notice about your bodily sensations?

How about feelings and thoughts?

What did you feel like doing?

How easy or difficult was it to stay in the present with the activity?

Clients also create personal self-monitoring forms to track each time they practice, recording the time, place, pre- and post-SUDS ratings, and any reflections about the activity.

NEUROSCIENCE IN ACTION

Daryl is a 16-year-old African American male who was referred by his mother for symptoms of depression and anxiety. He has a history of treatment for depression, including antidepressant medication, but no longer used medication at the time of our work together. His mother described him as a nervous child who became easily frustrated. Early in life, his father left, and the family had to move from Detroit to the New Orleans area. Daryl reported that he had always been a worrier and feels "wired" much of the time. He admitted that he was tired of feeling this way and was open to trying something different. The DSM Level 1 measure indicated symptoms in the depression and anxiety domains. His PHQ-9A depression was 12 (indicating moderate depression), and his DSM Level 2 Anxiety measure was 30 (indicating mild anxiety). Goal setting was introduced by asking the client to reflect on his average worry rating in terms of SUDS: "In a typical week, how worried do you get with 10 being as worried as you can be and 1 being not worried at all?"

Similarly, Daryl was asked to do ratings for feeling wired and for feeling depressed. Then he was asked, "If you were doing better, what would that average weekly rating be?" From these baseline points, goals were agreed upon for the following three targets:

Reduce daily worry from an average of 6 or more to 3 or less.

Reduce daily feelings of being wired from an average of 7 to 3 or less.

Increase average daily mood rating to 6 or more with 10 being a positive mood.

The *Bottom-Up Neuromodulation* activity was framed as a piece of the plan to accomplish each of these goals. After conducting the initial assessment and setting preliminary treatment goals, I began the *Bottom-Up Neuromodulation* activity with education about danger detection, hyper-reactivity, and avoidant coping:

Counselor: We have a system in our brain that is like a danger detective that alerts us to any potential threat. Like any good detective, the brain looks for clues whether the environment is safe or poses some kind of danger. If danger is detected, then the emotional part of our brain turns on a system that hypes us up for action—like pressing down on the gas pedal to go—like that wired feeling. On the other hand, if safety clues are detected, another system calms our body down, allowing us to chill out and recover; it pumps the brakes on that gas pedal. When a lot of stressful things have happened in a person's life, like the things you described earlier, that danger detection system can be overly sensitive, and thinking can be more prone to anticipate danger. So you can feel wired and worried a lot of the time. And we can deal with that discomfort by avoiding situations that trigger the feeling—like the time you got so anxious about going to a party that you decided not to go. What do you think of all that?

Daryl: Like I've got to let up on the pedal and learn to chill more? That's my problem—it just feels like the engine is running all the time. So how do I chill more?

Counselor: Research shows that two general approaches help: engaging in activities that encourage your safety system to activate and checking your thinking to be sure that you haven't misread the clues. Things that help that safety system gear up are calm breathing and relaxing movements, which are like messaging that safety system to turn on and chill out. Then later we can talk about ways of checking your thinking more specifically and also discuss what you can do to handle the situation. What do you think about giving some of those activities a try?

Daryl: Never thought of it that way. Mm. I know I can do the breathing part (laughs).

During the second and third weeks of treatment, I introduced Daryl to diaphragmatic breathing and interoceptive awareness exercises. An example of an interoceptive exercise I often us is as follows: "As you are breathing notice that sensation at the tip of your nose where the air feels slightly cooler as you breathe in and slightly warmer as you breathe out. Allow your attention to focus on that sensation of coolness as you breathe in and warmth as you breathe out." We constructed a self-monitoring log to record each time he practiced his breathing exercise. His SUDS ratings following the exercise fell from an average of six the initial week of training to three after the second week.

Next, movement was introduced as another way to calm the emotional brain. I first modeled the yoga movements and then we practiced them together in the office. In a seated position, we started with simple neck movements:

> Drop your head forward and focus on the stretched muscle on the back of your neck. Inhale and exhale slowly. Then lift your head up slowly to the starting position. Inhale and exhale slowly. Then drop your head all the way back and notice the stretch on the front of your neck. Inhale and exhale slowly. Then lift your head back up to the starting position. Inhale and exhale slowly. Next, tip your head to the left and notice the stretched muscle on the right side of your neck. Inhale and exhale slowly. Lift your head up to the starting position. Inhale and exhale slowly. Next, tip your head to the right and again notice the stretched muscle on the left side of your neck. Inhale and exhale slowly. Then lift your head up slowly back to the starting position. Inhale and exhale slowly.

I framed these basic movements as exercises that can be done anywhere to alert us to body tension and serve as a quick way of unwinding and engaging the chill system. Daryl commented that these were like calisthenics from his gym class but slower. Jokingly, he commented that it was "smooth training." We talked about when he might be able to implement the exercises into his life each day, and then I asked him to try to practice daily. In the following session, however, he reported that he had only done the exercises two of the days. We discussed ways of setting up reminders with his phone and finding more feasible practice times. The following week he showed considerable improvement, and his SUDS ratings were all 3 or below, and his average mood rating improved from 3 to 6. The PHQ-9 dropped 3 points, placing him at the top end of the mild range.

Once he gained facility with these bottom-up activities, I added top-down interventions, such as cognitive restructuring and exposure for situational avoidance. For example, Daryl often avoided situations where he would need to interact with unfamiliar peers. We selected an exposure activity to attend a school dance. Prior to going, he practiced his breathing and yoga movements. He then engaged in more positive self-talk on the way there, focusing on more adaptive ways of managing the situation (e.g., nodding and smiling as he moved through crowds).

ETHICAL AND MULTICULTURAL CONSIDERATIONS

Contraindications for this activity include acute suicidality, psychotic features, acute mania, uncontrolled substance use, and high levels of dissociative symptoms, as is often seen in clients with complex trauma. Although the activity is indicated for the majority of individuals with anxiety and depressive presentations, individuals with predominantly anhedonic depression may benefit more from interventions targeting the enhancement of the positive valences system through behavioral activation (Blom et al., 2014). It is important to have the parents or guardians involved in the overall treatment plan so that they understand the rationale and support the therapeutic assignments. These interventions have been implemented with teens from both urban and rural settings.

Three ethical issues should be considered when including yoga movements in the treatment protocol (Kamradt, 2017). First, although the activity is not formal yoga training, it does require a competence in implementing and teaching the positions appropriately. Personal yoga experience (e.g., a class) and consultation with a local certified yoga instructor are both recommended, especially for counselors with limited yoga training and experience. Web Ed (http://yogaed.com) is also a useful resource for educators and health-care professionals who want to implement yoga with a school-age population. A second ethical consideration is to do no harm. In this regard, the contraindications listed earlier address mental health considerations. In addition, if there are any physical problems (e.g., low back pain, knee problem), clients should obtain clearance from their personal physician. Lastly, informed consent should include the benefits and potential risks of both psychotherapy and yoga. In this discussion, potential yoga benefits that can be highlighted include improved mood, anxiety, stress reactivity and well-being (Balasubramaniam et al., 2013; Streeter et al., 2012). The most common risk that should be mentioned is straining muscles and joints.

ANCILLARY MATERIALS

The following are useful resources for implementing yoga poses and further yoga training:

- Ansari, M. & Lark, L. (1999). *Yoga for beginners*. Harper.
- D'Arrigo, C. (n.d.). *Seven standing beginner yoga poses to increase strength and flexibility*. https://www.yogiapproved.com/yoga/standing-beginner-yoga-poses/
- Stevenson, S. & Brock, S. (2017). *8 yoga poses for beginners*. https://www.beachbodyondemand.com/blog/standing-yoga-poses-for-beginners
- Yoga Ed. (2018). *The yoga ed curriculum*. http://yogaed.com/resource/the-yoga-ed-curriculum/ (online training for teaching teens yoga)

EVERYONE WANTS TO DRIVE THE BUS

Noticing What the Passengers Are Saying (and Feeling)

Mark Woodford

The neural connections in humans that run through the central nervous system in the body and brain (e.g., the brain stem, the limbic region, and the prefrontal cortex) form an affective (emotional), value-based appraisal system that has evolved to be adaptable for surviving and thriving in diverse environments (Fogel, 2009; Siegel, 2012b). Importantly, the limbic system in the midsection of the brain (e.g., the amygdala, anterior cingulate cortex) and the neural connections that run throughout the entire mesolimbic dopamine system lie at the heart of our psychological and emotional *drives* and affect our sense of well-being in various situational contexts. This affective-emotional-neural system at its base is hardwired (through a combination of genetics and environmental influences) to seek out what is of value and avoid what is not. "Value" in the context of our affective appraisal and arousal response systems means valuing both surviving (avoiding death) and thriving (approaching pleasure) (Siegel, 2012b).

Panksepp (2009) used animal models to describe seven basic emotional drives that exist as instinctual emotional responses to stimuli across species of mammals, including human beings: (1) seeking, (2) fear, (3) rage, (4) lust, (5) care, (6) panic, and (7) play. In humans, these systems shift into states of mind: the "seeking" system (urgent interest and desire state of mind), the "fear" system (anxious state of mind), the "rage" system (angry state of mind), the "lust" system (erotic state of mind), the "care" system (nurturing state of mind), the "panic" system (sad state of mind), and the "play" system (joyful state of mind) (as cited in Woodford, 2012). These emotional neural networks are the ancient instinctual systems that give us information about what is happening around us and what might be important for us to pay attention to in order to survive and thrive in our respective environments.

Emotional awareness happens in three phases: (1) initial orientation, appraisal, and arousal; (2) sensing primary emotions; and (3) having categorical (or basic) emotions, including the ability to describe them with words (such as "fear," "anger," "sadness," "surprise," or "joy") (Fogel, 2009; Seigel, 2012b). In *Everyone Wants to Drive the Bus,* individuals are guided through the process of increasing emotional awareness using information about our ancient neural circuitry system for appraisal and meaning making (Panksepp, 2009) and the acceptance and commitment therapy (ACT) metaphor "Passengers on the Bus" (Hayes et al., 2012). The neuroeducation activity can help move individuals from the precontemplation to contemplation stages and then into the preparation and action stages (Miller & Rollnick, 2013) related to the importance of being aware of basic emotions in various situations. Ultimately, *Everyone Wants to Drive the Bus* is aimed at fostering "awareness of awareness" or an observing/witnessing self that notices bodily and mental-emotional processes through prefrontal cortical functioning. As approach/avoidance survival systems, several of the basic emotional drives discussed in this activity are intimately linked to the fight, flight, or freeze responses that help us to "approach what is life-sustaining and avoid that which is dangerous" (Cozolino, 2014, p. 28). For example, in fear, panic, and rage states, our subcortical brain stem and lower limbic structures are fundamental to our survival. Yet being *reactive* (with subcortical and autonomic reactions in our bodies) is less adaptive in our daily lives when we are facing emotionally challenging situations that require more *responsive* (higher cortical response) behaviors. The latter process begins with practices that foster awareness of awareness. By helping clients create a witnessing self that can see and feel how emotional processes may be "driving their bus" in various situational contexts, we can assess how they are choosing to be more responsive in these situations, even as their emotional bodies are experiencing self-protective reactive processes. It is worth noting that the word "drives" in this activity functions as both a descriptor of basic physiological functioning that humans share with other mammals and a metaphor for increasing awareness for what "drives our bus" in terms of basic human emotional processes and leads to emotional awareness and expression of wants and needs.

MATERIALS NEEDED

- *Passengers on the Bus* script (detailed in the following section)
- Chairs (to function as bus seats)
- An imagination
- A sense of humor

PROCESS OF THE ACTIVITY

Everyone Wants to Drive the Bus is adaptable to multiple adolescent and adult client populations, as long as individuals have the basic cognitive ability to imagine that their thoughts, feelings, and bodily sensations could take on personalities that are riding on an imaginative mental bus that represents their inner world. When describing what you want to do with clients, call this activity "Passengers on the Bus" (see Hayes et al., 2012, pp. 250–253, for a full description of this core ACT exercise). To make this activity more visual and physically interactive, set up chairs in the configuration of an imaginary bus, having one chair be the driver's seat and the other seven chairs representative of the seven basic emotional drives. Once the scene is set, read the following script, pausing when noted for reflection and discussion:

> Imagine that you are driving a bus full of passengers. This bus is special because it represents you—all of you. You are both the driver and the passengers, and you are heading in a direction that says something about who you have been, who you are right now, and who you want to be in the future. Therefore, where you are heading on this bus is very important to you right now and in the future. However, the passengers on your bus keep yelling out directions about which way to go, telling you to "turn left" or "turn right," or saying things like "you missed your turn" or "slow down" or "speed up!" They all seem to think that they should be driving the bus, that they know what is best for you. Have you ever noticed yourself having a debate in your head—between yourself and various parts of yourself—your passengers?
>
> ***(Pause here and process the question as needed.)***
>
> What happens when you let the passengers drive your bus?
>
> ***(Pause again here as needed to process this question.)***
>
> (Summarize client responses and continue.) Sometimes we get so annoyed with our passengers that we just let them drive the bus. Out of exasperation, we give in to their demands and turn the wheel over to them. For most people, when that happens, at first, we do not even realize that it has happened, and then we find that we end up headed in a direction that was not where we wanted to go.
>
> ***(Pause here to ask for examples—or use the following example—of what this might look like.)***
>
> For example, how often have you said or did something that was detrimental in the middle of a fight with someone you cared about? Because the relationship was important to you, when

things calmed down, did you find yourself wondering, "What was I thinking?" Let us imagine that in that scenario who you are or who you want to be in that relationship gave up your driver's seat to a passenger that was yelling out distracting and detrimental things. In that scenario, you were not thinking. Rather, your passenger was "acting out" and driving your bus in the opposite direction of what you valued; in this case, away from the relationship that was meaningful to you.

Who are these passengers on the bus anyway—and what do they want? Do you have any ideas?

(Process this question as needed. At this point, the metaphor will likely begin to make sense to clients, but if not, process additional examples as needed.)

These passengers can represent many aspects of who we are. They can be parts of ourselves that have developed to protect us from danger or to help us manage tough situations that may have arisen in our lives. We call these parts "adaptive selves" because they have helped us to adapt to challenging—and even dangerous—situations. In fact, our bodies have built-in systems that function for this exact purpose.

Built into our neurocircuitry as humans are basic drive systems that operate below our awareness. We call this process "subcortical" because it operates in a part of our brain that is below ("sub-") our neo-cortex—"neo" meaning new, the newest part of our brain that thinks through decisions and sets goals for ourselves.

We have seven basic drives that we share with other mammals (mice, dogs, cats, etc.). These drives relate to seeking, fear, rage, lust, care, panic, and play. The main purpose of these drives is to help us to survive and to thrive in the world. Let us take a quick look at each one of them as the starting point for getting to know who the passengers on our bus might be and what they might be doing there.

First, we have a basic drive to seek. For mammals, this means to find things that we need, to consume those things, and/or to hoard them for later on if the need arises. You can see how this would be very helpful as a survival mechanism. However, what might happen if our drive to seek passenger hopped in the driver's seat of our bus?

(Pause and reflect on what that might look like with examples from the client's life.)

If this "seek" passenger were driving the bus below our awareness (subcortical), what would our behaviors look like? What might "seeking" be saying to you?

(It is important to understand that the seeking drive can work in concert with other basic drives—e.g., seek and lust or seek and care. Therefore, examples might include obsessive behaviors related to seeking and desire, such as addictive processes to avoid emotional experiences—e.g., alcohol and other drug misuse, binge eating, and hoarding, to name only a few—where "seeking" might be saying things like, "I can't live without this ____________." Similarly, seeking could pair with a need for care or nurturance for oneself and/or for others, where "seeking" may be saying, "I need affection right now.")

Can you think of a name for this passenger that would help us to be able to refer quickly to this emotional drive?

(Whatever name the client gives for the seeking drive, begin to use that named "person" moving forward in the activity and in the counseling process beyond the activity. This can

also be one potential point in the activity where you can demonstrate a "hijacked bus" with the chairs, showing a basic emotional drive taking over the driver's seat of one's mental bus.)

Second, if our basic emotional drive of fear hijacks the bus, what would that look like?

(Pause and reflect.)

What makes fear an important basic emotional drive for mammals (and for your life)?

(At this point, use the fundamental processes of asking for examples and naming the basic emotional drive—in this case fear—to help clients to gain awareness of the drive and to see how their awareness is larger than the drive itself. By naming and personifying the drives and physically placing them in the driver's seat one at a time, we attach visual images to the drives that help to separate them from the witnessing or observing self. Often, clients will name their drives after real or fictional people that they have known. This process gives a name(s) for basic value- and affective-based appraisal systems in the mind and body that speaks for what gives life meaning, salience, and value. Make sure to ask what each emotional drive would say if it could speak.)

How might the mind turn basic fear into human anxiety? Can you think of examples? What might "fear" be saying to you as a passenger on your bus?

(Pause and consider examples from the client's life experiences. The basic difference is that the mind can turn a bodily sensation—fear—into a mind-body state—anxiety. The point of making this distinction is to increase awareness about how the mind has the ability to amplify basic emotional drives—such as moving fear into anxiety—that begins as an affective arousal system whose function is to alert the person to danger in the environment).

Third, what would the basic emotional drive of rage look like? What function would rage serve as an adaptive drive? What does it look like when it drives your bus? What is your name for rage? What does rage have to say?

(Pause and reflect.)

Fourth, even though it is sometimes challenging for people to talk about their sex drive, how does the basic emotional drive of lust function when it is driving the bus?

(Continue to pause and reflect, ask for examples, and give this drive a name that has meaning for the client.)

Fifth, in what direction does your bus head when care is driving? What are the upsides and downsides of letting "care" drive the bus?

(Pause and reflect.)

Sixth, what about the basic emotional drive of panic? In animals, panic looks like hiding behaviors or freezing in place. In humans, panic can look like sadness or hopelessness. Can you think of examples from your life when panic was steering your bus? When it was driving, were you heading in the direction of what was important to you?

(Pause and reflect.)

Lastly, think of play as joy in motion. When we play, we are enjoying the ride. When does play have a chance to drive your bus? What does "play" have to say to you?

(Pause and reflect.)

Finish the activity by summarizing that these drives are built-in to our development as human beings for survival and for thriving and that with awareness—taking time to pause and reflect on our experiences—we can feel when our drives are speaking to us, listen to what they are letting us know that we need, and move flexibly in directions that align with our values and desires given the context.

FOLLOW-UP

Potential process questions that help to solidify learning are included throughout the script. However, ask additional questions immediately following the activity to continue fostering awareness of awareness. Example follow-up questions may include the following: What is it like to "witness" yourself? What are you noticing in this process (e.g., sensations in your body, thoughts about "how it's going," or feelings about the activity)? How might you work outside of the group to strengthen a "witnessing" or "observing self" that can see and feel what is "driving your bus" in various situations? What might get in your way with this practice?

Counselors can also cocreate behavioral experiments with clients that have them test out their reactions/responses in real-life situations and then ask them to report back to you or their counseling group by asking, "How did it go?" One can devise Likert scale questions that may help to quantify change to a degree (i.e., using a scaling question such as, "On a scale of 1 to 10, 1 being 'I was completely reactive on autopilot' and 10 being 'I was completely mindfully responsive,' how would you rate your behavior in response to that situation?"). Modify your follow-up questions based on the client's language and abstract thinking capabilities and the context of their specific behavioral experiments.

NEUROSCIENCE IN ACTION

This case study illustrates Bob's experience applying *Everyone Wants to Drive the Bus* after a group session that included the activity described earlier. Bob, a 54-year-old divorced, Caucasian male, was skeptical that he would notice his emotional drives "in a real-life situation." Upon returning to the next group session, however, he reported that he was riding on public transportation—a literal public bus—when he had the opportunity to witness one of his basic emotional drives nearly "hijack" his mental bus. He described the experience as follows:

> It was a crowded bus, and I was standing there minding my own business when these "punks"—there were three of them—got on the bus and started acting like they owned the place. One of them was smoking a cigarette and trying to hide it while he was passing it around to his friends. I started to get so pissed off because there were women and children on the bus—one of them had a baby even—and they don't need to hear that language or be exposed to cigarette smoke. Plus, I quit smoking a while back, which was really hard for me, and the fact that I had to breathe their smoke pissed me off even more! I almost lost it. I'll be honest—I wanted to strangle one of them. I was definitely feeling like...almost like my body was being taken over by how angry I was. Fortunately, I noticed how pissed off I was. My heart was pounding. I started to get all sweaty. And I could tell that I was a split second away from going off on those kids. And that's when I realized that I was in a rage. That "rage drive" that we talked about last week was right there in my face. I thought I was going to explode, but I saw it happening and I was able to back off and breathe and remind myself that these are kids who don't know any better. And I am a grown man who does. I know...I knew when I cooled down that I don't want to act like that. Can you imagine if I had let my rage take over? It would have been bad.

Bob processed this experience within the counseling setting and built self-efficacy to deal with other contextual situations where rage, or one of the other seven basic emotional drives, seemed to be driving his mental bus. Importantly, Bob was able to see his basic emotional response as information about what was important to him—what he valued—in that situation. Specifically, his rage response—his anger—let him know that he cared about the "women and children on the bus." Anger in this instance gave him information about his sense of self as a man who valued the "protector role." In addition, this example opened up the group conversation, allowing others to describe how their own basic emotional drives have taken the driver's seat in various situations with both positive and negative results. For example, the drives of "care" or "play" may lead to the positive mental states of nurturing and joy around loved ones.

ETHICAL AND MULTICULTURAL CONSIDERATIONS

Gender, culture, and ethnicity shape our values and identity. They form the context of our lives. What we eat, how we work and choose to relax, how we celebrate holidays and rituals, and how we process basic emotions all speak to our familial and ethnocultural upbringing. Our personal contextual issues provide the lens through which we will see and understand interventions such as *Everyone Wants to Drive the Bus*. This activity is focusing on basic emotional states—*seeking, fear, rage, lust, care, panic, and play,* but those states may be described and experienced in culturally specific ways. Being curious about these differences and modifying the activity accordingly to meet the clients' salient content areas and the various cultural contexts of your clients' lives leads to culturally responsive delivery of this activity. In addition, one has to be cognizant of clients' cognitive processing abilities; specifically, the use of metaphors may confuse young children who are unable to think abstractly or adults who are cognitively impaired (e.g., suffering from dementia and/or psychosis).

HELPING PARENTS PUT FLO IN THE DRIVER'S SEAT

An Approach to Neuroeducation for Managing Stress and Anger With Amy and FLo

Naomi J. Wheeler and Dalena Dillman Taylor

Individuals are constantly assessing and responding to the needs of their environments to survive (Porges, 2011). When individuals detect danger (often at an unconscious level), they respond to the perceived threat through a series of primal and instinctual behaviors: fight (mobilize and engage the threat), flight (withdraw and evade the threat), or freeze (feign death and become immobile). Neural structures within the limbic system are particularly active in detecting and responding to threat (LeDoux, 1996; Ohman, 2005). The limbic system includes the amygdala, hippocampus, hypothalamus, thalamus, basal ganglia, and cingulate gyrus and is associated with emotion, arousal, and memory formation (Patterson & Schmidt, 2003). The amygdala, in particular, is known for playing a key role in this process (Ohman, 2005; Siegel, 2012b). Neural activity in the amygdala increases when threatening stimuli are introduced, and injury to the amygdala attenuates the fight or flight response (LeDoux, 1996). Similarly, a person's efforts to regulate their emotions results in diminished activity in the amygdala (Buhle et al., 2014). Thus, the amygdala helps us to detect threats and control physiological responses to cope and survive.

When individuals are not in a state of reacting to a perceived threat, the prefrontal cortex (PFC) is typically more active (Garcia et al., 1999). The PFC is an area of the frontal lobe that is associated with tasks such as planning, problem solving, decision making, and reasoning. Siegel (2012a, 2012b) described the role of the PFC in higher order cognitive processes and noted that individuals can learn to engage this part of the brain to regulate arousal through intentional effort. For example, in a meta-analysis of neuroimaging research, Buhle and colleagues (2014) determined that the PFC was activated when individuals engaged in cognitive reappraisal strategies (i.e., efforts to change a person's interpretation of affective stimuli). Specifically, studies of reappraisal showed activation of the cognitive control and lateral temporal cortex and subsequent diminished activity in the amygdala. Thus in response to stimuli, individuals can at times consciously engage the PFC to facilitate regulation of their emotions.

One innate way individuals regulate arousal, also referred to as emotion regulation, is through connection with a trusted other (Beckes & Coan, 2011). Children's capacity for emotion regulation develops primarily within the context of relationships with parents and primary caregivers (Beckes & Coan, 2011; Holt-Lunstad, 2018; Schore, 2003a, 2003b). Researchers have identified three ways parents influence a child's regulatory capacity: (1) parent modeling of self-regulatory behavior, (2) emotional climate of the family, and (3) emotionally supportive parenting practices (Morris et al., 2017). Counseling interventions that strengthen a parents' ability to regulate themselves, and thus increasing their ability to respond effectively to their children's dysregulation, are vitally important.

The Prevention and Relationship Enhancement Program (PREP, 2011) is one such intervention. The PREP Inc. includes independent lessons that require no additional training to facilitate. The PREP Inc. *Letting FLo Drive: Anger and Stress* lecture doodle is about the role different parts of the brain play during stressful or challenging situations. The video is a brief (approximately 3½ minutes) animated clip that introduces Amy (amygdala) and FLo (frontal lobe). The amygdala, Amy, responds to threat-inducing situations by sending hormones that initiate adaptive reactions (i.e., psychophysiological responses, such as heart rate acceleration, increased blood pressure, startle reflex potentiation). Amy's responses are intended to be helpful in the moment but are limited (i.e., fight or flight) and are not always accurate or helpful in the long run. In part, the challenge of allowing Amy to take the lead for how we respond comes from her lack of distinction between physical threats to safety (e.g., a tiger about to attack us) and emotional threats to safety (e.g., relationship or work stress). The frontal lobe, FLo, is critical in evaluating Amy's responses and adjusting reactions when necessary. FLo acts as the body's mainframe for strategizing, problem solving, and planning actions in line with personal goals and long-term needs. FLo, when she works together with Amy, helps us to move from just surviving to thriving in stressful, challenging, or emotionally difficult situations.

The purpose of *Helping Parents Put FLo in the Driver's Seat* is to share information about the brain structures and functions associated with emotion regulation to ultimately improve co-regulation within the caregiver-child relationship. By using the PREP Inc. *Letting FLo Drive: Anger and Stress* lecture doodle within the context of a parent consultation or counseling session, counselors can promote an increased understanding of the adaptive yet limited range of responses associated with the amygdala and the increased problem-solving capacity of the frontal lobe region of the brain. The activity can also prompt discussions about current situations in the parent's life or the parent-child relationship that are experienced as emotional threats, promoting insight and encouraging new actions that allow for greater emotion regulation.

MATERIALS NEEDED

- Computer and monitor
- Internet access
- Amy and FLo Lecture Doodle from PREP, Inc. (see link listed in "Ancillary Materials")

PROCESS OF THE ACTIVITY

The PREP program was designed for individuals within a group setting. However, I (Naomi) have used the *Helping Parents Put FLo in the Driver's Seat* activity during counseling with individual parents of young children and with families of adolescents. In addition, I have used this video with counselors in training during courses associated with skill acquisition and practicum experience. Therefore, I believe this video is fairly adaptable to most audiences and a wide range of ages and presenting concerns. The process described in the following paragraphs and illustrated in the case study assumes the establishment of a working alliance and judgment on the part of the counselor that sharing information about the neuroscience of emotion regulation would be relevant and helpful to the clients' presenting concerns.

Step 1: Help Clients Identify a Time of Emotion Dysregulation in Their Parenting

The first step in this activity is to help individuals identify and explore current situations that evoke a stress response. For example, you can ask a couple to identify parenting situations with their child that create the most distress for them. As the clients share their stressors and triggering situations, you may prompt them to also identify associated physical reactions (e.g., heart pounding, muscle tightness) and look for patterns or themes in how they respond to triggering events.

Step 2: Introduce and Show Video Lesson

As you introduce the Letting FLo Drive: Anger and Stress video, inform clients of the purpose by saying something like, "I want to share a video with you that builds on the situations you've both described related to distressing interactions within the family. I'm hoping the video can help us develop a shared language to use as we try to understand what's happening in those moments with you and your child. The video moves a little fast, and some families have asked to watch it a few times, so let me know if you want to pause or replay as we go along." Check in with the clients to assess their readiness and desire to continue and then play the PREP Amy and FLo video.

Step 3: Discuss Reactions to the Video

After the video, facilitate a discussion about the content and experience of watching the video. When possible, help parents connect the content to their presenting concerns. Possible process questions include the following:

- What stood out to you from the information the video provided?
- How does the video relate to you/your family/the presenting issue?
- What does it look like when Amy is driving for you? For your child?
- How do you help Amy and FLo work together for yourself? For your child?

FOLLOW-UP

Moving forward in the counseling process, continue to reference the shared language and metaphor of Amy and FLo to support clients' awareness of their internal states (e.g., "It seems like Amy might have been running the show in that moment.") and to promote greater regulation through techniques that increase FLo's role in responding to stressful or threating situations. You can also help clients create a method of self-evaluation to enact the skills outside of session and track progress formally and informally.

NEUROSCIENCE IN ACTION

Juan and Anisa presented to counseling to address increased couple and parenting stress related to severe and frequent emotional outbursts by their oldest child, Gabe, age 4. The couple had two children, Gabe and his younger sister, Maria (age 3). In addition, Anisa was pregnant with their third child and due in a few months. Anisa, a stay-at-home mom, had grown overwhelmed trying to manage Gabe's behavioral challenges, which seemed to escalate at lunchtime, before bed, and when Juan would arrive home from work. Juan worked as a line cook and recently enrolled in culinary school on the weekends with hopes to improve the family's financial situation and his own job opportunities. When he returned home from work during the week, he reported feeling exhausted from the demands of his job and depleted and unable to respond to Gabe's outbursts in the ways he wanted to. The couple explored their hopes and expectations for their family relationships, as well as the roles, routines, and rituals they had developed as a family. Anisa shared her tendency to walk away from Gabe during his outbursts and avoid discussion with him afterward, given her feelings of frustration, inadequacy as a mother, and perceived inability to help him change his behavior. Juan discussed his tendency to respond to Gabe's outbursts with a harsh and direct approach, which he acknowledged tended to escalate the situation.

After the first few sessions, I shared the Amy and FLo video with Juan and Anisa. They both laughed watching the humorous situations depicted in the video, and once it ended Juan stated, "That's us! I want to fight and she [Anisa] wants to get out of there when he [Gabe] acts up. That Amy's got control of our car for real!" The couple spent several sessions discussing the emotional threats and fears that Gabe's behavior and their recent stressors triggered in each of them as parents. Juan shared fears about being unsuccessful in life, for Gabe and himself. He identified seeing himself in his son, including his problematic behaviors within the family that reminded him of his own childhood. He expressed concern that all his effort at work would be in vain if Gabe didn't learn to show respect. Anisa discussed feeling powerless and out of control during Gabe's tantrums. She explored fears that she could not protect her son and patterns from her own childhood during which she would run and hide when her parents would yell or argue.

We later discussed the importance for parents to be able to manage their own emotions to be fully present and respond to their child's needs (i.e., being the thermostat instead of the thermometer; Bratton et al., 2006). Amy and FLo became a shared language and metaphor for Juan and Anisa to encourage and support one another as a team in the management of their own individual sources of stress, as well as Gabe's behavior, in line with their goals for the family. The video also opened discussion and exploration around their perception of the "danger or threats" experienced by Gabe. In recent months, Gabe had observed more arguments between Juan and Anisa prior to the initiation of counseling, and he had to manage a range of emotions as the family transitioned to welcome another child and adjust to Juan's new work/school schedule. Moreover, we discussed developmental expectations for emotion regulation by Gabe within the metaphor "Gabe's FLo is just beginning to develop, so he really has fewer options in response to stress and needs our help as his parents." Together, we applied principles of neuroeducation to parenting, the parent-child relationship, and the development of co-regulation strategies within the family.

ETHICAL AND MULTICULTURAL CONSIDERATIONS

The video references relational situations most relevant for adults (e.g., driving, dating, interviewing for a job, managing finances); therefore, the video may not be appropriate for use with children or early adolescents. However, the concepts and language of Amy and FLo to reference parts of the brain may be used with younger ages. The video is also brief and moves at a fast pace. Some clients may need to watch the video more than once to capture and retain the information, especially clients with challenges in auditory processing or English as a second language.

ANCILLARY MATERIALS

- The PREP lecture doodle is a component of The Anger and Stress Leader Kit, which may be purchased for $24.00 on the following website: https://www.prepinc.com/shopping/ProductDetail.aspx?ID=106.
- The lecture doodle may also be watched or downloaded from the PREP Vimeo page by following the links found at https://www.prepinc.com/content/CURRICULA/Anger-Stress-Video.htm
- Bratton, S. C., Landreth, G. L., Kellam, T., & Blackard, S. R. (2006). *Child parent relationship therapy (CPRT): A 10-session filial therapy model.* Taylor and Francis Group.

MIRROR NEURONS' CONTRIBUTIONS TO THE BRAIN AS A SOCIAL ORGAN

Working With Clients to Teach Emotional Cues of Others

Kristina Scott, Laurie Dickstein-Fischer, and Justine Thomas

Researchers first discovered mirror neurons in macaque monkeys, finding that specific motor neurons would fire as a monkey performed an action or when they watched another monkey perform an action they had previously engaged in (Fabbri-Destro & Rizzolatt, 2008; Gallese & Goldman, 1998). After this phenomenon was researched in monkeys, researchers began to look at mirror neuron activity in humans.

In humans, mirror neurons are postulated to be one of the reasons people wince when they see someone get hurt, cry when watching a romantic comedy, and smile when someone smiles at them (Ferrari & Coude, 2018). Mirror neurons are theorized to be a catalyst that helps humans to see things from others' perspectives (Rizzolatti & Craighero, 2004). Research seems to indicate that learning in social animals, which humans are, requires functional mirror neurons (Oztop et al., 2013), and these functional mirror neurons must be able to communicate across brain regions (amygdala, hippocampus, caudate nuclei, cerebellum, frontal, and temporal regions) for social learning to encode successfully (Dapretto et al., 2006; de Waal & Preston, 2017; Perkins et al., 2010).

In the past 2 decades, dysfunctions found in human mirror neuron systems (MNS) have been correlated with deficits in social behavior, social cognition, language development, emotional interpretation, and communication (Pineda et al., 2014; Saffin & Tohid, 2016). Individuals with autism spectrum disorder (ASD), because of the social deficits associated with this condition, have been a focal area of this mirror neuron neurobiological theory. Mirror neurons are thought to be impaired in individuals with autism, which hinders learning through observation, verbal and nonverbal communication, emotional attunement, and empathy (Dapretto et al., 2006; Perkins et al., 2010; Saffin & Tohid, 2016).

Even though there are studies that suggest a "broken mirror neuron system" is associated with ASD, there is also much controversy and scrutiny associated with this claim (Brass et al., 2007; Heyes, 2018; Hickok, 2014; Uddin et al., 2007). Hamilton (2013) conducted a meta-analysis of published research using neuroscience methodologies to investigate the role of mirror neuron systems in various tasks and found that there was little evidence of global dysfunction in the mirror neuron systems of individuals with ASD. Although this review provides strong evidence against global dysfunction, it brings into question how top-down executive functioning processes and mirror neurons interact so that learning through observing others is possible (Catmur et al., 2007; Catmur et al., 2009; Heyes, 2001, 2018). The executive learning tasks of selecting what to attend to, making connections between others' actions and consequences, and applying flexible thinking to carry out observed actions in new situations are all needed in this top-down process (Campbell & Cunnington, 2017; Campbell et al., 2018; Dawson & Guare, 2018). Once these executive functioning tasks are done, mirror neuron activity then makes learning from others possible (Catmur et al., 2009; Heyes, 2018).

Individuals with ASD have difficulties with many of the strategic aspects of social learning, which include understanding what to attend to, identifying appropriate models to learn from, and matching contexts and social circumstances to learned information (Saffin & Tohid, 2016; Vivanti & Rogers, 2014). Individuals with ASD can find imitation in spontaneous contexts particularly difficult, especially when they were never given the opportunity to master imitation in a controlled context (Ingersoll, 2008; Saffin & Tohid, 2016).

In fact, one of the biggest barriers to the development of appropriate peer relationships in this population is the lack of social reciprocity in the context of peer-to-peer interaction (Fein, 2015;

Krasny et al., 2003; Schlopler & Mesibov, 1986; Weiss & Harris, 2001). The abnormalities in social reciprocity are observable when individuals with autism do not attempt to aid listeners' understanding, ask ritualized and repetitive questions about one area of interest, and do not regulate conversation to match their partners' interests (American Psychiatric Association, 2013; Bellini et al., 2007; Fein, 2015; Landa, 2000). These characteristics, referred to as theory of mind, show that individuals with autism have a hard time adjusting to the needs (knowledge and/or interests) of others (Baron-Cohen et al., 2013; Fine et al., 1994; Premack & Woodruff, 1978). Theory of mind abilities, just like executive functioning tasks, are linked to the control of imitation and actions of the mirror neuron system (Baron-Cohen, et al., 2013; Spengler et al., 2010). In general, theory of mind refers to understanding behaviors that are not explicitly taught. These behaviors can be seen in people's facial expressions, which can indicate their feelings, intentions, beliefs, thoughts, and/or perceptions. Theory of mind is associated with being able to take others' perspectives and identify other's emotions. These behaviors are considered essential to having appropriate conversations (Bellini, 2006; Bora & Pantelis, 2016; Ozonoff & Miller, 1995). Perspective taking is a skill deficit area for many individuals with ASD because they tend to see the world through one viewpoint, their own. Mirror neurons, as mentioned earlier, are the catalyst for an individual to be able to take another's perspective, show empathy, and act upon emotional sensory information that is collected (Bora & Pantelis, 2016; de Waal & Preston, 2017). In young children with autism, this is seen when they have difficulty engaging with others in imaginary play. These deficits become more pronounced in adolescents and adults with ASD who have an inability to sustain reciprocal communications (Baron-Cohen et al., 1985; Bellini, 2006; Bora & Pantelis, 2016; Tager-Flusberg, 1985). Theory of mind abilities are thought to be prerequisite skills for executive functioning (Bora & Pantelis, 2016; Perner & Lang, 2000).

In individuals with ASDs, the amygdala, also called the "social brain," is generally less engaged and developed (Baron-Cohen et. al, 2000; Clements et al., 2018). The amygdala is involved in social cognition and retrieving information about emotions (Clements et al., 2018; Corbett et al., 2009), and mirror neurons in the amygdala region in neurotypical individuals are activated when both imitating and observing emotions of others (Carr et al., 2003). This part of the brain is believed to be where deficits in theory of mind initiate (Clements et al., 2018). Dapretto et al. (2006) theorized that deficits in theory of mind associated with ASD develop because of MNS dysfunction.

Because the current prevalence of ASD in the United States is 1 in 59 (Centers for Disease Control and Prevention, 2019), it is important for counselors to be equipped to support clients with this diagnosis. Educating clients with ASD about mirror neurons and their role in theory of mind may help clients develop strategies to compensate for the deficits in their mirror neurons' functionality. The *Mirror Neurons* activity can be used with clients to explore the role of mirror neurons and to help clients strengthen their mirror neurons to better recognize and respond to the emotions of others. The ultimate goal of the activity is to equip and empower the client with skills to decode and act upon the emotions of others.

MATERIALS NEEDED

- Penn Emotion Recognition Task (ER-40) https://www.millisecond.com/download/library/pennemotionrecognitiontest_er_40/

PROCESS OF THE ACTIVITY

This activity is appropriate to use with clients once rapport has been established. It is used to promote social-emotional growth with clients who are diagnosed with ASD and emphasizes the importance of practicing and implementing their new skills outside of session.

Position yourself so that you are across from the client and facing them.

1. Begin by saying something like, "Your brain has a special kind of neuron called a 'mirror neuron.' Think about a real mirror. When you do something, your reflection does the exact same thing you are doing. Mirror neurons allow you to imitate another person's physical reaction, even though you may not have encountered the stimulus that caused their physical reaction. So, like a mirror, you imitate the other person. How would you feel about doing an exercise that could help us appreciate the ways that mirror neurons function? I would make a face, and then you would copy the facial expression. What do you think?"
2. Once the client expresses an interest in engaging in the activity, start by going through a series of facial expressions (i.e., happy, sad, angry). Prompt the client to mimic the facial expressions. I use the Penn Emotion Recognition Task (ER-40), which is a standardized test of various facial emotion expressions (sad, happy, angry, scared) and represents a mixture of female and male stimulus faces. After they finish the Penn Emotion Recognition Task, go through a series of their own facial expressions. This process assists in the transfer of information.
3. Go through the same set of facial expressions. This time ask the client to identify the possible stimulus or emotion for each physical reaction (i.e., sadness, happiness).
4. Then ask the client to explain what they would want another person to do for them if they were experiencing that emotion.
5. Explain that mirror neurons help people do this automatically. Say something like, "Mirror neurons help us know what another person might need or want from us, even when we are not *feeling* the same emotion they are. For some people, that knowledge happens automatically. For some people, it doesn't, and those people might have to work a little harder to understand what others are feeling based on facial expressions alone."
6. Next, go through the same set of facial expressions, but this time, ask the client to identify what you (the person experiencing the emotion) might want or need. You can share that this process helps them expand their theory of mind and make room for others' perspectives.

FOLLOW-UP

Counselors should have a general understanding of the effectiveness of the activity by the way the client responds to each prompt. If the client is able to (a) imitate the facial expression, (b) identify the underlying emotion, and (c) provide an appropriate response to the emotion, the activity can be deemed successful within the context of the counseling session. More importantly, however, is the implementation of the skills outside of the counseling session. This success can be measured formally or informally with self-report and/or other collateral contacts as treatment progresses.

NEUROSCIENCE IN ACTION

Evan is a 15-year-old male student who was diagnosed with high-functioning ASD. Socially, Evan was secluded from his peers. He chose to eat lunch alone because he did not know what to say to his classmates. In addition, Evan often spoke out of turn during classes (sometimes dominating discussions) was easily aggravated during class discussions when others disagreed with him, and he publicly criticized his teachers and peers when he perceived they have made a mistake. In his history class, another student began to cry during a debate with Evan, and despite the teacher's instructions to end the debate, Evan continued to argue his point. The following dialogue represents the author's experiences working with students, like Evan, using the *Mirror Neuron* activity described next.

Counselor: What you just did was act like a mirror neuron. You saw a physical reaction—my facial expression—and imitated it. Mirror neurons help us with our theory of mind and our ability to take another person's perspective and show empathy. We are going to add another element to this activity, which will help explain how mirror neurons and theory of mind work together. We are going to repeat what we did before, but this time, in addition to imitating the facial reaction, I want you to try to identify the emotion that could have caused the physical reaction.

Counselor smiles. Evan imitates.

Evan: Smiling means happy.

Counselor: Good. [*Frowns*]

Evan: [*Frowns*] Frowning means sad or angry.

Counselor: Good. Now, I want you to think about that emotion. What would you want someone to do if you were sad?

Evan: It depends. I might want them to leave me alone or maybe say something to make me feel better.

Counselor: Exactly. Mirror neurons help us know what another person might need or want from us, even when we are not *feeling* the same emotion they are. For some people, that knowledge happens automatically. For some people, it doesn't, and those people might have to work a little harder to understand what others are feeling based on facial expressions alone. The exercise that we just completed might help you understand what your classmates might need. Let's try the activity again, but this time, mimic the facial expression and tell me what I might need.

Counselor makes an angry face. Evan imitates.

Evan: That was angry, and when I'm angry, I either like to be alone or sometimes I want to talk about it.

Counselor: Good. So what could you do?

Evan: I don't know. I could ask them what they want me to do.

Counselor: Great! Even if you don't know what to do, you can still identify the emotion and then ask another person what they want you to do. That is helping expand your theory of mind and making space for other's perspectives and experiences.

Follow-Up Session

Counselor: It's been one week since our last meeting; how are your peer interactions in history class going?

Evan: We had another debate this week in class.

Counselor: Were you able to implement some of the strategies we discussed in our last session?

Evan: Yes, I didn't agree with one of my classmates, so I keep on repeating my side of the debate. I remembered the card sorting task you know it had those people making all the faces and then we practiced the faces. I asked my classmate if he was making an angry face.

Counselor: What did your classmate say?

Evan: He said he was feeling angry.

Counselor: So his facial expression matched his actual feelings?

Evan: I guess it did, anyway I asked him why he was angry because I was really confused.

Counselor: That's wonderful that you felt empowered to ask.

Evan: He told me that he was feeling frustrated that I kept on repeating myself and that my voice was getting very loud.

Counselor: Have you ever noticed that your voice changes when you are experiencing anger?

Evan: I never really thought about this.

Counselor: The session is almost over, and we covered a lot of useful information today. Between now and our session next week, would you be willing to notice if your classmates' voices change when they are experiencing excitement, happiness, or anger? I think paying attention to those things might expand your knowledge on mirror neurons and empathy.

ETHICAL AND MULTICULTURAL CONSIDERATIONS

ASD is, even by name, a spectrum disorder, and as a result, symptomology and manifestation vary greatly from person to person. Although this activity deals with mirror neurons and theory of mind, it also, at its heart, deals with empathy. In helping clients with ASD be more aware of others' emotions, desires, and needs, counselors are being empathetic toward their clients and considering *their* emotions, desires, and needs. Ultimately, this activity is best used with a client who is seeking change and wants to learn the skills to connect with others.

In addition, counselors must be aware of their clients' cultural backgrounds, as there is cultural variation in emotional expression, identification, and valence. A counselor may find, for instance, that an American client may attribute more extreme emotions to a facial expression that a Japanese client may see as more subdued (Pogosyan, 2016). Pogosyan (2016) also argued that different cultures direct attention to different facial features; people from East Asian cultures may tend to focus on the central region of the face and place more importance on the eyes and gaze direction, whereas Western Caucasian people may focus more on the mouth and eyebrows. We encourage counselors to explore their clients' cultural norms for emotional expression before engaging in this activity and then check in with the client during the activity to check for resonance and modify as needed.

Finally, emotions are complex and do not always match stereotyped expectations about facial expressions. For example, a smile does not always mean happiness; it can be a cover for embarrassment or shrewd smile. Counselors should acknowledge the limitations of the idea of reading facial expressions and work with individuals on holistic social-emotional learning.

FLIPPED LIDS, ANIMALS, AND BUBBLES

Promoting Regulation Through Neuroeducation

Dalena Dilman Taylor and Naomi J. Wheeler

A child's first six years of life are the most instrumental period for neuronal growth (National Scientific Council on the Developing Child, 2010). Therefore, early childhood is a critical time for development and learning. Teachers provide consistent care to children (Abidin & Robinson, 2002) and may be best positioned to identify and respond early to the needs of children exhibiting disruptive behaviors. The importance of a teacher's role is exemplified by the amount of time children spend in school (7+ hours), with younger children spending the majority of their school time with a single teacher. However, teachers have little to no preparation in mental health assessments and are required to balance the demands of many roles (Ball et al., 2016). Without early intervention or preventive services, children who exhibit disruptive behaviors (i.e., acting out, aggression, inattention, hyperactivity) are likely to develop long-term consequences, such as conduct, social, internalizing, and academic problems (Pardini & Fite, 2010). There are several neuroscience concepts, such as the social engagement system, brain development and communication, and regulation strategies, that we find helpful to include in various prevention and early intervention programs, and these concepts serve as the foundation for the *Flipped Lids, Animals, and Bubbles: Promoting Regulation Through Neuroeducation* activity.

The social engagement system is engaged subconsciously within the neuroception of safety (Porges, 2011). When individuals are engaged in social connection and perceived danger is low, the social engagement system pumps the ventral vagus brakes on the sympathetic nervous system that overrides stress hormones and activates the parasympathetic nervous system for the individual to remain calm. In this state, the brain is at an optimal level of arousal and open to new learning experiences. Therefore, the social engagement system is an important and foundational concept for the subsequent activity and process we provide.

According to the seminal work of Paul MacLean (1990) the brain develops in three hierarchical regions: the neofrontal cortex (e.g., upstairs brain), the limbic system (e.g., amygdala—downstairs brain), and the basal ganglia (e.g., brain stem—downstairs brain). Siegel and Bryson (2012) discuss this concept using the "hand model of the brain" (Siegel & Bryson, 2012), which uses the hand to visually explore these three regions of the brain, the primary roles, and how they communicate.

Siegel and Bryson (2012) broke this concept down even more by describing the upstairs (e.g., cortical regions) and downstairs (e.g., subcortical) brain to help younger children grasp the concept. Finally, Dan Siegel (2012a) coined the phrase "flipping one's lid" to indicate when the upstairs and downstairs brains are not communicating well and the parasympathetic nervous system is disengaged and the sympathetic nervous system is engaged (e.g., fight-flight).

Flipped lids require the practice of regulation strategies. There are several regulation strategies that are helpful for children. In this activity, we focus on the importance of diaphragmatic or "deep" breathing, an effective technique to support the regulation of emotional states (Varvogli & Darviri, 2011). Even young children can implement deep or diaphragmatic breathing strategies to calm their nervous systems and engage their "upstairs brains." Deep and slow breathing is facilitative of the relaxation response (Busch, et al., 2012), helping children to calm their sympathetic nervous systems when triggered by stressors.

Despite the importance of these concepts, neuroscience is complex. Most young children will not understand neuroscience concepts, such as the difference in frontal lobe (e.g., upstairs brain) and amygdala (e.g., downstairs brain), nor how to calm themselves when the amygdala is in

MATERIALS NEEDED

- Stuffed animals
- Bubbles

overdrive. Therefore, it is important to break down neuroscience principles and tasks in a developmentally appropriate manner using concrete steps. *Flipped Lids, Animals, and Bubbles: Promoting Regulation Through Neuroeducation* is a developmentally appropriate approach for the implementation of neuroeducation in the classroom. The activity includes experiential approaches that exemplify neuroeducation concepts and help children to recognize, regulate, and respond more appropriately to their feelings/reactions.

PROCESS OF THE ACTIVITY

Flipped Lids, Animals, and Bubbles: Promoting Regulation Through Neuroeducation is a three-week, 5- to 10-minute weekly activity to be integrated into preschool to kindergarten classrooms (ages 3–6); however, it can be adapted for older children or modified into one longer activity. Because of the simplicity of the intervention, school counselors or teachers can implement this activity as a part of the social-emotional curriculum that is required by many school districts.

Week 1. Review "Hand Model of the Brain" (Siegel & Bryson, 2012)

Duration: 5–10 minutes. It is important for the teacher to select a time in which most children are present, calm, and engaged. Most likely, the teacher will select the morning to increase the likelihood of establishing a neuroception of safety, allowing the child to be open to learning about new skills. The presenter will introduce the hand model of the brain first through modeling and then engaging students to demonstrate the model. Through discussion of the hand model, the presenter will acknowledge big emotions (e.g., anger, sadness)—feelings that the child may experience in which they have a difficult time controlling their actions or reactions to an event—and different parts of the child's brain (i.e., upstairs, downstairs). The presenter may define the upstairs brain—"the upstairs brain has an important job. It helps us to play, to come up with solutions, and understand how our friends or how we feel" (i.e., primarily responsible for complex actions, such as decision making, regulating emotions, and critical thinking)—and the downstairs brain—"the downstairs brain has an important job too! It helps us to breathe and keeps us safe when we are in danger" (i.e., primarily responsible for basic functions, such as breathing, experiencing big emotions, and perceiving danger).

The presenter will explore reactions to when children experience big emotions, acknowledging that children may "flip their lids" (Siegel, 2012b). As described in the brief video (https://www.youtube.com/watch?v=gm9CIJ74Oxw), children who flip their lids have a hard time regulating big emotions because their amygdala is working really hard to keep them safe. In more child-friendly terms, when a child flips their lid, their downstairs brain is in charge. The presenter will then have the class practice using a tactile display of flipping their lids, naming the emotion, and reaching out for support from their teacher. In addition, the presenter will encourage the teacher to implement the activity regularly in the classroom over the next week.

Week 2. Explore Deep Breathing Through Use of Stuffed Animals

Duration: 5–10 minutes. The presenter will review the hand model of the brain that was introduced in the previous week. The presenter will explore deep breathing through the use of stuffed animals as a means to calm the downstairs brain and close the lid (Siegel, 2012a; see Figure 7.12).

The presenter will ask the children to lie down and place a stuffed animal on each of their bellies. Then the presenter will instruct them to breathe in and focus on the animal going up. Next, the presenter will instruct them to let the air out and focus on the animal going down. The presenter will call attention to the stuffed animal going up and down, and this process helps children to

FIGURE 7.12 Deep Breathing With Stuffed Animals

create awareness of their breath. After the children have practiced these breaths two to three times, the presenter will connect the purpose of deep breathing exercise to the hand model of the brain and emphasize that as children "flip their lids" or experience big emotions, it can be helpful to grab a stuffed animal and practice this activity. Again, the presenter will request that the teacher encourage this practice throughout the week.

Week 3. Explore Deep Breaths Through Bubble Blowing

Duration: 5–10 minutes. The presenter will summarize the hand model of the brain, allowing the children to practice using a tactile display of flipping their lids and naming the "big" emotion at least once, and summarize the purpose of deep breathing as it connects to the hand model. Then the presenter will have children practice deep breathing again using bubbles. First, the presenter will model taking a deep breath and then slowly letting it go to form bubbles. The presenter can encourage children to take in a deep breath as modeled, count to three, and then inform them to release their breaths slowly as they count to three in their heads (presenter counts out loud). The children could then practice with a partner for the duration of the activity. Again, the presenter will request that the teacher encourage the practice of the deep breaths throughout the week.

FOLLOW-UP

The activity can include informal forms of evaluation, such as the following process questions:

1. When did you use your "bubbles" this week?
2. When did you use your animal to help calm down this week?
3. What big emotions did you feel?
4. When did you help a friend do "bubbles" or "animals" this week?

Furthermore, the teacher and student will now have a shared language and metaphor that may be used and referenced when the student experiences big emotions or is on the verge of flipping their lid.

NEUROSCIENCE IN ACTION

I (Dalena) implemented this activity in a 4-year-old class at a local preschool. I conducted each of the three activities in 5- to 10-minute segments 1 week apart. The teacher was invested in the process and used the same language and terminology throughout the week. It was evident that the children practiced each week through the different modifications they implemented on their own and through the empathy that emerged to help their "friends" practice these exercises as they learned big emotions, thus promoting social engagement. The following is an excerpt from Week 1 to illustrate this intervention.

Week 1. Review "Hand Model of the Brain" (Siegel, 2012b)

Counselor: Did you know each of you has a model of your brain in your own hands? [Excited tone.] Show me your hands. Hold them up very high. OK. I am going to teach you something really cool. This is called the hand model of the brain [hold up your fist]. Your brain has two pieces—an upstairs brain and a downstairs brain. See my palm [point to it]. This part of my hand shows me where my big emotions come from. Sometimes you have big emotions that are hard to control. Sometimes you may get mad and want to hit your friends or feel really sad and want to cry or scream. These feelings are okay. When you have these feelings and you scream, hit, or cry, we can call that flipping our lid [raise fingers up and away from palm]. This can be scary, and you may feel out of control and not sure what to do. I will teach you several ways to help control or calm these big emotions. When we calm our big emotions, we engage our upstairs brain [fold fingers over thumb to form a fist]. Let's practice. When you experience big emotions, you may flip your lid [demonstrate by raising fingers up]. However, by naming those big emotions, you can engage the upstairs brain [bring fingers back down over the thumb to touch the palm]. For this week, when you feel you are flipping your lid [fingers go up], tell your teacher. She will know how to help [look at teacher and nod to gain her approval and commitment].

The students practiced a tactile display of flipping their lids, naming the emotion, and reaching out for support, showing the person next to them and wanting me (Dalena) to also see their hands.

Week 2. Explore Deep Breathing Through Use of Stuffed Animals

Counselor: Good morning everyone. I am excited to be back. I have something fun in store. Remember last week? We learned about the hand model of the brain. Hold up your hands. Show me your fists. That's right [holding up a fist too]. This is our hand model of the brain. When it is in a fist, we know that we are using our upstairs brain and can control our big emotions. What happens when I do this [raise fingers up away from palm]?

Children: You flip your lid!

Counselor: You remembered! When we flip our lids, we are engaging our downstairs brain and have a very tough time controlling those big emotions we talked about last week. Did anyone flip their lids this past week?

Anna [pseudonym]: I did [shyly].

Counselor: Thanks for sharing, Anna. And what did you do after?

Anna: I told my teacher.

Counselor: Anna, you found something you could do! And I bet your teacher helped you control those big emotions. [Anna nodded.] Anyone else?

Freddie: Zach did. And I helped him.

Counselor: Freddie, you saw a friend that may need your help and you helped. Tell me what you did.

Freddie: I told my teacher.

Counselor: You found something to help Zach. [Freddie nodded.] And Zach, tell me about how that was for you.

Zach: My teacher helped me. I felt better.

Counselor: Many good things happened this past week! This week, I am going to show you something you can do to help control those big emotions *all by yourself* [children at this age like to feel competent so emphasize this statement]. Ms. Smith has a stuffed animal for each of you. Pick the animal you want for this activity. Give it a big hug while we wait for our friends to get their animals [choose an animal for yourself and model hugging the animal as each kid makes a selection]. Show me how you can lie on your back with your animal sitting on your belly. Ready? [Look around to make sure all kids are lying down. If you wait is too long, the children will get restless, so move quickly into the next step.] Take a deep breath in [model the breath with the children]. Do you see how your animal goes up? Your belly is pushing the animal high in the sky. Now breathe out [blow out the breath to model]. Watch as your animal comes back down closer to you. Let's try that again. Breathe in. 1 – 2 – 3. Your animal is going high into the sky. Breathe out. 1 – 2 – 3. And now, your animal is coming closer to you. Let's see if you can make the animal go higher this time. Breathe in. 1 – 2 – 3. Climbing higher. And breathe out. 1 – 2 – 3. Give your animal a big hug and sit up. How did that feel?

Sarah: Doggie went so high!

Counselor: You took big breaths in and out. Anyone else?

Max: I want to do it again.

Counselor: Max, you enjoyed practicing breathing with your animal. And you will. This week when you experience big emotions and "flip your lid" [model this using the hand model], you can grab an animal and practice. Did you know that when you take big breaths you are working to close your lid? Remember earlier, we practiced what our brain looks like when we flip our lid? That's right [as some children hold up their fists with fingers in the air]! So when you use the animal or your hand to practice deep breaths, you are working hard to close your lid and your big emotions. Your teacher will leave the animals over in that corner for when you need them [talk with the teacher ahead of time as to where she would like to store the animals for the children to use]. Next week, we will practice one more activity. See you all next Friday.

Week 3. Explore Deep Breaths Through Bubble Blowing

Counselor: Good morning. Today, we are going to go outside to practice our deep breathing. Who remembers what this is [holding up a fist]?

Alaina: The brain.

Counselor: Yes, this is the hand model of the brain. Everyone, hold up your hands. Make a fist. When our fingers round over our thumb, we know that we are using our upstairs brain and have an easier time controlling our big emotions. What happens when I do this? [Raise fingers up.]

Children: Flip the lid!

Counselor: Yes, sometimes this happens when emotions are really big, and we are struggling to bring ourselves under control. What was something you learned last week to help?

Anna: Animals on my belly.

Counselor: That's right. We practiced breathing with animals. We made them go up when we breathed in and down when we breathed out. Sometimes when we take deep breaths, we can calm down and use our upstairs brain again. Did anyone practice last week? Did anyone practice with a friend?

Max: I was really mad, and Zach asked me to breathe with him. Ms. Smith pulled out the animals and we did it!

Ms. Smith: We have been working in class to help each other out. At first, I would remind them to use the animals, but now they are doing it on their own.

Counselor: Great! You all are making deep breathing a part of your time here at school. Today, we are going to practice another way to do deep breaths. You each are going to get some bubbles [pass out the bubbles]. Watch me first. I want you to take a deep breath in [model for the child]. Now, blow all the air out, making big bubbles [blow into the wand to demonstrate]. Ok, you can try. Take a deep breath [breathe in with the children] and now blow out making big bubbles [release the breath]. This could be a way to calm down when you are outside on the playground or at home with your family. Now you have two ways to calm down.

Outcome

The teacher wholeheartedly believed in this activity and implemented daily alerts at the beginning of class to remind students of their new strategies. She also encouraged the notion of social engagement, community well-being, and family, informing students that they had a responsibility to care for each other and help when their friends were struggling. At our end of the year conference, she reported that students, without prompting, would engage in these strategies with each other if a student was exhibiting behavioral outbursts (i.e., flipping their lid), and some students adapted the strategies. One student modified the deep breathing exercise to be a growing flower. She would start in a ball on the floor with hands touching the ground then "grow" as her hands stretched to the ceiling as high as she could while breathing in. She would release her breath as she walked her hands down her body back to the ground (see Figure 7.13).

FIGURE 7.13 Growing Flower

ETHICAL AND MULTICULTURAL CONSIDERATIONS

Because of developmental delays or mobility concerns, this intervention may be a challenge for some, as it requires a certain level of cognitive understanding and mobility (in Week 2). The language used and materials can be modified to address any concerns regarding inclusivity. In this classroom, we had one student who was in a wheelchair. He held his animal on his belly and watched his hands and the animal move outward as he breathed in and inward as he released his breath. If students do not have mobility in their hands, the students could partner up and model for each other as they are able.

ANCILLARY MATERIALS

- *Hand Model of the Brain* by Dan Siegel for a reference to adapt for children: https://www.youtube.com/watch?v=gm9CIJ74Oxw
- Additional recommended readings: Siegel and Bryson (2012).

CLOSING THOUGHTS

The purpose of this chapter was to explore the neuroscience of emotion and emotion regulation theory and techniques. The neuroeducation exercises in this chapter demonstrated various ways clinicians can apply these concepts. Each activity in some way aimed to enhance awareness and strengthen emotion regulation capacity. As you reflect on the activities in this chapter, consider the way that you reacted to each activity. Before moving on to the next chapter, consider the following reflection questions:

REFLECTION QUESTIONS

1. What theory of emotion resonates most strongly with your knowledge and experiences?
2. How do you help clients foster emotion regulation capacity? Are there ways you could enhance these approaches by incorporating neuroeducation?
3. Which neuroeducation activities seem most interesting and/or applicable to clients you work with?

CREDITS

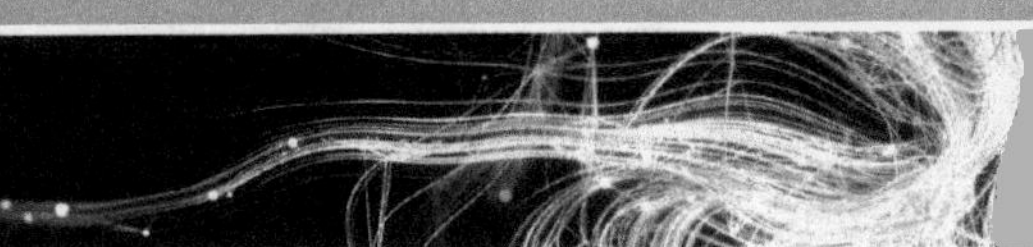

CHAPTER 8

Memory Systems

The purpose of memory is not to let us recall the past, but to let us anticipate the future. Memory is a tool for prediction.
—Alain Berthoz

CHAPTER OBJECTIVES

1. Understand the process of memory formation, consolidation, and reconsolidation.
2. Identify strategies to use the neuroscience of memory to inform clinical work.
3. Identify useful memory-related neuroscience concepts to explore with clients.

INTRODUCTION

As you begin this chapter, and as you are comfortable, take a moment to reflect on your earliest memory. What is your earliest memory? How old are you? Where are you? What are you doing? Who are you with? What do you feel? How does this memory influence the way you experience the world today? What is the purpose of this memory?

Asking clients about their earliest recollections is a staple in our clinical work. As we put ourselves through this task, we often wonder why a specific memory appears and others do not. Sometimes we want to remember, and sometimes we want to forget. Sometimes we control this retrieval, and other times it is intrusive and automatic. Sometimes we can make ourselves remember, and other times the retrieval of the memory seems out of our control. The nuance in how we experience memory is just one indicator of the complexity of our memory systems, as well as their effect on our therapeutic work.

Memory is a never-ending process through which sensory information is encoded and stored (Baddeley et al., 2009). Memories differ in speed of encoding (e.g., immediate vs. repeated exposure), duration (short term vs. long term), accessibility (implicit vs. explicit), and content (semantic vs. emotional) that is influenced by the dynamic interaction of a variety of interconnected neurons in various brain regions, structures, and networks, including the hippocampus, prefrontal cortex, medial temporal lobe, neocortex, striatum, amygdala, and cerebellum (Dahlitz, 2017; Kredlow et al., 2018; Ross et al., 2017). Yes, the construct of memory is complex!

The construct of memory is not new, and the wealth of literature outlining its evolution is covered in many books that exceed the purposes of this chapter. However, recent advances in neuroscience have provided new insights into how our experiences are encoded or not, as well as how memories are stored, accessed, remembered, misremembered, consolidated, and reconsolidated that will be briefly reviewed here. Whereas memory used to be considered a stable entity, research within the past decade has suggested that our memories are flexible, dynamic, vulnerable to influence, and editable (Lee, et al., 2017; Monfils et al., 2009; Nader & Einarsson, 2010; Schiller et al., 2010). Lee et al. (2017) discussed the evolution of our understanding of memory from a singularly consolidated phenomenon to a dynamically evolving and updating process that is amenable to intervention. These scholars affirm that memories need to be destabilized and the reconsolidation efforts disrupted long enough for incongruent information (prediction error, meaning what was expected to happen does not occur) to be absorbed.

Kredlow et al. (2018) provided a helpful overview of the memory formation, retrieval, and reconsolidation process, as well as recommendations for how pharmacological interventions, cognitive-behavioral strategies, sleep, brain stimulation and neuromodulation, and physical activity can be used to augment memory consolidation following initial exposures, memory reconsolidation following retrieval of initial memories, and enhancement to therapeutic memories. Their review captures the tremendous potential for memory work to serve as a guiding framework for clinical intervention. To review this process, we created a synthesized conceptual model to guide your review of the neuroeducation exercises in this chapter, as well as your future innovation in your clinical work. To review this model, we will use fear-based memories as an example because they are the most commonly studied memories; although, several other applications to addictive, declarative, and emotional memories are emerging (Kredlow et al., 2018).

Think back to your Psych 100 course or some other first exposure to behavioral theorists. Do you recall Ivan Pavlov's salivating dog experiments, which formalized the process we now know as classical conditioning? Okay, we have trouble remembering back that far too; maybe our protein was not fully synthesized and synapses never reached long-term potentiation? So, let us review Pavlovian classical conditioning as a primer for understanding how the neuroscience of memory can inform our work.

According to the theory of classical conditioning (Figure 8.1), we respond to stimuli in many ways; our responses are at least initially unconditioned (UCR) and related to various stimuli that are also unconditioned (UCS). UCS can range from innocuous stimuli, such as a street sign, to more intense stimuli, such as a traumatic event. UCR can include a variety of emotions, behaviors, feelings, cognitions, and physiological reactions, to name a few. Each UCS (e.g., traumatic event) creates a UCR (e.g., increased sympathetic nervous system [SNS] arousal), and when that UCS is paired with some neutral stimuli (NS; location, smells, images, etc.), often in the same moment of space and time, future exposure to the NS alone, now referred to as the conditioned stimulus (CS) in absence of the UCS, can produce the same physiological reactions, which are now referred to as the conditioned response (CR). This learning creates a stable memory that when compared to new stimuli predicts the necessary outcome and needed response. Whether it be N-methyl-D-aspartate (NMDA) receptors, basolateral nucleus of the amygdala, periaqueductral gray, dorsolaterial prefrontal cortex, thalamocortical pathways, or, most likely, the complex interaction of them all, neuroscience has provided tremendous insight into the precision of how, when, and for whom the classical conditioning process evolves, but much is yet to be known (Ferreira de Sá et al., 2019; Yau & McNally, 2018).

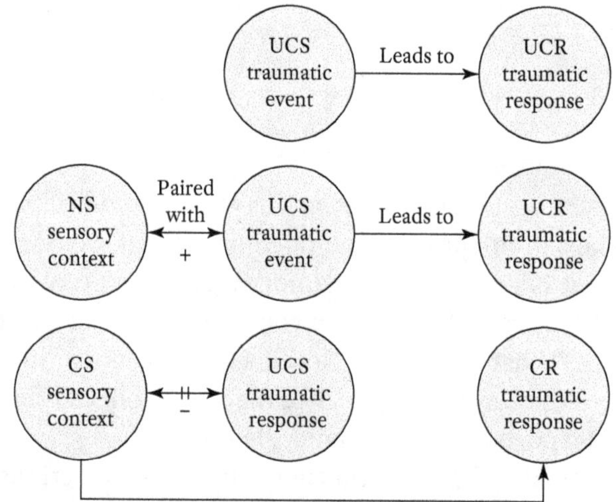

FIGURE 8.1 Classical Conditioning Process Following a Traumatic Event

Let us look at an example. Imagine a person deployed to a conflict-ridden area. They experience constant sensory stimuli (UCS; gunfire, smell of gun powder, etc.) that is related to increased hypervigilance, defensive posture, and related SNS activity (UCR). These UCS are generalized to all similar stimuli (CS; gunshots are like a door slamming) that create the same hypervigilance, defense posture, and SNS activity (now the CR). This memory helps the person predict future responses to the same stimuli to remain

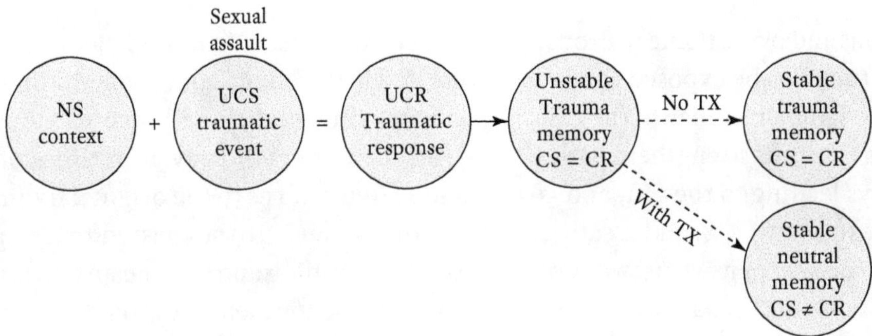

FIGURE 8.2 The Development of Stable Trauma or Neutral Memories Following a Sexual Assault

safe ("I need to be on alert to protect myself and my comrades"). While initially adaptive in nature, this response often causes problems in postdeployment life, when the context changes but similar stimuli exist. For instance, the soldier needs increased SNS arousal (UCR) when they hear gunfire (UCS). When this veteran returns home, they may have the same arousal to a door closing or car backfiring (CS), which can promote similar hypervigilance and potential aggression (CR). So what used to be helpful in one context is now causing problems in another context. It is possible that interventions could be delivered quickly after the initial exposure (Kredlow et al., 2018) to the gunfire to prevent a memory association between the gunfire and increased SNS response, but this would be counterproductive in the context of war, so treatment is often delivered much later after the established memory network between CS and CR is stabilized. Let us look at this process in terms of sexual assault (Figure 8.2).

A college student is walking to their dorm when they are sexually assaulted, leading to automatic SNS arousal promoting a fight response, followed by an attempt to flee, and then eventually complete dissociation, what we call a necessary traumatic response. It is possible that this interaction could lead to a fear-based memory network that creates this same response in similar contexts when the trauma or threat is not apparent, which could result in several challenges (e.g., avoiding class). However, if this student immediately presents to the university's intervention center, it might be possible to intervene quickly (e.g., pharmacological, cognitive-behavioral, stimulation) after the initial exposure while the memory is still in an unstable state. Immediate and effective intervention might prevent the full traumatic memory from being consolidated, and the entire consolidated memory could include elements of safety, care, and compassion delivered during the intervention. The quicker the intervention, the better able the intervention is to prevent new synaptic connections between stimuli and response becoming consolidated as a long-term memory in larger brain networks. However, this type of immediate intervention is often not possible, and the full traumatic memory often becomes stabilized, leading to a number of problems, especially when exposed to related stimuli.

When exposed to new stimuli, Kredlow et al. (2018) explained the process of assimilation (new information that confirms the existing networks) and accommodation (new information that disrupts the existing networks) in relation to an existing memory network (see Figure 8.3). If the new stimuli continue to produce the CR, then it becomes more stable in the long-term memory network, strengthening the

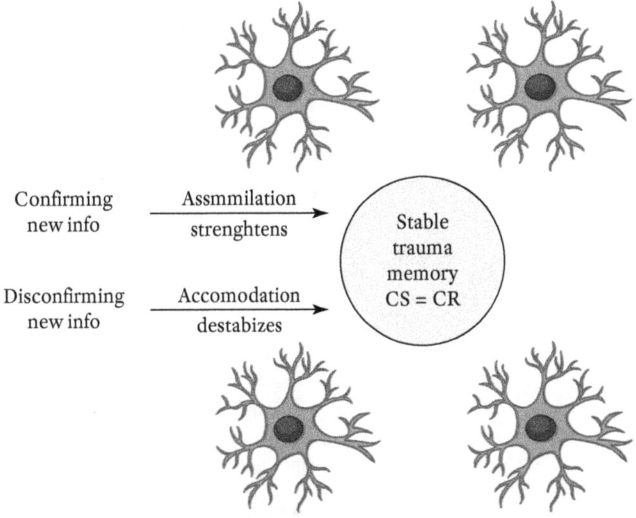

FIGURE 8.3 The Impact of New Information on Existing Trauma Memory Networks

cortico-limbic connections and overlapping neurons. So the person likely continues to be exposed to new stimuli that is exactly the same or similar to the CS, which promotes ongoing CR, thus strengthening the neurobiological pathways leading to the CR, and is generalized to new contexts, new UCS, and creating more CS. This creates an ever-expansive network of memories, feelings, emotions, and behavioral consequences. However, if the new stimuli do not confirm the existing memory network, then the memory network becomes disrupted. This incongruence (Grawe, 2007) or mismatch experience (Ecker et al., 2012) is often essential to sustained memory change at the heart of our clinical work (Grawe, 2007).

Research has suggested that traditional trauma treatments (e.g., extinction training), although effective in the short term, actually create a competing alternative memory that subsides over time, especially in times of increased stress, leading to a return to the original traumatic memory (e.g., LeDoux, 2015; Lee et al., 2017). In response, Kredlow et al. (2018) suggested that it is possible for an intervention to focus on increasing consolidation of these therapeutic gains through various strategies (e.g., praise, oxytocin, brain stimulation, naps) so that the memory of therapeutic gains become more solidified and prevent the return of the traumatic memory (see Figure 8.4). For instance, let's imagine the college student who endured the sexual assault does not receive treatment until much longer after the assault. They likely have a stabilized trauma memory that has been reinforced through encounters with stimuli similar to the initial assault. After receiving traditional extinction training without exposure, a competing alternative memory is created in which the conditioned stimuli no longer produces the conditioned response during therapeutic encounters; however, in times of stress, the person often returns to the original trauma memory. Kredlow et al. (2018) suggested that bypassing the extinction training and/or focusing on creating competing therapeutic memories could prevent the return of the original traumatic memory. For instance, the safety of the therapeutic relationship could create a mismatch experience, and when capitalized in the therapeutic encounter, it could lead to an edit of the old trauma memory.

Another approach that shows promise is to provide treatment postexposure in a therapeutic setting (Kredlow et al., 2018; Lee et al., 2017). It has been suggested that brief exposure (Figure 8.5) to the original trauma (e.g., telling a story about the trauma, imagining the trauma) retrieves and destabilizes the traumatic memory for about 10 minutes to 6 hours—a time frame that has been referred to as the reconsolidation window (Kredlow et al., 2018). After a brief pause postretrieval, the treatment continues with any number of interventions, including extinction training, counterconditioning, interference, and eye movements, among others. Rather than creating a competing memory, these interventions prevent the reconsolidation of old traumatic material and update the original memory absent of the CR, leading to more relief. In addition to preventing the reconsolidation, it is also possible to add an alternative emotional story to the original memory. In some ways, this creates a new CR of safety, relief, resilience, and/or growth

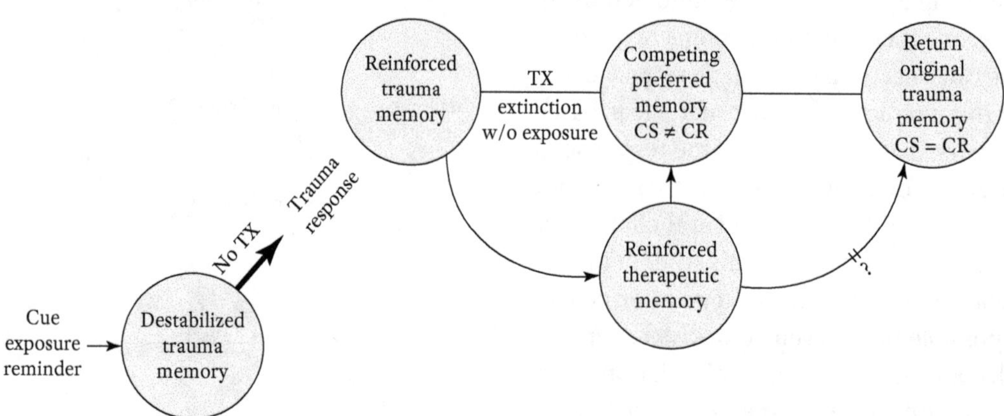

FIGURE 8.4 The Impact of Extinction Without Exposure on the Trauma Memory Network and the Potential for New Therapeutic Memories to Compete

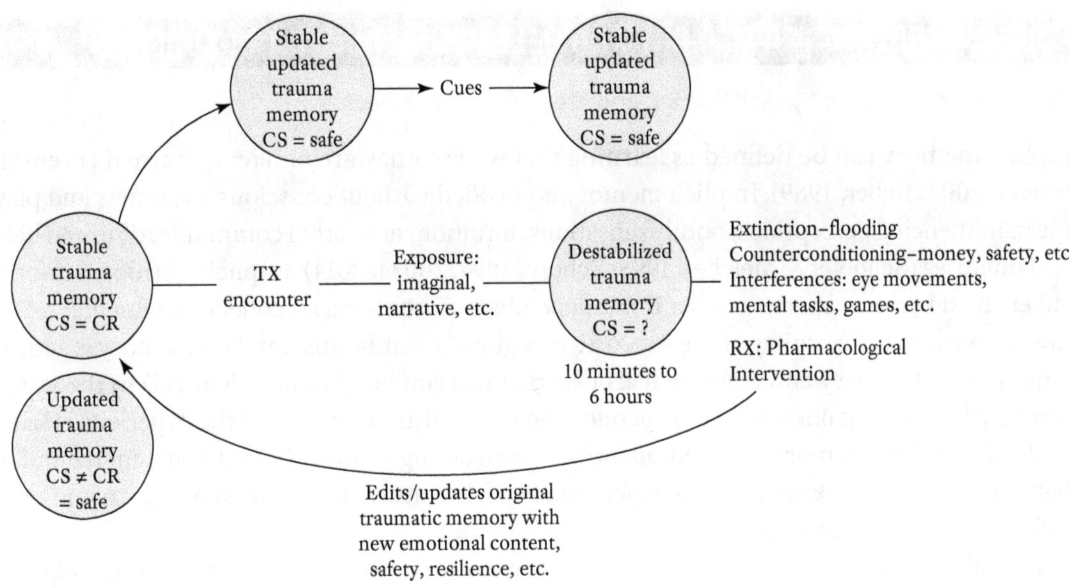

FIGURE 8.5 Potential Pathway to Memory Reconsolidation Lead to Stable, Updated Trauma Memories With Safe Valence

so that when future cues are met, the new, updated, traumatic memory with the new CRs is activated, and the person can react in a way that the context requires.

This newer view of the dynamic, editable nature of memory has led to new processes in existing treatments (e.g., extinction training), as well as the creation of entirely new treatment protocols, such as eye-movement desensitization and reprocessing (EMDR; see Wilson et al., 2018, for a review) and accelerated resolution therapy (ART; see Kip & Diamond, 2018, for a review), among others. In addition, using a memory reconsolidation framework may lead to better delivery of existing treatments, such as cognitive behavioral therapy (Kredlow et al., 2018). Although there is much to be excited about in this new era of trauma and memory work, there is still much to understand in terms of risks that are possible (e.g., updating to a more severe response, creating false memories, removing unwanted content). Kredlow et al. (2018) summarized these cautions, noting, "Be careful what you enhance" (p. 280). Future research will continue to elucidate the underlying mechanisms of change and specific types of updating techniques that are most effective for which memories, in which individuals, and under which circumstances.

As with all concepts in this book, this review is a simplified description of how memory consolidation and reconsolidation occur. Also, it is likely that much new research will be published, and some of these concepts will have new caveats or be replaced altogether. Therefore, it is important to remain current in this body of literature to evaluate if and when the interventions in this text are replicated in your own clinical work.

NEUROEDUCATION ACTIVITIES

This chapter presents four unique neuroeducation activities that use the neuroscience of memory to aid in the client's self-exploration, insight, and future changes. We will revisit a classic iceberg metaphor with a new twist, learn a fancy acronym (RECON), experience the power of song to elevate pre-pain memories, and explore the emerging value of eye movement.

UNDERWATER MEMORY AND RELEARNING ABOVE THE SURFACE

Stephannee Standefer, Russell Fulmer, and Megan Stocker Headley

Implicit memory can be defined as learning that we are unaware of having learned (Frensch & Rünger, 2003; Reber, 1989). Implicit memory is encoded without conscious awareness and plays a role in influencing perceptions, bodily sensations, intuition, nonverbal communication, and behavioral impulses (Schooler & Melcher, 1995; Schore, 1994, 2003a, 2014). Implicit learning is informed and enabled by past experiences but is not dependent on conscious recollection (Roediger, 1990). Interwoven into the circuitry of the subcortical regions of our brains, implicit memory is activated in moments of sensory and emotional arousal that feel similar (but not identical) to the state we were in when we first unconsciously encoded the material associated with the experience (Lane et al., 2015). Implicit memory is largely adaptive, constructing a nonverbal yet coherent mental map that converts past experiences into expectations of the future to help us avoid harm and ensure well-being (Van der Kolk, 2014).

Learning formed in the presence of intense negative emotion or infancy and early toddlerhood before the hippocampus is fully developed, however, can lead to misperceptions of threats and become less helpful, driving unwanted responses of behaviors, feelings, or thoughts (Tyng et al., 2017). The synapses associated with these responses become increasingly durable, making it feel like we are fighting an unyielding and unseen force (Ecker et al., 2012).

The influence of implicit memory has far-reaching clinical implications, from treating clients suffering from emotional dysregulation to those having difficulty with romantic relationships. Emotional learning unlocks and becomes modifiable only when a new experience mismatches what one has learned to expect (Ecker, 2015). The repair and security experienced in the therapeutic relationship not only induces an emotional extinction of sorts by creating a vivid contradiction to the learned pattern, but it also stimulates neuroplasticity in the cortical and subcortical systems of the right hemisphere (Schore, 2014).

Trauma or emotionally disturbing memories are often associated with a lack of cognitive integration that interferes in hippocampal-mediated consolidation processes (Lane et al., 2015). In such cases, the traumatic memory is encoded in amygdala-mediated implicit processes, resulting in a memory that is not easily or willingly retrievable. The psychotherapeutic environment offers an opportunity for the activation of emotionally arousing/distressing memory, as well as a place for corrective emotional learning (Bridges, 2006). In fact, transference has been described as an expression of clients' implicit memories (Schore, 2014). Our subcortical minds can be changed deeply and transformatively, liberating us from psychic determinism, expanding psychological flexibility within intimate relationships, and increasing our capacity for conscious responsiveness to life's challenges. The *Underwater Memory and Relearning Above the Surface* activity provides clinicians with an illustratable and comprehensible way to explore the human propensity to repeat less helpful behavior, empowering our clients to release the shackles of their past and to become more active authors of their present and future.

MATERIALS NEEDED

- A whiteboard or piece of paper
- A writing utensil

PROCESS OF THE ACTIVITY

The *Underwater Memory and Relearning Above the Surface* activity, which explores implicit memory and how it can keep us stuck, can be introduced across a fairly inclusive population but is especially helpful with populations who have experienced trauma. With individuals who have experienced trauma (or those with which trauma history is suspected), trust and safety should be firmly established before introducing this activity. It can be presented at any point in the session but is likely to be most compelling when individuals are questioning a disproportionate reaction they had or the self-defeating patterns they reenact despite their self-proclaimed "knowing better." These kinds of automatic behaviors can be described as clues that something unconscious, or *implicit*, is at play, thereby introducing the concept of "underwater memory."

Implicit memory can be explored and drawn in session using a similar model as Freud's iceberg model, proposing that the part of the brain "above water" houses our explicit memory, whereas the parts of the brain "underwater" house our implicit memory (Fechner, 1860; Jones, 1953; Miller, 2016). To elucidate the differences in the memory systems, it can be helpful to say that explicit memory stores information we have learned and can consciously recall more easily, while implicit memory stores information we were unaware of learning and are generally not consciously recalled. An appreciation of the role implicit memory plays in our emotional—and corporeal—sense of self can be facilitated by exploring how implicit memory activates emotions, which are best described in this activity as sensations arising in our bodies. This connection between the senses and emotions is often compellingly exemplified by acknowledging the immediacy with which certain odors trigger strong emotions and memories. To aid with an integrated processing of the underwater memory drawing, labels and bullet points can be added, describing the hallmark characteristics of implicit memory as unconscious, nonverbal, emotionally and somatically based, and harder to access and change.

Moving on to explore what happens when the emotions connected to an implicit memory are intense or negative, the drawing's profile orientation becomes useful. On the illustration, point out the subcortical brain stem and midbrain, which correspond with body-oriented and emotional/motivational functions, respectively, and then the cortical forebrain, which corresponds with cognitive/rational functions. Next, note how emotionally laden memories can sometimes get trapped "underwater" in the emotional centers of the brain and body and never make it up to our cognitive minds or into our awareness (Siegel, 2010a, 2010b). Introducing a discussion around triggers or situations in which the emotional distress is similar, inciting the same survival response learned at the time of the original event, helps to connect the dots between the past and the present. This concept of emotional arousal reactivating implicit learning can be clarified with the underwater metaphor; that is, when "water" conditions feel threatening and similar to some we have experienced before, we react the same way we did back then.

What feels vital to explore at this point is how these reactions we learned in the past that helped us to adapt to our conditions are now no longer necessary or helpful. Shifting these once-adaptive past patterns into ones more adaptive for the present requires first unlocking these memories and their imprinted responses. To help elucidate the esoteric process of rewriting implicit learning with a client, you can say something like the following:

> Modifying these automatic responses involves activating the underwater memories in a place or with a person that feels safe, bringing them above water so to speak, and realizing that we can respond differently this time. Each time an implicitly learned experience resolves in a way that is different from what we have come to expect, our brains and bodies begin to update and re-encode our emotional learning, allowing for more conscious control over our responses.

FOLLOW-UP

Assessment of this activity is primarily informal and involves a client's understanding of the difference between implicit and explicit memory, as well as an indication that the information offers insights around unhelpful or unwanted patterns of responding. After engaging in the activity, clinicians can pose open-ended questions such as the following:

- How do you make sense of this concept that we have conscious and unconscious memory?
- What areas of your life, if any, do you see implicit memory at play?
- Are there times you find yourself more likely to respond automatically or from an underwater place?

Such questions serve to gauge not only clients' big-picture comprehension of these concepts but also their interest level, which becomes an important motivator in the ultimate work of memory reconsolidation.

Another way to assess and reinforce the utility of this neuroeducation and its mode of delivery is to ask clients to monitor their reactions between sessions, returning with examples of times that their thoughts, feelings, or behaviors may have been influenced by implicit learning. The between-session exercise strengthens the clients' inner reflections around the effect of implicit memory while offering the counselor a glimpse at how accessible and readily available the concepts and information are applied by clients' in their day-to-day lives. Once comprehension is established, observed client behaviors indicative of progress in implicit memory integration include less dissociated affect, increased tolerance of emotional activation, regulation of heightened affective moments, and, finally, verbal expression of difficult emotions in a manner largely free from rationalizing or intellectualizing defenses. Reported behaviors indicative of the activity's positive effect on a client include an increased awareness of automatic patterns of responding, a wider window of tolerance for emotional reactivity, and a narrative that reflects increased agency and conscious flexibility of choice. Clients reveal enduring change when reconsolidation takes place in myriad settings and contexts (Lane et al., 2015).

NEUROSCIENCE IN ACTION

Sally, a 24-year-old newly married graduate student, presented with extreme anxiety, feelings of panic in her chest and throat, difficulty focusing, creative blocks, and trouble at work. Her family of origin included a father who displayed disproportionate reactions of rage, causing Sally to "hide" during much of her childhood, and a mother who, to accommodate him, had shut down her capacity to support her children emotionally. Sally learned to disappear around her father and only appear for her mother as an ally or emotional container. Sally came to me (Stephannee) seeking a new therapist after two years of work in which she experienced little relief.

In working with Sally, it became clear that anytime her father was mentioned or that she perceived a threat in her environment like the types of threats her father presented, her *water* level rose and she was flooded by implicit memories, often resulting in dissociation. She also described times at work where she would "check out" when her male boss would talk to her. The goal was to use the *Underwater Memory and Relearning Above the Surface* activity to explore with Sally how her response to male authority figures, as well as memories of her father, became trapped underwater and how therapy can help to free it and rewrite it.

To introduce the concept of implicit memory, a quick sketch (see Figure 8.6) of the brain was made with a marker on a piece of paper with a waterline labeled as the level of awareness. Descriptors of explicit and implicit memory characteristics were listed as bullet points. The drawing was used to show Sally where the emotional centers of her brain are and how her fearful memories of her father never traveled beyond that and instead became linked with the survival/protective response to hide. By connecting that response of the past with her "checking out" response of the present, Sally gained insight into how "underwater," locked, and automatic this learning became. She remarked, "This makes so much sense—it's as if the minute I sense even a hint of those same scary waters, I just shut down and stop breathing." It was clear that she was already incorporating new language (e.g., scary waters) of the metaphor into her description.

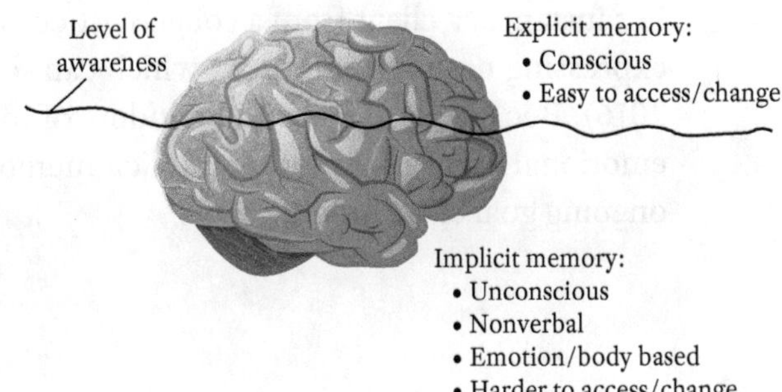

FIGURE 8.6 Visual Depiction of Implicit and Explicit Memory Using Underwater Imagery

Using the sketch, Sally saw that unlocking this learning required safely activating her implicit memories, enabling an integrated awareness of them, and how her therapy sessions in the past had not enabled the process of reactivation or reconsolidation. Rather than tapping into that deep-seated emotional learning that took place during that early visceral distress (and subsequently each time it was triggered by a similar situation, like at work or in past therapy), she was disengaging and keeping the memory and pattern of responding trapped underwater in her body and the subcortical regions of her brain. She also extended the initial metaphor by stating how her baseline water level had risen to the point that even the smallest reminder would prompt her defenses. Sally recognized that by dissociating and then intellectualizing, she was circumventing her painful emotions and bodily distress. With this recognition and by bringing the body and felt sense into the room, paired with safety in the therapeutic relationship, Sally began to discuss memories of her childhood without dissociating and reported considerable relief in her anxiety, her ability to focus, and her dissociative episodes at work. She remarked that the rising turbulent waters had subsided, and she was able to be present with the full range of her experiences.

ETHICAL AND MULTICULTURAL CONSIDERATIONS

Ethical considerations for this activity include an awareness of what negative memories may have been experienced and what reexperiencing them might mean to the client's well-being and the therapeutic process. Fear-based implicit memories formed before the age of 2, such as in cases of early child abuse, are not integrated and have no narrative attached and therefore may be reexperienced as terrifying and chaotic. Anytime troubling implicit memories are brought up in session, it is a good idea to prepare the client for potential dysregulation when they leave counseling. Clients have often spent a long time avoiding the events or explicit memories tied to the implicit learning, and thus bringing them to the surface can be initially destabilizing for the memory and the person. Helping the client plan for ways to cope with any distress that emerges as a result of accessing implicit memories (e.g., spending time with a trusted friend, taking a walk in nature, listening to comforting music) can help prevent unhelpful coping strategies (e.g., drinking alcohol in excess, overeating, lashing out at loved ones).

Multicultural considerations include an awareness that the way a client encoded a particular memory—as well as how they responded to it—is dependent on a confluence of factors related to their subjective experience and worldview. When using this activity, use the same sensitivity you would apply when exploring any type of traumatic memory with other existing approaches.

For instance, a client from a collectivist culture may have experienced feelings of shame around expressing negative emotions, which can serve to endanger group cohesion or harmony (Lim, 2016). Because of the limited window of tolerance and engagement that such a client has for emotional arousal, exploring implicit memory in session will be both a prerequisite for and an ongoing goal of treatment.

RECON

A Simple Five-Step Protocol for Reconsolidating a Traumatic Memory

Courtney Armstrong

At the turn of the 21st century, neuroscientists discovered the brain has an innate process for updating fear-based memories, called memory reconsolidation (Schwabe et al., 2014). Prior to this discovery, prolonged exposure and systematic desensitization were considered the best treatment options for trauma and anxiety disorders, but researchers realized that exposure does not completely eliminate a fear; it only creates a new memory network that competes for expression with the old fear memory network (LeDoux, 2015). As a result, fear memories treated with prolonged exposure tend to resurface after a period of time or when the client is under extreme stress. Memory reconsolidation actually updates learning associated with the original fear memory and seems to change the memory permanently. This process can happen naturally, but it can also be harnessed intentionally during therapy.

Reconsolidation is triggered when the brain encounters a reminder of a traumatic memory and simultaneously encounters a "mismatch experience"—a new experience that contradicts what the brain expects and changes the meaning of the memory (Ecker et al., 2012). Encountering a "mismatch experience" while recalling the old memory causes the memory to become malleable from about 10 minutes to 6 hours (Kredlow et al., 2018; Monfils et al., 2009; Nader & Einarsson, 2010; Schiller et al., 2010). During this reconsolidation window, the brain updates the old memory with any new information it deems relevant. After this period, the reconsolidation window closes, and the memory is put back into storage with this updated information. I created the *RECON: A Simple 5-Step Protocol for Reconsolidating a Traumatic Memory* activity to illustrate how therapists can foster memory reconsolidation using a simple protocol that I call RECON—an acronym for the following five steps of the reconsolidation process:

1. Recall one moment of the traumatic memory, briefly (no longer than 1 minute).
2. Explore undesirable beliefs attached to the event and the client's new desired beliefs.
3. Create a *new meaning experience* that evokes the client's desired beliefs about the event.
4. Objectively describe the memory while integrating the new meaning experience.
5. New narrative integration—repeat and revise the story until the new meaning of the memory *feels* true.

MATERIALS NEEDED

- No materials are required, but it can help to have paper and pen to write down the client's undesirable beliefs and desired new beliefs.

PROCESS OF THE ACTIVITY

Introduce the client to the concept of memory reconsolidation, highlighting that the brain can update a traumatic memory into a new context so that it will not haunt them anymore. Provide information about the three sequential phases of brain development: (1) the reptilian region, primarily responsible for our body's responses; (2) the mammalian region, which controls our emotional responses; and (3) the neocortex, which controls our rational thinking.

When we are in a calm state, these three regions of the brain work well together, and we are able to control our impulses and thoughts. Yet when we encounter a life-threatening or disturbing event, the survival and emotional brain regions override our thinking regions to mobilize a survival response. The emotional region then encodes the images, sensations, emotions, and behaviors we used to survive the event into an implicit memory network. This memory network can get activated any time we encounter reminders of the traumatic event and cause us to feel, think, and act as if we are in danger again.

Tell your client that with memory reconsolidation, you will help them create a new experience while reviewing the memory, so they can update the memory with new information. Then guide them through the following five steps of RECON:

Step 1 ("R"): Recall One Moment of the Traumatic Memory, Briefly

Ask your client to briefly bring the memory of the event to mind and describe any images, feelings, and physical sensations they notice. This need not last longer than a minute, just enough time to open the implicit memory network without retraumatizing the client.

Step 2 ("E"): Explore Undesirable Beliefs Attached to the Event and the Client's Desired Beliefs

Exploring traumatic events can dramatically change a person's beliefs about themselves, other people, and the world. Because stress hormones, like cortisol, inhibit the neocortex and verbal centers during a traumatic event, these undesirable beliefs are not stored as conscious, intellectual thoughts. They feel like essential truths about our lives that we cannot reason away. You can help your client name their implicit felt beliefs by asking the following:

1. What did it *feel* like this event meant about you?
2. What did it *feel* like the event meant about other people?
3. What did it *feel* like this event meant about your life, future, or the world?

To aid your client in identifying their desired beliefs about the event, ask the following:

1. What would you like to believe about yourself and your life now?
2. What do you know now that you did not know then?
3. What would you like your younger self to understand about that event now?
4. Let's imagine "future you" looking back now and realizing that you coped in the best way you could with the resources you had at that time. Imagine "future you" having moved forward with increased wisdom, power, integrity, compassion, or other positive qualities that you want to possess. What does "future you" *feel* and know to be true?

Step 3 ("C"): Create a New Meaning Experience That Evokes the Client's Desired Beliefs About the Event

Once you and your client agree on the beliefs they would like to associate with the memory, the next step is to create an *experience* that evokes a felt sense of these beliefs. It is not enough to intellectually identify desired beliefs. The emotional brain has to *feel it to believe it*, creating a new embodied memory. There are several ways to promote this felt sense, including symbolic imagery, visualization, music, and movement.

For example, you could invite your client to create a symbolic image that represents their desired beliefs. I have had clients identify as resilient oak trees, powerful lions, compassionate spiritual figures, and even antivirus computer software as symbolic images of desired beliefs. In addition, the client could visualize their desired future self or a positive memory of something that happened later in their lives that gives the event a new context. The client could also imagine stepping back into the scene of the traumatic event as a compassionate, competent adult who can comfort, guide, or protect their younger selves. With traumatic grief, you could invite the client to have an imaginal conversation with the deceased or a spiritual figure who can comfort them. If your client is not responsive to imagery, you could invite them to select a song or create a playlist of songs that evoke their desired beliefs. Movement can also evoke desired emotional responses. Engaging in physical motions, such as moving one's legs, raising one's arms into a victory pose, or pushing against something, evokes a sense of power and completion. Likewise, you could invite the client to say what they wish they could have said or act out what they wish they could have done. Any experiential intervention that helps the client tap into what it feels like to embody their desired beliefs is essentially creating the "mismatch" experience required to spark the memory reconsolidation process.

Step 4 ("O"): Objectively Describe the Memory While Integrating the New Meaning Experience

Next, invite your client to describe the memory from an objective perspective while integrating these new beliefs. Describing the memory objectively as if they were watching it on a small television screen helps your client stay in the present moment and avoid reliving the event.

Suggest that your client finish the story with a new ending—a point where they realized they escaped, survived, overcame, gained new wisdom, and so on. Integrating new endings also updates the memory network. Telling the story aloud helps the neocortex integrate the memory into a coherent narrative that can now be stored as a contextual explicit memory.

Step 5 ("N"): New Narrative Integration—Repeat and Revise the Story Until the New Meaning of the Memory Feels True

Once you and your client have reviewed and revised the memory with new endings and beliefs, have them repeat the story back to you again. This helps solidify new beliefs and gives you an opportunity to see if there are any places in the story where the client still feels stuck. In this step, you may create new meaning experiences to help your client change their beliefs. You will know the memory has been reconsolidated when the client can tell the story in a coherent narrative and their desired meaning of the event feels true.

You can space the steps of RECON protocol across three or more sessions, depending on your client's needs. For instance, you might use one full session for Steps 1 and 2 as you guide the client briefly to recall the memory, work through undesirable beliefs attached to the event, and explore new desired beliefs. Likewise, you may use a full session for Step 3 as you and your client explore a way to use imagery, music, or movement to create a felt experience that evokes their desired beliefs. In the next session, you could invite your client to recall the new meaning experience from Step 3, then objectively describe the memory while integrating their desired beliefs (Step 4) and repeat this new narrative until it *feels* true (Step 5). For memory reconsolidation to occur, the client has to juxtapose the memory of the trauma directly with the new meaning experience (Ecker et al., 2012). It's this simultaneous recollection of the old memory and the new meaning experience side by side that causes the synapses holding the memory to unlock and update the memory network.

FOLLOW-UP

You can evaluate the effectiveness of this activity via the client's self-report, your observation of their affect, and how they organize their story. Clients usually report feeling lighter and notice the memory has less emotional intensity. They will be able to see the event from their desired perspective and report a decrease in anxiety, nightmares, or intrusive thoughts and images. Their narrative of the event will be less fragmented, more coherent, and free of the prior undesired beliefs. After the intervention, clients' affects are usually broader and their posture more relaxed.

You can also administer self-report inventories before and 1 week after the RECON intervention. One such tool could be Weiss and Marmar's (1997) *Impact of Events Scale-Revised (IES-R)*. The IES-R is a 22-item measure that asks participants to rate the distress caused by a traumatic memory on a scale from 0 (not at all) to 4 (extremely) over the last 7 days and has shown adequate evidence of reliability and validity.

NEUROSCIENCE IN ACTION

The following case shows each step of the RECON protocol I used with my client, whom I will call Carol. She had an intense fear of the ocean after seeing her mother almost drown. Carol came to therapy for this issue because her son desperately wanted to go on a beach trip with his Boy Scout troop, but she had refused to let him go because of her fear. Her refusal to let him go was causing a great deal of conflict between them. She knew her fears were irrational and decided she wanted to overcome her ocean phobia once and for all.

Step 1: Recall One Moment of the Traumatic Memory, Briefly

Prior to asking Carol to start the memory reconsolidation process, I explained how the brain stores a disturbing memory, noting that it can continue to send danger signals anytime we encounter anything similar. I explained that we could use a gentle five-step protocol to help her emotional centers put the memory into proper context. Carol was eager to begin but admitted that she felt a little nervous about revisiting the memory of her mother almost drowning.

To calm her nervous system, I asked her to imagine a place that could symbolize peace and healing for her and breathe in and out slowly for a few minutes. She imagined being in her backyard garden. After 3 minutes of this exercise, she said she felt calmer and was ready to begin the RECON process.

I asked her to briefly recall a moment of the memory and describe it to me, remembering that her mom survived. Carol recalled,

> I went on a trip to the beach with my parents when I was 6 years old. I was playing on the beach with my dad while my mom was sunbathing on a float in the ocean. My dad suddenly ran toward the ocean because he saw a rip current pull my mom and her float under the water. He managed to swim out to her and pull her to the shore, but I was afraid she was going to die.

Step 2: Explore Undesirable Beliefs Attached to the Event and the Client's Desired Beliefs

Next, we explored the undesired beliefs that Carol's mind had attached to this event. Carol realized her undesirable belief was *"the ocean almost killed my mother and could kill my son too."* This belief showed the potential for her son's death, but to her surprise, Carol also spontaneously recalled a miscarriage she had when she was 20 years old. Carol was shocked to realize that she still felt guilty about the miscarriage, as if she caused it. This led her to realize that she was also harboring the undesired belief, *"I killed one child and better make sure I don't kill another one."* This belief was more definitive. She knew this belief was irrational, but her emotional system *felt* like it was true and compelled her to fiercely protect her son.

Step 3: Create a New Meaning Experience That Evokes the Client's Desired Beliefs About the Event

As I discussed earlier, researchers have found the key to revising a traumatic memory is to induce a "mismatch experience" or an experience that disconfirms the undesirable beliefs the client's mind attached to the event. We agreed that Carol's desired belief was not *"the ocean is always safe,"* because it is not. Her desired belief was *"my son can swim safely in the ocean if he recognizes safe swimming conditions and knows how to protect himself if he encounters a riptide."*

To create a felt experience for Carol that would validate her desired beliefs, I asked her to vividly recall her mother surviving the rip current and resting calmly in their hotel room after the event with no further problems. Then we did another imagery exercise where she visualized the day her mother learned swimming skills to manage a riptide and taught Carol and her son these skills too. Last, I suggested Carol imagine her son returning safely from the beach trip with a big grin on his face, sharing positive stories of his trip. She found that the image of him returning feeling happy not only overrode her fearful images but also caused her to feel a little excited about letting him go on the trip.

Step 4: Objectively Describe the Memory While Integrating the New Meaning Experience

Next, we wanted to integrate Carol's new beliefs into the old memory so that it could be updated. I asked Carol to objectively describe the memory, but this time finish the story by vividly recalling that her mother survived. Carol proceeded as follows:

> I went on a trip to the beach with my parents when I was 6 years old. I was playing on the beach with my dad while my mom was sunbathing on a float in the ocean. My dad suddenly ran toward the ocean because he saw a rip current pull my mom and her float under the water. He managed to swim out to her and pull her to the shore. She coughed up a lot of water, but after a while, she was able to breathe normally and survived. We even went out to dinner that night, and she had no further problems. Then, she took swimming lessons from a diver who showed her how to survive a rip current. My mom taught me and my son these skills too, which are to stay calm, float or tread water, and get your toes and nose parallel to the beach.

Carol turned her body so that it was parallel to me and demonstrated her rip current swimming skills as she finished the story. I asked her how she was feeling about the event now. She closed her eyes to briefly review the event again, then blurted, "Wow! I feel calmer and can think about it much more rationally now." The physical acting out of the survival swimming skills provided evidence for the body's integration of an evolving, reconsolidated memory containing safety and excitement.

Step 5: New Narrative Integration—Repeat and Revise the Story Until the New Meaning of the Memory Feels True

Next, I asked Carol to recount the story one more time to fully integrate the updated narrative of the event. Although Carol did not feel as troubled by this memory anymore, she still noticed she had a fear of her son dying because she had already lost one child to a miscarriage. As Carol and I explored possible experiences that would invalidate her belief that she caused the loss of her first child, she revealed that she had polycystic ovary syndrome (PCOS) and that this was the most likely reason she miscarried.

To create a felt experience that would help Carol's emotional system integrate this realization, I guided Carol in another imagery exercise. I suggested she imagine comforting her younger self at the time of the miscarriage, reassuring her that she did not cause the miscarriage, and a condition called PCOS caused the miscarriage. Then I invited her to show her younger self that she would go on to have a healthy pregnancy and be a very loving mother to her son. This brought tears of relief to Carol's eyes.

By the end of this session, Carol commented that she was able to think about both the beach incident and her miscarriage without feeling anxious or guilty. As a result, she felt more secure about letting her son go on the beach trip. Weeks later, she called to tell me that not only did her son return home from the trip safely but also that he showed up with that big grin on his face excitedly sharing stories about his adventure, just as she imagined in our session.

ETHICAL AND MULTICULTURAL CONSIDERATIONS

Reconsolidating traumatic memories is not recommended until you have developed a strong therapeutic alliance with your client. Likewise, it is not recommended to reconsolidate traumatic memories if your client is in crisis or in an unstable living environment. Facing traumatic memories can cause clients to feel very vulnerable and emotionally dysregulated. They need to feel safe and stable before revisiting painful memories in detail. This safe and stable holding environment can actually be a mismatch experience itself. In addition, it is useful to build emotional regulation skills prior to reviewing traumatic memories. This will help them stay grounded and manage any strong emotional responses that may arise while reviewing a traumatic memory.

If your client has multiple traumas, only focus on one memory at a time. You may not have to reconsolidate every traumatic memory they have. The emotional sections of the brain will generalize new learning to any memories that are similar. For example, if a client suffered childhood abuse, they may find they only need to reconsolidate two or three memories of the abuse. After that, the emotional sections tend to apply their desired new beliefs to any related memories.

If a client is diagnosed with dissociative identity disorder, preliminary work must be done to help the client manage dissociative episodes and understand all their personality parts before memory reconsolidation can be done. Otherwise, the client could be prone to reliving the event, or other parts could try to thwart the reconsolidation process.

In terms of multicultural considerations, it is important to understand and honor the values your client has within their culture and family system. For example, in some cultures, rape brings great shame to the family, and it is very difficult for a client to admit to anyone that this has happened to them. In cases like these, you need to carefully work with your client to help them attach a new meaning to an event that brings them relief but does not further isolate them from their family or cultural belief systems.

Formal training in using the RECON protocol is not required, but it is recommended that you at least have training in emotional regulation skills and grounding techniques you can use to help your client stay present as they review a traumatic memory. You may find training in other modalities that has similar processes for reconsolidating traumatic memories such as coherence therapy, eye-movement desensitization and reprocessing (EMDR), accelerated resolution therapy, or sensorimotor psychotherapy.

ANCILLARY MATERIALS

For ideas and examples for using the RECON protocol for complex trauma, see my book *Rethinking Trauma Treatment: Attachment, Memory Reconsolidation, and Resilience* (2019) and visit my website: https://realworldtherapy.com. Likewise, Ogden and Fisher's (2015) *Sensorimotor Psychotherapy: Interventions for Trauma and Attachment* has suggestions for helping clients manage physiological responses to trauma. Last, if you are working with clients diagnosed with dissociative identity disorder, I recommend Boon, Steel, and van der Hart's (2011) *Coping with Trauma Related Dissociation: Skills Training for Patients and Therapists.*

ACCELERATED RESOLUTION OF SYMPTOMS RELATED TO TRAUMATIC MEMORY

Amy Shuman, Kevin E. Kip, and Laney Rosenzweig

Grounded in new insights from memory research and limitations in the practice of EMDR, Laney Rosenzweig, LMFT, created accelerated resolution therapy (ART) in 2008. Since then, thousands of licensed professionals have been trained, and several peer-reviewed studies have been conducted, most under the leadership of Kevin Kip, PhD at the University of South Florida (Kip et al., 2012; Kip et al., 2013; Kip et al., 2014; Kip et al., 2016; Kip & Diamond, 2018). This body of literature is beginning to uncover the mechanistic evidence for the effectiveness of this therapy, but more research is necessary. Memory reconsolidation and the use of eye movements are two principle mechanisms that show promise for inducing therapeutic gains during ART.

MEMORY RECONSOLIDATION

Diamond et al. (2007) noted that an intrusive memory repeatedly reactivates the trauma memory circuit in the limbic system between the hippocampus (facts) and amygdala (emotion). For example, imagine a male soldier who is alone and in the course of searching a town is shot at and almost killed. He then begins experiencing intrusive memories of this experience whenever his limbic system is exposed to any triggering event (e.g., sound of a firecracker, the way the buildings looked), and he develops what many refer to as post-traumatic stress. External events often trigger the fight/flight/freeze responses and engage his amygdala and hippocampus into a "positive feedback condition" (Diamond, personal communication, February 12, 2014), meaning that each triggering incident and associated affect causes an intensification of the fearful aspects of the memory and emotions. Hence, the post-traumatic stress is based on a hippocampal-amygdala circuit lacking a controlling mechanism. Such a controlling mechanism could be the prefrontal cortex, which can help with reasoning out a solution (Diamond, personal communication, Voluntary Image Replacement in ART, January 4, 2001).

Remembering a fear-based memory opens the finite reconsolidation window (about 10 minutes to 6 hours postretrieval), making the memory malleable and receptive to the introduction of new protein synthesis (Kredlow et al., 2018; Monfils et al., 2009; Nader & Einarsson, 2010; Schiller et al., 2010). If new material (e.g., imagined material by rescripting the trauma memory) is created and introduced during the reconsolidation window, then the memory *and the corresponding emotional and sensorial affect* can be changed, and the change can be long lasting (Monfils et al., 2009; Schiller et al., 2010).

EYE MOVEMENTS

How is this emotional valence updated to create a new memory devoid of the earlier traumatic response? Although still being empirically explored, the process of eye movements seems to be one potential mechanism to enhance the memory reconsolidation process. At the very least, eye movements induce a relaxation response in the client (Hedstrom, 1991; Kapoula et al., 2010) by providing just the right amount of distraction from the imagined material (van den Hout et al., 2001). Another theory is that the eye movements while awake may grossly replicate rapid eye movement (REM), triggering effective processes of memory reconsolidation during REM sleep (Kip et al., 2014). This effect, paired with the introduction of new imagined material created during ART, is selectively used to replace any aspects of the emotional or sensory memory that is uncomfortable to the individual. This early research, anecdotal evidence of thousands of counselors and therapists who have been using ART since its introduction to the professional community in 2009, and emerging empirical evidence (Kip et al., 2012; Kip et al., 2013; Kip et al., 2014; Kip et al., 2016) adds to the credibility and consistency of positive change through ART.

The *Accelerated Resolution of Symptoms Related to Traumatic Memory* activity that follows will describe the effectiveness of combining eye movements with the imaginative rescripting of upsetting memories, a core process in ART.

MATERIALS NEEDED

Materials for this activity include the following:

- Something for the client to follow with their eyes (e.g., hand, wand, benign object on top of the hand)
- A modified Subjective Units of Distress Scale (Kim et al., 2008) referred to as the ARTometer® (see Figure 8.7).

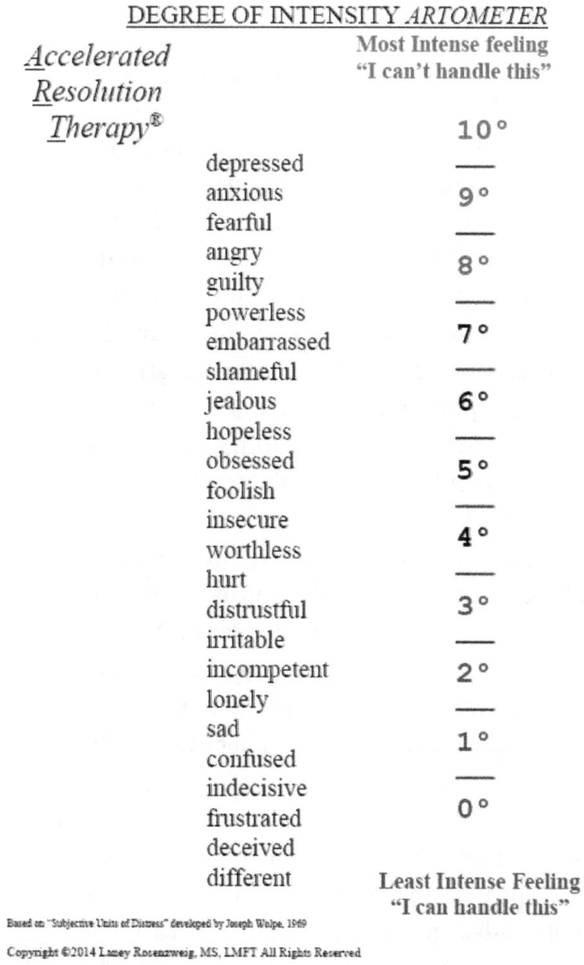

DEGREE OF INTENSITY *ARTOMETER*

Accelerated Resolution Therapy®

Most Intense feeling
"I can't handle this"

10°
—
9°
—
8°
—
7°
—
6°
—
5°
—
4°
—
3°
—
2°
—
1°
—
0°

depressed
anxious
fearful
angry
guilty
powerless
embarrassed
shameful
jealous
hopeless
obsessed
foolish
insecure
worthless
hurt
distrustful
irritable
incompetent
lonely
sad
confused
indecisive
frustrated
deceived
different

Least Intense Feeling
"I can handle this"

Based on "Subjective Units of Distress" developed by Joseph Wolpe, 1969

FIGURE 8.7 Example ARTometer to Measure Pre-post Intervention Distress
Assessing the effect of all interventions is essential to effective treatment, and the ARTometer provides an easy-to-use method for evaluating the outcomes of the ART process. It is important to explore the meaning emotional words have to you and how this compares to a word's meaning to your client (e.g., sad to one client might mean an unbearable state that leads to negative consequences, but to another sad might mean a tolerable state that indicates something is important). Clients might work toward or away from a certain emotional word based on this unique meaning and a sound assessment to operationalize any scale of measurement is important.

PROCESS OF THE ACTIVITY

As previously mentioned, the memory reconsolidation window is said to be open for about 6 hours postexposure, and a complete ART session is usually completed within a typical hour-long therapy session. The timing of when to begin the ART sessions is unique to each client and counselor. ART can commence as long as the following three criteria are met: (1) the client can move their eyes back and forth for several eye-movement sets during the clinical session; (2) the client is able to hold on to the thoughts and the "story" about the targeted problem throughout the story; and (3) the client is willing and motivated to allow any changes, including reducing or eliminating the symptoms, to occur. Before starting ART, it is important to recognize that the client controls all the content in an ART session. The counselor can make suggestions about what changes the client may want to make, but the final decision lies within the client. The client can even decide not to share details about the content of the targeted problem that they are working on and still reach their goal of relief from the symptoms associated with the targeted problem. Often, first responders and people with military experience choose not to share their targeted memories. Therefore, a lengthy period of rapport building between the client and counselor is not always necessary before engaging in the therapy.

The ART session typically includes the following protocol: (1) neuroeducation and introduction to ART, (2) exposure and desensitization (with eye-movement sets), (3) rescripting (with eye-movement sets), and (4) neutralizing future environmental triggers (with eye-movement sets).

Neuroeducation and Introduction to ART

Once the client and counselor agree that ART will be a proper intervention, the session begins with an introduction to the therapy. The client is given an overview of the neuroscience information that is relevant to ART (e.g., autonomic nervous system functioning, memory reconsolidation, eye movement) using language and depth of explanation that is proper for that client. An example of how we would explore this with a client would be as follows:

> Scientific study has shown that emotionally based memories are not fixed, such as a computer program, which could be located and plugged in. Rather, it turns out that whenever we recall a memory that has emotions tied to it, that memory becomes malleable and open to change. Scientists think that our brains are designed that way so that we can include important information to a newly recalled memory to make it more likely that we will survive if that incident should reoccur. Because we naturally make these edits, when sharing an emotional memory with others, we find that the details of the memories often differ from person to person. So, when you recall the upsetting memory that you came in with, you bring that recalled memory into what is called "the reconsolidation window." This is a period of time, thought to be from 2 minutes after you remember it, up until about 6 hours after you remember it. During this "reconsolidation window," we can take advantage of the natural opportunity to edit the images and/or sensations/emotions that you experience [check in with the client before continuing with the neuroeducation process]. You can make the images as neutral or as pleasant as you want. And it seems that these changes that you decide to make can last indefinitely. In the studies conducted so far, when people checked their memories up to a year later, the positive changes that the person made lasted (Schiller et al., 2010). Also, it is important for you to know that you will still be able to remember the facts of the original memory. While the images you see in your mind's eye can be altered to your liking, you will still keep the information about the incident, just not the upsetting images or sensations. [Check in with the client before continuing with the neuroeducation process.] Secondly, while you are recalling or editing the images, you will be following my hand with your eyes (see Figure 8.8). My hand will be moving back and forth like this [demonstrates smooth pursuit eye movements while following a hand moving side to side]. You will be moving through a series of eye-movement sets. You do not have to worry about that though. I will be guiding you through each step of the way,

FIGURE 8.8 Example Eye-Movement Sets

and you will have full control over choosing what kinds of edits you would like to make as we go along when we get to that part of the protocol. The reason that we use eye movements is that there is a lot of evidence that people seem to have a relaxation response to the eye movements and that we think, but don't know yet, that the eye movements catalyze (deepen and speed up) the positive changes that you make to your original upsetting memory images and sensations. You do not have to remember what I just told you. I will guide you through the process every step of the way. What are your thoughts?

It is important to check in with clients regularly when exploring neuroscience concepts during a session. Care should be taken to explore the meaning the client is making of this information in comparison to their lived experience. Next, the client is oriented to the general format of the therapy and the next phases of the protocol: exposure and desensitization, rescripting and reinforcing the rescripting, and neutralizing environmental triggers for future application.

During each step of the ART protocol, the counselor sits face-to-face with their client and slightly askew (as "ships passing in the night"). The counselor checks in with the client to determine how close they can get to them without causing any discomfort. The counselor then shows the client how they will move their extended hand from side to side in front of the client's eyes while the client tracks the hand movement to engage in eye movements for an abbreviated period of time, referred to as an eye-movement set. If the counselor has some physical challenges that impede their ability to move their hand in this fashion, some adjustments are possible. For example, the counselor can use a wand with a benign image about the size of a hand on top, which the client can track instead of the counselor's hand. The counselor also uses the ARTometer at the beginning to raise awareness of sensations and at the end of the session in order for the client to see evidence of the changes in effect and symptoms that have occurred over the course of the session. The ARTometer is usually numbered from zero to 10, with each unit representing an incremental intensification of the symptom that is being measured at the time, such as units of anxiety or pain.

Exposure and Desensitization

The activation of the memory is needed to open the reconsolidation window (Kip et al., 2012). In ART, the client is encouraged to recall their memory as a "scene" or "movie" while completing eye-movement sets. The first part of this phase, which can be uncomfortable for the client, is shorter than previous exposure therapies, usually between 1 and 15 minutes depending on how many eye-movement sets the client must go through to recall the entire "scene" or "movie" that illustrates the targeted issue. More eye-movement sets are needed when the scene is complex or long and/or when the scene brings about the need to frequently soothe uncomfortable emotions or sensations along the way. Also, clinicians using ART can start the exposure phase using metaphors if the client cannot tolerate the direct recall of the upsetting material, thus avoiding the actual upsetting images.

This "exposure phase," which includes two complete "viewings" of the targeted scene, is commonly about 5 minutes to 30 minutes in duration (Rosenzweig, personal communication, June 28, 2018). The client, with coaching from the counselor, has composed themselves into a relaxed and alert state of mind, has exposed themselves to the reactivation of the targeted memory with eye-movement sets for a short period of time, followed by a brief processing of sensations that have been activated. Moving back and forth between these two segments of the protocol, the therapist steers the client through two complete phases of short-lived exposure to the targeted memory. Usually, the client notices a feeling of emotional distance and/or comparative emotional calm and relaxation by the end of this phase, which is referred to as "desensitization." Occasionally, when a client begins the ART protocol and is working on soothing the sensations elicited by the recall of the memory, the uncomfortable sensations will either not decrease or will increase. After the counselor brings the client through a few eye-movement sets and the symptoms remain or are exacerbated, which is often the result of deeper related memories from the past, the counselor may choose to do what is called a "scene match." During this part of the protocol, the counselor uses eye-movement sets (the counselor has the client engage in smooth pursuit eye movements for a short, consistently prescribed period of time) in which the client is instructed to allow the brain to find an earlier time when they felt the similar uncomfortable sensations that matches what is being experienced in the present moment. If the client produces an earlier memory in this way, the counselor continues the ART protocol using this deeper memory as the "scene" and follows the same protocol as above. The use of this process is illustrated in the case presentation that follows.

Rescripting

After completing the exposure and desensitization phase of ART, the counselor leads the client into the "rescripting" phase. During this phase in ART, the client has complete control over selecting any imaginative visualizations that they choose. They are instructed to replace any part of their recalled upsetting memory with their newly imagined scenes. The counselor will instruct the client to change the targeted scene in any way they would like. It is explained to the client that the newly imagined replacements do not need to "make sense" or be "realistic" and are compared to a "good dream." It is explained that they will still "know" or retain facts of the recalled issue. The counselor usually does not interrupt while the eye-movement sets are performed, saving any questions or dialogue for between or after eye-movement sets.

The introduction of newly chosen imagined material to the reactivated memory is referred to in the ART protocol as "imaginal exposure." After the successful completion of the desensitization phase (as described earlier), the client is encouraged to change any of the sensory components of the memory (imaginal rescripting). The client then continues to engage in the eye-movement sets as directed by the therapist, while adding, deleting, or changing any part of the content of the recalled material that they choose. The client checks to see if the images have been changed by recalling the memory after the eye-movement set is over to determine whether, and to what degree, the desired changes have taken place. To ensure that all upsetting material is replaced, the counselor has the client check for any remaining negative images or sensations. Within the ART protocol, the client then "erases" the negative image from view. The client continues to be able to retrieve the "facts" of the original memory; however, they report that the visual/sensorial aspects of the memory have been changed, which changes the resultant emotional affect to that of benign or what Laney has coined "positized" (i.e., "positive") sensations.

Neutralizing Future Environmental Triggers

Finally, the counselor helps the client to "practice" neutralizing (or "positizing") any imagined future environmental incidents that had, up until the session, triggered the problematic symptoms. The counselor leads the client through a set of eye movements while imagining the triggering scene and making any changes to the scene that help to relax the client. The counselor may also help the client to soothe any uncomfortable somatic experiences while imagining the scene.

An ART session is concluded using a few sets of eye movements to have the client focus on imaginative exercises designed to increase confidence to help the client leave the newly synthesized memory to stabilize during the 6-hour period of memory reconsolidation. Clients typically resolve the identified trauma in one to five sessions, with an average of 3.6 sessions. Clients are often asked to return for a subsequent session to check in to determine if the targeted symptoms have sufficiently diminished or resolved. If more symptomatology has presented during the time between sessions, then the counselor can support the client through another ART session targeted to resolve these emerging symptoms.

If the client has not experienced the return of any of the targeted symptoms, it is not uncommon for them to begin to become aware of another layer of troubling symptoms associated with a personal challenge that was inaccessible before they resolved the earlier issue using ART. If this happens, the counselor can continue the ART process with this new layer of awareness.

FOLLOW-UP

At the conclusion of an ART session, the counselor presents the ARTometer used to measure the level of distress at the beginning of the session and asks the client to move the gauge to the corresponding number on the continuum. A successful ART session is thought to be demonstrated when the gauge is moved to a value of 0 to 3.

Physiological measures (e.g., galvanic skin response, quantitative electroencephalogram) may also be added to the evaluation of ART, although the study of the physiological effects of employing ART is just starting to appear. These methods can be explored given counselor training, access to equipment, and safety, as well as the importance of such measurement devices to the client.

NEUROSCIENCE IN ACTION

A 38-year-old Portuguese American male law student presented himself to a small private college counseling center. During intake, he reported that, for many years, more than he could count, he experienced heightened general anxiety daily, accompanied by frequent panic attacks. He kept this personal information to himself all these years, feeling that revealing this ongoing problem would cause others to think less of him. His previous job before coming back to school was as a firefighter, and he felt in that role that he would lose the respect of his colleagues and the trust of those he served if they were to know this truth about him. However, he noticed that the anxiety and panic were interfering with his ability to focus and retain the information needed to be successful as a law student.

The first session included the intake, neuroeducation, and practice of an anxiety-reducing technique known as diaphragmatic breathing (Ma et al., 2017). In this segment of the meeting, Amy offered the neuroscientific information behind its effectiveness for reducing anxiety:

> First, we inhale slowly while expanding our lower abdomen, as if we were slowly blowing up a balloon in our bellies [gave demonstration]. Next, after holding our breath gently for 1 second, we exhale even more slowly than we inhaled, again while focusing on and contracting our lower abdomen, followed by a 1-second gentle breath hold [gave another demonstration]. Breathing in and out this way has been shown to influence our vagus nerve to give a message of "relax" to our nervous system. Also, as we inhale, we are engaging our sympathetic nervous system, which can make us feel anxious. We lengthen our exhales because when we exhale, this engages our parasympathetic nervous system to reduce anxiety and helps us rest and digest.

As Amy gave the information to the client, she checked in verbally and looked for signs of understanding or confusion from the client and responded in-kind. For example, he indicated that he was not familiar with the vagus nerve or autonomic nervous system but that he was interested in learning more about them, so Amy pulled up a picture of the vagus nerve and a diagram of the sympathetic and parasympathetic nervous systems functioning on her computer. While they viewed this information together, she answered the client's questions and took part in a discussion about these systems and functions until the client was satisfied that he had reached a level of understanding of the material. Some clients want more explanation about the science and the research behind this technique, and others are satisfied with very little of this information and would rather just do the technique. As with all techniques, meet the client where they are and proceed accordingly.

Next, the client described his problem and symptoms, and the counselor determined that it would be appropriate to introduce ART as a therapy that he could consider choosing. He was given a brief introduction, the neuroscience of memory reconsolidation was explored, and he was provided a website address (www.artworksnow.com) to research on his own and determine if he would like to engage in ART therapy during the next session. The client chose to engage in ART at the next session. He reported that he had been practicing the diaphragmatic breathing, and it gave some temporary relief, but as soon as he stopped and went on with his business (and thinking), the anxiety and panic returned.

Amy helped him target the specific problem he wanted to work on (the panic attacks) and then to find a memory that would represent that problem throughout the session. He chose to remember recent events that would commonly elicit the panic attacks: shopping in a supermarket or department store, especially when looking down the aisles. While it is not necessary for a client to disclose the content of his material to the counselor to make meaningful changes, this client chose to share. He gauged his level of emotional discomfort at an "8" on the ARTometer.

After a few eye-movement sets in which the client moved back and forth between the "scene" and the somatic sensations, it became clear that the uncomfortable sensations were not decreasing, as a matter of fact, they worsened. At this point, the counselor chose to use a "scene match" and asked the client to, during the next eye-movement set, allow the mind to find the earliest time that he felt this way. The client followed these instructions, and at the conclusion of the eye-movement set, he reported, with surprise, that he remembered being a baby in his crib and watching his parents in a heated verbal fight. He remembered this was frequent, and he "saw" this memory in his mind's eye as a baby watching through the slats of the crib. It occurred to the counselor that watching these upsetting incidents through the crib slats might have resembled what he saw in his current life as he looked down the aisles of a store. Amy shared her thoughts about this comparison, and she and the client shared a stunned amazement as the likelihood of this parallel scene seemed apparent.

The client then went through the ART protocol using the memory as a baby as his new "scene." When he got to the rescripting phase, while "seeing his rescripted scene" during eye-movement sets, he decided to take his 38-year-old self back through time and rescue his "baby self" from that crib to a loving and protected space to sleep and be under his 38-year-old self's protection.

At the conclusion of the session, the client was asked to look at the ARTometer and note that he had chosen an "8" at the beginning of the session. He was asked to move the indicator to the level of emotional discomfort he was experiencing now as he thought about the problem. He moved the gauge to a "1," which was considered to be an indicator of a significant improvement of the symptoms. He was asked to note how he felt throughout the week and report at the next session.

During the next session, the client reported that he'd had no panic attacks since the last session, even though he had gone shopping at the supermarket. He still experienced ongoing anxiety, but he believed that the intensity and frequency decreased. He also brought up a new issue to work on: his anxiety increased when spending time with a woman he had a romantic interest in. The more she acted interested in pursuing a meaningful relationship, the more anxious he became, and he wanted to see if he could work on not having the interference of intensified anxiety while he pursued this movement toward intimacy.

He returned for four more ART sessions, alongside person-centered counseling. The frequency and intensity of his anxiety continued to decrease to a manageable level. He was able to focus and complete law school and pass the bar examination. At the final session, he reported that he and the woman were planning to continue their relationship as he graduated and moved to a different state. They would continue to date, and if all continued to go well, she would consider moving to his state. He did not feel that he needed to continue with counseling at his new location but was instructed on how to find an ART therapist there if needed.

ETHICAL AND MULTICULTURAL CONSIDERATIONS

Training is essential. While the protocol for ART is replicable and has been manualized for training, the step-by-step protocol is only taught to counselors who are licensed to practice and complete the specialized ART training. These training requirements are in place for two reasons: (1) client safety and (2) treatment fidelity. Because the response from clients is, not uncommonly, highly emotive during the short-lived initial exposure to the traumatic memory material, it requires a trained and licensed clinician with the competence to help the client tolerate and regulate any abreactions. In addition, the developer of ART, Laney Rosenzweig, is careful to protect the fidelity of the ART protocol to ensure the highest level of empirical evaluation and mandates that anyone learning ART take the required course before she will allow or condone the use of these protocols (Rosenzweig, personal communication, June 28, 2018).

Because the client is solely in control of the content of their rescripted images and scenes, they can keep their content in line with their unique personal values, culture, and religious beliefs. Another unique feature of ART is that the client has the choice to keep some or all of the content of their scenes to themselves. An effective ART counselor will be mindful of the intersectionality of all cultural identities when making suggestions to their clients about what they may want to do about the upsetting materials. Often, I (Amy) ask the client if they have any spiritual beliefs, and if so, and the client chooses to share, those beliefs will be incorporated into suggestions about rescripting changes that the client may choose to make. This can be especially helpful when a client is dealing with an issue that involves the death of a significant person in their life.

ANCILLARY MATERIALS

- The website for the Rosenzweig Center for Rapid Recovery, which provides a good deal of information about ART, how to find an ART therapist state by state, and how a licensed therapist or counselor can find ART Training: www.artworksnow.com
- The website for one other agency that has been licensed to train ART practitioners: https://artherapy-international.org/
- There is also a website for the organization that provides certification for licensed counselors and therapists who have taken the basic ART training. This organization provides an annual conference in which ART therapists present research and their practice of art with specific populations (i.e., children, substance use disorder recovery, eating disorders, psychotic disorders): www.is-art.org

YOUR SONG

Dawn M. Wirick

The incorporation of music into clinical counseling improves clients' moods and overall outlook on life (Bernatzky et al., 2011). More specifically, the inclusion of music when counseling those with chronic pain (e.g., fibromyalgia) has been shown to assist in decreasing pain and functional mobility (Garza-Villarreal et al., 2014). Outcomes are typically enhanced when clients choose the music rather than when counselors choose the music for the client. Furthermore, music expressing contentment as perceived by the client, no matter its genre, was found to be the most effective in reducing the experience of pain (Knox et al., 2011).

In working with clients who live with daily chronic lower back pain (CLBP) in clinical practice, the overriding theme is that of hopelessness. They have exhausted all medicinal and surgical options, thereby existing in a constant state of anxiety and fear. Instead of adding to the already high level of anxiety by talking more and more about pain in counseling sessions, picking a pleasurable song at the very beginning of the counseling process is straightforward and helps the client to employ a means by which they can put their pain into a landscape that contains a sense of pleasure and hope instead of talking about a loss of hope, functional limitations, and overall fears about the present and future.

The infusion of music interventions into counseling practices designed to assist with CLBP will be approached by first discussing the relationship between music and dopamine. Dopamine is a neurotransmitter in the brain that has been shown to be linked to motivation and reward-seeking behavior (Dayan & Balleine, 2002; Stegemoller, 2014), working memory (Carr et al., 2017; Dayan & Balleine, 2002), and reinforcement learning (Dayan & Ballenie, 2002; Glimcher, 2011). More importantly, researchers have noted that the response of dopaminergic neurons is transferred to stimuli during learning (DeBoer et al., 2019; Montague et al., 1996; Wassum et al., 2013). For example, when an auditory cue precedes a food reward for completing a new task, dopaminergic neurons fire in response to the food reward initially. Once the task is learned, dopaminergic neurons transfer firing to the auditory cue, demonstrating that the dopaminergic system may be responsible for predicting with temporal precision future reward events (Montague et al., 1996; Steinberg et al., 2013). This type of reinforcement signaling has been shown to be mediated by dopaminergic neurons in the nucleus accumbens (NAc) and ventral tegmental area (VTA), which have widespread projections to the cortex (Bao et al., 2001; Holmes & Fam, 2013). Thus paired stimulation of dopaminergic neurons in the VTA and sensory stimuli have been shown to result in cortical remapping (Bao et al., 2001; O'Kelly et al., 2016). Taken together with research that has demonstrated that dopamine modulates long-term potentiation (Gurden et al., 2000; Voss et al., 2017), it is well accepted that dopamine plays a vital role in neuroplasticity.

Music-focused research has discovered that listening to music may stimulate the same neural network as that involved in reinforcement learning and reward (Chanda & Levitin, 2013; Gold et al., 2019). Moreover, researchers have found a strong link between these regions and cognitive subsystems, including the orbito-frontal cortex, an area of frontal cortex responsible for encoding the temporal aspects of memory and emotional prosodic processing (Duarte et al., 2010). The results of these studies are linked to music listening, mainly listening to pleasurable music, and demonstrate the potential of music when applied therapeutically to facilitate neuroplasticity.

Bringing mental health expertise and neuroeducation to pain management physicians about the role of music in affecting neuroplasticity could be helpful in showing that counseling is not merely talking about the pain experience; it can lead to a pre-pain memory before the onset of CLBP. Also, the role of dopamine in this process could prove to be highly enlightening in the context of chronic pain experiences in general, and CLBP specifically. Therefore, I created the *Your Song* activity to bring these concepts and the benefits of music to life for clients with CLBP.

MATERIALS NEEDED

- Computer, smartphone, or another device that can be used to search for songs
- Music players (e.g., mp3, CD, cassette tape, record players)

PROCESS OF THE ACTIVITY

As part of counseling that uses music as a primary intervention, I supply clients with options to assist them in locating their favorite music genre and favorite song. When the client enters the initial session, I explain my counseling approach to CLBP as one that embraces music as the central healing mechanism in the counseling process. Then I introduce the client to a few websites, such as https://melodyfull.com and https://musicmap.info, and various apps that permit them to download their favorite songs. If a client does not have access to a computer or phone, then I spend the session assisting them in defining their favorite genre of music, downloading their favorite song if they desire to download it, and beginning discussion around their favorite genre and favorite song. In these early sessions, mp3 players, CD players, cassette tape players, and record players are in the office and can be checked out by the clients for 1 week at a time, if desired. Since I work primarily with clients who are 60+ years old, many of my clients do not respond favorably to websites, phone apps, and computers as delivery methods for music, so the overwhelming majority bring vinyl records, cassette tapes, and CDs that contain their favorite songs. Clients report feeling comforted by having record players, mp3 players, cassette tape players, and CD players to use and/or check out.

In my work with clients who are experiencing CLBP, I infuse music centrally into the first session and in-between session work. I ask clients to select one song that they deem to be uplifting and personally meaningful, as well as perceived as containing a hopeful theme or message that applies directly to their daily lives in the context of experiencing debilitating CLBP. Every client I have worked with communicates a sense of relief when they learn that these counseling sessions do not solely involve talking about their pain experiences, as many have reported feeling "tired" about being asked to continually talk about their pain and rate its severity in medical appointments (e.g., emergency room, chiropractic, surgeons).

In the first session, I share with clients how music-related interventions form the basis for each counseling session, and then I ask them about their relationship with music prior to the onset of their chronic pain. Most of my clients share that music, prior to the onset of chronic pain, played a role in their lives and that it took them to a happier place of calm and peace. I permit clients to share this part of their narrative for as long as they need to in the first session because I want to establish an informal "pre-onset" frame of reference.

In the second session, I encourage clients to discuss their "post-onset" narrative, meaning how music plays a role in their lives now that they live with CLBP on a daily basis. The beauty of this "pre-post" informal assessment is that it permits me to hear their relationship with music prior to pain onset and to see if the relationship has changed post-pain onset; I am trying to figure out if they listened to music more prior to the chronic pain onset, more with chronic pain onset, or if their music listening is similar between pre- and post-pain onset. Most of my clients are not aware of the power of music in reducing pain, so I spend time sharing with them how using time travel through music can assist them in returning to life before the onset of CLBP. By teaching my clients distraction through music skills, I am teaching them about the emotional effects that arise from listening to music—namely, distraction from the pain, pleasantness, pleasure, memory-evoked emotions, and relaxation (Garza-Villarreal et al., 2014). I also share that self-chosen music is likely to be the most proficient at reducing pain, as self-chosen music is already liked, which provides an easily achievable sustained attention to the song. The pleasant recall associated with a song prior to the onset of CLBP creates a sense of psychological time travel in that many clients communicate being able to take themselves back to a time when they were pain-free, carefree, and happy. By permitting clients to choose a song that represents life prior to CLBP onset, clients can share how they experience an instillation of hope because they learn that listening to a song that evokes positive emotions leads them to a state where they can distance themselves from their CLBP, even if the positive evocation of emotion is fleeting.

I use visual aids (see Figure 8.9) to assist them with being able to see the benefits of music and how picking one "song" that inspires a sense of calm or pleasantness within will assist in providing an avenue to explore creative outlets with the intent of distracting clients from the pain experience and upholding neuroplasticity. With this visual, I discuss music as a distractor and how music can occupy the mind with something familiar and soothing—namely, a self-chosen song. I also share with clients that picking a song that speaks to one's life experience prior to CLBP onset sets up a positive emotional state in which clients can anticipate a reward—namely, psychological time travel to a prior time period where they did not experience chronic, debilitating pain.

As the client discusses this visual with me, I reiterate that music can assist in rewiring/upholding neuroplasticity because a self-chosen song helps the client connect the favorite song to nonrelated

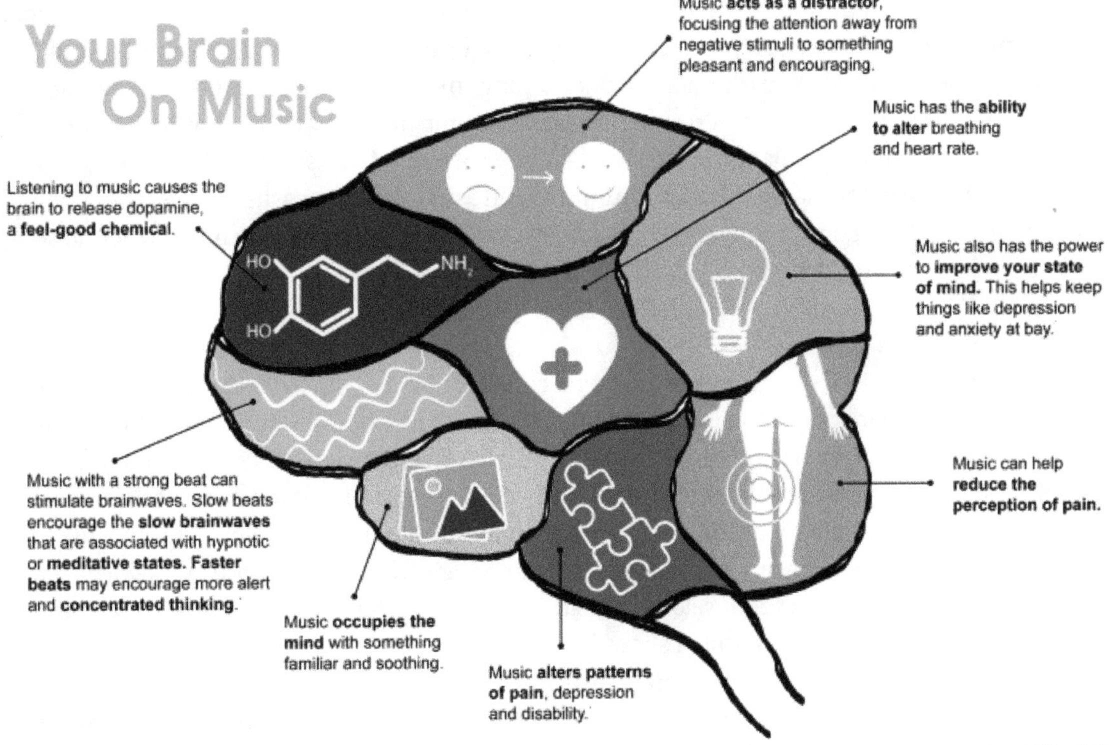

FIGURE 8.9 Potential Effect of Music on Various Brain Structures and Functions
Music normally has intrinsic value, but neuroscience might not. This image shows ways that music might influence brain functioning. By connecting regions of the brain with potential benefits of music, images like this can help clients visualize potential outcomes that aid in consent and the processing of neuroeducation exercises. From neurotransmitters to brain waves, perceptions, and more, this image engages the client in the neuroeducation process by capitalizing on the intrinsic value of music. As with all concepts, remember that these benefits are not localized to only one region or structure; rather, they require complex interactions with multiple regions and structures.

entities involved in CLBP, such as anxiety, stress, and feelings of control. In addition, I have found that the *Your Song* activity works most effectively as clients learn how music affects different parts of the brain and how music works to activate dopamine, as well as the associated reward of a pleasant memory (or memories) from one's past, especially prior to the onset of CLBP.

I use the *Your Song* activity solely in individual counseling sessions, as I recognize that clients appreciate that the selection of their song is private, idiosyncratic to their experience of pre- and post-onset of CLBP and connected to individual pain level, type, and intensity. Taking all these factors into account, the client picks one favorite song that instills a sense of hope, listens to the song repeatedly between sessions, and reports back the following themes:

1. What type of overall theme does this song impart to you about your development of hope because of CLBP?
2. What, in particular, about the lyrics give you a sense of hope? List one lyric in detail.
3. What do you find pleasurable about listening to this song repeatedly? Please list specific memories of happier times/pre-pain and what experiencing this song brings up for you. Please list your current experience of pain in the moment of listening to the song repeatedly. Do you find yourself distracted from your pain while listening to the song?

FOLLOW-UP

I administer the Pain Catastrophizing Scale (PCS; Sullivan et al., 1995) in the second session of counseling and readminister the scale during the last session of counseling. In all individual counseling sessions, I engage a high level of emotional processing and discussion around the selection of the pleasurable/instillation of a hope song, meanings attached to it, and memories that are brought to the surface as a result. This scale permits me to have a baseline measure of a client's level of rumination, magnification, and feelings of helplessness related to CLBP (Sullivan et al., 1995). Having these scores from beginning to end assists me in measuring levels of catastrophizing, magnification, and helplessness, as well as how the type of music genre and actual song might correlate with reducing these entities.

NEUROSCIENCE IN ACTION

Anna (hypothetical based on composite of several cases) is a 67 year old female referred by her pain management physician for counseling. She reported CLBP sustained in injuries in a motor vehicle accident. She had four spinal surgeries in the last 7 years. Anna reported the limited ability to stand or walk, resulting in a weight gain of 60 pounds in 1 year and subsequent physical deconditioning. She experienced pain when sitting or lying in bed with significant insomnia. She described the pain as "dominating" her life. When I introduced the *Your Song* activity, Anna seemed taken aback at first. She stated that with other counselors, she had discussed "negative self-talk" and wondered why I did not employ the same technique. I shared that picking a song that evoked a sense of pleasure would help her recall more pleasant and happy times, leading to increased hope and decreased pain. I spent time explaining to Anna that being able to travel back in her mind to a time prior to the onset of debilitating pain could help to cue her associational memory so that she could associate the song with pleasurable memories and experiences. Because Anna lived in a constant state of pain and experienced a high level of agitation related to this constant pain, she appeared to push back on picking a song, as she stated that she was old and out of touch with contemporary music. I explained to Anna that she did not have to choose a contemporary song and that she could select a song from her pre-pain onset. Anna semismiled and then stated that she remembered attending community hall dances and dancing the entire night. I also communicated with Anna that she did not have to pick her song in session one and that she might find it more helpful to pick a song in session two. Anna thanked me for allowing her more time to pick her song.

In the second session, Anna shared that she had picked her favorite song, entitled "Long Cool Woman in a Black Dress" by the Hollies. She immediately recalled wearing a snug black dress to one of the community dances and how everyone at the dance commented on how wonderful she looked and above all else how well she danced. She used the song to travel back to 1971 as if it were yesterday. She shared that picking this song helped her to go back and revisit a time period in her life that was free from pain. She also shared that having CLBP prohibited her from engaging in her favorite activity—namely, dancing. Anna was a client who had and continues to have a strong relationship with music. She was able to state by the end of counseling that she appreciated how much listening to her favorite music distracted her from her chronic daily experience of pain and activated her positive memories around sights, sounds, and images at those community hall dances. She stated that by listening to her favorite song, she was able to recall positive memories, which helped her to distance herself from her pain through her positive memories and to anticipate positives when she listened to her self-chosen song.

When scoring Anna's pre-test responses to items on the PCS, she obtained an overall score of 39 out of 52, with higher scores representing more pain catastrophizing. She endorsed scores of 3, to a great degree, for the 13 items on the scale. She shared that she'd considered assigning a score of 4, all the time on the item "I keep thinking about how badly I want the pain to go away," as she reported that she really felt challenged in this particular area of facing her pain on a daily basis. When I administered a post-test of the PCS, her overall score dropped to a 26, and she endorsed a score of 2, to a moderate degree on the item "I keep thinking about how badly I want the pain to go away." When she and I discussed this lower score, she stated that she turned to the song she picked in session, and when she found herself ruminating, she played the song until she experienced a decrease in repetitious thinking about how she would do anything to reduce her pain. She reported that she found herself turning to the self-chosen song as many as 6 times per day, especially, when she experienced an increase in her overall CLBP.

ETHICAL AND MULTICULTURAL CONSIDERATIONS

Music is transcultural. It possesses meanings that speak to the human spirit universally. However, the counselor must suspend judgment toward a song that, from the counselor's perspective, does not embody an instillation of hope and/or pleasure. My experience with having the client pick *Your Song* at the beginning of counseling has been well-received by minority groups who seek out counseling because of CLBP. Many of my minority clients explain that "talk is cheap" and that not everyone speaks the "same language." Because music preference is highly subjective, instillation of hope means something different to each client with whom I have worked. For some, a song from a heavy metal genre, such as Judas Priest's "Beyond the Realms of Death," instills a sense of hope, whereas for someone else, a selection from the classical genre, such as Chopin's "Spring Waltz," instills a sense of hope. In addition, because I work with clients who are 60+ years of age, many have hearing-related limitations and wear hearing aids. I spend time with these clients discussing their hearing loss and how it may affect their ability to hear a song. Many have contacted their hearing aid distribution company for help. In addition, I provide a printed fact sheet from the National Institute on Deafness and other Communication Disorders that outlines various assistive devices, current research findings related to hearing loss, and how to locate more information if needed. I also provide the website link during the first session: https://www.nidcd.nih.gov/sites/default/files/Documents/health/hearing/NIDCD-Assistive-Devices-FS.pdf.

CLOSING THOUGHTS

The purpose of this chapter was to introduce practical strategies to infuse the neuroscience of memory into your clinical practice. The neuroeducation exercises in this chapter showed ways that the reconsolidation process is harnessed for therapeutic gain. We learned about a unique acrostic (RECON) to remember the clinical process of memory reconsolidation, explored the power of eye movements to destabilize memories and promote accelerated outcomes, revisited a classic image of consciousness with a modern twist of implicit and explicit memory, and even connected music to the learning process. As you reflect on the activities in this chapter, we hope that you are making some direct applications to your own life as well as your clinical work. Before moving on to the next chapter, consider the following reflection questions:

REFLECTION QUESTIONS

1. How has your view of memory changed while reviewing this chapter?
2. What are your most practical takeaways from this chapter?
3. How do you see these activities having meaning in your personal life?

CREDITS

Fig. 8.3a: Copyright © 2016 Depositphotos/interactimages.
Fig. 8.6a: Copyright © 2016 Depositphotos/macrovector.
Fig. 8.7: Copyright © 2014 by Laney Rosenzweig. Reprinted with permission.
Fig. 8.9: Source: https://www.kakou.org.uk/your-brain-on-music/.

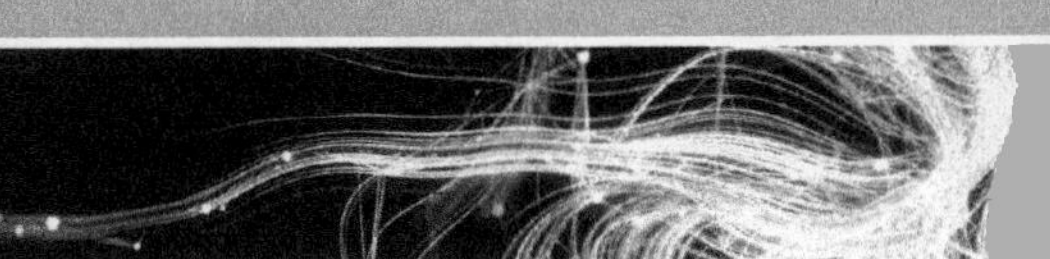

CHAPTER 9

Technological Applications of Neuroscience

The field of behavioral and mental health is now fully entering the world of technology-enhanced services.
—Jeffrey J. Magnavita

CHAPTER OBJECTIVES

1. Understand the basic uses of technology in mental health treatment.
2. Demonstrate applications of technology as neuroeducation interventions.
3. Identify additional training venues for the advanced practice of brain stimulation and biofeedback.

INTRODUCTION

Take a moment to visualize someone applying sensors to your scalp or even directly to your brain, and these sensors are connected to a piece of technology. What do you experience? For some individuals, this scenario might bring up images from a science fiction movie or illicit fears of mind control. For other individuals, this image might bring up feelings of excitement or curiosity. Perhaps sensors and technology just bring to mind feelings of familiarity—another day at the clinic. Regardless of our positive or negative associations with such images, technology is ever present in our lives and increasingly being infused in the development of health and wellness and as a treatment for mental and emotional disorders. Examples of technology-involved interventions include direct brain stimulation; use of email, text messaging, and phone applications to supplement or even replace traditional in-person therapy; virtual reality environments and artificial intelligence chatbots; and measures of physiological and electrical activity (e.g., biofeedback, neurofeedback). We believe the increased use of technology in counseling and psychotherapy creates many opportunities to apply neuroscience and neuroeducation. For example, using a biofeedback tool (e.g., heart rate monitor) can provide the opportunity to talk with clients about the relationship between the mind and body and how certain exercises (e.g., breath awareness, visual imagery) can regulate nervous system arousal. Using neurofeedback devices can lead to conversations about functions associated with each network of the brain and states associated with various brain waves. Virtual reality training modules can provide opportunities for counselors to share the value of repetitive practicing of new thoughts or behaviors in relative safety (e.g., topics related to neuroplasticity, the social engagement system). Perhaps even more important than providing opportunities to share relevant neuroscience information, the technology gives clients the opportunity to *experience* the neuroscience concepts in a felt-sense manner. They get to see physiological changes happening in real time and can experience the psychological benefits of such changes.

Although many forms of technology are involved in the treatment of mental and emotional disorders and the promotion of wellness, we will primarily focus on brain stimulation and biofeedback in this chapter.

Noninvasive	Noninvasive + convulsions	Invasive
Electrodes placed externally and provide mild electric manipulation	Electrodes placed externally and induce seizures	Electrodes placed directly on brain area or nerve
TMS, rTMS, tCDS, CES	ECT, MST	DBS, VNS

FIGURE 9.1. Continuum of Brain Stimulation Technologies
Deep brain stimulation (DBS). Vagus nerve stimulation. Electroconvulsive therapy. Magnetic seizure therapy. Transcranial magnetic stimulation (TMS). Transcranial direct current stimulation (tDCS). Cranial electrical stimulation (CES)

Brains stimulation interventions (BSI) promote neural modulation using electrical activity, either through direct induction of electric current or magnetic fields (NIMH, n.d.).

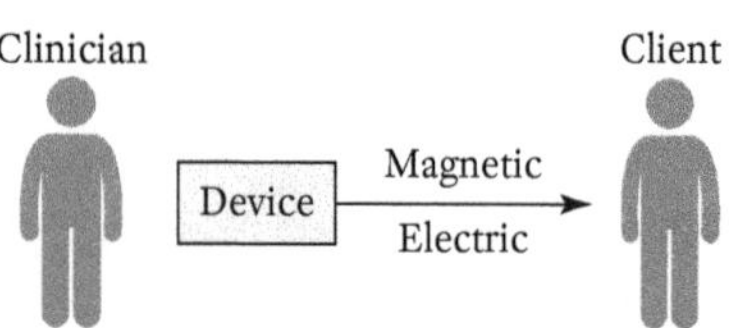

FIGURE 9.2 Direct Brain Stimulation

BSIs began in the 19th century but have grown in popularity and application in the treatment of mental disorders in the past 30 years (Steinberg, 2013). BSIs exist on a continuum (see Figure 9.1) from invasive to noninvasive (see Figure 9.2; Brunoni et al., 2019). Deep brain and vagus nerve stimulation are the most common invasive techniques, followed by electroconvulsive and magnetic seizure therapy that are the most common noninvasive techniques that require induced convulsions, and TMS, tDCS, and CES are the most common noninvasive techniques that do not require induced convulsions. Brunoni et al. (2019) synthesize the literature to review the advantages and disadvantages, as well as current application and Food and Drug Administration (FDA)-clearance levels. Although using BSIs to treat mental and emotional disorders (e.g., depressive disorders, schizophrenia) is gaining evidence, there are also some noted limitations (e.g., cognitive impairment, tremors) depending on the method (Chalah & Ayache, 2019). Although most counselors will not use direct stimulation therapies alone, noninvasive approaches, especially CES, are more accessible and being incorporated as stand-alone treatments, adjunctive to counseling and psychotherapy, and even home use by clients (Marksberry & Kirsch, 2018). Regardless of approach, it is useful to be aware of these interventions to facilitate adequate referrals and seek additional training.

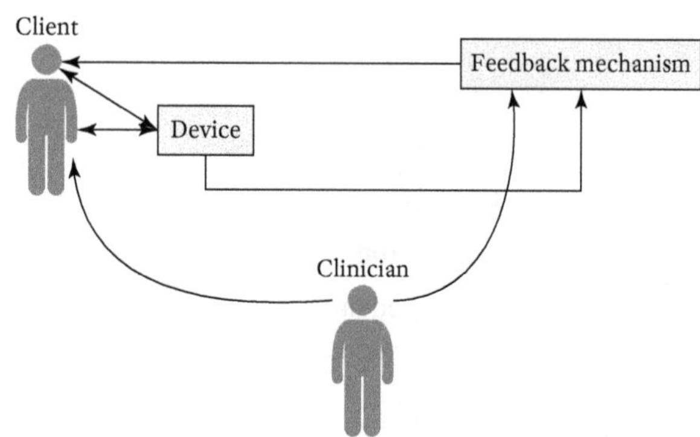

FIGURE 9.3 Biofeedback Setup Demonstrating the Technology and Counselor as a Feedback Mechanism

Biofeedback is another noninvasive approach to the technological application of neuroscience in practice. Grounded in principles of autonomic arousal, self-regulation, and operant and classical conditioning, biofeedback promotes awareness and regulation of physiological arousal by monitoring peripheral physiological activity and providing feedback to the individual. Different from brain stimulation, biofeedback (see Figure 9.3) involves no direct stimulation; rather, the biofeedback device monitors physiological activity and sends that information to a feedback device (e.g., computer monitor, headphones), and then the person self-regulates based on the feedback received. The clinician also serves as an important method of feedback that completes a complex inter-/intrapersonal technological system of intervention.

The official origins of biofeedback as an interdisciplinary field trace back to the late 1960s with several key publications, the definition of the term, and formation of the Biofeedback Research Society, the predecessor to the Association of Applied Psychophysiology and Biofeedback (AAPB) (Moss,

1999). Biofeedback is a specialized intervention with standards for training outlined by the Biofeedback Certification International Alliance (www.bcia.org). In addition, the AAPB (www.aapb.org) continues to advance the field through ongoing scientific study, publications, conferences, and member services. Although often criticized for small sample sizes, the use of biofeedback (e.g., Goessl et al., 2017) and neurofeedback (Hammond & Novian, 2018) has a long history of support in the treatment of many medical conditions, as well as general stress.

There are several forms of biofeedback that are important to be aware of, and each focuses on a different peripheral measure of physiological activity, including the following:

- Electromyography monitors the electrical activity of muscle fibers used in contraction.
- Peripheral temperature measures blood vessel dilation.
- Galvanic skin response measures skin conductivity through sweat on the extremities.
- Heart rate variability measures heart rate data using chest straps and/or ear/finger clip.
- Electroencephalogram (EEG) measures electrical signals on the scalp correlated with neural activity in various areas of the brain.

Technology permeates our daily lives, from smartphones to watches, Fitbits, and beyond. This technology is now being used for various direct and indirect health-care interventions. The brief exposure to some of these methods in this chapter is important given the rapid growth of these interventions. Although some are more accessible to counselors and psychotherapists than others, it is important to stay up to date with these advances for referral, additional training, and clinical intervention. It is also important to note that technology is not required for neuroscience-informed practice; however, technology is another tool available as you consider the application of neuroeducation in your practice.

NEUROEDUCATION ACTIVITIES

This chapter offers three neuroeducation activities that incorporate technology in practice. You will see two forms of brain monitoring and feedback, as well as one strategy to bring breath work to life with technological monitoring. The authors in this chapter offer tangible applications of technology and neuroscience in practice, with a focus on biofeedback.

TRAIN YOUR BRAIN

Neurofeedback Training to Assist in the Mitigation of ADHD Symptoms

Shaywanna Harris

Neurofeedback, also known as EEG biofeedback, is a drug-free, noninvasive training protocol designed to foster optimal brain wave activity that is ideal for counseling practice (Myers & Young, 2012). Neurofeedback as a practice has its roots in experimental research conducted on cats. In 1969, Barry Sterman serendipitously came to the realization that cats who had been trained to control electrical activity in their brains were less likely to experience seizures when exposed to a toxic seizure-inducing chemical. Since Sterman's work, neurofeedback has grown in popularity with many researchers examining the efficacy of neurofeedback as a treatment for various disorders, including epilepsy, attention-deficit/hyperactivity disorder (ADHD), substance use disorders, anxiety, and many others (e.g., Hardt & Kamiya, 1978; Lubar & Shouse, 1976; Shouse & Lubar 1979; Sterman 2000; Twemlow & Bowen, 1977).

For the purpose of this activity, I will focus on my work with clients experiencing symptoms of ADHD. The existing literature on neurofeedback and ADHD has mixed results. However, researchers have found that neurofeedback can be effective in mitigating the symptoms of ADHD in children and adults (Bink et al., 2015; Doren et al., 2018; Enriquez-Geppert et al., 2019; Gonzalez-Castro, Cueli, Rodriguez, Garcia, & Alvarez, 2016; Mayer et al., 2012). Although some research (Duric et al., 2012) found that neurofeedback was just as effective in treating ADHD symptoms as methylphenidate, other research (Escolano et al., 2014) found that individuals receiving neurofeedback experienced larger reductions in symptoms than those on medication.

There are several types of neurofeedback. Whereas many researchers use targeted neurofeedback protocols in clinical populations to impact specific areas in the brain directly, more generalized forms of neurofeedback, such as NeurOptimal, tend to be applied to nonclinical populations to promote overall mental efficiency (Luctkar-Flude et al., 2019). The largest difference between NeurOptimal and targeted neurofeedback is that the NeurOptimal system does not set a specific protocol based on a diagnosis or the results of quantitative electroencephalography; rather, the system measures electrical activity and bases the feedback on an individual's activity in the moment, providing feedback when electricity spikes beyond a range calculated by the software. Specifically, Harris and colleagues (2019) examined the effects of NeurOptimal neurofeedback on ADHD symptoms in college students. The researchers found significant reductions in ADHD symptoms (inattention, hyperactivity, and self-concept as it relates to ADHD) after 16 sessions of NeurOptimal neurofeedback. The findings are promising; however, the study design did not include a comparison group, and thus the ability to make causal inferences is limited.

The purpose of *Train Your Brain* is to demonstrate the application of the NeurOptimal system with adult clients who are experiencing symptoms of ADHD. Even if you are not interested in practicing neurofeedback, you can use your understanding to talk with clients about potential treatment options and referrals.

MATERIALS NEEDED

Materials needed to provide NeurOptimal neurofeedback training include the following:

- The NeurOptimal neurofeedback training system (available for purchase at www.neuroptimal.com)
  - A computer with the NeurOptimal software installed
  - zAmp
- Conductive paste
- Sensors
- Earbuds
- Gentle wipes for skin (to help remove the paste after the session)
- Alcohol wipes (to clean the sensors)

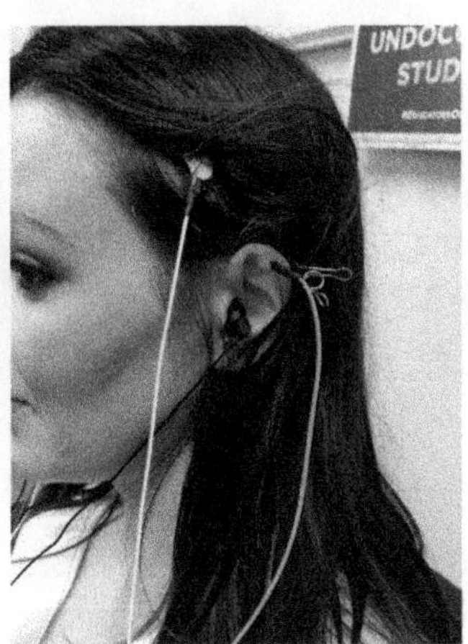

FIGURE 9.4 Connecting Electrodes to the Left Side

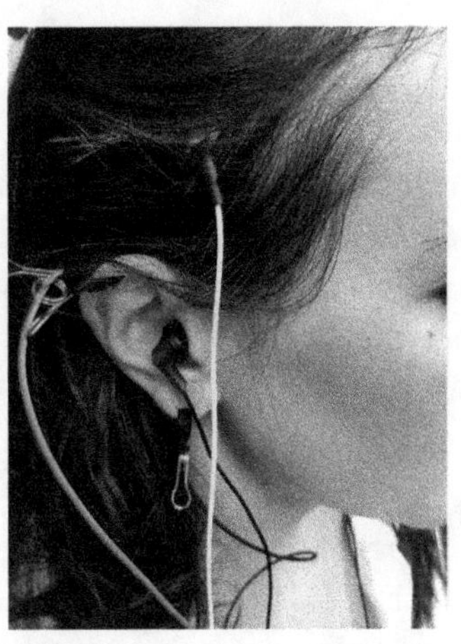

FIGURE 9.5 Connecting Electrodes to the Right Side

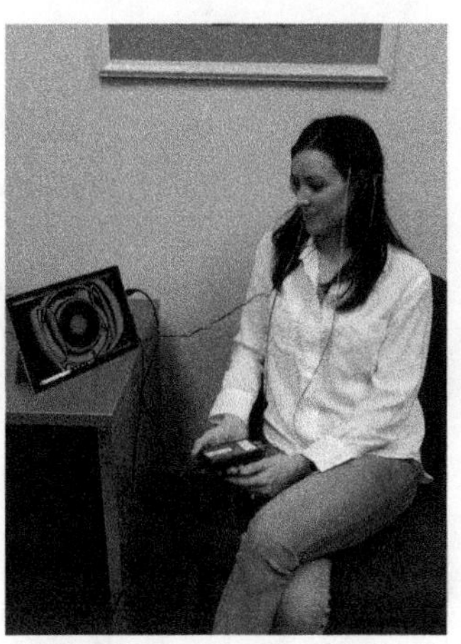

FIGURE 9.6 Connecting Electrodes to the NeurOptimal System

PROCESS OF THE ACTIVITY

Neurofeedback can be integrated at any point during the therapeutic process. However, neurofeedback may be more useful in the beginning of the therapeutic process to mitigate severe behavioral symptoms that are immediately affecting the client's life and could be a barrier to traditional treatment. The counselor can help the client cope with the acute symptoms before exploring deeper emotions in therapy. Neurofeedback can be used with children, adolescents, and adults with ADHD, and research exists to support the use of neurofeedback with each population. The first session of NeurOptimal neurofeedback includes the following steps: (1) explanation of neurofeedback and what the client can expect, (2) setup of the system, (3) facilitation of the neurofeedback session, (4) taking down of the system, and (5) processing of the client's experience.

Begin the process with a brief explanation of neurofeedback. You can say something like the following: "Neurofeedback is a noninvasive process in which electrical activity is measured and analyzed and then feedback is given to your brain that helps the brain waves move into a more optimal range. The feedback is in the form of small interruptions in the music you will be listening to. You do not have to do or think about anything."

To set up the client for a NeurOptimal session, allow the client to get comfortable (seated or lying down). Attach the sensors using electroconductive paste. Three sensors are attached to the left side of the client's head (one at the earlobe, one at the top of the ear, and one on the client's scalp, approximately one inch above the ear; see Figure 9.4), and two sensors are attached to the client's right side (at the top of the ear, on the scalp, one inch above the ear; see Figure 9.5). Ensure the sensors are connected to the zAmp, and that the zAmp is connected to the computer USB port (see Figure 9.6). This will ensure that the system is measuring the electrical activity from the client. Once the sensors are attached, assist the client in placing earbud headphones in their ears (earbuds are most effective because larger headphones may interfere with the electrodes located on the client's ears). The earbuds will play music during the training session. After the client has been set up, begin the session by clicking start on the computer. Once the session begins, the client will hear the music begin. The session is programmed to last 33.5 minutes, the optimal time as determined by the NeurOptimal developers (Zengar, 2016). During the session, the music will be interrupted as feedback to the client that the brain activity is venturing out of the desired range. The client may notice the slight interruptions in the music, yet some interruptions may be so slight—if the degree of differentiation measured by the machine is slight—that they are only noticeable at the subconscious level. The counselor also remains active while in session with observation skills, as well as maintaining nonverbal attunement.

Once the session has ended, the program on the computer will stop the music, and you can remove the sensors and the conductive paste. You may want to use some type of wipes to ensure that all the paste is removed. You will also need to clean the sensors with alcohol wipes to sterilize them for the next session. Once the cleanup has concluded, talk with the client about their experience during the neurofeedback session.

FOLLOW-UP

Ask individualized process questions based on the needs of your clients and their presenting concerns. Some questions you may ask include, "How have you noticed your symptoms changing since beginning neurofeedback?" Or, "Have others mentioned noticing any changes in your behavior since you've begun neurofeedback?" Further, you may incorporate the use of formal ADHD and outcome assessments to monitor the progress of their clients while they are receiving neurofeedback. For example, you can administer paper-and-pencil ADHD assessments (e.g., Conners' Adult ADHD Rating Scale; Conners et al., 1999) after a set number of sessions to track the client's progress (e.g., every 10 sessions). Also, you can incorporate journal writing by encouraging the client to journal daily or weekly about their symptoms. Journaling may help the client become aware of subtle changes in their symptoms by writing them down.

NEUROSCIENCE IN ACTION

Chloe, a 24-year-old woman who sought help managing her ADHD symptoms, contacted Shaywanna, a licensed counselor intern and certified neurofeedback practitioner, and set up an appointment. Shaywanna and Chloe began their relationship with an intake session in which Chloe explained to Shaywanna that she was having issues with sleep, concentration, and hyperactivity because of her ADHD diagnosis. Shaywanna explained the process of counseling to Chloe and offered neurofeedback as an option. Chloe agreed to try neurofeedback, as well as psychotherapy, to help her symptoms of ADHD.

In the first session, Shaywanna explained the process of neurofeedback to Chloe, indicating that neurofeedback is a noninvasive process in which the NeurOptimal system will measure her cortical electric activity and provide her brain feedback in the form of slight interruptions in music. Shaywanna further explained that neurofeedback, similar to exercise or learning a new skill, takes time and consistency to produce noticeable differences. Chloe expressed confusion and asked Shaywanna if the system would "shock" her as she has seen in movies and on TV. Shaywanna explained that contrary to deep brain stimulation, the feedback given in neurofeedback is noninvasive and would be in the form of interruptions in the music Chloe would be listening to. After the clarification of her concerns, Chloe was curious and excited to see if neurofeedback would actually work. Shaywanna then administered a formal ADHD assessment (i.e., the Conner's Adult ADHD Rating Scale [CAARS]) and asked Chloe to write down her ADHD symptoms and rate their intensity so that they could track this information over time. Once Shaywanna had consent from Chloe, they completed the neurofeedback session.

After the session, Shaywanna asked Chloe to describe her experience, and Chloe expressed that she did not feel different, but she felt calm. Shaywanna explained to Chloe that it is expected for her to feel calm after a session of neurofeedback because of the relaxing nature of the sessions. Shaywanna and Chloe then began their counseling session, after which Shaywanna and Chloe scheduled their next meeting, and Shaywanna asked Chloe to journal any changes she noticed daily. After approximately 10 sessions, Shaywanna administered the CAARS again, and Chloe's scores on the hyperactivity subscale decreased. Chloe also reported, via journaling, feeling calmer, being better able to focus, and being able to sleep better at night. Chloe mentioned that her significant other had noticed that she was "less fidgety" and was able to listen better during conversations. Shaywanna also noticed that Chloe was more focused in session and did not story tell or jump from topic to topic as she did initially. Here, it seemed the NeurOptimal training also aided in psychotherapy progress. Shaywanna and Chloe continued their sessions until they reached an agreement that Chloe had met her therapeutic goals and was ready for termination.

ETHICAL AND MULTICULTURAL CONSIDERATIONS

Clinicians may need to exercise caution when providing neurofeedback to individuals with pacemakers or other electrical implants, as the additional electrical activity in the body may interfere with the neurofeedback system's measurement of electrical activity in the brain, causing excess noise and potentially affecting the feedback being given to the brain. Further, as some neurofeedback systems require sensors to be attached to the scalp with an electroconductive adhesive, individuals with severe skin allergies may react to the conductive gel.

There have been documented cases in which individuals have not experienced significant improvements after receiving neurofeedback training. However, the adverse effects of NeurOptimal neurofeedback are limited to increased feelings of tiredness or relaxation, as NeurOptimal neurofeedback is a generalized form of neurofeedback. With targeted forms of neurofeedback, there are issues of adverse effects that may occur because of improper training protocols and a lack of proper training (Hammond & Kirk, 2008). Therefore, clinicians should ensure that they are properly trained and certified to perform the protocols they are performing, keeping in mind our ethical duty to perform services within our respective scopes of practice and boundaries of competence. Clinicians should also consider that much of the existing research on neurofeedback and ADHD includes little racial or ethnic diversity, and cultural variables related to the neurofeedback process and outcomes have not been examined in the literature. Further, as the feedback given is based on electrical activity, the possibility of the feedback being culturally biased is reduced. Developmentally, neurofeedback has shown promise in assisting individuals with developmental disorders or epilepsy.

BRAIN MAPPING TO EFFICACIOUS TREATMENT

Lori A. Russell-Chapin

Quantitative electroencephalography (qEEG), often referred to as brain mapping, is a method of statistically analyzing electrical activity on the human scalp that correlates to brain activity through an electroencephalogram (EEG). For certain types of neurofeedback (NFB), qEEG is often a prerequisite, but a referral for qEEG can add value to your clinical practice by adding objective data to inform case conceptualization and treatment planning, thus elevating a holistic view of the treatment process. This *Brain Mapping to Efficacious Treatment* activity will introduce you to the basics of qEEG so that you may more comfortably refer clients for a qEEG and even consider additional training to conduct qEEG and NFB yourself.

To conduct a qEEG, you need various hardware to collect EEG data from the scalp of a client. Generally, electrodes are placed on various sites of the scalp that are related to specific brain regions. The International 10/20 System (Jasper, 1958) is often used to guide the placement of 19 electrodes, which can be directly placed on the scalp, or the client can wear a cap that already includes the electrodes according to the 10/20 system. EEG data is collected by the electrodes, filtered through an amplifier, and analyzed using computer software. I use the Nexus 32 system, as well as Biotrace and NeuroGuide software, but there are several other systems that record the same data, such as BrainMaster, Deymed, and Thought Technology. The Head Map of Brain Functions (see Figure 9.7) illustrates the actual placements of the sensors and the typical corresponding brain functions.

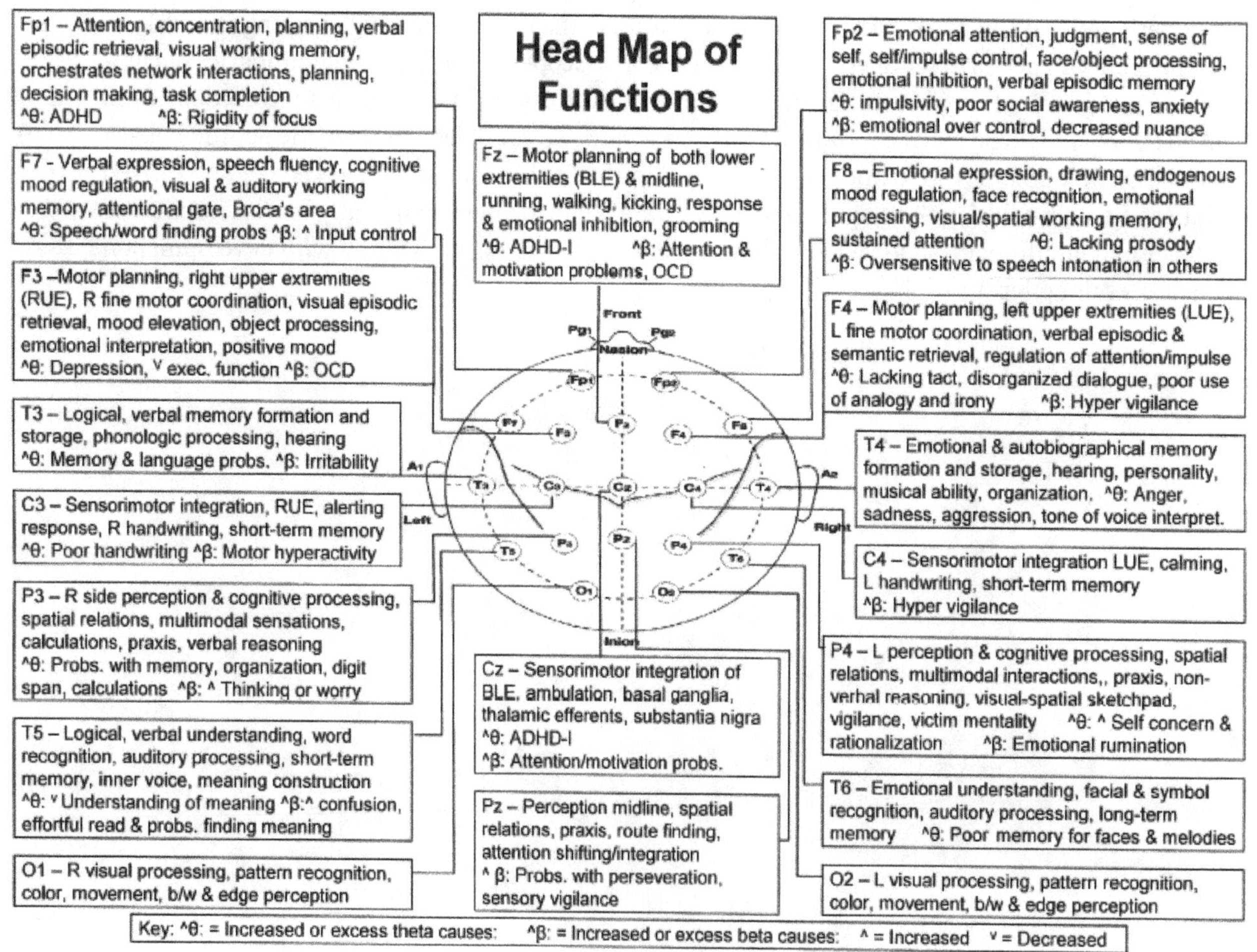

FIGURE 9.7 Head Map of Brain Functions Aligned With International 10-20 Classification System

When collecting EEG data, the integrity of the signal is essential. It is important to limit interference, such as electromagnetic pollution, like that from cell phones and overhead lighting, which could affect the accuracy of the EEG recording. Impedance levels are collected to ensure that the interference is below acceptable thresholds, generally below 5 kohms. Once the electrodes are in place and the signal is strong, the EEG is then recorded continuously in the awake state under three conditions: (1) with eyes closed, (2) with eyes open, and (3) while completing one task of silently counting backward from 1,000 subtracting by 7. Although this is my general protocol, there are other methods of qEEG that include different tasks based on client needs. The entire qEEG takes approximately 1 hour to complete depending on your client's needs.

Once the data is collected, it is visually inspected and artifacts (i.e., unwanted electrical activity, such as muscle movements and eye blinks) are deleted from the recording. Split-half and test-retest coefficients are also created to evaluate the reliability of the analysis (Thatcher & Lubar, 2008). An absolute and normalized spectral analysis is computed for each condition using T-tests and Z-scores. The brain maps are then produced, demonstrating a comparison of the client's recording to a normative database.

According to Budzynski et al. (2009), the importance of the qEEG to the diagnosis and prognosis of brain dysfunction arises from the fact that qEEG can reliably and objectively measure the distribution and amount of brain electrical activity. This can then be compared to a normative database using T-tests, Z-scores, means, and standard deviations, which generally show some degree of over- or underactivation and/or dysregulation. Think back to your assessment and research courses, the brain map will show you standardized scores that indicate specific sites and networks where brain wave activity is significantly different, typically 1.5 to 3.9 standard deviations, from the representative norm group. These scores can be helpful to evaluate a number of conditions from ADHD to anxiety and traumatic brain injury, often with corresponding brain EEG signatures (Chapin & Russell-Chapin, 2014). If correlated with their self-report, then this can aid in more precise diagnosis and treatment planning.

As counseling professionals, we are constantly dealing with the health of our clients' brains, directly or indirectly. Research has demonstrated that counseling changes the brain (Ivey et al., 2018). Knowing how and why change occurs seems fundamental to the entire process of counseling. Using qEEG helps clinicians observe dysregulation in the brain, another critical piece of information to guide therapeutic goals.

Even if your client does not want to complete, or cannot afford, NFB, the qEEG offers data that you, the counselor, can integrate into your counseling practice. For example, if you see that there is overactivation in the right prefrontal cortex with 16–20 hertz or high beta, then developing and implementing techniques to calm the brain would be important. Teaching parasympathetic interventions, such as heart rate variability, skin temperature control, and diaphragmatic breathing would be recommended. The qEEG promotes holistic care and provides additional outcome measures. Given

MATERIALS NEEDED

To complete this activity, you will need a qEEG report, or brain map, of a client. Therefore, you will need to find a trained neurotherapist in your area, preferably one who is board certified in NFB (BCN) and/or a qEEG diplomate. One method of locating a BCN is to visit www.bcia.org, which is the website for the Biofeedback Certification International Alliance (BCIA). There is a section titled "BCIA Credentials." Underneath is a category labeled "Finding a Practitioner." You can search by zip code to find practitioners in the surrounding area. Build a professional relationship with that person so that they can be a referral source for your clients, and you can be a referral source for theirs. Once the referral is made and the 19 channel qEEG (full head map) completed, brain maps will be created, along with a narrative report explaining the brain maps and their functions. Recommendations will also be offered for NFB, biofeedback, talk therapy, and other possible interventions.

the benefit of qEEG, I created the *Brain Mapping to Efficacious Treatment* activity as a step-by-step method for obtaining and collaborating with a qEEG specialist.

PROCESS OF THE ACTIVITY

Once you receive the qEEG report, you will want to review it independently before meeting with your client or have the qEEG specialist join you in your session to explain the results. You can use the sample brain maps in this chapter to follow along in this activity (see Figure 9.8).

TABLE 9.1 **TYPICAL BRAIN WAVES EVALUATED WITH QEEG**

Brain Wave	Frequency Bands	Typically Related To
Delta	0.1 to 3 HZ	Dreamlike state
Theta	3 to 8 HZ	Deep meditation and creativity
Alpha	8 to 12 HZ	Alertness and idling to next action
Beta	13 to 18 HZ	Thinking and task completion
High Beta	19 to 40 HZ	Problem solving
Note. The higher the HZ, the faster the wave and more cycles per second.		

Notice that the brain map presents data for five brain wave categories (delta to high beta—see Table 9.1) organized in columns and five metrics (absolute power to phase lag) organized in rows. Each brain wave category and the related frequency bands and typical states associated with it can be found in Table 9.1. It should also be noted that certain types of NFB also focus on infraslow waves (< 0.5 HZ) and gamma waves (38–42 HZ), but those are not normally captured in a brain map. Each brain wave is measured using each of the five metrics at each of the 19 channel sites and compared to a normative database. This matrix provides a comprehensive view of how each brain wave category is functioning at the various sites measured by the qEEG.

The first row is absolute power, which is the actual power or voltage in the client's EEG. In the sample brain map, we see the absolute power for all bandwidths is overactive, especially in the beta and high beta frequency bands. If localized to a certain brain region, such as the right prefrontal cortex, this may be suggestive of anxiety. This is helpful information to any counselor in talk therapy, as building emotional and self-regulation skills to regulate this overactivation would be essential to the success of counseling.

The second row is relative power, which shows the percentages of bandwidth power in each band compared to the total power in the client's EEG (Chapin & Russell-Chapin, 2014; Russell-Chapin, 2017). However, relative power is seldom used for diagnostic and treatment planning purposes.

The third row is amplitude asymmetry. Brains have all five main types of brain waves everywhere, but there is a normative asymmetry. This means a healthy, regulated brain would have more delta, theta, and alpha in the back of the head and lower beta in the left hemisphere. Looking at this distribution is helpful. For example, if a client had too much alpha in the front, this may lead to or be a signature of inattentiveness. With this client's brain map, observing the activity in the fourth and fifth column labeled beta, there appears to be not enough beta, especially in the left prefrontal cortex and yet too much beta in the middle and back of the head. This may help the counselor better understand the limits of talk therapy with this client, who has a lower IQ. Counseling could start with sensorimotor activities to better engage this client.

The fourth row is brain coherence. This construct focuses on how well the brain can communicate locally, regionally, and globally. In other words, how well does this brain talk from the amygdala to the prefrontal cortex, or how well does the left side of the brain communicate with

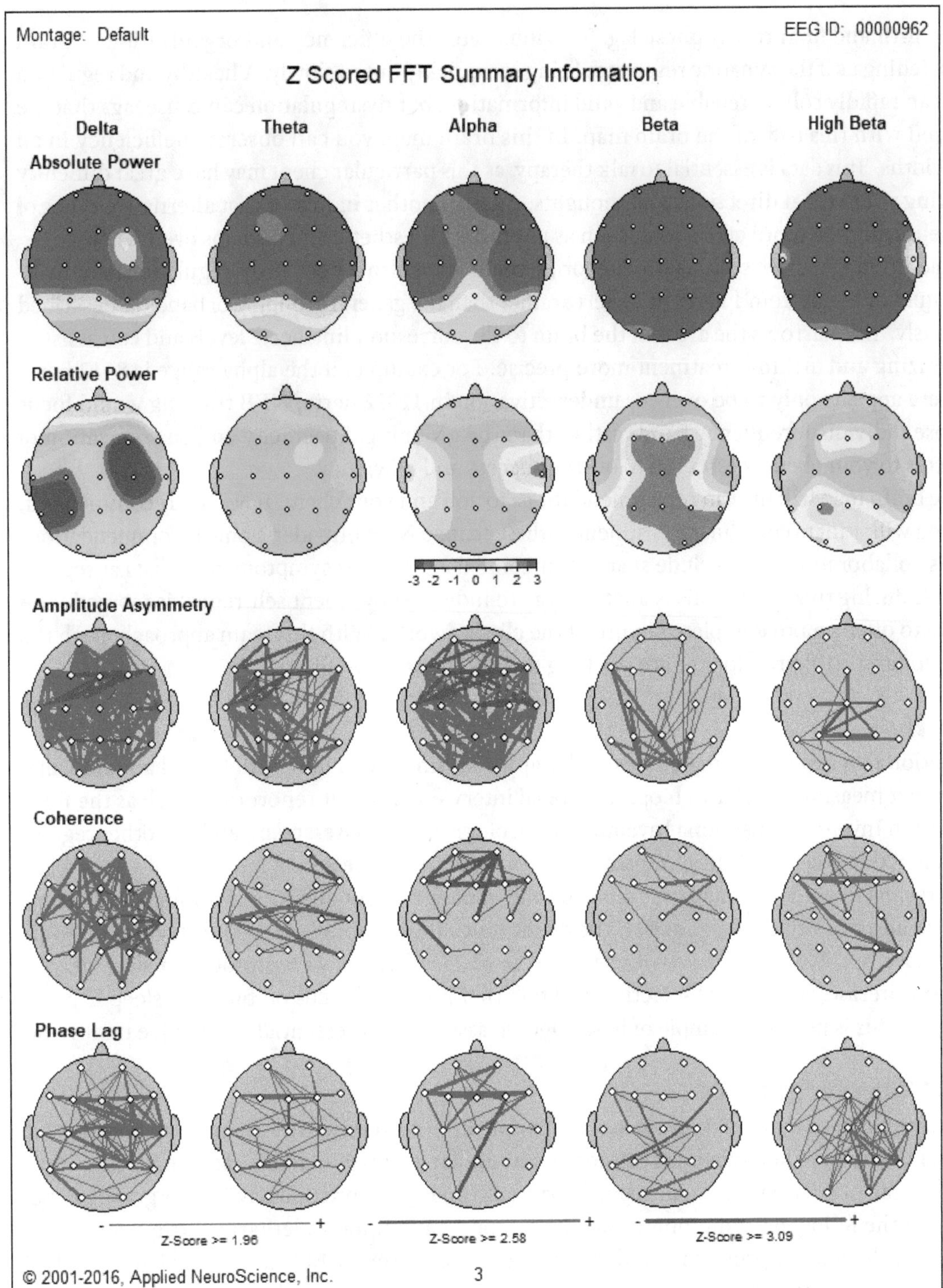

FIGURE 9.8 Pretreatment qEEG Results

the right side of the brain? These metrics help the counselor and client better understand patterns of coherence/communication. In this brain map, the client's left and right prefrontal cortices are under communicating with each hemisphere in alpha. Again, this makes sense, especially seeing visually that there is overcommunication occurring with high beta in the left and right prefrontal cortices. In counseling, you may observe this client to be a bit lethargic because of undercommunication, yet possibly anxious because of overactivation and overcommunication of high beta.

The fifth and final row is phase lag. This illustrates the efficiency and organization of brain waves, telling us if the synaptic responses firing too quickly or too slowly. A healthy and regulated brain can rapidly collect reliable and valid information, but dysregulation can cause lags that are captured with this row of the brain map. In this brain map, you can observe inefficiency in all bandwidths. This data is essential to talk therapy, as this particular client may have great difficulty following your verbal directions and thoughts. Again, another indicator that alternative types of counseling may be more efficacious, such as anything kinesthetic and perhaps even NFB.

In addition to the five bandwidth categories, brain maps also report on dysregulation in individual frequency bands from 1 hertz to 30 hertz rather than the general grouping of bands as described previously. This narrows the areas of the brain to the corresponding hertz levels and can assist in customizing and making treatment more precise. For example, if the alpha range is 8–12 hertz but there appears only to be over- or underactivation in 11–12 hertz, NFB training would focus on those individual frequency bands rather than the grouping. Specificity and customization of protocols to your client is essential to overall success and efficiency.

The brain map will inform recommendations to you and your client. If NFB is recommended, then you will want to coordinate treatment with a certified NFB provider. Some recommendations for this collaboration may include sharing outcome data, such as symptom checklists at regular intervals during treatment. This is another way to indicate how client self-report is merged with biodata to offer a more complete picture of the client's world. With this team approach, both the counselor and NFB practitioner are working toward the same goals.

FOLLOW-UP

In addition to a qEEG, a complete neurotherapy assessment includes both formal and informal assessment measures, such as a biopsychosocial interview, and self-report tools such as the Beck Depression Inventory, Insomnia Inventory, Neurological Risk Assessment, and any other regular assessment that you include in your practice. These additional assessment measures often correlate to the results of the brain maps. Comparing the qualitative and quantitative information helps establish and prioritize client goals. If the client states that "falling asleep and staying asleep" is the number 1 problem, and this is observed in the qEEG, then an NFB protocol for sleep may be the first criterion for protocol selection and talk therapy could focus on building sleep hygiene practices. This is just one example of how ongoing assessment is essential to effective treatment.

NEUROSCIENCE IN ACTION

The brain map (see Figure 9.8) reviewed previously in this exercise was a pretreatment qEEG of a former client, but I have changed the demographics for discussion in this case study. This client was a 12-year-old Caucasian female named Suzy, with an IQ of approximately 75. Her grandmother identified the following symptoms as needing improvement: focus, lethargy, little attention to detail, and sleep onset problems. In this case, I conducted the qEEG and proceeded with NFB as the primary treatment method; however, traditional counseling skills and an emphasis on the therapeutic relationship was necessary throughout. In addition to the qEEG, I conducted a thorough biopsychosocial history, a clinical five-channel EEG comparing her results to a clinical population, and the Test of Variable Attention, as well as symptom checklists and pertinent self-reports focusing on sleep, depression, and anxiety. After exploring the qEEG results with the other scores, we decided on a course of NFB for Suzy.

The symptom checklists were completed after every 10 sessions. After 20 sessions of NFB, a second qEEG illustrated major changes, especially in the area of alpha and theta. Twenty more sessions of NFB were administered, and the third qEEG again showed some remarkable changes in the brain. After 60 sessions of NFB, a post-treatment qEEG was administered. Take a look at the post qEEG brain map (see Figure 9.9) and compare it to the pretreatment brain map (see Figure 9.8).

Notice how much of the topography of the brain maps have changed from pre- to post-EEG.

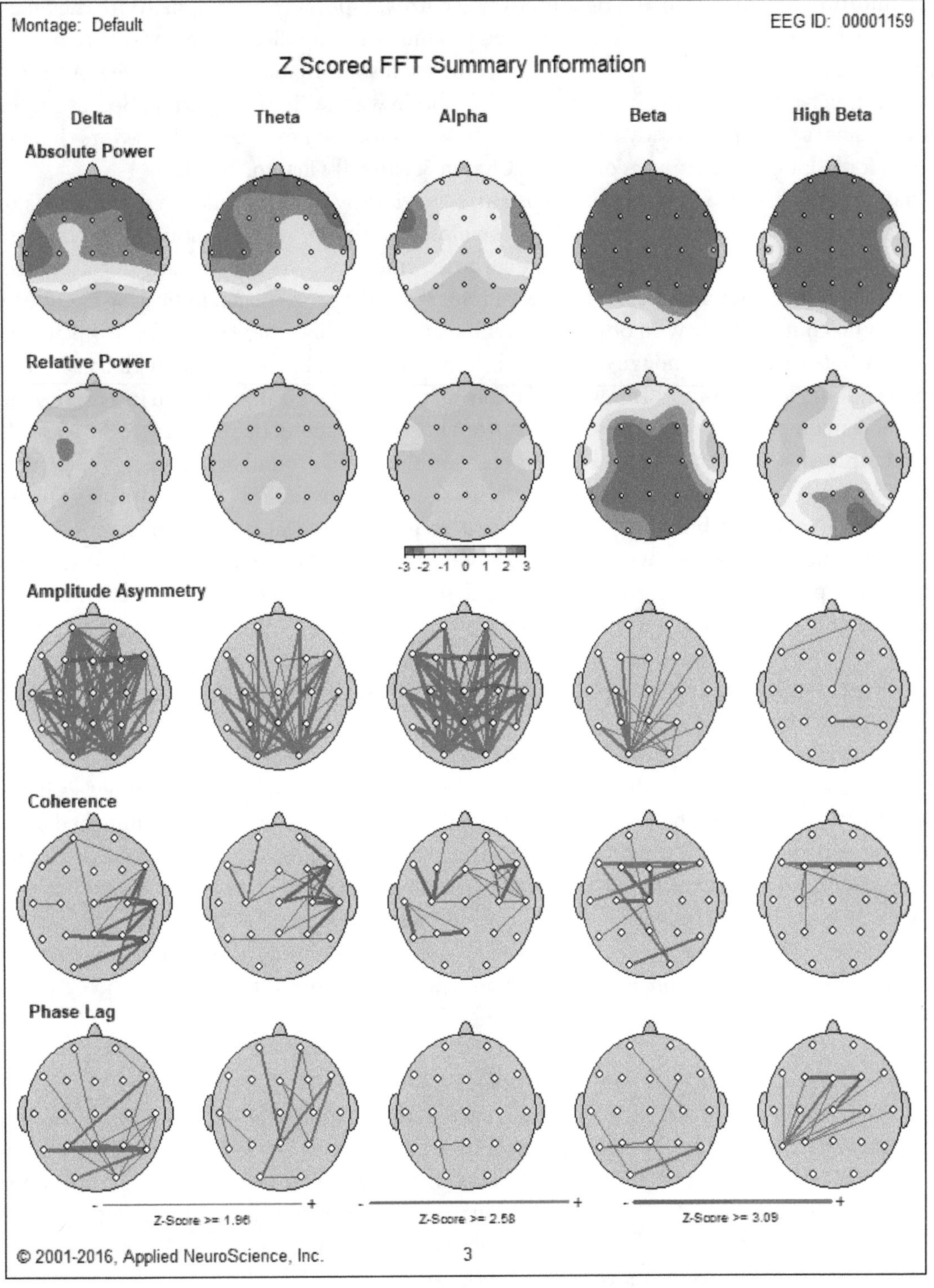

FIGURE 9.9 Post-Treatment qEEG

In the pretest EEG, there appears to be overactivation in all brain waves. The amplitude asymmetry shows too many unwanted brain waves in the front of the head. Some of the "noodle-like" depictions may be from the brain not working well, but it may also be confounded by many of the prescribed medications Suzy is taking. As the brain begins to work more efficiently, with the help of a psychiatrist, some of those medications may be weaned. In the coherence row, the pretest shows too much cross talk within all bandwidths, especially in the delta range, yet not enough communication within the left and right prefrontal cortex, especially with alpha. With the phase lag row, the brain is firing too much in delta and too much and too little in the other brain wave categories. Compare the posttest brain maps to the pretest brain maps. In absolute power, the overactivation has improved, especially in the alpha brain waves. This is important because alpha waves are seen as an idling, ready to change brain waves for the next needed behaviors that are essential for helping us function at our best. (Chapin & Russell-Chapin, 2014).

Changes are observed in the brain maps and behaviorally in amplitude asymmetry. Major changes occurred in the brain, especially in the alpha bandwidths. Even though low and high beta bandwidths continue to be overactivated, those same waves are functioning in the correct place in the brain. Coherence displays the most remarkable improvements, indicating her ability to access and communicate with other brain regions more readily. There are still a few places in the brain where there is not enough or too much communication, but overall, all regions of Suzy's brain are talking to each other. This will definitely help Suzy process information in a more valid and reliable manner. The world will begin to make a little more sense. In Suzy's case, she was able to receive information more reliably and comprehend the world around her easier.

Finally, phase lag demonstrates that synaptic firing has improved in all bandwidths. The phase lag maps indicate Suzy's ability to receive information in a more organized and efficient manner. There is still more work to be accomplished; however, stopping this client at 60 NFB sessions seemed wise to allow this healthier brain to work and monitor changes in daily life. Of course, additional NFB can happen, if needed, at any time. Typically, NFB improvements will remain stable across time, unless another brain trauma or dysregulation happens, such as another high fever or head injury. Changes during NFB generally promote more successful and efficacious talk therapy throughout as well.

Even though the qEEG suggested progress, it was important to filter this information through Suzy's real-life experiences. At the end of NFB, Suzy's behaviors changed measurably, as if she had suddenly woken up. In the beginning, Suzy walked slowly with her shoulders hunched over, her hair was in her face, and she rarely spoke. At her exit interview, she was very talkative and smiling, telling jokes, and mad at her brother. These behaviors were quite normal and healthy. Although Suzy couldn't acknowledge what these brain maps meant to her, her grandparents both commented on the differences in Suzy's behaviors, mostly with homework completion and her talkative demeanor. In addition, a new IQ test after the NFB sessions indicated an increase of 6 IQ points.

ETHICAL AND MULTICULTURAL CONSIDERATIONS

To incorporate qEEG into a clinical practice, there must be significant additional training and equipment funds available to purchase computers and software. To do so, please go to www.bcia.org, where you can find pertinent information about the needed training and certification for biofeedback, NFB, and qEEG. Of course, the purpose of this chapter is not to recommend that this training be taken but to understand enough about brain mapping to make necessary referrals for clients and incorporate this knowledge into your practice.

OBSERVING MY BREATH AT WORK

Deborah L. Duenyas, PhD

In the past decade, there has been an increase of professional research focused on the use of mindful breathing as an intervention in clinical settings (Bing-Canar et al., 2016; Eisenbeck et al., 2018; Keng & Tan, 2017). Breathing is a fundamental physiological function; breathing occurs automatically, often without our conscious thought or focused attention. Empirical findings include the use of breathing with intention for improved physiological functioning, such as influencing heart rate variability, cardiac vagal activity, and autonomic nervous system functioning (Chapin, 2017; Goessl et al., 2017). Such interventions require moving awareness of our breathing patterns from the unconscious, automatic area of the human brain stem to the conscious, intentional areas of the forebrain and prefrontal cortex (Bing-Canar et al., 2016).

Mindful breathing is a form of mindfulness that focuses on paying attention to your breath in the moment. For example, asking clients to feel their abdomen rise during a breath (aka., diaphragmatic breathing) or to notice the sensation of air temperature as they breathe in through the nose. Mindful breathing results from, as well as leads to, improved self-monitoring and attention to self-regulation, decreased symptoms of stress and anxiety, reduced symptoms associated with attention-deficit/hyperactivity disorder, and improved sleep quality (Bing-Canar et al., 2016; Eisenbeck et al., 2018; Russell et al., 2017; Tsai et al., 2015).

Biofeedback is a neuroscience-informed intervention that helps individuals become aware of the automatic functions of their bodies to provide them with more control over those functions (Myers & Young, 2012). Technological biofeedback interventions use digital and mechanical apparatuses to aid individuals in becoming more aware of physiological functions (Crockett et al., 2017). A pulse oximeter is a small piece of equipment that uses a visual display to show an individual's heartbeat and rhythm. The use of a pulse oximeter can help younger clients gain physiological awareness and facilitate meaningful connections between their cognitions and affect (Crockett et al., 2017). The goal is to help clients identify physical cues of arousal sooner to promote regulation prior to distress, dysregulation, and behavioral consequences.

The purpose of the *Observing My Breath at Work* intervention is to help clients, specifically children, gain awareness of their bodies' automatic response processes, practice mindful breathing, and build confidence in their ability to manage their physical and behavioral responses to strong emotion. My experience is that when children feel empowered in their bodies, they are better able to use positive coping strategies to work through challenging situations.

MATERIALS NEEDED

You will need a children's pulse oximeter. There are numerous pulse oximeters to choose from online. Although I cannot endorse any one specific brand, I have used ACC U Rate's 430P Animal Themed Fingertip Pulse Oximeter (https://amzn.to/2zSBzjn).

PROCESS OF THE ACTIVITY

This activity is designed for children aged 3–13 and can be used with various presenting concerns, including anxiety, inattention, hyperactivity, impulsivity, emotion regulation, and aggressive behaviors. Prior to using this activity, the parent/guardian of the client should be consulted to make sure the activity is appropriate and that the client has no underlying medical condition(s) (e.g., asthma) that could cause harm. The procedure is as follows:

1. Introduce the activity by talking with your client about a recent event or experience in which they felt one or more intense emotions (i.e., anxiety, anger, fear). For example, fighting with a sibling over a toy at home or transitioning between activities at school. Talk about the identified event with your client; ask them to show you what their face and body looked like when they were feeling this emotion. Your client may be able to act out these physical cues, but if not, drawing pictures, talking, or pointing to different illustrations found in children's books are also good methods for helping clients show you these physical cues. Next, ask how they experienced their breathing and heartbeat before, during, and after the event.
2. Prompt the client to reflect on the clues in their facial expression and body language (i.e., frowning, scrunching their eyebrows, making fists) that can help them to better understand their emotional experience. Once the client has identified a few physical clues, process the ones they might feel inside their body (i.e., rapid heartbeat, tense muscles, butterflies in the stomach) in relation to their emotional experience.
3. Show them the pulse oximeter; let them explore and play with it (i.e., put it on their finger, open and close it). Inform the client that this gadget can give them some information about their heartbeat. At this time, you can use the pulse oximeter to establish a baseline heart rate for the activity.
4. Ask the client to engage in a physical activity that will raise their heart rate (i.e., jumping jacks, running in place, running outside). After, on average, 60 seconds of time, place the pulse oximeter back on their finger and show them their new heart rate. It should have increased because of the physical activity. Ask your client if this is how their heart and breath feel when they are angry?
5. Have the client take a few deep belly breaths (diaphragmatic breaths). Ask your client what changes they observe on the pulse oximeter (i.e., heart rate slowing down with each breath). What changes do they observe while they are in a resting state? Provide positive reinforcement for the breath work they are doing and how good they are at slowing down their heart rate. Let them know this is a mindful breath and can be used as a "calm down" skill. Ask your client if and how it would be easier to make "good" behavioral choices when their breathing and heart rate are moving very fast or after they have taken a few deep breaths and slowed down their breath and heart rate.
6. You can repeat this activity a number of times to gain practice, build awareness, and create a fun experience in which they are in control of their own body and breath. The activity is also a fun way to build rapport with the client.
7. Finally, process their experience with the physiological activity (i.e., jumping jacks, running in place, running outside). How was the activity similar to having an intense emotion and how was it different? Review the event and clues the client mentioned in Step 1. Next time the client starts to feel this emotion, they will have the power to take a deep belly breath and use this new "calm down" skill. Let your client know they did excellent self-detective work today!

FOLLOW-UP

After completing this activity with the client, ask the parent/guardian to come in and have the client demonstrate their new "calm down" breathing skill. Demonstrating the skill at this time provides positive reinforcement to the client, assesses their comprehension of the activity, and models how to use this skill with the parent/guardian. Ask the parent/guardian to watch for examples of when the client uses their "calm down" breathing skill over the next few weeks. Children are often excited to do this activity, and as a result, they feel empowered by the awareness that they have control over some of their physiological functions. This experience also gives parents/guardians the opportunity to use this intervention and focus on the positive progress of the child.

NEUROSCIENCE IN ACTION

Noah is a 5-year-old male enrolled in kindergarten. He was brought to counseling by his mother upon referral by his school counselor. Noah's mother reported "disruptive" behavior both in his classroom and at home. She stated that Noah has "tantrums" (e.g., he becomes tearful and kicks or hits others), a short attention span, and difficulty following directions. Noah's mother explained that his symptoms started 6 months ago after his father was incarcerated for his third driving under the influence offense. This meeting was my fourth session with Noah.

Counselor: I heard you were feeling a little upset at school today. Can you tell me what happened?

Noah: My teacher said it was time to clean up, but I wasn't finished with my puzzle.

Counselor: Sounds like you felt sad that you had to stop playing with the puzzle.

Noah: Yeah, and I was angry!

Counselor: Can you show me what you looked like when you were angry? [*Noah hunched his shoulders, balled up his fists, furrowed his eyebrows, and frowned in demonstration.*]

Counselor: Yes, I can see by looking at your face and body that you were very angry. Did you have any other feelings in your body? Was your heart beating very fast? Did you feel a change in your breath?

Noah: Oh yeah, I felt hot; my heart was beating really fast. I could tell I was breathing faster, and I threw the puzzle on the floor. I was really mad!

Counselor: Noah, do you know what a heartbeat sounds like? [*I made the heartbeat sound.*] Doctors listen to your heartbeat with a stethoscope to make sure it sounds healthy. This little machine can show you your heartbeat and tell you how fast it is going. Can I show you? [*I put the oximeter on Noah's finger.*] See, the waves are showing you your heartbeat. [*I made the heartbeat sound in rhythm with Noah's heartbeat.*] The number shows us how fast it is going. Wow, your heart is going 106 beats per minute.

Noah: Wow, my heart is fast!

Counselor: Okay, now run to the other side of the playground and back. [*Noah runs.*]

Counselor: Great, you are really fast! Now, let's see how fast your heart is going. Wow, 130 beats per minute. Now take a deep belly breath, just like we practiced. [*Noah takes a breath.*]

Counselor: Look your heartbeats are slowing down. You are calming down with each good belly breath. Excellent breathing Noah!

Noah: Look it is slowing down!

Counselor: How does it feel to use your breathing to calm down?

Noah: Really good. I can't believe I'm doing that!

Counselor: Did you feel any similarities between your heart rate running and your heart rate at school this morning?

Noah: Yes, my heart was beating so fast when I threw my puzzle on the floor, just like it was now.

Counselor: Wow, so when you feel strong emotions, like you did today at school with your teacher, your breath and heart rate may have become quicker, just like they did when you ran for me right now. What was different about your experience in school and your experience now?

Noah: I don't feel angry right now.

Counselor: Right. That is different. Do you think you can focus on your breath and calm down when you are feeling angry?

Noah: Yes, I think it would be helpful. I can pay attention to my body clues and let my teacher know how I am feeling before I do something that I get in trouble for.

Counselor: So you think if you listen to your body clues and use your breath to calm down that it might be easier to tell your teacher how you're feeling?

Noah: Yes, I think so.

Counselor: Noah, you are an amazing self-detective. I can't wait to hear how you use your new skill. Let's keep practicing!

ETHICAL AND MULTICULTURAL CONSIDERATIONS

This activity has been designed for children ages 3–13. The Acc U Rate pediatric pulse oximeter used in this activity is not a medical device and is not intended for medical use. Children with medical conditions that could be exacerbated by physical activity, such as asthma, should not participate in this activity. As noted earlier, counselors should always discuss the activity with the child's parent/guardian prior to engaging in the activity. Although no formal training is required, counselors using a nonmedical pulse oximeter with clients should read the operating manual that comes with the purchase of their pulse oximeter and feel competent in their ability to use and interpret its features and functions prior to use with a client.

CLOSING THOUGHTS

The purpose of this chapter was to introduce readers to the technological applications of neuroscience. When many clinicians think of neuroscience, they automatically think about expensive technology. As we have learned so far in this book, most application of neuroscience in practice does not require any technology. However, this chapter introduces readers to how technology can enhance, adjunct, or serve as an option for referral. If technology is used, the relationship and the first-person account of the client self-report remain essential to the technological integration of neuroscience in practice. Before moving on to the next chapter, consider the following reflection questions:

REFLECTION QUESTIONS

1. What do you think about incorporating this technology into your practice?
2. Who are the biofeedback and neurofeedback practitioners in your area?
3. How might you balance the client's lived experience with the technological data?

CREDITS

Fig. 9.2a: Copyright © 2011 Depositphotos/leremy.
Fig. 9.3a: Copyright © 2011 Depositphotos/leremy.
Fig. 9.7: Copyright © by John Anderson. Reprinted with permission.
Fig. 9.8: Copyright © by Applied Neuroscience, Inc.
Fig. 9.9: Copyright © by Applied Neuroscience, Inc.

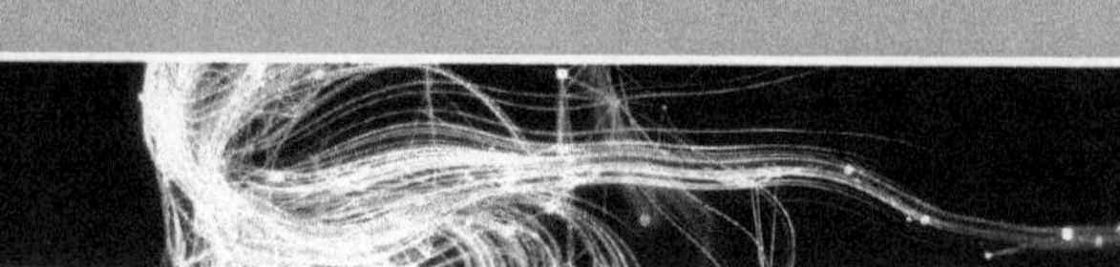

CHAPTER 10

Summary and Next Steps in Research

Research is formalized curiosity. It is poking and prying with a purpose.
—Zora Neale Hurston

CHAPTER OBJECTIVES

1. Summarize key neuroeducation content and processes.
2. Review ethical and multicultural considerations.
3. Identify opportunities for future research into neuroeducation.

NEUROEDUCATION CONTENT AND PROCESS

If you have made it this far in your reading, you have been introduced to a wide range of neuroeducation content areas. From principles of brain development and memory to neuroscience-informed theories of emotion and the embodied brain, we hope some of the concepts in this text resonated with you and perhaps sparked some creative ideas of your own. We would like to stress once more the importance of process when it comes to applying neuroeducation. We encourage you to flip back to the first two chapters of this book and consider the many uses of neuroeducation, helpful and less helpful ways to integrate neuroeducation into your work, and the value of microskills and metaprinciples underlying all neuroeducation activities. You may want to ask yourself the following questions when thinking about applying neuroeducation:

- What neuroscience principles are most relevant to my clients' strengths and challenges?
- When might be the best time to introduce a neuroeducation activity?
- How will I know if the neuroeducation activity is resonating with a client?
- When is it better to pull back from the neuroscience, reestablish a connection, and pivot in a new direction?
- Whose interests am I serving with the neuroeducation activity—my own enthusiasm for the topic, my need to appear competent or in control of the session, or truly the client's benefit?
- In what ways can I directly link the information to the client's lived experience? Or better yet, how can I create an experience for the client in which the neuroscience ideas resonate in an embodied way?

ETHICAL AND MULTICULTURAL CONSIDERATIONS

In Chapter 2, we introduced essential metaprinciples related to the neuroeducation process. This might be a good time to flip back to Table 2.3 and ground yourself in the crucial ethical and multicultural considerations relevant to the neuroeducation process. These principles were extended by each contributor as they explored the value of ethics and culture specific to their activities. Primary themes included the following:

- ***Practitioners' Competence.*** Contributors highlighted the importance of clinicians' training and knowledge related to whatever neuroscience concepts they are introducing to clients. They stressed that clinicians should be aware of their scope of practice and only represent themselves and their activities within this scope. In addition, as we noted in the early chapters of the book, it's best to qualify any neuroscience concepts you are sharing in tentative terms. The field is continually evolving, sometimes leading to modifications of prior understandings and theories. Our translations may be a little off or not quite true to the basic science research. So embrace what you do know while acknowledging what you do not and present information as the starting point for continued exploration and meaning making.
- ***Supporting Client Autonomy.*** The importance of giving clients a choice to engage in neuroeducation activities was noted throughout the various contributors' writings. Contributors shared that clients are at various levels in their openness and readiness to change, and clinicians should be mindful of these factors when facilitating activities.
- ***Using a Trauma-Informed Lens.*** Contributors noted the importance of recognizing that their activities could awaken memories and/or embodied experiences in clients that lead to a trauma response (e.g., dissociation, panic). Clinicians should be equipped to assess and respond to such occurrences. Along the same lines, many contributors noted that their activities would not be appropriate for clients in a crisis state; in such cases, crisis intervention should take precedence. With all techniques, timing is crucial and clinical judgment is paramount.
- ***Attention to the Developmental Levels of Clients.*** Contributors noted the importance of aligning language, content, and process to clients' developmental levels. In general, overly cognitive approaches and talk-based interventions are less effective with young children. Throughout the life span, individuals often respond to more experiential methods of learning.
- ***Attention to Clients' Abilities.*** Clients vary in terms of their physical and cognitive abilities—including movement, vision, hearing, and so forth. Some activities may need to be modified or avoided altogether.
- ***Elevation of Clients' Culture.*** Contributors highlighted the need to be aware of and lean into cultural variables throughout. Practicing cultural humility and embracing the intersectionality of all identities will reduce the chance of oversimplifying the client's experiences while helping connect metaphors, examples, and other information to their language, worldview, symbols, customs, and other culturally relevant material. Genuine curiosity and openness can go a long way in understanding clients' cultural values and perspectives.

NEXT STEPS IN EVALUATION AND RESEARCH

Neuroeducation is a relatively new intervention in the mental health field. Although pain neuroscience education has a growing body of empirical support during physical therapy (Louw et al., 2011; Robins et al., 2016), the exploration of neuroeducation in counseling and psychotherapy is primarily anecdotal. Any technique is only as good as the process that follows and the outcomes it generates. Evaluation methods can be informal (e.g., general processing questions, such as, "How was that experience for you?" Or, "What sense do you make of that information?") or formal (e.g., pre- and post-assessments of the Beck Depression Inventory or the Attitudes Towards Mental Health Problems' Self Rating scale), and the contributors in this text have provided sound methods to evaluate their specific neuroeducation activities. We encourage you to take a look back over those suggestions and consider how you will monitor and assess your own effectiveness as you implement the neuroeducation process.

In addition to general process and outcome evaluation at a clinical level, you might be interested in more empirical research on your own or in partnership with colleagues and local universities. Whether it be single-subject research design (Lenz, 2015) or more complex randomized control studies, various quantitative and qualitative methods can be useful in exploring important research questions related to neuroeducation, including the following:

- What are the experiences of clients engaging in (specify the neuroeducation activity)?
- How do clients perceive clinicians who deliver neuroeducation? How do these perceptions compare to perceptions of clinicians who do not practice neuroeducation?
- How does the use of neuroeducation affect common factors and therapeutic outcomes?
- What are the neuroscience concepts clinicians most frequently share with clients via neuroeducation interventions?
- How does (specify the neuroeducation activity) affect (client population) (specify the symptom or behavior [e.g., avoidance, shame, panic attacks, locus of control, agency])?
- What is the relationship between (specify the neuroeducation activity/ies) and clients' motivation to change?
- Does (specify the neuroeducation activity) change clients' (specify the physiological experience [e.g., heart rate, skin conductance]) in session?

These research questions, along with many other possibilities that you might be thinking about, are the beginning of the research process and guide research design, but the design of neuroscience research can be daunting. Luckily, the National Institute of Health's Research Domain Criteria (RDoC; https://www.nimh.nih.gov/research) provides researchers with a framework to guide study design. The RDoC Matrix defines constructs of inquiry (e.g., reward anticipation), reviews units of analysis (e.g., from genes to physiology and even self-report), identifies existing research paradigms, and informs methods of data collection. Although lab-based methods of collecting molecular and cellular data might not be as common among practicing clinicians, networks, physiology, behaviors, and self-report are commonplace in our work and serve as prime research variables. Also, RDoC-informed research and the constructs themselves might inform future neuroeducation activities that you could implement in your practice.

CONCLUDING THOUGHTS

As we come to the end of this text, we hope that you have found some meaningful insights, both personally and professionally. The concepts explored in this book have meant a lot to our personal and professional development, and we hope that they will inspire innovative ideas for your clinical work, as well as inspire your own creativity. As the mental health field continues to explore the complexities of human experiences, neuroscience is just another way of exploring these experiences and requires continued evaluation like any other theoretical or scientific proclamations. Neuroscience can be an integrative framework for the biological, psychological, and social experiences of us all. However, it is essential to practice neurohumility, to embrace the tension of what we know, and acknowledge the vast array of issues that we do not. The intention of the neuroeducation process is to provide a framework and ideas to help lean into this tension and curiously explore the world of those we serve, as well as to help them create meaning that will aid in their pursuit of what is most important to them.

REFLECTION QUESTIONS

1. How will you balance content and process in your engagement in neuroeducation activities with clients?
2. How will you address ethical concerns and elevate cultural diversity when applying neuroeducation?
3. What do you want to know about the effectiveness of neuroeducation and its future in clinical practice? Where is your curiosity taking you?

References

Abidin, R. R. (2012). *Parenting stress index* (4th ed.). PAR.

Abidin, R. R., & Robinson, L. L. (2002). Stress, biases, or professionalism: What drives teachers' referral judgments of students with challenging behaviors? *Journal of Emotional and Behavioral Disorders, 10*(4), 204–212. https://doi.org/10.1177/10634266020100040201

Acevedo, E. O., & Ekkekakis, P. (2006). *Psychobiology of physical activity*. Human Kinetics.

Adames, H. Y., Chavez-Dueñas, N. Y., Sharma, S., & La Roche, M. J. (2018). Intersectionality in psychotherapy: The experiences of an AfroLatinx Queer immigrant. *Psychotherapy, 55*(1), 73–79. https://doi.org/10.1037/pst0000152

Adedoyin, C., Burns, N., Jackson, H. M., & Franklin, S. (2014). Revisiting holistic interventions in substance abuse treatment. *Journal of Human Behavior in the Social Environment, 24*(5), 538–546. https://doi.org/10.1080/10911359.2014.914718

Ahmed, M. (2018). Rationale for the use of movement experience as adjunct to psychotherapy and counseling in working with clients across life spans. *International Society for Psychological and Social Approaches to Psychosis—US Chapter Newsletter, 17*(1), 8–10. http://www.isps-us.org/newsletters/ISPS-US-newsletter-s17-3.pdf

Ahmed, M., & Boisvert, C. M. (2013). *Mind stimulation therapy: Cognitive interventions for persons with schizophrenia*. Routledge/Taylor & Francis Group.

Ainsworth, B., Eddershaw, R., Meron, D., Baldwin, D., & Garner, M. (2013). The effect of focused attention and open monitoring meditation on attention network function in healthy volunteers. *Psychiatry Research, 210*(3), 1226–1231. https://doi.org/10.1016/j.psychres.2013.09.002

Ainsworth, M. D. S. (1991). Attachments and other affectional bonds across the life cycle. In C. M. Parkes, J. Stevenson-Hinde, & P. Marris (Eds.), *Attachment across the life cycle* (pp. 33–51). Tavistock/Routledge.

Allen, T. M., Wren, A. A., Anderson, L. M., Sabholk, A., & Mauro, C. F (2018). A group CBT-yoga protocol targeting pain-related and internalizing symptoms in youth. *Clinical Practice in Pediatric Psychology, 6*(1), 7–18. https://doi.org/10.1037/cpp0000206

Alt, S. R., Turner, J. D., Klok, M. D., Meijer, O. C., Lakke, E. A., Derijk, R. H., & Muller, C. P. (2010). Differential expression of glucocorticoid receptor transcripts in major depressive disorder is not epigenetically programmed. *Psychoneuroendocrinology, 35*(4), 544–556. https://doi.org/10.1016/j.psyneuen.2009.09.001

Alvarez, J. A., & Emory, E. (2006). Executive function and the frontal lobes: A meta-analytic review. *Neuropsychology Review, 16*(1), 17–42. doi:10.1007/s11065-006-9002-x

American College of Sports Medicine (ACSM). (2018). *ACSM's exercise testing and prescription* (10th ed.). Wolters Kluwer Health.

American College of Sports Medicine (ACSM). (n.d.a). *Exercise is medicine*. http://www.exerciseismedicine.org

American College of Sports Medicine (ACSM). (n.d.b). *Healthcare providers action guide*. https://www.exerciseismedicine.org/assets/page_documents/HCP_Action_Guide(5).pdf

American College of Sports Medicine (ACSM). (n.d.c). *Starting an exercise program*. https://exerciseismedicine.org/assets/page_documents/8_StartingExProgram.pdf

American College of Sports Medicine (ACSM). (n.d.d). *Your prescription for health*. https://www.exerciseismedicine.org/assets/page_documents/EIM%20Prescription%20pad%201-up.pdf

American Counseling Association. (2014). *ACA code of ethics*. Author.

American Counseling Association (ACA). (n.d.). *Mental health month*. https://www.counseling.org/events/mindandbodyfitness

American Mental Health Counselors Association. (2019). *What is a clinical mental health counselor?* https://www.amhca.org/about

American Psychiatric Association. (2013). *Diagnostic and statistical manual of mental disorders* (5th ed.). Author.

American Psychiatric Association. (n.d.). *Online assessment measures*. http://www.psychiatry.org/practice/dsm/dsm5/online-assessment-measures

American Psychological Association (APA). (2013a). *What is resilience?* http://www.apa.org/helpcenter/road-resilience.aspx

American Psychological Association (APA). (2013b). *How stress affects your health*. https://www.apa.org/helpcenter/stress.aspx

Amighi, J. K., Loman, S., Lewis, P., & Sossin, K. M. (1999). *The meaning of movement: Developmental and clinical perspectives of the Kestenberg Movement Profile*. Gordon and Breach Publishers.

Amir, T., Gati, I., & Kleiman, T. (2008). Understanding and interpreting career decision-making difficulties. *Journal of Career Assessment, 16*(3), 281–309. https://doi.org/10.1177/1069072708317367

Amodeo, L. R., McMurray, M. S., & Roitman, J. D. (2017). Orbitofrontal cortex reflects changes in response–outcome contingencies during probabilistic reversal learning. *Neuroscience*, 345, 27–37.

Anda, R. F., Felitti, V. J., Bremner, D. J., Walker, J. D., Whitfield, C., Perry, B. D., Dube, S. R., & Giles, W. H. (2006). The enduring effects of abuse and related adverse experiences in childhood: A convergence of evidence from neurobiology and epidemiology. *European Archives of Psychiatry and Clinical Neuroscience, 256*(3), 174–186. https://doi.org/10.1007/s00406-005-0624-4

Ansari, M., & Lark, L. (1999). *Yoga for beginners.* HarperCollins.

Aqel, S. I., Hampton, J. M., Bruss, M., Jones, K. T., Valiente, G. R., Wu, L., Young, M. cC., Willis, W. L., Ardoin, S., Agarwal, S., Bolon, B., Powell, N., Sheridan, J., Schlesinger, N., & Jarjour, W. N., & Young, N. A. (2017). Daily moderate exercise is beneficial and social stress is detrimental to disease pathology in murine lupus nephritis. *Frontiers in Physiology, 8*(236). https://doi.org/10.3389/fphys.2017.00236

Archibald, S. L., Fennema-Notestine, C., Gamst, A., Riley, E. P., Mattson, S. N., & Jernigan, T. L. (2001). Brain dysmorphology in individuals with severe prenatal alcohol exposure. *Developmental Medicine and Child Neurology, 43*(3), 148–154. https://doi.org/10.1017/S0012162201000299

Armour, J. A. (2008). Potential clinical relevance of the "little brain"on the mammalian heart. *Experimental Physiology, 93,* 165–176. https://doi.org/10.1113/expphysiol.2007.041178

Arnsten, A. F. T. (2009). Stress signaling pathways that impair prefrontal cortex structure and function. *Nature Reviews Neuroscience, 10*(6), 410–422. https://doi.org/10.1038/nrn2648

Arnsten, A. F. T., Raskind, M. A., Taylor, F. B., & Connor, D. F. (2015). The effects of stress exposure on prefrontal cortex: Translating basic research into successful treatments for post-traumatic stress disorder. *Neurobiology of Stress, 1,* 89–99. https://doi.org/10.1016/j.ynstr.2014.10.002

Arpawong, T. E., Rohrbach, L. A., Milam, J. E., Unger, J. B., Land, H., Sun, P., Spruijt-Metz, D., & Sussman, S. (2017). Stressful life events and predictors of post-traumatic growth among high-risk early emerging adults. *Journal of Postiive Psychology, 11*(1), 1–14. https://doi.org/10.1080/17439760.2014.994223

Association for Play Therapy (n.d). *Guidelines.* https://www.a4pt.org/page/ClarifyingUseofPT

Astley, S. J., Aylward, E. H., Olson, H. C., Kerns, K., Brooks, A., Coggins, T. E., Davies, J., Dorn, S., Gendler, B., Jirikowic, T., Kraegel, P., Maravilla, K., & Richards, T. (2009a). Magnetic resonance imaging outcomes from a comprehensive magnetic resonance study of children with fetal alcohol spectrum disorders. *Alcoholism: Clinical and Experimental Research, 33*(10), 1671–1689. https://doi.org/10.1111/j.1530-0277.2009.01004.x

Astley, S. J., Richards, T., Aylward, E. H., Olson, H. C., Kerns, K., Brooks, A., Coggins, T. E., Davies, J., Dorn, S., Gendler, B., & Jirikowic, T., Kraegel, P., Maravilla, K., & Richards, T. (2009b). Magnetic resonance spectroscopy outcomes from a comprehensive magnetic resonance study of children with fetal alcohol spectrum disorders. *Magnetic Resonance Imaging, 27*(6), 760–778. https://doi.org/10.1016/j.mri.2009.01.003

Aston-Jones, G., & Cohen, J. D. (2005). An integrative theory of locus coeruleus norepinephrine function: Adaptive gain and optimal performance. *Annual Review of Neuroscience, 28,* 403–450. https://doi.org/10.1146/annurev.neuro.28.061604.135709

Baars, B. J., & Gage, N. M. (2010). *Cognition, brain, and consciousness: Introduction to cognitive neuroscience* (2nd ed.). Elsevier Academic Press.

Baddeley, A., Eysenck, M. W., & Anderson, M. C. (2009). *Memory.* Psychology Press.

Badenoch, B. (2008). *Being a brain-wise therapist: A practical guide to interpersonal neurobiology.* W. W. Norton & Company.

Badenoch, B. (2018). *The heart of trauma: Healing the embodied brain in the context of relationships.* W. W. Norton & Company.

Baker, L. M. (2009). Nature's pervading influence: A therapy of growth. *International Journal of Disability, Development And Education, 56*(1), 93–96. https://doi.org/10.1080/10349120802682091

Baker, P. M., Raynor, S. A., Francis, N. T., & Mizumori, S. J. Y. (2017). Lateral habenula integration of proactive and retroactive information mediates behavioral flexibility. *Neuroscience,* 345, 89–98.

Balasubramaniam, M., Telles, S., & Doraiswamy, P. M. (2013). Yoga on our minds: A systematic review of yoga for neuropsychiatric disorders. *Frontiers in Psychiatry, 3,* 117. https://doi.org/10.3389/fpsyt.2012.00117

Ball, A., Iachini, A. L., Bohnenkamp, J. H., Togno, N. M., Brown, E. L., Hoffman, J. A., & George, M. W. (2016). School mental health content in state in-service K–12 teaching standards in the United States. *Teaching and Teacher Education, 60,* 312–320. https://doi.org/10.1016/j.tate.2016.08.020

Banich, M. T. (2009). Executive function the search for an integrated account. *Current Directions in Psychological Science, 18*(2), 89–94. doi:10.1111/j.1467-8721.2009.01615.x

Bao, S., Chan, V. T., & Merzenich, M. M. (2001). Cortical remodelling induced by activity of ventral tegmental dopamine neurons. *Nature, 412*(6842), 79–83. https://doi.org/10.1038/35083586

Barbas, H., & Zikopoulos, B. (2007). The prefrontal cortex and flexible behavior. *Neuroscientist, 13*(5), 532–545. https://doi.org/10.1177/1073858407301369

Barlow, J. S. (2009). *The cerebellum and adaptive control.* Cambridge University Press. https://doi.org/10.1017/CBO9780511529771

Barnett, S. A., & Cowan, P. E. (1976). Activity, exploration, curiosity and fear: An ethological study. *Interdisciplinary Science Reviews, 1*(1), 43–62. https://doi.org/10.1179/030801876789768534

Baron-Cohen S., Leslie, A. M., & Frith, U. (1985). Does the autistic child have a 'theory of mind'? *Cognition, 21*(1), 37–46. https://doi.org/10.1016/0010-0277(85)90022-8

Baron-Cohen, S., Ring, H. A., Bullmore, E. T., Wheelwright, S., Ashwin, C., & Williams, S. C. R. (2000). The amygdala theory of autism. *Neuroscience and Biobehavioral Reviews, 24*(3), 355–364. https://doi.org/10.1016/S0149-7634(00)00011-7

Baron-Cohen, S., Tager-Flusberg, H., & Lombardo, M.V. (2013). *Understanding other minds: Perspectives form developmental social neuroscience* (3rd ed.). Oxford University Press.

Barrett, L. F. (2017). *How emotions are made: The secret life of the brain.* Houghton Mifflin Harcourt.

Barrett, L. F., Lewis, M., & Haviland-Jones, J. M. (Eds.). (2016). *The handbook of emotions* (4th ed.). Guilford Press.

Barrus, M. M., Hosking, J. G., Cocker, P. J., & Winstanley, C. A. (2017). Inactivation of the orbitofrontal cortex reduces irrational choice on a rodent betting task. *Neuroscience*, 345, 38–48.

Bartenieff, I., & Lewis, D. (2002). *Body movement: Coping with the environment.* Routledge.

Bassett, D. S., & Gazzaniga, M. S. (2011). Understanding complexity in the human brain. *Trends in Cognitive Science*, *15*(5), 200–209. https://doi.org/10.1016/j.tics.2011.03.006

Bava, S., & Tapert, S. (2010). Adolescent brain development and the risk for alcohol and other drug problems. *Neuropsychology Review*, *20*(4), 398–413. https://doi.org/10.1007/s11065-010-9146-6

Bear, M. F., Connors, B. W., & Paradiso, M. A. (2016). *Neuroscience: Exploring the brain* (4th ed.). Lippincott, Williams, & Wilkins Publishers.

Beck, L., Kumschick, I. R., Eid, M., & Klann-Delius, G. (2012). Relationship between language competence and emotional competence in middle childhood. *Emotion*, *12*(3), 503–514. https://doi.org/10.1037/a0026320

Beckes L., & Coan J. A. (2011). Social baseline theory: The role of social proximity in emotion and economy of action. *Social and Personality Psychology Compass*, *5*(12), 976–988. https://doi.org/10.1111/j.1751-9004.2011.00400.x

Beeson, E. T., & Field, T. A. (2017). Neurocounseling: A new section of the Journal of Mental Health Counseling. *Journal of Mental Health Counseling*, *39*(1), 71–83. https://doi.org/10.17744/mehc.39.1.06

Beeson, E. T., Field, T. A., Reckner, J. L., Luke, C., & Jones, L. K. (2019). Neuroscience research, training, and practice: Adding to or subtracting from counselor identity? *Journal of Counselor Leadership and Advocacy*, *6*(2), 97–113. https://doi.org/10.1080/2326716X.2019.1617210

Beeson, E. T., Kim, S. R., Zalaquett, C. P., & Fonseca, F. (2019). Neuroscience attitudes, exposure, and knowledge among counselors. *Teaching and Supervision in Counseling*, *1*(2), 1–19. https://doi.org/10.7290/tsc010201

Beggs, S., Liu, X. J., Kwan, C., & Salter, M. W. (2010). Peripheral nerve injury and TRPV1-expressing primary afferent C-fibers cause opening of the blood-brain barrier. *Molecular Pain*, *6*(74). https://doi.org/10.1186/1744-8069-6-74

Bellini, S. (2006). *Building social relationships: A systematic approach to teaching social interactions skills to children and adolescents with autism spectrum disorders and other social difficulties.* Autism Asperger Publishing Company.

Bellini, S., Peters, J. K., Benner, L., & Hopf, A. (2007). A meta-analysis of school-based social skills interventions for children with autism spectrum disorders. *Remedial and Special Education*, *28*(3), 153–162. https://doi.org/10.1177/07419325070280030401

Belmaker, R. H., & Agam, G. (2008). Mechanisms of disease: Major depressive disorder. *New England Journal of Medicine*, *358*(1), 55–68. https://doi.org/10.1056/NEJMra073096

Berg, M., & Sarnyai, Z. (2015). "More than skin deep": Stress neurobiology and mental health consequences of racial discrimination. *Stress: The International Journal on the Biology of Stress*, *18*(1), 1–10. https://doi.org/10.3109/10253890.2014.989294

Bernatzky, G., Presch, M., Anderson, M., & Panksepp, J. (2011). Emotional foundations of music as a non-pharmacological pain management tool in modern medicine. *Neuroscience and Biobehavioral Reviews*, *35*(9), 1989–1999. https://doi.org/10.1016/j.neubiorev.2011.06.005

Bicknell-Hentges, L., & Lynch, J. J. (2009, March). *Everything counselors and supervisors need to know about treating trauma* [Paper presentation]. American Counseling Association Annual Conference and Exposition, Charlotte, NC, United States.

Bingaman, K. A. (2011). The art of contemplative and mindfulness practice: Incorporating the findings of neuroscience into pastoral care and counseling. *Pastoral Psychology*, *60*(3), 477–489. https://doi.org/10.1007/s11089-011-0328-9

Bing-Canar, H., Pizzuto, J., & Compton, R. J. (2016). Mindfulness-of-breathing exercise modulates EEG alpha activity during cognitive performance. *Psychophysiology*, *53*(9), 1366–1376. https://doi.org/10.1111/psyp.12678

Bink, M., van Nieuwenhuizen, C., Popma, A., Bongers, I. L., & van Boxtel, G. J. M. (2015). Behavioral effects of neurofeedback in adolescents with ADHD: A randomized controlled trial. *European Child & Adolescent Psychiatry*, *24*(9), 1035–1048. https://doi.org/10.1007/s00787-014-0655-3

Birmaher, B., Arbelaez, C., & Brent, D. (2002). Course and outcome of child and adolescent major depressive disorder. *Child and Adolescent Psychiatric Clinics of North America*, *11*(3), 619–638. https://doi.org/10.1016/S1056-4993(02)00011-1

Bisby, J. A., Horner, A. J., Bush, D., & Burgess, N. (2018). Negative emotional content disrupts the coherence of episodic memories. *Journal of Experimental Psychology: General*, *147*(2), 243–256. https://doi.org/10.1037/xge0000356

Bishop, W., & Fish, J. M. (1999). Questions as interventions: Perceptions of Socratic, solution-focused, and diagnostic questioning styles. *Journal of Rational-Emotive & Cognitive-Behavior Therapy*, *17*(2), 115–140. https://doi.org/10.1023/A:1023005015329

Bissonette, G. B., & Roesch, M. R. (2017). Neurophysiology of rule switching in the corticostriatal circuit. *Neuroscience*, 345, 64–76.

Blom, E. H., Duncan, L. G., Ho, T. C., Connolly, C. G., LeWinn, K. Z., Chesney, M., Hecht, F., & Yang, T. T. (2014). The development of an RDoC-based treatment program for adolescent depression: 'Training for awareness, resilience, and action' (TARA). *Frontiers in Human Neuroscience*, *8*, 630. https://doi.org/10.3389/fnhum.2014.00630

Blom, E. H., Tymofiyeva, O., Chesney, M. A., Ho, T. C., Moran, P., Connolly, C. G., Duncan, L G., Baldini, L., Weng, H. Y., Acree, M., Goldman, V., & Yang, T. T. (2017). Feasibility and preliminary efficacy of a novel RDoC-based treatment program for adolescent depression: 'Training for awareness resilience and action' (TARA)—a pilot study. *Frontiers in Psychiatry*, *7*, 208. https://doi.org/10.3389/fpsyt.2016.00208

Blood, A. J., & Zatorre, R. J. (2001). Intensely pleasurable responses to music correlate with activity in brain regions implicated in reward and emotion. *Proceedings of the National Academy of Sciences of the United States of America, 98*(20), 11818–11823. https://doi.org/10.1073/pnas.191355898

Boening, M., Southwell, C., & Westland, G. (2012). *Body psychotherapy competencies.* https://www.eabp.org/forum-body-psychotherapy-competencies.php

Bogels, S., Hoogstad, B., van Dun, L., de Schutter, S., & Restifo, K. (2008). Mindfulness training for adolescents with externalizing disorders and their parents. *Behavioural and Cognitive Psychotherapy, 36*(2), 193–209. https://doi.org/10.1017/S1352465808004190

Boisvert, C. M., & Ahmed, M. (2018). *Using diagrams in psychotherapy: A guide to visually enhanced therapy.* Routledge.

Boon, S., Steele, K., & van der Hart, O. (2011). *Coping with trauma-related dissociation: Skills training for patients and therapists.* W. W. Norton & Company.

Bora, E., & Pantelis, C. (2016). Meta-analysis of social cognition in attention-deficit/hyperactivity disorder (ADHD): Comparison with healthy controls and autistic spectrum disorder. *Psychological Medicine, 46*(4), 699–716. https://doi.org/10.1017/S0033291715002573

Borre, Y. E., O'Keeffe, G. W., Clarke, G., Stanton, C., Dinan, T. G., & Cryan, J. F. (2014). Microbiota and neurodevelopmental windows: Implications for brain disorders. *Trends in Molecular Medicine, 20*(9), 509–18. https://doi.org/10.1016/j.molmed.2014.05.002

Boswell, J. F., Farchione, T. J., Sauer-Zavala, S., Murray, H. W., Fortune, M. R., & Barlow, D. H. (2013). Anxiety sensitivity and interoceptive exposure: A transdiagnostic construct and change strategy. *Behavior Therapy, 44*(3), 417–431. https://doi.org/10.1016/j.beth.2013.03.006

Bott, N. T., Radke, A. E., & Kiely, T. (2016). Ethical issues surrounding psychologists' use of neuroscience in the promotion and practice of psychotherapy. *Professional Psychology: Research and Practice, 47*(5), 321–329. https://doi.org/10.1037/pro0000103

Bowen, S., Chawla, N., & Marlatt, G. A. (2011). *Mindfulness-based relapse prevention for addictive behaviors: A clinician's guide.* Guilford Press.

Bowlby, J. (1982). Attachment and loss: Retrospect and prospect. *American Journal of Orthopsychiatry, 52*(4), 664–678. https://doi.org/10.1111/j.1939-0025.1982.tb01456.x

Bowlby, J. (1988). *A secure base: Clinical applications of attachment theory.* Routledge.

Boyson, G. A. (2009). A review of experimental studies of explicit and implicit bias among counselors. *Journal of Multicultural Counseling & Development, 37*(4), 240–249. https://doi.org/10.1002/j.2161-1912.2009.tb00106.x

Brass, M., Schmitt, R. M., Spengler, S., & Gergely, G. (2007). Investigating action understanding: Inferential processes versus action simulation. *Current Biology, 17*(24), 2117–2121. https://doi.org/10.1016/j.cub.2007.11.057

Bratton, S. C., Landreth, G. L., Kellam, T., & Blackard, S. R. (2006). *Child parent relationship therapy (CPRT) treatment manual: A 10-session filial therapy model for training parents.* Routledge/Taylor and Francis Group.

Bridges, M. R. (2006). Activating the corrective emotional experience. *Journal of Clinical Psychology, 62*(5), 551–568. https://doi.org/10.1002/jclp.20248

Briere, J., & Scott, C. (2006). *Principles of trauma therapy: A guide to symptoms, evaluation, and treatment.* Sage Publications.

Brom, D., Stokar, Y, Lawi, C, Nuriel-Porat, V., Ziv, Y., Lerner, K., & Ross, G. (2017). Somatic experiencing for posttraumatic stress disorder: A randomized controlled outcome study. *Journal of Traumatic Stress, 30*(3), 304–312. https://doi.org/10.1002/jts.22189

Brooks, K. P., Gruenewald, T., Karlamangla, A., Hu, P., Koretz, B., & Seeman, T. E. (2014). Social relationships and allostatic load in the MIDUS study. *Health Psychology, 33*(11), 1373–1381. https://doi.org/10.1037/a0034528

Brown, K., & Stanforth, D. (2017). Go green with outdoor activity. *ACSM's Health & Fitness Journal, 21*(1), 10–15. https://doi.org/10.1249/FIT.0000000000000264

Brown, K. W., & Ryan, R. M. (2003). The benefits of being present: Mindfulness and its role in psychological wellbeing. *Journal of Personality and. Social Psychology, 84*(4), 822–848. https://doi.org/10.1037/0022-3514.84.4.822

Brown, K. W., Ryan, R. M., & Creswell, J. D. (2007). Mindfulness: Theoretical foundations and evidence for its salutary effects. *Psychological Inquiry, 18*(4), 211–237. https://doi.org/10.1080/10478400701598298

Brown, R. P., Gerbarg, P. L., & Muench, F. (2013). Breathing practices for treatment of psychiatric and stress-related medical conditions. *Psychiatric Clinics of North America, 36*(1), 121–140. https://doi.org/10.1016/j.psc.2013.01.001

Brunoni, A. R., Sampaio-Junior, B., Moffa, A. H., Aparício, L. V., Gordon, P., Klein, I., Rios, R. M., Razza, L. B., Loo, C., Padberg, F., & Valiengo, L. (2019). Noninvasive brain stimulation in psychiatric disorders: A primer. *Brazilian Journal of Psychiatry, 41*(1), 70–81. https://doi.org/10.1590/1516-4446-2017-0018

Bryan, C. J., Rudd, M. D., & Wertenberger, E. (2013). Reasons for suicide attempts in a clinical sample of active duty soldiers. *Journal of Affective Disorders, 144*(1–2), 148–152. https://doi.org/10.1016/j.jad.2012.06.030

Budde, H., Velasques, B., Ribeiro, P., Machado, S., Emeljanovas, A., Kamandulis, S., Skurvydas, A., & Wegner, M. (2018). Does intensity or youth affect the neurobiological effect of exercise on major depressive disorder? *Neuroscience & Biobehavioral Reviews,84*, 492–494. https://doi.org/10.1016/j.neubiorev.2016.09.026

Budzynski, T. H., Budzynski, H. K., Evans, J. R., & Abarbanel, A. (Eds.) (2009). *Introduction to quantitative EEG and neurofeedback: Advanced theory and applications* (2nd ed.). Academic Press.

Buhle, J. T., Silvers, J. A., Wage, T. D., Lopez, R., Onyemekwu, C., Kober, H., Weber, J., & Oschner, K. N. (2014). Cognitive reappraisal of emotion: A meta-analysis of human neuroimaging studies. *Cerebral Cortex, 24*(11), 2981–2990. https://doi.org/10.1093/cercor/bht154

Bullock-Yowell, E., Peterson, G. W., Reardon, R. C., Leierer, S. J., & Reed, C. A. (2011). Relationships among career and life stress, negative career thoughts, and career decision state: A cognitive information processing perspective. *Career Development Quarterly, 59*(4), 302–314. https://doi.org/10.1002/j.2161-0045.2011.tb00071.x

Busch, V., Magerl, W., Kern, U., Haas, J., Hajak, G., & Eichhammer, P. (2012). The effect of deep and slow breathing on pain perception, autonomic activity, and mood processing—an experimental study. *Pain Medicine*, *13*(2), 215–228. https://doi.org/10.1111/j.1526-4637.2011.01243.x

Butler, A. B., & Hodos, W. (2005). *Comparative vertebrate neuroanatomy. Evolution and adaptation* (2nd ed.). John Wiley & Sons.

Butler, D. S., & Moseley, G. L. (2003). *Explain pain*. Noigroup Publications.

Buzsaki, G., & Gage, F. H. (1989). The cholinergic nucleus basalis: A key structure in neocortical arousal. *Experientia Supplementum*, *57*, 159–171.

Cabral, P., Meyer, H. B., & Ames, D. (2011). Effectiveness of yoga therapy as a complementary treatment for major psychiatric disorders: A meta-analysis. *Primary Care Companion for CNS Disorders*, *13*(4). https://doi.org/10.4088/PCC.10r01068

Cacciaglia, R., Nees, F., Grimm, O., Ridder, S., Pohlack, S. T., Diener, S. J., Liebscher, C., & Flor, H. (2017). Trauma exposure relates to heightened stress, altered amygdala morphology and deficient extinction learning: Implications for psychopathology. *Psychoneuroendocrinology*, *76*, 19–28. https://doi.org/10.1016/j.psyneuen.2016.11.012

Cadman, B. (2018, January 17). Dopamine deficiency: Symptoms, causes, and treatment. https://www.medicalnewstoday.com/articles/320637.php

Caldwell, C., & Koch, S. C. (2018). Working with embodied memory: The moving cycle as a phenomenological body psychotherapy method. *Journal of Consciousness Studies*, *25*(7–8), 242–255.

Campbell, M. E. J., & Cunnington, R. (2017). More than an imitation game: Top-down modulation of the human mirror system. *Neuroscience and Biobehavioral Reviews*, *75*, 95–102. https://doi.org/10.1016/j.neubiorev.2017.01.035

Campbell, M. E. J., Mehrkanoon, S., & Cunnington, R. (2018). Intentionally not imitating: Insula cortex engaged from top-down control of action mirroring. *Neuropsychologia*, *111*, 241–251. https://doi.org/10.1016/j.neuropsychologia.2018.01.037

Canbeyli, R. (2013). Sensorimotor modulation of mood and depression: In search of an optimal mode of stimulation. *Frontiers in Human Neuroscience*, *7*, 428. https://doi.org/10.3389/fnhum.2013.00428

Cann, A., Calhoun, L. G., Tedeschi, R. G., Taku, K., Vishnevsky, T., Triplett, K. N., & Danhauer, S. C. (2010). A short form of the Posttraumatic Growth Inventory. *Anxiety Stress Coping*, *23*, 127–37.

Cannon, W. B. (1963). *The wisdom of the body*. Norton & Company, Inc.

Carabotti, M., Scirocco, A., Maselli, M.A., & Severi, C. (2015). The gut-brain axis: Interactions between enteric microbiota, central and enteric nervous systems. *Annals of Gasteroenterology*, *28*(2), 203–209.

Carlson, N. R. (2013). *Foundations of behavioral neuroscience* (9th ed.). Pearson.

Carr, G. V., Maltese, F., Sibley, D. R., Weinberger, D. R., & Papaleo, F. (2017). The dopamine D5 receptor is involved in working memory. *Frontiers in Pharmacology*, *8*, 666. https://doi.org/10.3389/fphar.2017.00666

Carr, L., Iacoboni, M., Dubeau, M. C., Mazziotta, J. C., & Lenzi, G. L. (2003). Neural mechanisms of empathy in humans: A relay from neural systems for imitation to limbic areas. *Proceedings of the National Academy of Sciences of the United States of America*, *100*(9), 5497–5502. https://doi.org/10.1073/pnas.0935845100

Carson, D. K., & Becker, K. W. (2004). When lightning strikes: Reexamining creativity in psychotherapy. *Journal of Counseling and Development*, *82*(1), 111–115. https://doi.org/10.1002/j.1556-6678.2004.tb00292.

Casa, B. L., Negi, N. J., & Hong, M. (2012). Culturally competent social work research: Methodological considerations for research with language minorities. *Social Work*, *57*(1), 1–10. doi:10.1093/sw/swr002

Caspersen, C. J., Powell, K. E., & Christenson, G. M. (1985). Physical activity, exercise, and physical fitness: Definitions and distractions for health-related research. *Public Health Reports*, *100*(2), 126–131.

Cassilhas, R. C., Lee, K. S., Fernandes, J., Oliveira, M. G., Tufik, S., Meeusen, R., & de Mello, M. T. (2012). Spatial memory is improved by aerobic and resistance exercise through divergent molecular mechanisms. *Neuroscience*, *202*, 309–317. https://doi.org/10.1016/j.neuroscience.2011.11.029

Catmur, C., Walsh, V., & Heyes, C. (2007). Sensorimotor learning configures the human mirror system. *Current Biology*, *17*(17), 1527–1531. https://doi.org/10.1016/j.cub.2007.08.006

Catmur, C., Walsh, V., & Heyes, C. M. (2009). Associative sequence learning: The role of experience in the development of imitation and the mirror system. *Philosophical Transactions of the Royal Society of London, Series B: Biological Sciences*, *364*(1528), 2369–2380. https://doi.org/10.1098/rstb.2009.0048

Centers for Disease Control and Prevention (CDC). (2016). *Prevention status reports: National summary*. US Department of Health and Human Services. https://wwwn.cdc.gov/psr/NationalSummary/NationalSummary.aspx

Chalah, M. A., & Ayache, S. S. (2019). Noninvasive brain stimulation and psychotherapy in anxiety and depressive disorders: A viewpoint. *Brain Sciences*, *9*(4), 82. https://doi.org/10.3390/brainsci9040082

Chanda, M. L., & Levitin, D. J. (2013). The neurochemistry of music. *Trends in Cognitive Sciences*, *17*(4), 179–193. https://doi.org/10.1016/j.tics.2013.02.007

Chandiramani, K. & Tripathi, B.M. (1993). Psychoeducational group therapy for alcohol and drug dependence recovery. *Indian Journal of Psychiatry, 35(3)*, 169–172.

Chao, L., Weiner, M., & Neylan, T. (2013). Regional cerebral volumes in veterans with current versus remitted posttraumatic stress disorder. *Psychiatry Research*, *213*(3), 193–201.

Chapin, T. J. (2017). Wellness and optimal performance. In T. A. Field, L. K. Jones, & L. A. Russell-Chapin (Eds.), *Neurocounseling: Brain based clinical approaches* (pp. 133–146). American Counseling Association.

Chapin, T. J., & Russell-Chapin, L. A. (2014). *Neurotherapy and neurofeedback: Brain-based treatment for psychological and behavioral problems*. Routledge/Taylor & Francis Group.

Chen, K. W., Berger, C. C., Manheimer, E., Forde, D., Magidson, J., Dachman, L., & Lejuez, C. W. (2012). Meditative therapies for reducing anxiety: A systematic review and meta-analysis of randomized controlled trials. *Depression and Anxiety, 29*(7), 545–562. https://doi.org/10.1002/da.21964

Chen, M., & Lacey, R. E. (2018). Adverse childhood experiences and adult inflammation: Findings from the 1958 British birth cohort. *Brain, Behavior, and Immunity, 69*, 582–590. doi: 10.1016/j.bbi.2018.02.007.

Choi, E. J., Taylor, M. J., Hong, S. B., Kim, C., & Yi, S. H. (2018). The neural correlates of attachment security in typically developing children. *Brain and Cognition, 124*, 47–56. https://doi.org/ 10.1016/j.bandc.2018.04.003

Chrobak, A. A., Nowakowski, J., & Dudek, D. (2016). Interactions between the gut microbiome and the central nervous system and their role in schizophrenia, bipolar disorder, and depression. *Archives of Psychiatry and Psychotherapy, 18*(2), 5–11. https://doi.org/10.12740/APP/62962

Clark-Polner, E., Wager, T. D., Satpute, A. B., & Barrett L. F. (2016). Neural fingerprinting: Meta-analysis, variation, and the search for brain-based essences in the science of emotion. In L. F. Barrett, M. Lewis, & J. M. Haviland-Jones (Eds.), *Handbook of emotions* (4th ed., pp. 146–165). Guilford Press.

Clements, C. C., Zoltowski, A. R., Yankowitz, L. D., Yerys, B. E., Schultz, R. T., & Herrington, J. D. (2018). Evaluation of the social motivation hypothesis of autism: A systematic review and meta-analysis. *JAMA Psychiatry, 75*(8), 797–808. https://doi.org/10.1001/jamapsychiatry.2018.1100

Coan, J. A., Schaefer, H. S., & Davidson, R. J. (2006). Lending a hand: Social regulation of the neural response to threat. *Psychological Science, 17*(12), 1032–1039. https://doi.org/10.1111/j.1467-9280.2006.01832.x

Conners, C. K., Erhardt, D., & Sparrow, E. P. (1999). *Conners' Adult ADHD Rating Scales (CAARS): Technical manual.* Multi-Health Systems, Inc.

Connor, K. M. & Davidson, J. R.T. (2003). Development of a new resilience scale: The Connor-Davidson resilience scale (CD-RISC). *Depression and Anxiety, 18*, 76–82. https://doi.org/10.1002/da.10113

Corbett, B. A., Constantine, L. J., Hendren, R., Rocke, D., & Ozonoff, S. (2009). Examining executive functioning in children with autism spectrum disorder, attention deficit hyperactivity disorder and typical development. *Psychiatry Research, 166*(2–3), 210–222. https://doi.org/10.1016/j.psychres.2008.02.005

Cotman, C. W., & Berchtold, N. C. (2002). Exercise: A behavioral intervention to enhance brain health and plasticity. *Trends in Neurosciences, 25*(6), 295–301. https://doi.org/10.1016/S0166-2236(02)02143-4

Coutinho, J. F., Perrone-McGovern, K. M., & Gonçalves, O. F. (2017). The use of neuroimaging methodology in counselling psychology research: Promises, pitfalls, and recommendations. *Canadian Journal of Counselling and Psychotherapy, 51*(4), 327–348.

Coutinho, J. F., Silva, P. O., & Decety, J. (2014). Neurosciences, empathy, and healthy interpersonal relationships: Recent findings and implications for counseling psychology. *Journal of Counseling Psychology, 61*(4), 541–548. https://doi.org/10.1037/cou0000021

Covey, S. (2008). Foreward. In A. L. Pattakos (Ed.), *Prisoners of our thoughts: Viktor Frankl's principles for discovering meaning in life and work* (2nd ed.). Berrett-Koehler Publishers, Inc.

Cozolino, L. (2014). *The neuroscience of human relationships* (2nd ed.). W. W. Norton & Company, Inc.

Cozolino, L. J. (2010). *The neuroscience of psychotherapy: Healing the social brain* (2nd ed.). W. W. Norton & Company, Inc.

Cozolino, L., & Sprokay, S. (2006). Neuroscience and adult learning. *New Directions for Adult & Continuing Education, 110*, 11–19. https://doi.org/10.1002/ace.214

Craft, L. L., & Perna, F. M. (2004). The benefits of exercise for the clinically depressed. *Primary Care Companion to the Journal of Clinical Psychiatry, 06*(03), 104–111. https://doi.org/10.4088/pcc.v06n0301

Cramer, S. C., Sur, M., Dobkin, B. H., O'Brien, C., Sanger, T. D., Trojanowski, J. Q., . . . Vinogradov, S. (2011). Harnessing neuroplasticity for clinical applications. *Brain: A Journal of Neurology, 134*(6), 1591–1609. https://doi.org/10.1093/brain/awr039

Crenshaw, K. (1989). Demarginalizing the intersection of race and sex: A black feminist critique of antidiscrimination doctrine, feminist theory and antiracist politics. *University of Chicago Legal Forum, 1*, 8. https://chicagounbound.uchicago.edu/uclf/vol1989/iss1/8

Crenshaw, K. (1991). Mapping the margins: Intersectionality, identity politics, and violence against women of color. *Stanford Law Review, 43*(6), 1241–1299. https://doi.org/10.2307/1229039

Crockett, J. E., Gill, D. L., Cashwell, T. H., & Myers, J. E. (2017). Integrating non-technological and technological peripheral biofeedback in counseling. *Journal of Mental Health Counseling, 39*(2), 163–179. https://doi.org/10.17744/mehc.39.2.06

Crum, A. J., Akinola, M., Martin, A., & Faith, S. (2017). The role of stress mindset in shaping cognitive, emotional, and physiological responses to challenging and threatening stress. *Anxiety, Stress & Coping: An International Journal, 30*(4), 379–395. https://doi.org/10.1080/10615806.2016.1275585

Crum, A. J., Salovey, P., & Achor, S. (2013). Rethinking stress: The role of mindsets in determining the stress response. *Journal of Personality and Social Psychology, 104*(4), 716–733. https://doi.org/10.1037/a0031201

Cuthbert, B. N., & Insel, T. R. (2013). Toward the future of psychiatric diagnosis: The seven pillars of RDoC. *BMC Medicine, 11*, 126. https://doi.org/10.1186/1741-7015-11-126

Czamanski-Cohen, J., & Weihs, K. (2016). A bio-behavioural model for the conduct of the mechanistic study of art therapy. *Psycho-Oncology, 25*(SP. S3), 29.

Dahlitz, M. (2017). *The psychotherapist's essential guide to the brain.* Dahlitz Media.

Dale, L. P., Shaikh, S. K., Fasciano, L. C., Watorek, V. D., Heilman, K. J., & Porges, S. W. (2018). College females with maltreatment histories have atypical autonomic regulation and poor psychological wellbeing. *Psychological Trauma: Theory, Research, Practice, and Policy, 10*(4), 427–434. https://doi.org/10.1037/tra0000342

Damasio, A., & Carvalho, G. B. (2013). The nature of feelings: Evolutionary and neurobiological origins. *Nature Reviews Neuroscience, 14*(2), 143–152. https://doi.org/10.1038/nrn3403

Damasio, A., Damasio, H., & Tranel, D. (2012). Persistence of feelings and sentience after bilateral damage of the insula. *Cerebral Cortex, 23*(4), 833–846.

D'Andrea, W., Pole, N., & DePierro, J. (2013). Heterogeneity of defensive responses after exposure to trauma: Blunted autonomic reactivity in response to startling sounds. *International Journal of Psychophysiology, 90*(1), 80–89.

Dapretto, M., Davies, M. S., Pfeifer, J. H., Scott, A. A., Sigman, M., Bookheimer, S. Y., & Iacoboni, M. (2006). Understanding emotions in others: Mirror neuron dysfunction in children with autism spectrum disorders. *Nature Neuroscience, 9*(1), 28–30. https://doi.org/10.1038/nn1611

D'Arrigo, C. (n.d.) *Seven standing beginner yoga poses to increase strength and flexibility.* https://www.yogiapproved.com/yoga/standing-beginner-yoga-poses/

Davidson, R. J., & Begley, S. (2012). *The emotional life of your brain.* Plume.

Davidson, R. J., & McEwen, B. S. (2012). Social influences on neuroplasticity: Stress and interventions to promote well-being. *Nature Neuroscience, 15*(5), 689–695. https://doi.org/10.1038/nn.3093

Davis, W. T., Campbell, L., Tax, J., & Lieber, C. S. (2002). A trial of "standard" outpatient alcoholism vs. a minimal treatment control. *Journal of Substance Abuse Treatment, 23*(1), 9–19.

Davis, D. E., DeBlare, C., Owen, J., Hook, J. N., Rivera, D. P., Choe, E., Van Tongeren, D., Worthington Jr., E. L., & Placeres, V. (2018). The multicultural orientation framework: A narrative review. *Psychotherapy, 55*(1), 89–100. https://doi.org/10.1037/pst0000160.supp

Dawson, P., & Guare, R. (2018). *Executive skills in children and adolescents: A practical guide to assessment and intervention* (3rd ed.). Guilford Press.

Dayan, P., & Balleine, B. W. (2002). Reward, motivation, and reinforcement learning. *Neuron, 36*(2), 285–298. https://doi.org/10.1016/s0896-6273(02)00963-7

Dell, P., & O'Neil, J. (2009). *Dissociation and the dissociative disorders: DSM-V and beyond.* Routledge.

Desbonnet, L., Clarke, G., Shanahan, F., Dinan, T. G., & Cryan, J. F. (2014). Microbiota is essential for social development in the mouse. *Molecular Psychiatry, 19*(2), 146–148. https://doi.org/10.1038/mp.2013.65

Descartes, R. (1984). *Principles of philosophy.* Springer.

Deslandes, A., Moraes, H., Ferreira, C., Veiga, H., Silveira, H., Mouta, R., Pompeu, F. A., Coutinho, E. S., & Laks, J. (2009). Exercise and mental health: Many reasons to move. *Neuropsychobiology, 59*(4), 191–198. https://doi.org/10.1159/000223730

de Waal, F. B. M., & Preston, S. D. (2017). Mammalian empathy: Behavioural manifestations and neural basis. *Nature Reviews Neuroscience, 18*(8), 498–509. https://doi.org/10.1038/nrn.2017.72

Diamond, D. M., Campbell, A. M., Park, C. R., Halonen, J., & Zoladz, P. R. (2007). The temporal dynamics model of emotional memory processing: A synthesis on the neurobiological basis of stress-induced amnesia, flashbulb and traumatic memories, and the Yerkes-Dodson Law. *Neural Plasticity, 2007*(60803). https://doi.org/10.1155/2007/60803

Diamond, D., Fleshner, M., & Rose, G. (1994). Psychological stress repeatedly blocks hippocampal primed burst potentiation in behaving rats. *Behavioural Brain Research, 62*(1), 1–9. doi: 10.1016/0166-4328(94)90032-9

Dickson, P. E., Cairns, J., Goldowitz, D., & Mittleman, G. (2017). Cerebellar contribution to higher and lower order rule learning and cognitive flexibility in mice. *Neuroscience,* 345, 99–109.

Dieringer, D. D., Lenz, J. G., Hayden, S. C. W., & Peterson, G. W. (2017). The relation of negative career thoughts to depression and hopelessness. *Career Development Quarterly, 65*(2), 159–172. https://doi.org/10.1002/cdq.12089

Dobkin, P. L., Irving, J. A., & Amar, S. (2011). For whom may participation in a mindfulness-based stress reduction program be contraindicated? *Mindfulness, 3*(1), 44–50. https://doi.org/10.1007/s12671-011-0079-9

Doidge, N. (2007). *The brain that changes itself: Stories of personal triumph from the frontiers of brain science.* Viking.

Dolan, R., & Dayan, P. (2013). Goals and habits in the brain. *Neuron, 80*(2), 312–325. https://doi.org/10.1016/j.neuron.2013.09.007

Doll, A., Holzel, B. K., Bratec, S. M., Boucard, C. C., Xie, X., Wohlschlager, A. M., & Sorg, C. (2016). Mindfulness attention to breath regulates emotions via increased amygdala-prefrontal cortex connectivity. *NeuroImage, 134,* 305–313. https://doi.org/10.1016/j.neuroimage.2016.03.041

Donker, T., Griffiths, K. M., Cuijpers, P., & Christensen, H. (2009). Psychoeducation for depression, anxiety, and psychological distress: A meta-analysis. *BMC Medicine, 7,* 79. https://doi.org/10.1186/1741-7015-7-79

Dorahy, M. J., Brand, B. L., Sar, V., Krüger, C., Stavropoulos, P., Martínez-Taboas, A., & Middleton, W. (2014). Dissociative identity disorder: An empirical overview. *Australian and New Zealand Journal of Psychiatry, 48*(5), 402–417. https://doi.org/10.1177/0004867414527523

Doran, G. T. (1981). There's a S.M.A.R.T way to write management's goals and objectives. *Management Review, 70*(11), 35–36.

Doren, J. V., Arns, M., Heinrich, H., Vollebregt, M. A., Strehl, U., & Loo, S. K. (2018). Sustained effects of neurofeedback in ADHD: A systematic review and meta-analysis. *European Child & Adolescent Psychiatry, 28*(3), 293–305. https://doi.org/10.1007/s00787-018-1121-4

Duarte, A., Henson, R. N., Knight, R. T., Emery, T., & Graham, K. S. (2010). The orbitofrontal cortex is necessary for temporal context memory. *Journal of Cognitive Neuroscience, 22*(8), 1819–1831. https://doi.org/10.1162/jocn.2009.21316

Duckworth, A. L., Peterson, C., Matthews, M. D., & Kelly, D. R. (2007). Grit: Perseverance and passion for long-term goals. *Journal of Personality and Social Psychology, 92*(6), 1087–1101. https://doi.org/10.1037/0022-3514.92.6.1087

Duncan, B. L., Miller, S. D., Sparks, J. A., Claud, D. A., Reynolds, L. R., Brown, J., & Johnson, L. D. (2003). The Session Rating Scale: Preliminary psychometric properties of a "working" alliance measure. *Journal of Brief Therapy, 3*(1), 3–12.

Duncan, B. L., Miller, S. D., Wampold, B. E., & Hubble, M. A. (Eds.) (2011). *The heart & soul of change: Delivering what works in therapy* (2nd ed.). American Psychological Association.

Dunn, A. D., Reed, B., Guariglia, C., Dunn, A. M., Hillman, J. M., & Kreek, M. J. (2018). Structurally related kappa opioid receptor agonists with substantial differential signaling bias: Neuroendocrine and behavorial effects in C57CL6 mice. *International Journal of Neuropsychopharmacology, 21*(9), 847–857. https://doi.org/10.1093/ijnp/pyy034

Duric, N. S., Assmus, J., Gundersen, D., & Elgen, I. B. (2012). Neurofeedback for the treatment of children and adolescents with ADHD: A randomized and controlled clinical trial using parental reports. *BMC Psychiatry, 12*, 107. https://doi.org/10.1186/1471-244X-12-107

Durston, S. (2003). A review of the biological bases of ADHD: What have we learned from imaging studies? *Mental Retardation and Developmental Disabilities Research Reviews, 9*(3), 184–195. https://doi.org/10.1002/mrdd.10079

Ecker, B. (2015). Memory reconsolidation understood and misunderstood. *International Journal of Neuropsychotherapy, 3*(1), 2–46. https://doi.org/10.12744/ijnpt.2015.0002-0046

Ecker, B., Ticic, R., & Hulley, L. (2012). *Unlocking the emotional brain: Eliminating symptoms at their roots using memory reconsolidation.* Routledge.

Edward, K. L. (2005). Resilience: A protector from depression. *Journal of the American Psychiatric Nurses Association, 11*(4), 241–243. https://doi.org/10.1177/1078390305281177

Eisenbeck, N., Luciano, C., & Valdivia-Salas, S. (2018). Effects of a focused breathing mindfulness exercise on attention, memory, and mood: The importance of task characteristics. *Behaviour Change, 35*(1), 54–70. https://doi.org/10.1017/bec.2018.9

Ekhtiari, H., Rezapour, T., Aupperle, R. L., & Paulus, M. P. (2017). Neuroscience-informed psychoeducation for addiction medicine: A neurocognitive perspective. *Progress in Brain Research, 235*, 239–264. doi: 10.1016/bs.pbr.2017.08.013

Ekkekakis, P., & Acevedo, E. O. (2006). Affective responses to acute exercise: Toward a psychobiological dose-response model. In E. O. Acevedo & P. Ekkekakis (Eds.), *Psychobiology of physical activity* (pp. 91–109). Human Kinetics.

Elbrecht, C. R., & Antcliff, L. (2014). Being touched through touch. Trauma treatment through haptic perception at the Clay Field: A sensorimotor art therapy. *International Journal of Art Therapy: Inscape, 19*(1), 1–12.

Elfenbein, H. A., & Ambady, N. (2002). On the universality and cultural specificity of emotion recognition: A meta-analysis. *Psychological Bulletin, 128*(2), 203–235. https://doi.org/10.1037/0033-2909.128.2.203

Elisei, S., Sciarma, T., Verdolini, N., & Anastasi, S. (2013). Resilience and depressive disorders. *Psychiatria Danubina, 25*, S263–S267.

Enriquez-Geppert, S., Smit, D., Pimenta, M. G., & Arns, M. (2019). Neurofeedback as a treatment intervention in ADHD: Current evidence and practice. *Current Psychiatry Reports, 21*(46), 1–7. https://doi.org/10.1007/s11920-019-1021-4

Epel, E., Prather, A. A., Puterman, E., & Tomiyama, A. J. (2016). Eat, drink, and be sedentary: A review of health behaviors' effects on emotions and affective states, and implications for interventions. In L. F. Barrett, M. Lewis, & J. M. Haviland-Jones (Eds.), *Handbook of emotions* (4th ed., pp. 685–706). Guilford Press.

Escher, M., Daali, Y., Chabert, J., Hopfgartner, G., Dayer, P., & Desmeules, J. (2007). Pharmacokinetic and pharmacodynamic properties of buprenorphine after a single intravenous administration in healthy volunteers: A randomized, double-blind, placebo-controlled, crossover study. *Clinical Therapeutics: The International Peer-Reviewed Journal of Drug Therapy, 29*(8), 1620–1631. https://doi.org/10.1016/j.clinthera.2007.08.007

Escolano, C., Navarro-Gil, M., Garcia-Campayo, J., Congedo, M., & Minguez, J. (2014). The effects of individual upper alpha neurofeedback in ADHD: An open-label pilot study. *Applied Psychophysiology and Biofeedback, 39*(3–4), 193–202. https://doi.org/10.1007/s10484-014-9257-6

Etkin, A., Buchel, C., & Gross, J. J. (2015). The neural bases of emotion regulation. *Nature Reviews Neuroscience, 16*(11), 693–700. https://doi.org/10.1038/nrn4044

Fabbri-Destro, M., & Rizzolatti, G. (2008). Mirror neurons and mirror systems in monkeys and humans. *Physiology, 23*, 171–179. https://doi.org/10.1152/physiol.00004.2008

Fals-Stewart, W., Birchler, G. R., & Kelley, M. L. (2006). Learning sobriety together: a randomized clinical trial examining behavioral couples therapy with alcoholic female patients. *Journal of Consulting and Clinical Psychology, 74(3)*, 579–591.

Faurholt-Jepsen, M., Kessing, L. V., & Munkholm, K. (2017). Heart rate variability in bipolar disorder: A systematic review and meta-analysis. *Neuroscience & Biobehavioral Reviews, 73*, 68–80. https://doi.org/ 10.1016/j.neubiorev.2016.12.007.

Feder, A., Nestle, E. J., Westphal, M., & Charney, D.S. (2010). Psychobiological mechanisms of resilience to stress. In J.W. Reich, A. J. Zautra, & J. S. Hall (Eds.), Handbook of adult resilience (pp. 35–54). Guilford Press.

Fechner, G. T. (1860). *Elemente der Psychophysik.* Druck und Valeg von Breitkopf und Härtel.

Fein, E. (2015). 'No one has to be your friend': Asperger's syndrome and the vicious cycle of social disorder in later modern identity markets. *Ethos, 43*(1), 82–107. https://doi.org/10.1111/etho.12073

Felitti, V. J., Anda, R. F., Nordenberg, D., Williamson, D. F., Spitz, A. M., Edwards, V., Koss, M. P., & Marks, J. S. (1998). Relationship of childhood abuse and household dysfunction to many of the leading causes of death in adults. *American Journal of Preventive Medicine, 14*, 245–258. https://doi.org/10.1016/s0749-3797(98)00017-8

Felmingham, K., Kemp, A., Williams, L., Das, P., Hughes, G., & Peduto, A. (2007). Changes in anterior cingulate and amygdala after cognitive behavior therapy of posttraumatic stress disorder. *Psychological Science, 18*(2), 127–129. https://doi.org/10.1111/j.1467-9280.2007.01860.x

Fernald, P. S. (2000). Carl Rogers: Body-centered counselor. *Journal of Counseling & Development, 78*(2), 172–179. https://doi.org/10.1002/j.1556-6676.2000.tb02575.x

Fernandez-Duque, D., Evans, J., Christian, C., & Hodges, S. D. (2015). Superfluous neuroscience information makes explanations of psychological phenomena more appealing. *Journal of Cognitive Neuroscience, 27*(5), 926–944. https://doi.org/10.1162/jocn_a_00750

Ferrari, P. F., & Coude, G. (2018). Mirror neurons, embodied emotions, and empathy. In K. Z. Meyza & E. Knapska (Eds.), *Neuronal correlates of empathy: From rodent to human* (pp. 67–77). Elsevier Academic Press.

Field, T. A., Jones, L. K., & Russell-Chapin, L. A. (Eds.). (2017). *Neurocounseling: Brain-based clinical approaches.* American Counseling Association.

Fine, J., Bartolucci, G., Szatmari, P., & Ginsberg, G. (1994). Cohesive discourse in pervasive developmental disorders. *Journal of Autism and Developmental Disorders, 24*(3), 315–329. https://doi.org/10.1007/BF02172230

Fingelkurts, A. A., & Fingelkurts, A. A. (2017). Information flow in the brain: Ordered sequences of metastable states. *Information, 8*(1), 22. https://doi.org/10.3390/info8010022

Finsterwald, C., & Alberini, C. M. (2014). Stress and glucocorticoid receptor-dependent mechanisms in long-term memory: From adaptive responses to psychopathologies. *Neurobiology of Learning and Memory, 112*, 17–29. https://doi.org/10.1016/j.nlm.2013.09.017

Fishbane, M. D. (2013). *Loving with the brain in mind: Neurobiology and couple therapy.* W.W. Norton & Company.

Flor, H. (2000). The functional organization of the brain in chronic pain. *Progress in Brain Research, 129*, 313–322. https://doi.org/10.1016/s0079-6123(00)29023-7

Flores, P. J, & Porges, S. W. (2017). Group psychotherapy as a neural exercise: Bridging polyvagal theory and attachment theory. *International Journal of Group Psychotherapy, 67*(2), 202–222. https://doi.org/10.1080/00207284.2016.1263544

Flynn, J. J., Hollenstein, T., & Mackey, A. (2010). The effect of suppressing and not accepting emotions on depressive symptoms: Is suppression different for men and women? *Personality and Individual Differences, 49*(6), 582–586. https://doi.org/10.1016/j.paid.2010.05.022

Fogel, A. (2009). *The psychophysiology of self-awareness: Rediscovering the lost art of body sense.* W. W. Norton & Company.

Follette, V., Palm, K. M., & Pearson, A. N. (2006) Mindfulness and trauma: Implications for treatment. *Journal of Rational-Emotive & Cognitive-Behavior Therapy, 24*, 45–61.

Forrest, K. A. (2001). Toward an etiology of dissociative identity disorder: A neurodevelopmental approach. *Consciousness and Cognition, 10*(3), 259–293.

Foster, J. A., Lyte, M., Meyer, E., & Cryan, J. F. (2016). Gut microbiota and brain function: An evolving field in neuroscience. *International Journal of Neuropsychopharmacology, 19*(5), 1–7. https://doi.org/10.1093/ijnp/pyv114

Frank, J. D., & Frank, J. B. (1993). *Persuasion and healing: A comparative study of psychotherapy* (3rd ed.). Baltimore, MD: Johns Hopkins University Press.

Frensch, P. A., & Rünger, D. (2003). Implicit learning. *Current Directions in Psychological Science, 12*(1), 13–18. https://doi.org/10.1111/1467-8721.01213

Frodl, T., & O'Keane, V. (2016). Integrating the stress systems and neuroimaging in depression. In T. Frodl (Ed.), *Systems neuroscience in depression* (pp. 269–308). Elsevier Academic Press.

Fryer, S. L., Tapert, S. F., Mattson, S. N., Paulus, M. P., Spadoni, A. D., & Riley, E. P. (2007). Prenatal alcohol exposure affects frontal–striatal BOLD response during inhibitory control. *Alcoholism: Clinical and Experimental Research, 31*(8), 1415–1424. https://doi.org/10.1111/j.1530-0277.2007.00443.x

Fuchs, T. (2012). The phenomenology of body memory. In S. C. Koch, T. Fuchs, T., M. Summa, & C. Müller (Eds.), *Body Memory, Metaphor and Movement* (pp. 9–22). John Benjamins.

Fujisawa, T., Jung, M., Kojima, M., Saito, D. N., Kosaka, H., & Tomada, A. (2015). Neural basis of psychological growth following adverse experiences: A resting-state functional MRI study. *PLoS One, 10*(8), 1–14. https://doi.org/10.1371/journal.pone.0136427

Gadek-Michalska, A., Spyrka, J., Rachwalska, P., Tadeusz, J., & Bugajski, J. (2013). Influence of chronic stress on brain corticosteroid receptors and HPA axis activity. *Pharmacological Reports, 65*(5), 1163–1175.

Gallahue, D. L, & Donnelly, F. C. (2003). *Developmental physical education for all children* (4th ed.). Human Kinetics.

Gallant, S. N. (2016). Mindfulness meditation practice and executive functioning: Breaking down the benefit. *Consciousness and Cognition, 40*, 116–130. https://doi.org/10.1016/j.concog.2016.01.005

Gallese, V., & Goldman, A. (1998). Mirror neurons and the simulation theory of mind reading. *Trends in Cognitive Sciences, 2*(12), 493–501. https://doi.org/10.1016/S1364-6613(98)01262-5

Gallese, V., & Lakoff, G. (2005). The brain's concepts: The role of sensory-motor system in conceptual knowledge. *Cognitive Neuropsychology, 22*(3–4), 455–479. https://doi.org/10.1080/02643290442000310

Galvan, A. (2010). Neural plasticity of development and learning. *Human Brain Mapping, 31*(6), 879–890. https://doi.org/10.1002/hbm.21029

Garcia, R., Vouimba, R. M., Baudry, M., & Thompson, R. F. (1999). The amygdala modulates prefrontal cortex activity relative to conditioned fear. *Nature, 402*(6759), 294–296. https://doi.org/10.1038/46286

Gard, T., Noggle, J. J., Park, C. L., Vago, D. R., & Wilson, A. (2014). Potential self-regulatory mechanisms of yoga for psychological health. *Frontiers in Human Neuroscience, 8*, 1–20

Garza-Villarreal, E. A., Wilson, A. D., Vase, L., Brattico, E., Barrios, F. A., Jensen, T. S., Romero-Romo, J. L, & Vuust, P. (2014). Music reduces pain and increases functional mobility in fibromyalgia. *Frontiers in Psychology, 5*, 90. https://doi.org/10.3389/fpsyg.2014.00090

Gaskill, R. L., & Perry, B. D. (2012). Child sexual abuse, traumatic experiences, and their impact on the developing brain. In P. Goodyear-Brown (Ed.), *Handbook of child sexual abuse: Identification, assessment, and treatment* (pp. 29–47). John Wiley & Sons, Inc.

Gazzaniga, M. S. (2011). *Who's in charge: Free will and the science of the brain.* HarperCollins.

Geller, S. M., & Porges, S. W. (2014). Therapeutic presence: Neurophysiological mechanisms mediating feeling safe in therapeutic relationships. *Journal of Psychotherapy Integration, 24*(3), 178–192. https://doi.org/10.1037/a0037511

Gerbarg, P. L., Brown, R. P., & American Association for Geriatric Psychology. (2016). Top-down plus bottom-up integrative treatments in psychology. *Psychiatric Times, 33*(4). www.psychiatrictimes.com/integrative-psychiatry/top-down-plus-bottom-integrative-treatments-psychiatry

Gershon, M. (1998). *The second brain.* Harper Collins.

Gibson, N., & Tantam, D. (2018). The best medicine? Psychotherapists' experience of the impact of humour on the process of psychotherapy. *Existential Analysis, 29*(1), 64–76.

Giese, M., Unternaehrer, E., Brand, S., Calabrese, P., Holsboer-Trachsler, E., & Eckert, A. (2013). The interplay of stress and sleep impacts BDNF level. *PloS ONE, 8*(10), e76050. https://doi.org/10.1371/journal.pone.0076050

Gifford, L. (1998). Pain, the tissues and the nervous system: A conceptual model. *Physiotherapy, 84*(1), 27–36. https://doi.org/10.1016/s0031-9406(05)65900-7

Gifford, L. (2014). *Aches and Pains.* Wordpress.

Gifford, L., & Muncey, H. (1999). *Explaining pain to patients* [Paper presentation]. International Association on the Study of Pain, Vienna, Austria.

Gladding, S. T. (2008). The impact of creativity in counseling. *Journal of Creativity in Mental Health, 3*(2), 97–104. https://doi.org/10.1080/15401380802226679

Gladding, S.T. (2011). *The creative arts in counseling.* American Counseling Association.

Glimcher, P.W. (2011). Understanding dopamine and reinforcement learning: The dopamine reward prediction error hypothesis. *Proceedings of the National Academy of Sciences of the United States of America, 108*(3), 15647–15654. https://doi.org/10.1073/pnas.1014269108

Goessl, V. C., Curtiss, J. E., & Hofmann, S. G. (2017). The effect of heart rate variability biofeedback training on stress and anxiety: A meta-analysis. *Psychological Medicine, 47*(15), 2578–2586. https://doi.org/10.1017/s0033291717001003

Goetz, G. L., Keltner, D., & Simon-Thomas. E. (2010). Compassion: An evolutionary analysis and empirical review. *Psychological Bulletin, 136*(3), 351–374. https://doi.org/10.1037/a0018807

Gogtay, N., Giedd, J. N., Lusk, L., Hayashi, K. M., Greenstein, D., Vaituzis, A. C., . . . Ungerleider, L. G. (2004). Dynamic mapping of human cortical development during childhood through early adulthood. *Proceedings of the National Academy of Sciences of the United States of America, 101*(21), 8174–8179. https://doi.org/10.1073/pnas.0402680101

Gold, B.P., Mas-Herrero, E., Zeighami, Y., Benovoy, M., Dagher, A., & Zatorre, R. J. (2019). Musical reward prediction errors engage the nucleus accumbens and motivate learning. *Proceedings of the National Academy of Sciences of the United States of America, 116*(8), 3310–3315. https://doi.org/10.1073/pnas.1809855116

Goldapple, K., Segal, Z., Garson, C., Lau, M., Bieling, P., Kennedy, S., & Mayberg, H. (2004). Modulation of cortical-limbic pathways in major depression. *Archives of General Psychiatry, 61*(1), 34–41. https://doi.org/10.1001/archpsyc.61.1.34

Goldberg, D. S., & McGee, S. J. (2011). Pain as a global public health priority. *BMC Public Health, 11,* 770. https://doi.org/10.1186/1471-2458-11-770

Goleman, D. (2011). *The brain and emotional intelligence: New insights.* https://www.amazon.com/Brain-Emotional-Intelligence-New-Insights-ebook/dp/B004WG5ANA

Gonzalez-Castro, P., Cueli, M., Rodríguez, C., García, T., & Álvarez, L. (2016). Efficacy of neurofeedback versus pharmacological support in subjects with ADHD. *Applied Psychophysiology and Biofeedback, 41*(1), 17–25. https://doi.org/10.1007/s10484-015-9299-4

Goodman, R. D., & Calderon, A. M. (2012). The use of mindfulness in trauma counseling. *Journal of Mental Health Counseling, 34*(3), 254–268.

Goosby, B. J., & Heidbrink, C. (2013). Transgenerational consequences of racial discrimination for African American health. *Sociological Compass, 7*(8), 630–643. https://doi.org/10.1111/soc4.12054

Gordon, N. (2007). The cerebellum and cognition. *European Journal of Paediatric Neurology, 11*(4), 232–234. https://doi.org/10.1016/j.ejpn.2007.02.003

Goss, D. (2016). Integrating neuroscience into counseling psychology: A systematic review of current literature. *Counseling Psychologist, 44*(6), 895–920. https://doi.org/10.1177/0011000016650263

Gottlieb, J., Oudeyer, P., Lopes, M., & Baranes, A. (2013). Information-seeking, curiosity, and attention: Computational and neural mechanisms. *Trends in Cognitive Sciences, 17*(11), 585–593. https://doi.org/10.1016/j.tics.2013.09.001

Goyal, M., Singh, S., Sibinga, E. M., Gould, N. F., Rowland-Seymour, A., Sharma, R., Berger, Z., Sleicher, D., Maron, D. D., Shihab, H. M., Ranasinghe, P. D., & Haythornthwaite, J. A. (2014). Meditation programs for psychological stress and well-being: A systematic review and meta-analysis. *JAMA Internal Medicine, 174*(3), 357–368. https://doi.org/10.1001/jamainternmed.2013.13018

Grawe, K. (2007). *Neuropsychotherapy. How the neurosciences inform effective psychotherapy.* Psychology Press.

Greene, C. A., Williams, A. E., Harris, P. N., Travis, S. P., & Kim, S. Y. (2016). Unfolding case-based practicum curriculum infusing crisis, trauma, and disaster preparation. *Counselor Education and Supervision, 55*(3), 216–232. https://doi.org/10.1002/ceas.12046

Greenbaum, R. L., Stevens, S. A., Nash, K., Koren, G., & Rovet, J. (2009). Social cognitive and emotion processing abilities of children with fetal alcohol spectrum disorders: A comparison with attention deficit hyperactivity disorder. *Alcoholism: Clinical and Experimental Research, 33*(10), 1656–1670. https://doi.org/10.1111/j.1530-0277.2009.01003.x

Greenberg, L. S. (2007). Emotion coming of age. *Clinical Psychology: Science and Practice, 14,* 414–421. https://doi.org/10.1111/j.1468-2850.2007.00101.x

Gremel, C., Chancey, J., Atwood, B., Luo, G., Neve, R., Ramakrishnan, C., Deisseroth, K., & Costa, R. (2016). Endocannabinoid modulation of orbitostriatal circuits gates habit formation. *Neuron, 90*(6), 1312–1324. https://doi.org/10.1016/j.neuron.2016.04.043

Gruber, M. J., Gelman, B. D., & Ranganath, C. (2014). States of curiosity modulate hippocampus-dependent learning via the dopaminergic circuit. *Neuron, 84*(2), 486–496. https://doi.org/10.1016/j.neuron.2014.08.060

Grzanka, P. R. (2014). Introduction: Intersectional objectivity. In P. R. Grzanka (Ed.), *Intersectionality: A foundations and frontiers reader* (pp. xiii–xxvii). Westview Press.

Guo, L., Ponvert, N. D., & Jaramillo, S. (2017). The role of sensory cortex in behavioral flexibility. *Neuroscience,* 345, 3–11.

Gurden, H., Takita, M., & Jay, T. M. (2000). Essential role of D1 but not D2 receptors in the NMDA receptor-dependent long-term potentiation at hippocampal prefrontal cortex synapses in vivo. *Journal of Neuroscience, 20*, 1–5.

Gysbers, N. C., Heppner, M. J., & Johnston, J. A. (2014). *Career counseling: Holism, diversity, and strengths* (4th ed.). American Counseling Association.

Haldeman, S. (1990). Presidential address, North American Spine Society: Failure of the pathology model to predict back pain. *Spine, 15*(7), 718-724. https://doi.org/10.1097/00007632-199007000-00019

Hall, S. B, & Walker, K. D. (2017). Clinical neuroscience of substance use disorders. In T.A., Field, L. K. Jones, & L. A. Russell-Chapin (Eds.), *Neurocounseling: Brain-based clinical approaches* (pp. 149–164). American Counseling Association.

Hamilton, A. F. de C. (2013). Reflecting on the mirror neuron system in autism: A systematic review of current theories. *Developmental Cognitive Neuroscience, 3*(1), 91–105. https://doi.org/10.1016/j.dcn.2012.09.008

Hammond, D. C., & Kirk, L. (2008). First, do no harm: Adverse effects and the need for practice standards in neurofeedback. *Journal of Neurotherapy, 12*(1), 79–88.

Hammond, D.C., & Novian, A. N. (2018). The ISNR comprehensive bibliography of neurofeedback research. https://www.isnr.org/isnr-comprehensive-bibliography

Hand, G. A., Phillips, K. D., & Wilson, M. A. (2006). Central regulation of stress reactivity and physical activity. In E. O. Acevedo & P. Ekkekakis (Eds.), *Psychobiology of physical activity* (pp. 189–2001). Human Kinetics.

Hanson, J. L., Nacewicz, B. M., Sutterer, M. J., Cayo, A. A., Schaefer, S. M., Rudolph, K. D., Shirtcliff, E. A., & Pollack, S. D., & Davidson, R. J. (2015). Behavioral problems after early life stress: Contributions of the hippocampus and amygdala. *Biological Psychiatry, 77*(4), 314–323. https://doi.org/10.1016/j.biopsych.2014.04.020

Hardt, J. V., & Kamiya, J. (1978). Anxiety change through electroencephalographic alpha feedback seen only in high anxiety subjects. *Science, 201*(4350), 79–81. https://doi.org/10.1126/science.663641

Harris, S., Lambie, G. W., & Hundley, G. (2019). The effects of neurofeedback training on college students' attention deficit hyperactivity disorder symptoms. *Counseling Outcome Research, 10*(2), 64-77. https://doi.org/10.1080/21501378.2018.1442679

Harvard Health Publishing (HHP). (2018, May 1). Understanding the stress response. https://www.health.harvard.edu/staying-healthy/understanding-the-stress-response

Haslam, N., & Kvaale, E. P. (2015). Biogenetic explanations for mental disorder: The mixed-blessing model. *Current Directions in Psychological Science, 24*(5), 399–404. https://doi.org/10.1177/0963721415588082

Hass-Cohen, N., Clyde Findlay, J., Carr, R., & Vanderlan, J. (2014). "Check, change what you need to change and/or keep what you want": An art therapy neurobiological-based trauma protocol. *Art Therapy: Journal of the American Art Therapy Association, 31*(2), 69–78. https://doi.org/10.1080/07421656.2014.903825

Hasson, U., Ghazanfar, A. A., Galantucci, B., Garrod, S., & Keysers, C. (2012). Brain-to-brain coupling: A mechanism for creating and sharing a social world. *Trends in Cognitive Science, 16*(2), 114–121. https://doi.org/10.1016/j.tics.2011.12.007

Hart, C. (2013). Held in mind, out of awareness. Perspectives on the continuum of dissociated experience, culminating in dissociative identity disorder in children. *Journal of Child Psychotherapy, 39*(3), 303–318.

Hatfield, B. D. (1991). Exercise and mental health: The mechanisms of exercise-induced psychological states. In L. Dimant (Ed.), *Psychology of Sports, Exercise, & Fitness: Social and Personal Issues* (pp. 17–49). Hemisphere Publishing Corp.

Hatfield, B. D. (2012). Kinesiology and mental health: The promise of exercise neuroscience research for diseases and disorders of the brain. *Kinesiology Review, 1*(1), 46–58. https://doi.org/10.1123/krj.1.1.46

Hayes, S. C., Strosahl, K. D., & Wilson, K. G. (2012). *Acceptance and commitment therapy: The process and practice of mindful change* (2nd ed.). Guilford Press

Heal, D. J., Cheetham, S. C., & Smith, S. L. (2009). The neuropharmacology of ADHD drugs in vivo: Insights on efficacy and safety. *Neuropharmacology, 57*(7–8), 608–618. https://doi.org/10.1016/j.neuropharm.2009.08.020

Hebb, D. O. (1949). *The organization of behavior.* Wiley.

Hecker, L. L., & Kottler, J. A. (2002). Growing creative therapists. *Journal of Clinical Activities, Assignments & Handouts in Psychotherapy Practice, 2*(2), 1–3. https://doi.org/10.1300/J182v02n02_01

Hedlund, L., & Gyllensten, A.L. (2013). The physiotherapists' experience of basic body awareness therapy in patients with schizophrenia and schizophrenia spectrum disorders. *Journal of Bodywork and Movement Therapies, 17*(2), 169–176. https://doi.org/10.1016/j.jbmt.2012.10.008

Hedstrom, J. (1991). A note on eye movements and relaxation. *Journal of Behavior Therapy and Experimental Psychiatry, 22*(1), 37–38. https://doi.org/10.1016/0005-7916(91)90031-y

Heffernan, T. M. (2008). The impact of excessive alcohol use on prospective memory: A brief review. *Current Drug Abuse Reviews, 1*(1), 36–41.

Heishman S. J., Singleton E. G., & Liguori A. (2001). Marijuana craving questionnaire: Development and initial validation of a self-report instrument. *Addiction, 96*, 1023–1034.

Heit, H. A., & Gourlay, D. L. (2008). Buprenorphine: New tricks with an old molecule for pain management. *Clinical Journal of Pain, 24*(2), 93–97. https://doi.org/10.1097/AJP.0b013e31815ca2b4

Helgeson, V. S., Reynolds, K. A., & Tomich, P. L. (2006). A meta-analytic review of benefit finding and growth. *Journal of Consulting and Clinical Psychology, 74*(5), 797–816. https://doi.org/10.1037/0022-006x.74.5.797

Herman, J. L. (1992). *Trauma and recovery: The aftermath of violence—from domestic abuse to political terror.* BasicBooks.

Herpertz-Dahlmann, B., Seitz, J., & Baines, J. (2017). Food matters: How the microbiome and gut-brain interaction might impact the development and course of anorexia nervosa. *European Child & Adolescent Psychiatry, 26*(9), 1031–1034. https://doi.org/10.1007/s00787-017-0945-7

Heyes, C. M. (2001). Causes and consequences of imitation. *Trends in Cognitive Science, 5*(6), 253–261. https://doi.org/10.1016/S1364-6613(00)01661-2

Heyes, C. M. (2018). Empathy is not in our genes. *Neuroscience and Biobehavioral Reviews, 95*, 499–507. https://doi.org/10.1016/j.neubiorev.2018.11.001

Hickok, G. (2014). *The myth of mirror neurons: The real neuroscience of communication and cognition.* W.W. Norton & Company.

Hill, R., & Rossi, E. L. (2017). *The practitioner's guide to mirroring hands: A client-responsive therapy that facilitates natural problem-solving and mind-body healing.* Crown House Publishing.

Ho, S. H., Lin, C. J., & Kuo, F. L. (2016, June 27). *The effects of gardening on quality of life in people with stroke.* https://www.ncbi.nlm.nih.gov/pubmed/27372897

Holmes, N. M., & Fam, J. (2013). How does dopamine release in the nucleus accumbens core relate to encoding of a Pavlonian incentive stimulus? *Journal of Neuroscience, 33*(25), 10191–10192. https://doi.org/10.1523/JNEUROSCI.1543-13.2013

Holt-Lunstad, J. (2018). Why social relationships are important for physical health: A systems approach to understanding and modifying risk and protection. *Annual Review of Psychology, 69*, 437–458. https://doi.org/10.1146/annurev-psych-122216-011902

Hong, S., & Mills, P. J. (2006). Physical activity and psychoneuroimmunology. In E. O. Acevedo & P. Ekkekakis (Eds.), *Psychobiology of physical activity* (pp. 177–188). Human Kinetics.

Hongu, N., Going, S. B., Orr, B. J., Merchant, N. C., Hingle, M. D., Roe, D. J., Greenblatt, Y. V., & Houtkooper, L. B. (2014). Tech savvy: Mobile technologies for promoting health and physical activity. *ACSM's Health & Fitness Journal, 18*(4), 8–15. https://doi.org/10.1249/FIT.0000000000000050

Hormes, J. M., Kearns, B., & Timko, C. A. (2014). Craving Facebook? Behavioral addiction to online social networking and its association with emotion regulation deficits. *Addiction, 109*(12), 2079-2088. https://doi.org/10.1111/add.12713

Hornung, J. P. (2003). The human raphe nuclei and the serotonergic system. *Journal of Chemical Neuroanatomy, 26*(4), 331–343.

Houlihan, B. (2008). *Sport and society: A student introduction* (2nd ed.). Sage Publications.

Hübener, M., & Bonhoeffer, T. (2014). Neuronal plasticity: Beyond the critical period. *Cell, 159*(4), 727–737. https://doi.org/10.1016/j.cell.2014.10.035

Hutchison, A., & Gerstein, L. (2017). Emotion recognition, emotion expression, and cultural display rules: Implications for counseling. *Journal of Asia Pacific Counseling, 7*(1), 19–35. https://doi.org/10.18401/2017.7.1.3

Hutson, P. H., Pennick, M., & Secker, R. (2014). Preclinical pharmacokinetics, pharmacology and toxicology of lisdexamfetamine: A novel d-amphetamine pro-drug. *Neuropharmacology, 87*41–8750. https://doi.org/10.1016/j.neuropharm.2014.02.014

Inaba, D. S., & Cohen, W. E. (2014). *Uppers, downers, all arounders: Physical and mental effects of psychoactive drugs* (8th ed.). CNS Productions, Inc.

Ingersoll, B. (2008). The effect of context on imitation skills in children with autism. *Research in Autism Spectrum Disorders, 2*(2), 332–340. https://doi.org/10.1016/j.rasd.2007.08.003

Institute of Medicine (US) Committee on Advancing Pain Research, Care, and Education. (2011). *Relieving pain in America: A blueprint for transforming prevention, care, education, and research.* National Academies Press.

Ivey, A. E., Ivey, M. B., & Zalaquett, C. P. (2018). *Intentional interviewing and counseling: Facilitating client development in a multicultural society* (9th ed.). Cengage Learning.

Ivey, A. E., & Zalaquett, C. P. (2011). Neuroscience and counseling: Central issue for social justice leaders. *Journal for Social Action in Counseling and Psychology, 3*(1), 103–116.

Jacob, Y., Gilam, G., Lin, T., Raz, G., & Hendler, T. (2018). Anger modulates influence hierarchies within and between emotional reactivity and regulation networks. *Frontiers in Behavioral Neuroscience, 12*, 60.

Jasanoff, A. (2018). *The biological mind: How brain, body, and environment collaborate to make us who we are.* Basic Books.

Jasper, H. H. (1958). The ten-twenty electrode system of the International Federation. *Electroencephalography and Clinical Neurophysiology, 10*, 371–375.

Johansen, J. P. (2013). Neuroscience: anxiety is the sum of its parts. *Nature, 496*(7444), 174.

Johannes, C. B., Le, T. K., Zhou, X., Johnston, J. A., & Dworkin, R. H. (2010). The prevalence of chronic pain in United States adults: Results of an internet-based survey. *Journal of Pain, 11*(11), 1230–1239. https://doi.org/10.1016/j.jpain.2010.07.002

Jones, E. (1953). *The life and work of Sigmund Freud.* Basic Books.

Jordan, J. S., Srinivasan, N., & van Leeuwen, C. (2015). The role of complex systems theory in cognitive science. *Cognitive Processing, 16*(4), 315–317. https://doi.org/10.1007/s10339015-0739-0

Joseph, S., & Linley, P. A. (Eds.). (2008). *Trauma, recovery, and growth: Positive psychological perspectives on posttraumatic stress.* John Wiley & Sons.

Juster, R. P., McEwen, B. S., & Lupien, S. J. (2010). Allostatic load biomarkers of chronic stress and impact on health and cognition. *Neuroscience and Biobehavioral Reviews, 35*(1), 2–16. https://doi.org/10.1016/j.neubiorev.2009.10.002

Kabat-Zinn, J. (2003). Mindfulness-based interventions in context: Past, present, and future. *Clinical Psychology: Science and Practice, 10*(2), 144–156. https://doi.org/10.1093/clipsy/bpg016

Kalberg, W. O., Provost, B., Tollison, S. J., Tabachnick, B. G., Robinson, L. K., Eugene Hoyme, H., Trujillo, P. M., Buckley, A. S., & Aragon, A. S., & May, P. A. (2006). Comparison of motor delays in young children with fetal alcohol syndrome to those with prenatal alcohol exposure and with no prenatal alcohol exposure. *Alcoholism: Clinical and Experimental Research, 30*(12), 2037–2045. https://doi.org/10.1111/j.1530-0277.2006.00250.x

Kalmanowitz, D. (2016). Inhabited studio: Art therapy and mindfulness, resilience, adversity and refugees. *International Journal of Art Therapy: Inscape, 21*(2), 75–84.

Kamradt, J. M. (2017). Integrating yoga into psychotherapy: The ethics of moving from the mind to the mat. *Complementary Therapies in Clinical Practice, 27*, 27–30. https://doi.org/10.1016/j.ctcp.2017.01003

Kandel, E. R. (2006). *In search of memory: The emergence of a new science of mind*. W. W. Norton & Company.

Kandel, E. R., Schwartz, J. H., Jessell, T. M., Siegelbaum, S. A., & Hudspeth, A. J. (Eds.). (2012). *Principles of neural science* (5th ed.). McGraw-Hill.

Kapoula, Z., Yang, Q., Bonnet, A., Bourtoire, P., & Sandretto, J. (2010). EMDR effects on pursuit eye movements. *PLoS ONE, 5*(5), 10762. https://doi.org/10.1371/journal.pone.0010762

Karr-Morse, R., & Wiley, M. S. (Collaborator). (2012). *Scared sick: The role of childhood trauma in adult disease*. Basic Books.

Kashdan, T. B., Barrett, L. F., & McKnight, P. E. (2015). Unpacking emotion differentiation: Transforming unpleasant experience by perceiving distinctions in negativity. *Current Directions in Psychological Science, 24*(1), 10–16. https://doi.org/10.1177/0963721414550708

Katz, L. F., Maliken, A. C., & Stettler, N. M. (2012). Parental meta-emotion philosophy: A review of research and theoretical framework. *Child Development Perspectives, 6*(4), 417–422. https://doi.org/10.1111/j.1750-8606.2012.00244.x

Katz, L. S. (2016). *Treating military sexual trauma*. Springer Publishing Company.

Kaut, K. P. (2011). Psychopharmacology and mental health practice: An important alliance. *Journal of Mental Health Counseling, 33*(3), 196–222. https://doi.org/10.17744/mehc.33.3.u357803u508r4070

Kaut, K. P., & Dickinson, J. A. (2007). The mental health practitioner and psychopharmacology. *Journal of Mental Health Counseling, 29*(3), 204–225. https://doi.org/10.17744/mehc.29.3.t670636302771120

Kawamichi, H., Yoshihara, K., Sasaki, A. T., Sugawara, S. K., Tanabe, H. C., Shinohara, R., Sugisawa, Y., Tokutake, K., & Mochizuki, Y., & Sadato, N. (2015). Perceiving active listening activates the reward system and improves the impression of relevant experiences. *Social Neuroscience, 10*(1), 16–26. https://doi.org/10.1080/17470919.2014.954732

Kendall, N. A. S., Linton, S. J., & Main, C. (1998). Psychosocial yellow flags for acute low back pain: 'Yellow Flags' as an analogue to 'Red Flags.' *European Journal of Pain, 2*(1), 87–89. https://doi.org/10.1016/S1090-3801(98)90050-7

Kenemans, J. L., & Kähkönen, S. (2011). How human electrophysiology informs psychopharmacology: From bottom-up driven processing to top-down control. *Neuropsychopharmacology, 36*(1), 26–51. https://doi.org/10.1038/npp.2010.157

Keng, S., & Tan, J. X. (2017). Effects of brief mindful breathing and loving-kindness meditation on shame and social problem solving abilities among individuals with high borderline personality traits. *Behaviour Research and Therapy, 97*, 43–51.

Kiema, H., Rantanen, A., Laukka, S., Siipo, A., & Soini, H. (2014). The connection between skilled counseling and client's heart rate variability. *Procedia: Social and Behavioral Sciences, 159*, 802–807. https://doi.org/10.1016/j.sbspro.2014.12.452

Kim, D., Bae, H., & Park, Y. C. (2008). Validity of the subjective units of disturbance scale in EMDR. *Journal of EMDR Practice and Research, 2*(1), 57–62. https://doi.org/10.1891/1933-3196.2.1.57

Kip, K. E., D'Aoust, R. F., Hernandez, D. F., Girling, S. A., Cuttino, B., Long, M. K., Rojas, P., Wittenberg, T., Abhayakumar, A., & Rosenzweig, L. (2016). Evaluation of brief treatment of symptoms of psychological trauma among veterans residing in a homeless shelter by use of accelerated resolution therapy. *Nursing Outlook, 64*(5), 411–423. https://doi.org/10.1016/j.outlook.2016.04.006

Kip, K. E., & Diamond, D. M. (2018). Clinical, empirical, and theoretical rationale for selection of accelerated resolution therapy for treatment of post-traumatic stress disorder in VA and DoD facilities. *Military Medicine, 183*(9–10), 314–321. https://doi.org/10.1093/milmed/usy027

Kip, K. E., Elk, C. A., Sullivan, K. L., Kadel, R., Lengacher, C. A., Long, C. J., . . . Diamond, D. M. (2012). Brief treatment of symptoms of post-traumatic stress disorder (PTSD) by use of accelerated resolution therapy (ART®). *Behavioral Sciences, 2*(2), 115-134. https://doi.org/10.3390/bs2020115

Kip, K. E., Rosenzweig, L., Hernandez, D. F., Shuman, A., Sullivan, K. L., Long, C. J., Rosenzweig, L., Shuman, A., Hernandez, D. F., Street, J. D., Girling, S. A., & Diamond, D. M. (2013). Randomized controlled trial of accelerated resolution therapy (ART) for symptoms of combat-related post-traumatic stress disorder (PTSD). *Military Medicine, 178*(12), 1298–1309. https://doi.org/10.7205/milmed-d-13-00298

Kip, K. E., Shuman, A., Hernandez, D. F., Diamond, D. M., & Rosenzweig, L. (2014). Case report and theoretical description of accelerated resolution therapy (ART) for military-related post-traumatic stress disorder. *Military Medicine, 179*(1), 31–37. https://doi.org/10.7205/milmed-d-13-00229

Kira, I. A., Ashby, J. S., Omidy, A. Z., & Lewandowski, L. (2015). Current, continuous, and cumulative trauma-focused cognitive behavior therapy: A new model for trauma counseling. *Journal of Mental Health Counseling, 37*(4), 323–340. https://doi.org/10.17744/mehc.37.4.04

Kita, I. (2014). Physical exercise can induce brain plasticity and regulate mental function. *Advances in Exercise and Sports Physiology, 20*(1), 1–7.

Kivlighan, D. M., Jr., Hill, C. E., Gelso, C. J., & Baumann, E. (2016). Working alliance, real relationship, session quality, and client improvement in psychodynamic psychotherapy: A longitudinal actor partner interdependence model. *Journal of Counseling Psychology, 63*(2), 149–161. https://doi.org/10.1037/cou0000134

Kjaer, P., Leboeuf-Yde, C., Korsholm, L., Sorensen, J. S., & Bendix, T. (2005). Magnetic resonance imaging and low back pain in adults: A diagnostic imaging study of 40-year-old men and women. *Spine, 30*(10), 1173–1180. https://doi.org/10.1097/01.brs.0000162396.97739.76

Klarer, M., Arnold, M., Gunther, L., Winter, C., Langhans, W., & Meyer, U. (2014). Gut vagal afferents differentially modulate innate anxiety and learned fear. *Journal of Neuroscience, 34*(21), 7067–7076. https://doi.org/10.1523/JNEUROSCI.0252-14.2014

Kleinbub, J. R. (2017). State of the art of interpersonal physiology in psychotherapy: A systematic review. *Frontiers in Psychology, 8*, 2053. https://doi.org/10.3389/fpsyg.2017.02053

Knox, D., Beveridge, S., Mitchell, L., & MacDonald, R. A. (2011). Acoustic analysis and mood classification of pain-relieving music. *Journal of the Acoustical Society of America, 130*(3), 1673–1682. https://doi.org/10.1121/1.3621029

Knutson, B., Adams, C. M., Fong, G. W., & Hommer, D. (2001). Anticipation of increasing monetary reward selectively recruits nucleus accumbens. *Journal of Neuroscience, 21*(16), RC159.

Kodituwakku, P. W. (2009). Neurocognitive profile in children with fetal alcohol spectrum disorders. *Developmental Disabilities Research Reviews, 15*(3), 218–224. https://doi.org/10.1002/ddrr.73

Kodituwakku, P. W., Kalberg, W., & May, P. A. (2001). The effects of prenatal alcohol exposure on executive functioning. *Alcohol Research and Health, 25*(3), 192–198.

Kolb, B. & Gibb, R. (2014). Searching for the principles of brain plasticity and behavior. *Cortex, 58*, 251–260. https://doi.org/10.1016/j.cortex.2013.11.012

Kolb, B., Mychasiuk, R., Muhammad, A., & Gibb, R. (2013). Brain plasticity in the developing brain. In M. M. Merzenich, M. Nahum, & T. M. Vleet (Eds.), *Progress in brain research: Vol. 207* (pp. 35–64). Academic Press.

Koole, S. L., & Tschacher, W. (2016). Synchrony in psychotherapy: A review and an integrative framework for the therapeutic alliance. *Frontiers in Psychology, 7*, 862. https://doi.org/10.3389/fpsyg.2016.00862

Kostanski, M., & Hassed, C. (2008). Mindfulness as a concept and a process. *Australian Psychologist, 43*(1), 15–21. https://doi.org/10.1080/00050060701593942

Koziol L. F., Budding D. E., & Chidekel, D. (2012). From movement to thought: Executive function, embodied cognition, and the cerebellum. *Cerebellum, 11*(2), 505–525. https://doi.org/10.1007/s12311-011-0321-y

Krasny, L., Williams, B. J., Provencal, S., & Ozonoff, S. (2003). Social skills interventions for the autism spectrum: Essential ingredients and a model curriculum. *Child and Adolescent Psychiatric Clinics of North America, 12*(1), 107–122. https://doi.org/10.1016/S1056-4993(02)00051-2

Kredlow, M. A., Eichenbaum, H., & Otto, M. W. (2018). Memory creation and modification: Enhancing the treatment of psychological disorders. *American Psychologist, 73*(3), 269–285. https://doi.org/10.1037/amp00001885

Kumar, A., Rinwa, P., Kaur, G., & Machawal, L. (2013). Stress: Neurobiology, consequences and management. *Journal of Pharmacy and BioAllied Sciences, 5*(2), 91–97. https://doi.org/10.4103/0975-7406.111818

Kuri, E. (2017). Toward an ethical application of intersectionality in art therapy. *Art Therapy, 34*(3), 118–122. https://doi.org/10.1080/07421656.2017.1358023

Lambert, M. J., Burlingame, G. M., Umphress, V., Hansen, N. B., Vermeersch, D. A., Clouse, G. C., & Yanchar, S. C. (1996). The reliability and validity of the Outcome Questionnaire. *Clinical Psychology & Psychotherapy, 3*(4), 249–258. https://doi.org/10.1002/(SICI)1099-0879(199612)3:4<249::AID-CPP106>3.0.CO;2-S

Lambie, D. (2016). Motivational interviewing to promote exercise behaviour change: A meta-ethnography using perspectives of patients and clinicians. *Physiotherapy, 102*(1), e49–e50. https://doi.org/10.1016/j.physio.2016.10.369

Landa, R. (2000). Social language use in asperger syndrome and high-functioning autism. In A. Klin, F. R. Volkmar, & S. S. Sparrow (Eds.) *Asperger syndrome* (pp.125–155). Guilford Press.

Lane, R. D., Ryan, L., Nadel, L., & Greenberg, L. (2015). Memory reconsolidation, emotional arousal, and the process of change in psychotherapy: New insights from brain science. *Behavioral and Brain Sciences, 38*, e1. https://doi.org/10.1017/s0140525x14000041

Langton, B., & King, J. (2018). Utilizing body weight training with your personal training clients. *ACSM's Health & Fitness Journal, 22*(6), 44–51. https://doi.org/10.1249/FIT.0000000000000433

Laska, K. M., Gurman, A. S., & Wampold, B. E. (2014). Expanding the lens of evidence-based practice in psychotherapy: A common factors perspective. *Psychotherapy, 51*(4), 467–481. https://doi.org/10.1037/a0034332

Layne, C. M., Ippen, C. G., Strand, V., Stuber, M., Abramovitz, R., Reyes, G., Ross, L., Lipscomb, L., & Pynoos, R. (2011). The core curriculum on childhood trauma: A tool for training a trauma-informed workforce. *Psychological Trauma: Theory, Research, Practice, and Policy, 3*(3), 243–252. https://doi.org/10.1037/a0025039

Lazarus, R. S., & Folkman, S. (1984). *Stress, appraisal, and coping.* Springer.

Lebel, C., Rasmussen, C., Wyper, K., Walker, L., Andrew, G., Yager, J., & Beaulieu, C. (2008). Brain diffusion abnormalities in children with fetal alcohol spectrum disorder. *Alcoholism: Clinical and Experimental Research, 32*(10), 1732–1740. https://doi.org/10.1111/j.1530-0277.2008.00750.x

Lebel, C., Roussotte, F., & Sowell, E. R. (2011). Imaging the impact of prenatal alcohol exposure on the structure of the developing human brain. *Neuropschological Review, 21*, 102–118. doi:10.1007/s11065-011-9163-0

Lebow, M. A., & Chen, A. (2016). Overshadowed by the amygdala: The bed nucleus of the stria terminalis emerges as key to psychiatric disorders. *Molecular Psychiatry, 21*(4), 450–463. https://doi.org/10.1038/mp.2016.1

Lebowitz, E. R., Gee, D. G., Pine, D. S., & Silverman, W. K. (2018). Implications of the research domain criteria project for childhood anxiety and its disorders. *Clinical Psychology Review, 64*, 99–109. https://doi.org/10.1016/j.cpr.2018.01.005

Lebowitz, M. S., Phil, M., & Ahn, W. (2015). Emphasizing malleability in the biology of depression: Durable effects on perceived agency and prognostic pessimism. *Behaviour Research and Therapy, 71*, 125–130. https://doi.org/10.1016/j.brat.2015.06.005.

Leckey, J. (2011). The therapeutic effectiveness of creative activities on mental well-being: A systematic review of the

literature. *Journal of Psychiatric Mental Health Nursing, 18*, 501–509.
LeDoux, J. (2015). *Anxious: Using the brain to understand and treat fear and anxiety.* Penguin Books.
LeDoux, J. E. (1996). *The emotional brain: The mysterious underpinnings of emotional life.* Simon and Schuster.
LeDoux, J. E., & Hofman, S. G. (2018). The subjective experience of emotion: A fearful view. *Current Opinion in Behavioral Sciences, 19*, 67–72. https://doi.org/10/1016/j.cobeha.2017.09.011
Lee, J. L. C., Nader, K., & Schiller, D. (2017). An update on memory reconsolidation updating. *Trends in Cognitive Sciences, 21*(7), 531–545. https://doi.org/10.1016/j.tics.2017.04.006
Leffler, J. M., Young, M. E., & Fristad, M. A. (2008). Psychoeducation. In F. T. L. Leong, E. M. Altmaier, & B. D. Johnson (Eds.), *Encyclopedia of counseling* (pp. 799–803). Sage Publishing.
Leith, L. M. (2010). *Foundations of exercise and mental health* (2nd ed.). Fitness Information Technology.
Lent, R. W., Brown, S. D., & Hackett, G. (1994). Toward a unifying social cognitive theory of career and academic interest, choice, and performance. *Journal of Vocational Behavior, 45*(1), 79–122. https://doi.org/10.1006/jvbe.1994.1027
Lenz, A. S. (2015). Using single-case research designs to demonstrate evidence for counseling practices. *Journal of Counseling & Development, 93*(4), 387–393. https://doi.org/10.1002/jcad.12036
Lesch, K. P. (2007). Linking emotion to the social brain: The role of the serotonin transporter in human social behaviour. *EMBO Reports, 8*(supp 1), 24–29. https://doi.org/10.1038/sj.embor.7401008
Lester, D. (1968). The effect of fear and anxiety on exploration and curiosity: Toward a theory of exploration. *Journal of General Psychology, 79*(1), 105–120. https://doi.org/10.1080/00221309.1968.9710458
Levine, P. A. (2010). *In an unspoken voice: How the body releases trauma and restores goodness.* North Atlantic Books.
Levine, P., & Frederick, A. (1997). *Waking the tiger: Healing trauma.* North Atlantic Books.
Levine, P., Porges, S., & Phillips, M. (2015). *Healing trauma and pain through polyvagal science.* www.maggiephillipsphd.com/courses.html
Levitt, H. M., Pomerville, A., & Surace, F. I. (2016). A qualitative meta-analysis examining clients' experiences of psychotherapy: A new agenda. *Psychological Bulletin, 142*(8), 801–830. https://doi.org/10.1037/bul0000057
Li, X., Jauquet, C. A., & Kivlighan, D. M., Jr. (2016). When is therapist metacommunication followed by more client collaboration? The moderation effects of timing and contexts. *Journal of Counseling Psychology, 63*(6), 693–703. https://doi.org/10.1037/cou0000162
Liang, S., Wu, X., Hu, X., Wang, T., & Jin, F. (2018a). Recognizing depression from the microbiota-gut-brain axis. *International Journal of Molecular Sciences, 19*(6), 1592. https://doi.org/10.3390/ijms19061592
Liang, S., Wu, X., & Jin, F. (2018b). Gut-brain psychology: Rethinking psychology from the microbiota-gut-brain axis. *Frontiers in Integrative Neuroscience, 12*, 33. https://doi.org/10.3389/fnint.2018.00033
Lilienfeld, S. O. (2014). The research domain criteria (RDoC): An analysis of methodological and conceptual challenges. *Behaviour Research and Therapy, 62*, 129–139. https://doi.org/10.1016/j.brat.2014.07.019
Lim, N. (2016). Cultural differences in emotion: Differences in emotional arousal level between the east and the west. *Integrative Medicine Research, 5*(2), 105–109. https://doi.org/10.1016/j.imr.2016.03.004
Locke, B. D., Buzolitz, J. S., Lei, P. W., Boswell, J. F., McAleavey, A. A., Sevig, T. D., Dowis, J. D., & Hayes, J. A. (2011). Development of the Counseling Center Assessment of Psychological Symptoms-62 (CCAPS-62). *Journal of Counseling Psychology, 58*(1), 97.
Lohrasbe, R. S., & Ogden, P. (2017). Somatic resources: Sensorimotor psychotherapy approach to stablising arousal in child and family treatment. *Australian and New Zealand Journal of Family Therapy, 38*(4), 573–581. https://doi.org/10.1002/anzf.1270
Louw, A. (2013). *Why do I hurt? A patient book about the neuroscience of pain.* Orthopedic Physical Therapy Products.
Louw, A. (2014). Therapeutic neuroscience education via e-mail: A case report. *Physiotherapy Theory and Practice, 30*(8), 588–596. https://doi.org/10.3109/09593985.2014.912255
Louw, A., & Butler, D. S. (2011). Chronic back pain and pain science. In S. B. Brotzman & R. C. Manske, (Eds.), *Clinical orthopaedic rehabilitation: An evidence-based approach.* (3rd ed., pp. 498–506). Elsevier.
Louw, A., Butler, D. S., Diener, I., & Puentedura, E. J. (2013). Development of a preoperative neuroscience educational program for patients with lumbar radiculopathy. *American Journal of Physical Medicine & Rehabilitation, 92*(5), 446–452. https://doi.org/10.1097/phm.0b013e3182876aa4
Louw, A., Diener, I., Butler, D. S., & Puentedura, E. J. (2011). The effect of neuroscience education on pain, disability, anxiety, and stress in chronic musculoskeletal pain. *Archives of Physical Medicine and Rehabilitation, 92*(12), 2041–2056. https://doi.org/10.1016/j.apmr.2011.07.198
Louw, A., Diener, I., Landers, M. R., & Puentedura, E. J. (2014). Preoperative pain neuroscience education for lumbar radiculopathy: A multicenter randomized controlled trial with 1-year follow-up. *Spine, 39*(18), 1449–1457. https://doi.org/10.1097/brs.0000000000000444
Louw, A., Diener, I., & Puentedura, E. (2014). Comparison of terminology in patient education booklets for lumbar surgery. *International Journal of Health Sciences, 2*(3), 47–56. https://doi.org/10.15640/ijhs.v2n3a5
Louw, A., Podalak, J., Zimney, K., Schmidt, S., & Puentedura, E. J. (2018). Can pain beliefs change in middle school students? A study of the effectiveness of pain neuroscience education. *Physiotherapy Theory and Practice, 34*(7), 542–550. https://doi.org/10.1080/09593985.2017.1423142
Louw, A., Puentedura, E. J., Diener, I., & Peoples, R. R. (2015). Preoperative therapeutic neuroscience education for lumbar radiculopathy: A single-case fMRI report. *Physiotherapy Theory and Practice, 31*(7), 496–508. https://doi.org/10.3109/09593985.2015.1038374

Louw, A., Puentedura, E., Schmidt, S., & Zimney, K. (2018). *Pain neuroscience education: Teaching people about pain* (2nd ed.). Orthopedic Physical Therapy Products.

Louw, A., Zimney, K., O'Hotto, C., & Hilton, S. (2016). The clinical application of teaching people about pain. *Physiotherapy Theory and Practice, 32*(5), 385–395. https://doi.org/10.1080/09593985.2016.1194652

Louw, A., Zimney, K., Puentedura, E. J., & Diener, I. (2016). The efficacy of pain neuroscience education on musculoskeletal pain: A systematic review of the literature. *Physiotherapy Theory and Practice, 32*(5), 332–355. https://doi.org/10.1080/09593985.2016.1194646

Lovheim, H. (2011). A new three-dimensional model for emotions and monoamine neurotransmitters. *Medical Hypotheses, 78*(2), 341–348. https://doi.org/10.1016/j.mehy.2011.11.016

Lubar, J. F., & Shouse, M. N. (1976). EEG and behavioral changes in a hyperkinetic child concurrent with training of the sensorimotor rhythm (SMR): A preliminary report. *Biofeedback and Self-regulation, 1*(3), 293–306.

Luctkar-Flude, M. F., Tyerman, J., & Groll, D. (2019). Exploring the use of neurofeedback by cancer survivors: Results of interviews with neurofeedback providers and clients. *Asia-Pacific Journal of Oncology Nursing, 6*(1), 35–42. https://doi.org/10.4103/apjon.apjon_34_18

Luke, C. C. (2016). *Neuroscience for counselors and therapists: Integrating the sciences of mind and brain.* Sage Publishing.

Lyon, L. (2018). 'All disease begins in the gut': Was Hippocrates right? *Brain: A Journal of Neurology, 141*(3), 1–5. https://doi.org/10.1093/brain/awy017

Ma, X., Yue, Z., Gong, Z., Zhang, H., Duan, N., Shi, Y., Wei, G. X., & Li, Y. (2017). The effect of diaphragmatic breathing on attention, negative affect and stress in healthy adults. *Frontiers in Psychology, 8*, 874. https://doi.org/10.3389/fpsyg.2017.00874

Macdonald, K., Germine, L., Anderson, A., Christodoulou, J., & McGrath, L. M. (2017). Dispelling the myth: Training in education or neuroscience decreases but does not eliminate beliefs in neuromyths. *Frontiers in Psychology, 8*, 1314. https://doi.org/10.3389/fpsyg.2017.01314.

Maclean, P. D. (1990). *The triune brain in evolution: Role in paleocerebral functions.* Plenum Press.

Magnavita, J. J. (Ed.). (2018). *Using technology in mental health practice.* American Psychological Association.

Makinson, R. A., & Young, J. S. (2012). Cognitive behavioral therapy and the treatment of posttraumatic stress disorder: Where counseling and neuroscience meet. *Journal of Counseling & Development, 90*(2), 131–140. https://doi.org/10.1111/j.1556-6676.2012.00017.x

Malchiodi, C. A. (Ed.). (2005). *Expressive therapies.* Guilford Press.

Manchikanti, L., Fellows, B., Ailinani, H., & Pampati, V. (2010). Therapeutic use, abuse, and nonmedical use of opioids: A ten-year perspective. *Pain Physician, 13*(5), 401–435.

Maniam, J., Antoniadis, C., & Morris, M. J. (2014). Early-life stress, HPA axis adaptation, and mechanisms contributing to later health outcomes. *Frontiers in Endocrinology, 5*, 73. https://doi.org/10.3389/fendo.2014.00073

March, J. S. & Vitiello, B. (2009). Clinical messages from the treatment for adolescent depression study (TADS). *American Journal of Psychiatry, 166*(10), 1118–1123. https://doi.org/10.1176/appi.ajp.2009.08101606

Marksberry, J. A., & Kirsch, D. L. (2018). Cranial electrotherapy stimulation. In J. J. Magnavita (Ed.), *Using technology in mental health practice* (pp. 85–100). American Psychological Association.

Marsella, A. J. (2010). Ethnocultural aspects of PTSD: An overview of concepts, issues, and treatments. *Traumatology, 16*(4), 17–26. https://doi.org/10.1177/1534765610388062

Marshall, C., Medves, J., Docherty, D., & Paterson, M. (2011). Interprofessional jargon: How is it exclusionary? Cultural determinants of language use in health care practice. *Journal of Interprofessional Care, 25*(6), 452–453. https://doi.org/10.3109/13561820.2011.597891

Martin, R. E., & Ochsner, K. N. (2016). The neuroscience of emotion regulation development: Implications for education. *Current Opinion in Behavioral Sciences, 10*, 142–148. https://doi.org/10.1016/j.cobeha.2016.06.006

Matta Mello Portugal, E., Cevada, T., Sobral Monteiro-Junior, R., Teixeira Guimarães, T., da Cruz Rubini, E., Lattari, E., Blois, C., & Camaz Deslandes, A. (2013). Neuroscience of exercise: From neurobiology mechanisms to mental health. *Neuropsychobiology, 68*, 1–14. https://doi.org/10.1159/000350946

Mattson, S. N., Crocker, N., & Nguyen, T. T. (2011). Fetal alcohol spectrum disorders: Neuropsychological and behavioral features. *Neuropsychology Review, 21*(2), 81–101. https://doi.org/10.1007/s11065-011-9167-9

Mayer, E. A. (2011). Gut feelings: The emerging biology of gut-brain communication. *Nature Reviews Neuroscience, 12*(8), 453–466. https://doi.org/10.1038/nrn3071

Mayer, J. D., Salovey, P., & Caruso, D. R. (2008). Emotional intelligence: New ability or eclectic trait? *American Psychologist, 63*(6), 503–517. https://doi.org/10.1037/0003-066X.63.6.503

Mayer, K., Wyckoff, S. N., Schulz, U., & Strehl, U. (2012). Neurofeedback for adult attention-deficit/hyperactivity disorder: Investigation of slow cortical potential neurofeedback—preliminary results. *Journal of Neurotherapy, 16*(1), 37–45. https://doi.org/10.1080/10874208.2012.650113

McEwen, B. S. (1998). Stress, adaptation, and disease: Allostasis and allostatic load. *Annals of the NY Academy of Sciences, 840*(1), 33–44. https://doi.org/10.1111/j.1749-6632.1998.tb09546.x

McEwen, B. S., & Morrison, J. H. (2013). The brain on stress: Vulnerability and plasticity of the prefrontal cortex over the life course. *Neuron, 79*(1), 16–29. https://doi.org/10.1016/j.neuron.2013.06.028

McHenry, B., Sikorski, A. M., & McHenry, J. (2014). *A counselor's introduction to neuroscience.* Routledge/Taylor & Francis Group.

McHugh, R. K., Fitzmaurice, G. M., Carroll, K. M., Griffin, M. L., Hill, K. P., Wasan, A. D., & Weiss, R. D. (2014). Assessing craving and its relationship to subsequent prescription opioid use among treatment-seeking prescription opioid dependent patients. *Drug and Alcohol Dependence, 145*, 121-126. doi: 10.1016/j.drugalcdep.2014.10.002

McKay, D., & Tolin, D. F. (2017). Empirically supported psychological treatments and the research domain criteria (RDoC). *Journal of Affective Disorders, 216*, 78–88. https://doi.org/10.1016/j.jad.2016.10.018

McMahon, S. B., & Koltzenburg, M. (Eds.) (2005). *Wall and Melzack's Textbook of pain* (5th ed.). Elsevier.

McNevin, N.H., Wulf, G., & Carlson, C. (2000). Effects of attentional focus, self-control, and dyad training on motor learning: Implications for physical rehabilitation. *Physical Therapy, 80*(4), 373–385. https://doi.org/10.1093/ptj/80.4.373

McRae, K., Misra, S., Prasad, A. K., Pereira, S. C., & Gross, J. J. (2012). Bottom-up and top-down emotion generation: Implications for emotion regulation. *Social Cognitive and Affective Neuroscience, 7*(3), 253–262. https://doi.org/10.1093/scan/nsq103

Meauley, E., & Courneya, K. S. (1994). The subjective exercise experiences scale (SEES): Development and preliminary validation. *Journal of Sport and Exercise Psychology, 16*(2), 163–177. doi:10.1123/jsep.16.2.163

Meeus, M., Nijs, J., Van Oosterwijck, J., Van Alsenoy, V., & Truijen, S. (2010). Pain physiology education improves pain beliefs in patients with chronic fatigue syndrome compared with pacing and self-management education: A double-blind randomized controlled trial. *Archives of Physical Medicine and Rehabilitation, 91*(8), 1153–1159. https://doi.org/10.1016/j.apmr.2010.04.020

Meeusuen, R. (2006). Physical activity and neurotransmitter release. In E. O. Acevedo & P. Ekkekakis (Eds.), *Psychobiology of physical activity* (pp. 129–143). Human Kinetics.

Melzack, R. (2001). Pain and the neuromatrix in the brain. *Journal of Dental Education, 65*(12), 1378–1382.

Merrick, M. T., Ports, K. A., Ford, D. C., O Afifi, T., Gershoff, E. T., & Grogan-Kaylor, A. (2017). Unpacking the impact of adverse childhood experiences on adult mental health. *Child Abuse & Neglect, 69*, 10–19. https://doi.org/10.1016/j.chiabu.2017.03.016

Metzl, E. S. & Morrell, M. A. (2008). The role of creativity in models of resilience: Theoretical exploration and practical applications. *Journal of Creativity in Mental Health, 3*(3), 303–318.

Michielsen, H. J., De Vries, J., & Van Heck, G. L. (2003). Psychometric qualities of a brief self- rated fatigue measure: The Fatigue Assessment Scale. *Journal of Psychosomatic Research, 54*, 345–352.

Mikkelsen, K., Stojanovska, L., Polenakovic, M., Bosevski, M., & Apostolopoulos, V. (2017). Exercise and mental health. *Maturitas, 106*, 48–56. https://doi.org/10.1016/j.maturitas.2017.09.003

Miller, R. (2016). Neuroeducation: Integrating brain-based psychoeducation into clinical practice. *Journal of Mental Health Counseling, 38*(2), 103–115. https://doi.org/10.17744/mehc.38.2.02

Miller, R. M., & Barrio Minton, C. A. (2016). Experiences learning interpersonal neurobiology: An interpretive phenomenological analysis. *Journal of Mental Health Counseling, 38*(1), 47–61. https://doi.org/10.17744/mehc.38.1.04

Miller, W. R., & Rollnick, S. (2013). *Motivational interviewing: Helping people change* (3rd ed.). Guilford Press.

Molteni, R., Barnard, R. J., Ying, Z., Roberts, C. K., & Gomez-Pinilla, F. (2002). A high-fat, refined sugar diet reduces hippocampal brain-derived neurotrophic factor, neuronal plasticity, and learning. *Neuroscience, 112*(4), 803–814. https://doi.org/10.1016/s0306-4522(02)00123-9

Monfils, M. H., Cowansage, K. K., Klann, E., & Ledoux, J. E. (2009). Extinction-reconsolidation boundaries: Key to persistent attenuation of fear memories. *Science, 324*(5929), 951–955. https://doi.org/10.1126/science.1167975

Mons, N., & Beracochea, D. (2016). Behavioral neuroadaptation to alcohol: From glucocorticoids to histone acetylation. *Front Psychiatry, 7*, 165. eCollection.

Montag, C., & Panksepp, J. (2017). Primary emotional systems and personality: An evolutionary perspective. *Frontiers in Psychology, 8*, 1–15.

Montague, P. R., Dayan, P., & Sejnowski, T. J. (1996). A framework for mesencephalic dopamine systems based on predictive Hebbian learning. *Journal of Neuroscience, 16*(5), 1936–1947.

Montgomery, A. (2013). *Neurobiology essentials for clinicians: What every therapist needs to know.* W.W. Norton & Company.

Monti, D., Peterson, C., Kunkel, E., Hauck, W., Pequignot, E., Rhodes, L., & Brainard, G. (2006). A randomized, controlled trial of mindfulness-based art therapy (MBAT) for women with cancer. *Psycho-Oncology, 15*(5), 363–373.

Moore, E. M., Migliorini, R., Infante, M. A., & Riley, E. P. (2014). Fetal alcohol spectrum disorders: Recent neuroimaging findings. *Current Developmental Disorders Reports, 1*(3), 161–172. https://doi.org/10.1007/s40474-014-0020-8

Moore, R. A., Derry, S., Aldington, D., Cole, P., & Wiffen, P. J. (2015). Amitriptyline for fibromyalgia in adults. *Cochrane Database of Systematic Reviews, 7*, CD011824. https://doi.org/10.1002/14651858.cd011824

Moore, R. A., Wiffen, P. J., Derry, S., & McQuay, H. J. (2011). Gabapentin for chronic neuropathic pain and fibromyalgia in adults. *Cochrane Database of Systematic Reviews, 16*(3), CD007938. https://doi.org/10.1002/14651858.cd007938.pub2

Morris, A. S., Criss, M. M., Silk, J. S., & Houtlberg, B. J. (2017). The impact of parenting on emotion regulation during childhood and adolescence. *Child Development Perspectives, 11*(4), 233–238. https://doi.org/10.1111/cdep.12238

Moseley, G. L. (2003). Joining forces—combining cognition-targeted motor control training with group or individual pain physiology education: A successful treatment for chronic low back pain. *Journal of Manual & Manipulative Therapy, 11*(2), 88–94. https://doi.org/10.1179/106698103790826383

Moseley, G. L. (2004). Evidence for a direct relationship between cognitive and physical change during an education intervention in people with chronic low back pain. *European Journal of Pain, 8*(1), 39–45. https://doi.org/10.1016/s1090-3801(03)00063-6

Moseley, G. L. (2007). Reconceptualising pain according to modern pain science. *Physical Therapy Reviews, 12*(3), 169–178. https://doi.org/10.1179/108331907x223010

Moseley, G. L., Nicholas, M. K., & Hodges, P. W. (2004) A randomized controlled trial of intensive neurophysiology education in chronic low back pain. *Clinical Journal of Pain, 20*(5), 324–330. https://doi.org/10.1097/00002508-200409000-00007

Moseley, L. (2002). Combined physiotherapy and education is efficacious for chronic low back pain. *Australian Journal of Physiotherapy, 48*(4), 297–302. https://doi.org/10.1016/s0004-9514(14)60169-0

Moss, D. (1999). Biofeedback, mind-body medicine, and the higher limits of human nature. In D. Moss (Ed.), *Humanistic and transpersonal psychology: A historical and biographical sourcebook* (pp. 145–161). Greenwood Press/ Greenwood Publishing Group.

Murawski, N. J., Moore, E. M., Thomas, J. D., & Riley, E. P. (2015). Advances in diagnosis and treatment of fetal alcohol spectrum disorders: From animal models to human studies. *Alcohol Research: Current Reviews, 37*(1), 97–108.

Myers, J., & Sweeney, T. (2004). The indivisible self: An evidence-based model of wellness. *Journal of Individual Psychology, 60*(3), 234–244.

Myers, J. E., & Young, J. S. (2012). Brain wave biofeedback: Benefits of integrating neurofeedback in counseling. *Journal of Counseling & Development, 90*(1), 20–28. https://doi.org/10.1111/j.1556-6676.2012.00003.x

Nadal, K. L. (2018). *Microaggressions and traumatic stress: Theory, research, and clinical treatment.* American Psychological Association.

Nader, K., & Einarsson, E. Ö. (2010). Memory reconsolidation: An update. *Annals of the New York Academy of Sciences, 1191*(1), 27–41. https://doi.org/10.1111/j.1749-6632.2010.05443.x

Nakagawa, S., Sugiura, M., Sekiguchi, A., Kotozaki, Y., Miyauchi, C. M., Hanawa, S., Araki, T., Takeuchi, H., Sakuma, A., Taki, Y., & Kawashima, R. (2016). Effects of post-traumatic growth on the dorsolateral prefrontal cortex after a disaster. *Scientific Reports, 6*, 343–364. https://doi.org/10.1038/srep34364

Naqvi, N., Shiv, B., & Bechara, A. (2006). The role of emotion in decision making: A cognitive neuroscience perspective. *Current Directions in Psychological Science, 15*(5), 260–264. https://doi.org/10.1111/j.1467-8721.2006.00448.x

National Institute of Mental Health (NIMH). (n.d.). *Brain stimulation therapies.* https://www.nimh.nih.gov/health/topics/brain-stimulation-therapies/brain-stimulation-therapies.shtml

National Institute of Mental Health (NIMH). (2013). What is post-traumatic stress disorder (PTSD)? http://www.nimh.nih.gov/about/index.shtml

National Institute on Drug Abuse (NIDA). (2014). Drugs, brains, and behavior: The science of addiction. https://www.drugabuse.gov/publications/drugs-brains-behavior-science-addiction/preface

National Scientific Council on the Developing Child. (2010). *Early experiences can alter gene expression and affect long-term development* (Working paper 10). http://developingchild.harvard.edu/resources/reports_and_working_papers/working_papers/wp10/

Neeru, D. C., Khakha, N.D.C., Satapathy, S., & Dey, A. B. (2015). Impact of Jacobson progressive muscle relaxation (JPMR) and deep breathing exercises on anxiety, psychological distress, and quality of sleep of hospitalized older adults. *Journal of Psychosocial Research, 10*(2), 211–223.

Nestler, E. J. (2002). From neurobiology to treatment: Progress against addiction. *Nature Neuroscience, 5*, 1076–1079. https://doi.org/10.1038/nn945

Nijs, J., Roussel, N., van Wilgen, C. P., Köke, A., & Smeets, R. (2013). Thinking beyond muscles and joints: Therapists' and patients' attitudes and beliefs regarding chronic musculoskeletal pain are key to applying effective treatment. *Manual Therapy, 18*(2), 96–102. https://doi.org/10.1016/j.math.2012.11.001

Nijs, J., & Van Houdenhove, B. (2009). From acute musculoskeletal pain to chronic widespread pain and fibromyalgia: Application of pain neurophysiology in manual therapy practice. *Manual Therapy, 14*(1), 3–12. https://doi.org/10.1016/j.math.2008.03.001

Nijs, J., Van Wilgen, C. P., Van Oosterwijck, J., Van Ittersum, M., & Meeus, M. (2011). How to explain central sensitization to patients with 'unexplained' chronic musculoskeletal pain: Practice guidelines. *Manual Therapy, 16*(5), 413–418. https://doi.org/10.1016/j.math.2011.04.005

Niles, S. G., & Harris-Bowlsbey, J. E. (2017). *Career development interventions* (5th ed.). Pearson.

Nowack, K., & Radecki, D. (2018). Introduction to the special Issue: Neuromythconceptions in consulting psychology—between a rock and a hard place. *Consulting Psychology Journal: Practice and Research, 70*(1), 1–10. http://dx.doi.org/10.1037/cpb0000108

Oana, C. R., Ciobica, A., & Timofte, D. (2018). The current state of knowledge on the link between the human microbiome and some neuropsychiatric disorders. *Bulletin of Integrative Psychiatry, 24*(2), 27–38.

Ochoa-Repáraz, J., & Kasper, L. H. (2018). The microbiome and neurologic disease: Past and future of a 2-way interaction. *Neurotherapeutics, 15*(1), 1–4. https://doi.org/10.1007/s13311-018-0604-9

Ochsner, K. N., Ray, R. R., Hughes, B., McRae, K., Cooper, J. C., Weber, J., Gabrieli, J. D., & Gross, J. J. (2009). Bottom-up and top-down processes in emotion generation: Common and distinct neural mechanisms. *Psychological Science, 20*(11), 1322–1331. https://doi.org/10.1111/j.1467-9280.2009.02459.x

Ogden, P., & Fisher, J. (2015). *Sensorimotor psychotherapy: Interventions for trauma and attachment.* W. W. Norton & Company.

Ogden, P., & Minton, K. (2000). Sensorimotor psychotherapy: One method for processing traumatic memory. *Traumatology, 6*(3), 149–173. https://doi.org/10.1177/153476560000600302

Ogden, P., Minton, K., & Pain, C. (2006). *Trauma and the body: A sensorimotor approach to psychotherapy.* W.W. Norton & Company.

Ohman, A. (2005). The role of the amygdala in human fear: Automatic detection of threat. *Psychoneuroendocrinology, 30*(10), 953–958. https://doi.org/10.1016/j.psyneuen.2005.03.019

O'Hare, E. D., Kan, E., Yoshii, J., Mattson, S. N., Riley, E. P., Thompson, P. M., Toga, A. W., & Sowell, E. R. (2005). Mapping cerebellar vermal morphology and cognitive correlates in prenatal alcohol exposure. *Neuroreport, 16*(12), 1285–1290. https://doi.org/10.1097/01.wnr.0000176515.11723.a2

O'Kelly, J., Fachner, J. C., & Tervaniemi, M. (2016). Editorial: Dialogues in music therapy and music neuroscience: Collaborative understanding driving clinical advances. *Frontiers in Human Neuroscience, 10*, 585. https://doi.org/10.3389/fnhum.2016.00585

Olex, S., & Olex, K. (2018). Effects of exercise on mental health. In D. A. Monti & A. B. Newberg (Eds.), *Integrative psychiatry and brain health* (2nd ed., pp. 50–96). Oxford University Press. https://doi.org/ 10.1093/med/9780190690557.001.0001

Oliveira-Silva, P., & Gonçalves, O. F. (2011). Responding empathically: A question of heart, not a question of skin. *Applied Psychophysiology and Biofeedback, 36*(3), 201–207. https://doi.org/10.1007/s10484-011-9161-2

Olsen, A., & McHose, C. (1991). *Body stories: A guide to experiential anatomy.* Station Hill Press, Inc.

Organization for Economic Cooperation and Development. (2002). *Understanding the brain: Towards a new learning science.* Paris, France: OECD.

Orlinsky, D. E., Ronnestad, M. H., & Willutzki, U. (2004). Fifty years of psychotherapy process-outcome research: Continuity and change. In M. J. Lambert (Ed.), *Bergin and Garfield's handbook of psychotherapy and behavior change* (5th ed., pp. 307–389). John Wiley & Sons, Inc.

Owen, J. (2013). Early career perspectives on psychotherapy research and practice: Psychotherapist effects, multicultural orientation, and couple interventions. *Psychotherapy, 50*(4), 496–502. https://doi.org/10.1037/a0034617

Owen, J., Drinane, J. M., Tao, K. W., DasGupta, D. R., Zhang, Y. S. D., & Adelson, J. (2018). An experimental test of microaggression detection in psychotherapy: Therapist multicultural orientation. *Professional Psychology: Research and Practice, 49*(1), 9–21. https://doi.org/10.1037/pro0000152

Owen, J., Tao, K. W., Imel, Z. E., Wampold, B. E., & Rodolfa, E. (2014). Addressing racial and ethnic microaggressions in therapy. *Professional Psychology: Research and Practice, 45*(4), 283–290. https://doi.org/10/1037/a0037420

Ozonoff, S., & Miller, J. N. (1995). Teaching theory of mind: A new approach to social skills training for individuals with autism. *Journal of Autism and Developmental Disorders, 25*(4), 415–433. https://doi.org/10.1007/BF02179376

Oztop, E., Kawato, M., & Arbib, M.A. (2013). Mirror neurons: Functions, mechanisms and models. *Neuroscience Letters, 540*, 43–55. https://doi.org/10.1016/j.neulet.2012.10.005

Paley, B., & O'Connor, M. J. (2011). Behavioral interventions for children and adolescents with fetal alcohol spectrum disorders. *Alcohol Research & Health, 34*(1), 64–75.

Panksepp, J. (1986). The neurochemistry of behavior. *Annual Review of Psychology, 37*, 77–107. https://doi.org/10.1146/annurev.ps.37.020186.000453

Panksepp, J. (2009). Brain emotional systems and qualities of mental life: From animal models of affect to implications for psychotherapeutics. In D. Fosha, D. J. Siegel, & M. F. Solomon (Eds.), *The healing power of emotion: Affective neuroscience, development & clinical practice* (pp. 1–26). W. W. Norton & Company.

Panksepp, J. (2010). Affective neuroscience of the emotional BrainMind: Evolutionary perspectives and implications for understanding depression. *Dialogues in Clinical Neuroscience, 12*(4), 533–545.

Panksepp J. (2011). Cross-species affective neuroscience decoding of the primal affective experiences of humans and related animals. *PLoS ONE, 6*(9), 21236. https://doi.org/10.1371/journal.pone.0021236

Panksepp J., Knutson B., & Pruitt, D. L. (1998). Toward a neuroscience of emotion: The epigenetic foundations of emotional development. In M. F. Mascolo, & S. Griffin (Eds.), *What develops in emotional development?* (pp. 53–84). Plenum Press.

Panksepp, J., & Watt, D. (2011). What is basic about basic emotions? Lasting lessons from affective neuroscience. *Emotion Review, 3*(4), 387–396. https://doi.org/10.1177/1754073911410741

Paquette, V., Levesque, J., Mensour, B., Leroux, J. M., Beaudoin, G., Bourgouin, P., & Beauregard, M. (2003). "Change the mind and you change the brain": Effects of cognitive-behavioral therapy on the neural correlates of spider phobia. *NeuroImage, 18*(2), 401–409. https://doi.org/10.1016/S1053-8119(02)00030-7

Parashar, A., & Udayabanu, M. (2016). Gut microbiota regulates key modulators of social behavior. *European Neuropsychopharmacology, 26*(1), 78–91. https://doi.org/10.1016/j.euroneuro.2015.11.002

Pardini, D. A., & Fite, P. J. (2010). Symptoms of conduct disorder, oppositional defiant disorder, attention-deficit/hyperactivity disorder, and callous-unemotional traits as unique predictors of psychosocial maladjustment in boys: Advancing an evidence base for DSM-V. *Journal of the American Academy of Child & Adolescent Psychiatry, 49*(11), 1134–1144. https://doi.org/10.1016/j.jaac.2010.07.010

Pascalau, R., Stănilă, R. P., Sfrângeu, S., & Szabo, B. (2018). Anatomy of the limbic white matter tracts as revealed by fiber dissection and tractography. *World Neurosurgery, 113*, E672–E689

Pasek, T. P. (2016). Hierarchical mazes in psychological research. *American Journal of Psychology, 129*(4), 443–459. https://doi.org/10.5406/amerjpsyc.129.4.0443

Patrick, S. W., Fry, C. E., Jones, T. F., & Buntin, M. B. (2016). Implementation of prescription drug monitoring programs associated with reductions in opioid-related death rates. *Health Affairs, 35*(7), 1324–1332. https://doi.org/10.1377/hlthaff.2015.1496

Patterson, D. W., & Schmidt, L. A. (2003). Neuroanatomy of the human affective system. *Brain and Cognition, 52*(1), 24–26. https://doi.org/10.1016/S0278-2626(03)00005-8

Paul, J. D. (2016). Understimulation of cerebellum in Asperger's syndrome: A personal perspective. *Schizophrenia Bulletin, 42*(5), 1086–1089. https://doi.org/10.1093/schbul/sbu107

Perkins, T., Stokes, M., McGillivray, J., & Bittar, R. (2010). Mirror neuron dysfunction in autism spectrum disorders. *Journal of Clinical Neuroscience, 17*(10), 1239–1243. https://doi.org/10.1016/j.jocn.2010.01.026

Perner, J., & Lang, B. (2000). Theory of mind and executive function: Is there a developmental relationship? In S. Baron-Cohen, H. Tager-Flusberg, & D. J. Cohen (Eds.), *Understanding other minds: Perspectives from developmental cognitive neuroscience* (2nd ed., pp. 150–181). Oxford University Press.

Perry, B. D. (2009). Examining child maltreatment through a neurodevelopmental lens: Clinical applications of the neurosequential model of therapeutics. *Journal of Loss and Trauma, 14*(4), 240–255. https://doi.org/10.1080/15325020903004350

Peterson, B. S., Wang, Z., Horga, G., Warner, V., Rutherford, B., Klahr, K. W., . . . Weissman, M. M. (2014). Discriminating risk and resilience endophenotypes from lifetime illness effects in familial major depressive disorder. *JAMA Psychiatry, 71*(2), 136–148. https://doi.org/10.1001/jamapsychiatry.2013.4048

Petrenko, C. L. M. (2015). Positive behavioral interventions and family support for fetal alcohol spectrum disorders. *(2015). Current Developmental Disorders Reports, 2*(3), 199–209. doi: 10.1007/s40474-015-0052-8

Pineda, J. A., Carrasco, K., Datko, M., Pillen, S., & Schalles, M. (2014). Neurofeedback training produces normalization in behavioural and electrophysiological measures of high-functioning autism. *Philosophical Transactions of the Royal Society of London. Series B, Biological Sciences, 369*(1644), 20130183. https://doi.org/10.1098/rstb.2013.0183

Pisarik, C. T., Rowell, P. C., & Thompson, L. K. (2017). A phenomenological study of career anxiety among college students. *Career Development Quarterly, 65*(4), 339–352. https://doi.org/10.1002/cdq.12112

Pogosyan, M. (2016, October 9). *Emotion perception across cultures: How culture influences the way we interpret facial expressions of emotion.* Psychology Today. https://www.psychologytoday.com/us/blog/between-cultures/201610/emotion-perception-across-cultures

Pollak, S. (2013). Teaching mindfulness in therapy. In C. K. Germer, R. D. Siegel, & P. R. Fulton (Eds.), *Mindfulness and psychotherapy* (2nd ed., pp. 133–147). Guilford Press.

Ponce-Garcia, E., Madewell, A. N., & Kennison, S. M. (2015) The development of the scale of protective factors: Resilience in a violent trauma sample. *Violence and Victims*, 30 (5), 735–755.

Popova, S., Lange, S., Probst, C., Gmel, G., & Rehm, J. (2017). Estimation of national, regional, and global prevalence of alcohol use during pregnancy and fetal alcohol syndrome: A systematic review and meta-analysis. *Lancet Glob Health, 5*(3), e290–e299. https://doi.org/10.1016/S2214-109X(17)30021-9.

Porges, S. W. (2003). The polyvagal theory: Phylogenetic contributions to social behavior. *Physiology & Behavior, 79*(3), 503–513. https://doi.org/10.1016/S0031-9384(03)00156

Porges, S. W. (2011). *The polyvagal theory: Neurophysiological foundations of emotions, attachment, communication, and self-regulation.* W.W. Norton & Company.

Porges, S. W. (2017). *The pocket guide to the polyvagal theory: The transforming power of feeling safe.* W. W. Norton & Company.

Prasad, J. A., Abela, A. R., & Chudasama, Y. (2017). Midline thalamic reuniens lesions improve executive behaviors. *Neuroscience*, 345, 77–88.

Prati, G., & Pietrantoni, L. (2009). Optimism, social support, and coping strategies as factors contributing to posttraumatic growth: A meta-analysis. *Journal of Loss and Trauma, 14*(5), 364–388. https://doi.org/10.1080/15325020902724271

Premack, D., & Woodruff, G. (1978). Does the chimpanzee have a theory of mind? *Behavioral and Brain Sciences, 1*(4), 515–526. https://doi.org/10.1017/S0140525X00076512

PREP, Inc. (2011). *Independent lesson: Anger and Stress: Letting FLo drive.* https://www.prepinc.com/Content/CURRICULA/Letting-FLo-Drive.htm

Prescott, D. S., Maeschalck, C. L., & Miller, S. D. (Eds.). (2017). *Feedback informed treatment in clinical practice: Reaching for excellence.* American Psychological Association.

Preston, A. R., & Eichenbaum, H. (2013). Interplay of hippocampus and prefrontal cortex in memory. *Current Biology, 23*(17), R764–773. https://doi.org/10.1016/j.cub.2013.05.041

Pujol, J., Harrison, B. J., Ortiz, H., Deus, J., Soriano-Mas, C., Lopez-Sola, M., Graniello, B., Wickramaratne, P., Garcia, F., Yu, S., Hao, X., Adams, P. B., Qian, M., Liu, J., Gerber, A., & Cardoner, N. (2009). Influence of the fusiform gyrus on amygdala response to emotional faces in the non-clinical range of social anxiety. *Psychological Medicine, 39*(7), 1177–1187. https://doi.org/10.1017/S003329170800500X

Purves, D., & Hadley, R. D. (1985). Changes in the dendritic branching of adult mammalian neurones revealed by repeated imaging in situ. *Nature, 315*(6018), 404–406. https://doi.org/0.1038/315404a0

Radley, J., Morilak, D., Viau, V., & Campeau, S. (2015). Chronic stress and brain plasticity: Mechanisms underlying adaptive and maladaptive changes and implications for stress-related CNS disorders. *Neuroscience and Biobehavioral Reviews, 58*, 79–91. https://doi.org/10.1016/j.neubiorev.2015.06.018

Raio, C. M., Orederu, T. A., Palazzolo, L., Shurick, A. A., & Phelps, E. A. (2013). Cognitive emotion regulation fails the stress test. *Proceedings of the National Academy of Sciences of the United States of America, 110*(37), 15139–15144. https://doi.org/10.1073/pnas.1305706110

Ramos, C., Leal, I. & Tedeschi, R.G. (2016). Protocol for the psychotherapeutic group intervention for facilitating posttraumatic growth in nonmetastatic breast cancer patients. *BMC Women's Health, 16*(22), 1–9. https://doi.org/10.1186/s12905-016-0302-x

Rappaport, L. (Ed.). (2014). *Mindfulness and the arts therapies: Theory and practice.* Jessica Kingsley Publishers.

Rapoport, M., Van Reekum, R., & Mayberg, H. (2000). The role of the cerebellum in cognition and behavior: A selective review. *Journal of Neuropsychiatry and Clinical Neurosciences, 12*(2), 193–198. https://doi.org/10.1176/appi.neuropsych.12.2.193

Rasmussen, C., & Bisanz, J. (2009). Executive functioning in children with fetal alcohol spectrum disorders: Profiles and age-related differences. *Child Neuropsychology, 15*(3), 201–215. https://doi.org/10.1080/09297040802385400

Ratey, J. J. (2002). *A user's guide to the brain: Perception, attention, and the four theaters of the brain.* Vintage Books.

Reardon, R. C., Lenz, J. G., Sampson, J. P., Jr., & Peterson, G. W. (2011). Big questions facing vocational psychology: A cognitive information processing perspective.

Journal of Career Assessment, 19(3), 240–250. https://doi.org/10.1177/1069072710395531

Reber, A. S. (1989). Implicit learning and tacit knowledge. *Journal of Experimental Psychology: General, 118*(3), 219–235. https://doi.org/10.1037/0096-3445.118.3.219

Reese, R. F., & Myers, J. E. (2012). EcoWellness: The missing factor in holistic wellness models. *Journal of Counseling & Development, 90*(4), 400–406. https://doi.org/10.1002/j.1556-6676.2012.00050.x

Reese, R. J., Usher, E. L., Bowman, D. C., Norsworthy, L. A., Halstead, J. L., Rowlands, S. R., & Chisholm, R. R. (2009). Using client feedback in psychotherapy training: An analysis of its influence on supervision and counselor self-efficacy. *Training and Education in Professional Psychology, 3*(3), 157–168. https://doi.org/10.1037.a0015673

Reger-Nash, B., Bauman, A. E., Smith, B. J., Craig, C. L., Abildso, C. G., & Leyden, K. M. (2011). Organizing an effective community-wide physical activity campaign: A step-by-step guide. *ACSM's Health & Fitness Journal, 15*(5), 21–27. https://doi.org/10.1249/FIT.0b013e318229cc4f

Reinders, A. S., Chalavi, S., Schlumpf, Y. R., Vissia, E. M., Nijenhuis, E. S., Jäncke, L., & Ecker, C. (2018). Neurodevelopmental origins of abnormal cortical morphology in dissociative identity disorder. *Acta Psychiatrica Scandinavica, 137*(2), 157–170. https://doi.org/10.1111/acps.12839

Relf, P. D. (2005). The therapeutic values of plants. *Pediatric Rehabilitation, 8*(3), 235–237. https://doi.org/10.1080/13638490400011140

Renna, M. E., Quintero, J. M., Fresco, D. M., & Mennin, D. S. (2017). Emotion regulation therapy: A mechanism-targeted treatment for disorders of distress. *Frontiers in Psychology, 8*, 98. https://doi.org/10.3389/fpsyg.2017.00098

Rieckmann, T., Daley, M., Fuller, B. E., Thomas, C. P., & McCarty, D. (2007). Client and counselor attitudes toward the use of medications for treatment of opioid dependence. *Journal of Substance Abuse Treatment, 32*(2), 207–215. https://doi.org/10.1016/j.jsat.2006.09.002

Riehl, M., & Michigan Medicine. (2018, January 23). Diaphragmatic breathing demonstration from Michigan Medicine [Video]. YouTube. https://www.youtube.com/watch?v=UB3tSaiEbNY&feature=youtu.be

Rizzolatti, G., & Craighero, L. (2004). The mirror-neuron system. *Annual Review of Neuroscience, 27*, 169–192. https://doi.org/10.1146/annurev.neuro.27.070203.144230

Roberts, G. (2019). *Feelings wheel.* https://feelingswheel.com

Robins, H., Perron, V., Heathcote, L. C., & Simons, L. E. (2016). Pain neuroscience education: State of the art and application in pediatrics. *Children, 3*(4), e43. https://doi.org/10.3390/children3040043

Rock, D., Siegel, D. J., Poelmans, S. A. Y., & Payne, J. (2012). *The healthy mind platter.* https://davidrock.net/files/02_The_Healthy_Mind_Platter_US.pdf

Roediger, H. L. (1990). Implicit memory: Retention without remembering. *American Psychologist, 45*(9), 1043–1056. https://doi.org/10.1037/0003-066x.45.9.1043

Rosenberg, M. (1965). *Society and the adolescent self-image.* Princeton University Press.

Rosenzweig, M. R., Bennett, E. L., & Diamond, M. C. (1972). Chemical and anatomical plasticity of brain: Replications and extensions, 1970. In J. Gaito (Ed.), *Macromolecules and behavior* (pp. 205–277). Springer.

Ross, D. A., Arbuckle, M. R., Travis, M. J., Dwyer, J. B., van Schalkwyk, G. I., & Ressler, K. J. (2017). An integrated neuroscience perspective on formulation and treatment planning for posttraumatic stress disorder: An educational review. *JAMA Psychiatry, 74*(4), 407–415. https://doi.org/10.1001/jamapsychiatry.2016.3325

Rossouw, J. G., Rossouw, P. J., Paynter, C., Ward, A., & Khnana, P. (2017). Predictive 6 factor resilience scale—domains of resilience and their role as enablers of job satisfaction. *International Journal of Neuropsychotherapy, 5*(1), 25–40. https://doi.org/10.12744/ijnpt.2017.1.0025-0040

Rossouw, P. J., & Rossouw, J. G. (2016). The predictive 6-factor resilience scale: Neurobiological fundamentals and organizational application. *International Journal of Neuropsychotherapy, 4*(1), 31–45. https://doi.org/10.1244/ijnpt.2016.0031-0045

Russell, M. E. B., Scott, A. B., Boggero, I. A., & Carlson, C. R. (2017). Inclusion of a rest period in diaphragmatic breathing increases high frequency heart rate variability: Implications for behavioral therapy. *Psychophysiology, 54*(3), 358–365. https://doi.org/10.1111/psyp.12791

Russell-Chapin, L.A. (2017). Neurocounseling assessment. In T. A. Field, L. K. Jones, & L. A. Russell-Chapin (Eds.), *Neurocounseling: Brain-based clinical approaches* (pp. 115–132). American Counseling Association.

Rustin, J. (2013). *Infant research & neuroscience at work in psychotherapy: Expanding the clinical repertoire.* W.W. Norton & Company.

Ryan, C. G., Gray, H. G., Newton, M., & Granat, M. H. (2010). Pain biology education and exercise classes compared to pain biology education alone for individuals with chronic low back pain: A pilot randomised controlled trial. *Manual Therapy, 15*(4), 382–387. https://doi.org/10.1016/j.math.2010.03.003

Rypma, B., Berger, J. S., Prabhakaran, V., Bly, B. M., Kimberg, D. Y., Biswal, B. B., & D'Esposito, M. (2006). Neural correlates of cognitive efficiency. *Neuroimage, 33*(3), 969–979. doi:10.1016/j.neuroimage.2006.05.065s

Saffin, J. M., & Tohid, H. (2016). Walk like me, talk like me. The connections between mirror neurons and autism spectrum disorder. *Neurosciences, 21*(2), 108–119. https://doi.org/10.17712/nsj.2016.2.20150472

Sah, P., & Westbrook, R. F. (2008). Behavioral neuroscience: The circuit of fear. *Nature, 454*(7204), 589.

Sale, A., Berardi, N., & Maffei, L. (2014). Environment and brain plasticity: Towards an endogenous pharmacotherapy. *Physiological Reviews, 94*(1), 189–234. https://doi.org/10.1152/physrev.0036.2012

Salovey, P., & Mayer, J. D. (1990). Emotional intelligence. *Imagination, Cognition and Personality, 9*(3), 185–211. https://doi.org/10.2190/DUGG-P24E-52WK-6CDG

Sandoval-Motta, S., Aldana, M., Martinez-Romero, E., & Frank, A. (2017). The human microbiome and the

Sapolsky, R. M. (2000). How do glucocorticoids influence stress responses? Integrating permissive, suppressive, stimulatory, and preparative actions. *Endocrine Reviews, 21*(1), 55–89. http://doi:10.1210/er.21.1.55

Sar, V., Unal, S. N., & Ozturk, E. (2007). Frontal and occipital perfusion changes in dissociative identity disorder. *Psychiatry Research, 156*(3), 217–223.

Sauer-Zavala, S., Gunter, C. A., Farchione, T. J., Boettcher, H. T., Bullis, J., & Barlow, D. H. (2017). Current definitions of "transdiagnostic" in treatment development: A search for consensus. *Behavior Therapy, 48*, 128–138. https://doi.org/10.1016/j.beth.2016.09.004

Scanlon, V. C., & Sanders, T. (2015). *Essentials of anatomy and physiology* (7th ed.). F. A. Davis Company.

Scarantino, A. (2016). The philosophy of emotions and its impact on affective science. In L. F. Barrett, M. Lewis, & J. M. Haviland-Jones (Eds.), *Handbook of emotions* (4th ed., pp. 3–48). Guilford Press.

Schaakxs, R. Wielaard, I., Verhoeven, J. E., Beekman, A. T. F., Penninx, W. J. H., & Comijs, H. C. (2016). Early and recent psychosocial stress and telomere length in older adults. *International Psychogeriatrics, 28*, 405–413. https://doi.org/10.1017/S1041610215001155

Schiller, D., Monfils, M., Raio, C. M., Johnson, D. C., LeDoux, J. E., & Phelps, E. A. (2010). Preventing the return of fear in humans using reconsolidation update mechanisms. *Nature, 463*(7277), 49–53. https://doi.org/10.1038/nature08637

Schmid, T. (2005). *Promoting health through creativity.* London: Whurr.Szeszko, P., Lehrner, A., & Yehuda, R. (2018). Glucocorticoids and hippocampal structure and functions in PTSD. *Harvard Review of Psychiatry, 26*(3), 142–157.

Schlopler E. & Mesibov, G.B. (Eds.) (1986). *Social behavior in autism.* Plenum Press.

Schooler, J., & Melcher, J. (1995). The ineffability of insight. In S. M. Smith, T. B. Ward, & R. A. Finke (Eds.), *The creative cognition approach* (pp. 97–133). MIT Press.

Schore, A. N. (1994). *Affect regulation and the origin of the self: The neurobiology of emotional development.* Lawrence Erlbaum Associates.

Schore, A. N. (2000). Attachment and the regulation of the right brain. *Attachment & Human Development, 2*(1), 23–47. https://doi.org/10.1080/146167300361309

Schore, A. N. (2001a). The effects of early relational trauma on right brain development, affect regulation, and infant mental health. *Infant Mental Health Journal, 22*(1–2), 201–269. https://doi.org/10.1002/1097-0355(200101/04)22:1<201::AID-IMHJ8>3.0.CO;2-9

Schore, A. N. (2001b). The effects of a secure attachment relationship on right brain development, affect regulation, and infant mental health. *Infant Mental Health Journal, 22*(1–2), 7–66 https://doi.org/10.1002/1097-0355(200101/04)22:1<7::AID-IMHJ2>3.0.CO;2-N

Schore, A. N. (2003a). *Affect dysregulation and disorders of the self.* W. W. Norton & Company.

Schore, A. N. (2003b). *Affect regulation and the repair of the self.* W. W. Norton & Company.

Schore, A. N. (2005). Attachment, affect regulation, and the developing right brain: Linking developmental neuroscience to pediatrics. *Pediatrics in Review, 26*(6), 204–217. https://doi.org/10.1542/pir.26-6-204

Schore, A. N. (2012). *The science of the art of psychotherapy.* W. W. Norton & Company.

Schore, A. N. (2014). The right brain is dominant in psychotherapy. *Psychotherapy, 51*(3), 388–397. https://doi.org/10.1037/a0037083

Schore, J. R., & Schore, A. N. (2008). Modern attachment theory: The central role of affect regulation in development and treatment. *Clinical Social Work Journal, 36*(1), 9–20. https://doi.org/10.1007/s10615-007-0111-7

Schore, A. N. (2017). Modern attachment theory. In S. N. Gold (Ed.), *APA handbook of trauma psychology: Foundations in knowledge* (Vol. 1, pp. 389–406). American Psychological Association. https://doi-org.turing.library.northwestern.edu/10.1037/0000019-020

Schulz, A., & Vögele, C. (2015). Interoception and stress. *Frontiers in Psychology, 6*(993), 1–23. https://doi.org/10.3389/fpsyg.2015.00993

Schwabe, L., Nader, K., & Pruessner, J. C. (2014). Reconsolidation of human memory: Brain mechanisms and clinical relevance. *Biological Psychiatry, 76*(4), 274–280. https://doi.org/10.1016/j.biopsych.2014.03.00

Sehgal, M., Sethi, K., & Vaneet, K. (2016). Psychosocial factors contributing to post traumatic growth. *Journal of Psychosocial Research*, 11, 437-445.

Shaffer, F., McCraty, R., & Zerr, C. L. (2014). A healthy heart is not a metronome: An integrative review of the heart's anatomy and heart rate variability. *Frontiers in Psychology, 5*(1040), 1–19. https://doi.org/10.3389/fpsycg.2014.01040

Shapiro, S., & Carlson, L. (2009). *The art and science of mindfulness.* American Psychological Association.

Shatz, C. J. (1992). The developing brain. *Scientific American, 267*(3), 60–67. https://doi.org/10.1038/scientificamerican0992-60

Shatz, C. J. (1996). Emergence of order in visual system development. *Proceedings of the National Academy of Sciences of the United States of America, 93*(2), 602–608. https://doi.org/10.1073/pnas.93.2.602

Shaver, P., & Mikulincer, M. (2007). Adult attachment strategies and the regulation of emotion. In J. J. Gross (Ed.), *Handbook of emotion regulation* (pp. 446–465). Guilford Press.

Shaw, S. L., & Murray, K. W. (2014). Monitoring alliance and outcome with client feedback measures. *Journal of Mental Health Counseling, 36*(1), 43–57. https://doi.org/10.17744/mehc.36.1.n5g64t3014231862

Shouse, M. N., & Lubar, J. F. (1979). Operant conditioning of EEG rhythms and Ritalin in the treatment of hyperkinesis. *Biofeedback & Self-Regulation, 4*(4), 299–311.

Siddiqui, S. V., Chatterjee, U., Kumar, D., Siddiqui, A., & Goyal, N. (2008). Neuropsychology of prefrontal cortex. *Indian Journal of Psychiatry, 50*(3), 202–208. https://doi.org/10.4103/0019-5545.43634

Siegel, D. (1999). *The developing mind: Toward a neurobiology of interpersonal experience.* Guilford Press.

Siegel, D. J. (2009). Mindful awareness, mindsight, and neural integration. *The Humanistic Psychologist, 37*(2), 137–158. https://doi.org/10.1080/08873260902892220

Siegel, D. J. (2010a). *Mindsight: The new science of personal transformation.* Bantam Books.

Siegel, D. J. (2010b). *The mindful therapist: A clinician's guide to mindsight and neural integration.* W.W. Norton & Company.

Siegel, D. J. (2012a). *Pocket guide to interpersonal neurobiology: An integrative handbook of the mind.* W. W. Norton & Company.

Siegel, D. J. (2012b). *The developing mind: How relationships and the brain interact to shape who we are* (2nd ed.). Guilford Press.

Siegel, D. J. (2014, September 16). *General interest, mental health, relationships.* https://www.drdansiegel.com/blog/2014/09/16/brain-insights-and-well-being/

Siegel, D. J. (2015). *Brainstorm: The power and purpose of the teenage brain.* Penguin.

Siegel, D. J. (2016). *Mind: A journey to the heart of being human.* W. W. Norton & Company.

Siegel, D. J., & Bryson, T. P. (2012). *The whole-brain child: 12 revolutionary strategies to nurture your child's developing mind.* Delacorte Press.

Siegel, E. H., Sands, M. K., Van den Noortgate, W., Condon, P., Chang, Y., Dy, J., Quigley, K. S., & Barrett, L. F. (2018). Emotion fingerprints or emotion populations? A meta-analytic investigation of autonomic features of emotion categories. *Psychological Bulletin, 144*(4), 343–393. https://doi.org/10.1037/bul0000128

Siegelmann, H. T. (2010). Complex systems science and brain dynamics. *Frontiers in Computational Neuroscience, 4,* 7. https://doi.org/10.3389/fncom.2010.00007

Silvers, J. A., & Moreira, J. F. G. (2019). Capacity and tendency: A neuroscientific framework for the study of emotion regulation. *Neuroscience Letters, 693,* 35–39. https://doi.org/10.1016/j.neulet.2017.09.017

Simpson, J. A., Collins, W. A., Tran, S., & Haydon, K. C. (2007). Attachment and the experience and expression of emotions in romantic relationships: A developmental perspective. *Journal of Personality and Social Psychology, 92*(2), 355–367. https://doi.org/10.1037/0022-3514.92.2.355

Singleton, E.G., Tiffany, S.T., & Henningfield, J. E. (1995). Development and validation of a new questionnaire to assess craving for alcohol. In L. S. Harris (Ed.), *Problems of drug dependence, 1994: Proceeding of the 56th Annual Meeting: The College on Problems of Drug Dependence, Inc., Volume II: Abstracts. NIDA Research Monograph, 153.* (p. 289). National Institute on Drug Abuse.

Sinha, R. (2013). The clinical neurobiology of drug craving. *Current Opinion in Neurobiology, 23*(4), 649–654. https://doi.org/10.1016/j.conb.2013.05.001

Sjoling, M., Lundberg, K., Englund, E., Westman, A., & Jong, M. C. (2011). Effectiveness of motivational interviewing and physical activity on prescription on leisure exercise time in subjects suffering from mild to moderate hypertension. *BMC Research Notes, 4,* 352. https://doi.org/10.1186/1756-0500-4-352

Skinner, M. D., & Aubin, H. (2010). Craving's place in addiction theory: Contributions of the major models. *Neuroscience and Biobehavioral Reviews, 34*(4), 606–623. https://doi.org/10.1016/j.neubiorev.2009.11.024

Sklare, G., Portes, P. R., & Splete, H. (1985). Developing questioning effectiveness in counseling. *Counselor Education and Supervision, 25*(1), 12–20. https://doi.org/10.1002/j.1556-6978.1985.tb00507.x

Sloan, T. J., & Walsh, D. A. (2010). Explanatory and diagnostic labels and perceived prognosis in chronic low back pain. *Spine, 35*(21), 1120–1125. https://doi.org/10.1097/brs.0b013e3181e089a9

Smith, B. H., Elliott, A. M., Chambers, W. A., Smith, W. C., Hannaford, P. C., & Penny, K. (2001). The impact of chronic pain in the community. *Family Practice, 18*(3), 292–299. https://doi.org/10.1093/fampra/18.3.292

Smith, J. C. (2005). *Relaxation, meditation, and mindfulness: A mental health practitioner's guide to new and traditional approaches.* Springer Publishing Company.

Somerville, L. H., Hare, T., & Casey, B. J. (2011). Frontostriatal maturation predicts cognitive control failure to appetitive cues in adolescents. *Journal of Cognitive Neuroscience, 23*(9), 2123–2134.

Soosalu, G., Henwood, S., & Deo, A. (2019). Head, heart, and gut in decision making: Development of a multiple brain preference questionnaire. *SAGE Open, 9*(1), 1–17. https://doi.org/10.1177/2158244019837439

Spengler, S., Bird, G., & Brass, M. (2010). Hyperimitation of actions is related to reduced understanding of others' minds in autism spectrum conditions. *Biological Psychiatry, 68*(12), 1148–1155. https://doi.org/10.1016/j.biopsych.2010.09.017

Spielmann, A. L., Forster, B. B., Kokan, P., Hawkins, R. H., & Janzen, D. L. (1999). Shoulder after rotator cuff repair: MR imaging findings in asymptomatic individuals—initial experience. *Radiology, 213*(3), 705–708. https://doi.org/10.1148/radiology.213.3.r99dc09705

Starr, L. R., Hershenberg, R., Shaw, Z. A., Li, Y. I., & Santee, A. C. (2019, June 27). The perils of murky emotions: Emotion differentiation moderates the prospective relationship between naturalistic stress exposure and adolescent depression. *Emotion.* Advance online publication. https://doi.org/10.1037/emo0000630

Steele, S., Boon, S., & van der Hart, O. (2017). *Treating trauma-related dissociation: A practical, integrative approach.* W. W. Norton & Company.

Stegemoller, E. L. (2014). Exploring a neuroplasticity model of music therapy. *Journal of Music Therapy, 51*(3), 211–227. https://doi.org/10.1093/jmt/thu023

Steinberg, E. E., Keiflin, R., Boivin, J. R., Witten, I. B., Deisseroth, K., & Janak, P. H. (2013). A causal link between prediction errors, dopamine neurons, and learning. *Nature Neuroscience, 16*(7), 966–973. https://doi.org/10.1038/nn.3413

Steinberg, H. (2013). Transcranial direct current stimulation (tDCS) has a history reaching back to the 19th century. *Psychological Medicine, 43*(3), 669–671. https://doi.org/10.1017/S0033291712002929

Steinberg, L. (2008). A social neuroscience perspective on adolescent risk-taking. *Developmental Review, 28*(1), 78–106. https://doi.org/10.1016/j.dr.2007.08.002

Sterling, M., Jull, G., & Kenardy, J. (2006). Physical and psychological factors maintain long-term predictive capacity post-whiplash injury. *Pain, 122*(1–2), 102–108. https://doi.org/10.1016/j.pain.2006.01.014

Sterman, M. B. (2000). Basic concepts and clinical findings in the treatment of seizure disorders with EEG operant conditioning. *Clinical Electroencephalography, 31*(1), 45–55.

Stevenson, S., & Brock, S. (2017). *8 yoga poses for beginners*. https://www.beachbodyondemand.com/blog/standing-yoga-poses-for-beginners

Streeter, C. C., Gerbarg, P. L., Saper, R. B., Ciraulo, & Brown, R. P. (2012). Effects of yoga on the autonomic nervous system, gamma-aminobutyric-acid, and allostasis in epilepsy, depression, and post-traumatic stress disorder. *Medical Hypotheses, 78*(5), 571–579. https://doi.org/10.1016/j.mehy.2012.01.021

Stults-Kolehmainen, M. A., & Sinha, R. (2013). The effects of stress on physical activity and exercise. *Sports Medicine, 44*(1), 81–121. https://doi.org/10.1007/s40279-013-0090-5

Stuss, D. T., & Knight, R. T. (2013). *Principles of frontal lobe function*. Oxford University Press.

Substance Abuse and Mental Health Services Administration. (SAMHSA). (2014). *Trauma-informed care in behavioral health services* (Treatment Improvement Protocol Series 57, HHS Publication No. SMA 14-4816).

Sue, D. W. (2010). *Microaggressions in everyday life*. Wiley.

Sullivan, R. M., PhD. (2013). The neurobiology of attachment to nurturing and abusive caregivers. *National Library of Medicine National Institute of Health*. Retrieved November 11, 2018. https://www.ncbi.nlm.nih.gov/pmc/articles/PMC3774302/pdf/nihms461646.pdf

Sullivan, M. J. L., Bishop, S. R., & Pivik, J. (1995). The pain catastrophizing scale: Development and validation. *Psychological Assessment*, *7*(4), 524–532. https://doi.org/10.1037/1040-3590.7.4.524

Sussman, T. J., Jin, J., & Mohanty, A. (2016). Top-down and bottom-up factors in threat-related perception and attention in anxiety. *Biological Psychology, 121(B)*, 160–172. https://doi.org/10.1016/j.biopsycho.2016.08.006

Swan, J., Hyland, P. (2012). A review of the beneficial mental health effects of exercise and recommendations for future research. *Psychology & Society, 5*(1), 1–15.

Szeszko, P. R., Lehrner, A., & Yehuda, R. (2018). Glucocorticoids and hippocampal structure and function in PTSD. *Harvard Review of Psychiatry, 26*(3), 142–157. https://doi.org/10.1097/HRP.0000000000000188

Tager-Flusberg, H. (1985). The conceptual basis for referential word meaning in children with autism. *Child Development, 56*(5), 1167–1178. https://doi.org/10.2307/1130231

Taylor, S. E. (2012). Tend and befriend theory. In P.A.M. Van Lange, & A. W. Kruglanski, (Eds.), *Handbook of theories of social psychology* (Vol. 1, pp. 32–49). Sage Publications.

Tedeschi, R. G., & Calhoun, L. G. (1996). The posttraumatic growth inventory: Measuring the positive legacy of trauma. *Journal of Traumatic Stress, 9*(3), 455–472. https://doi.org/10.1002/jts.2490090305

Teicher, M. H., Andersen, S. L., Polcari, A., Anderson, C. M., Navalta, C. P., & Kim, D. M. (2003). The neurological consequences of early stress and childhood maltreatment. *Neuroscience and Biobehavioral Reviews, 27*(1–2), 33–44. https://doi.org/10.1016/S0149-7634(03)00007-1

Thatcher, R. W. & Lubar, J. F. (2008). History of the scientific standards of QEEG normative databases. In T. H. Budzinsky, H. K. Budzinsky, J. R. Evans & A. Abarbanel (Eds.), *Introduction to quantitative EEG and neurofeedback: Advanced theory and applications* (2nd ed., pp. 29–59). Academic Press.

Tinsley, H.E.A. (1992). Career decision making and career indecision. *Journal of Vocational Behavior, 41*, 209–211.

Treadway, M. T., Buckholtz, J. W., & Zald, D. H. (2013). Perceived stress predicts altered reward and loss feedback processing in medial prefrontal cortex. *Frontiers in Human Neuroscience, 7*, 180. https://doi.org/10.3389/fnhum.2013.00180

Trow, J. E., Hong, N. S., Jones, A. M., Lapointe, J., MacPhail, J. K., & McDonald, R. J. (2017). Evidence of a role for orbital prefrontal cortex in preventing over-generalization to moderate predictors of biologically significant events. *Neuroscience*, 345, 49–63.

Tsai, H. J., Kuo, T. B. J., Lee, G., & Yang, C. C. H. (2015). Efficacy of paced breathing for insomnia: Enhances vagal activity and improves sleep quality. *Psychophysiology, 52*(3), 388–396. https://doi.org/10.1111/psyp.12333

Twardosz, S., & Lutzker, J. R. (2010). Child maltreatment and the developing brain: A review of neuroscience perspectives. *Aggression and Violent Behavior, 15*(1), 59–68. https://doi.org/10.1016/j.avb.2009.08.003

Twemlow, S. W., & Bowen, W. T. (1977). Sociocultural predictors of self-actualization in EEG-biofeedback-treated alcoholics. *Psychological Reports, 40*(2), 591–598. https://doi.org/10.2466/pr0.1977.40.2.591

Tyng, C. M., Amin, H. U., Saad, M. N. M., & Malik, A. S. (2017). The influences of emotion on learning and memory. *Frontiers in Psychology, 8*, 1454. https://doi.org/10.3389/fpsyg.2017.01454

Uddin, L. Q., Iacoboni, M., Lange, C., & Keenan, J. P. (2007). The self and social cognition: The role of cortical midline structures and mirror neurons. *Trends in Cognitive Sciences, 11*(4), 153–157. https://doi.org/10.1016/j.tics.2007.01.001

U.S. Department of Health and Human Services (HHS), Office of the Surgeon General. Facing addiction in America: The Surgeon General's Report on Alcohol, Drugs, and Health. Washington, DC: HHS, November 2016.

Van den Hout, M., Muris, P., Salemink, E., & Kindt, M. (2001). Autobiographical memories become less vivid and emotional after eye movements. *British Journal of Clinical Psychology, 40*(2), 121–130. https://doi.org/10.1348/014466501163571

Van der Kolk, B. A. (1994). The body keeps the score: Memory and the evolving psychobiology of posttraumatic stress. *Harvard Review of Psychiatry, 1*(5), 253–265. https://doi.org/10.3109/10673229409017088

Van der Kolk, B. A. (2014). *The body keeps the score: Brain, mind and body in the healing of trauma*. Penguin Books.

van der Werff, S. J. A., Elzinga, B. M., Smit, A. S., & van der Wee, N.J.A. (2017). Structural brain correlates of resilience to traumatic stress in Dutch police officers. *Psychoneuroendocrinology, 85*, 172–178. https://doi.org/10.1016/j.psyneuen.2017.08.019

Van Oosterwijck, J., Nijs, J., Meeus, M., Truijen, S., Craps, J., Van den Keybus, N., & Paul, L. (2011). Pain neurophysiology education improves cognitions, pain thresholds, and movement performance in people with chronic whiplash: A pilot study. *Journal of Rehabilitation Research and Development, 48*(1), 43–58. https://doi.org/10.1682/jrrd.2009.12.0206

Varvogli, L., & Darviri, C. (2011). Stress management techniques: Evidence-based procedures that reduce stress and promote health. *Health Science Journal, 5*(2), 74–89.

Vilaça-Alves, J., Muller, F., Rosa, C., Payan-Carreira, R., Lund, R., Matos, F., Garrido, N., & Saavedra, F. J., Reis, V. M. (2018). Cardiorespiratory, enzymatic and hormonal responses during and after walking while fasting. *Plos One,13*(3). https://doi.org/10.1371/journal.pone.0193702

Vivanti, G., & Rogers, S. J. (2014). Autism and the mirror neuron system: Insights from learning and teaching. *Philosophical Transactions of the Royal Society of London. Series B, Biological Sciences, 369*(1644), 20130184. https://doi.org/10.1098/rstb.2013.0184

Vlaeyen, J. W. S., Crombez, G., & Linton, S. J. (2016). The fear-avoidance model of pain. *Pain, 157*(8), 1588–1589. https://doi.org/10.1097/j.pain.0000000000000574

Volkow, N. D., Koob, G. F., & McLellan, A. T., (2016). Neurobiologic advances from the brain disease model of addiction. *New England Journal of Medicine, 374*(4), 363–371. https://doi.org/10.1056/NEJMra1511480

Voss, P., Thomas, M. E., Cisneros-Franco, J. M., & de Villers-Sidani, E. (2017). Dynamic brains and the changing rules of neuroplasticity: Implications for learning and recovery. *Frontiers in Psychology, 8*, 1657. https://doi.org/10.3389/fpsyg.2017.01657

Vuong, H. E., Yano, J. M., Fung, T. C., & Hsiao, E. Y. (2017). The microbiome and host behavior. *Annual Review of Neuroscience, 40*, 21–49. https://doi.org/10.1146/annurev-neuro-072116-031347

Vyas, A., Mitra, R., Shankaranarayana Rao, B. S., & Chattarji, S. (2002). Chronic stress induces contrasting patterns of dendritic remodeling in hippocampal and amygdaloid neurons. *Journal of Neuroscience, 22*(15), 6810-6818. https://doi.org/10.1523/JNEUROSCI.22-15-06810.2002

Wagener, A. E. (2017). Metaphor in professional counseling. *Professional Counselor, 7*(2), 144–154. https://doi.org/10.15241/aew.7.2.144

Wagner, D. (2015a). Polyvagal theory and peek-a-boo: How the therapeutic pas de deux heals attachment trauma. *Body, Movement and Dance in Psychotherapy, 10*(4), 256–265. https://doi.org/10.1080/17432979.2015.1069762

Wagner, D. (2015b), November 24). Is my anxiety attracting your depression? Polyvagal theory in romance. *Elephant Journal.* https://www.elephantjournal.com/2015/11/is-my-anxiety-attracting-your-depression-polyvagal-theory-in-romance/

Wagner, D. (2016, June 27). Polyvagal theory in practice. *Counseling Today.* https://ct.counseling.org/2016/06/polyvagal-theory-practice/

Wagner, D. (2017). Yoga and yogurt: What mindful people need to know about the vagus nerve. *Asana International Yoga Journal.* https://www.asanajournal.com/yoga-yogurt-mindful-people-need-know-vagus-nerve/

Wagner, D., & Hurst, S. M. (2018). Couples dance/movement therapy: Bringing a theoretical framework into practice. *American Journal of Dance Therapy, 40*(1), 18–43. https://doi.org/10.1007/s10465-018-9271-y

Wagnild, G. M. & Young, H. M. (1993). Development and psychometric evaluation of the resilience scale. *Journal of Nursing Measurement*, 1, 165–178.

Wald, J., & Taylor, S. (2007). Efficacy of interoceptive exposure therapy combined with trauma-related exposure therapy for posttraumatic stress disorder: A pilot study. *Journal of Anxiety Disorders, 21*(8), 1050–1060. https://doi.org/10.1016/j.janxdis.2006.10.010

Walton, D. M., Pretty, J., MacDermid, J. C., & Teasell, R. W. (2009). Risk factors for persistent problems following whiplash injury: Results of a systematic review and meta-analysis. *Journal of Orthopaedic and Sports Physical Therapy, 39*(5), 334–350. https://doi.org/10.2519/jospt.2009.2765

Wampold, B. E. (2001). *The great psychotherapy debate: Models, methods, and findings.* Mahwah, NJ: Erlbaum.

Wampold, B. E. (2011). *Qualities and actions of effective therapists.* American Psychological Association. https://www.apa.org/education/ce/effective-therapists.pdf

Wampold, B. E. (2015). How important are the common factors in psychotherapy? An update. *World Psychiatry, 14*(3), 270–277. https://doi.org/10.1002/wps.20238

Wampold, B. E., & Budge, S. L. (2012). The 2011 Leona Tyler award address: The relationship—and its relationship to the common and specific factors of psychotherapy. *Counseling Psychologist, 40*(4), 601–623. https://doi.org/10.1177/0011000011432709

Wampold, B. E., & Imel, Z. E. (2015). *The great psychotherapy debate: The evidence for what makes psychotherapy work* (2nd ed.). Routledge/Taylor & Francis Group.

Wassum, K. M., Ostlund, S. B., Loewinger, G. C., & Maidment, N. T. (2013). Phasic mesolimbic dopamine release tracks reward seeking during expression of Pavlonian-to-instrumental transfer. *Biological Psychiatry, 73*(8), 747–755. https://doi.org/10.1016/j.biopsych.2012.12.005

Watt, D. F. (2003). Psychotherapy in an age of neuroscience: Bridges to affective neuroscience. In J. Corrigall & H. Wilkinson (Eds.), *Revolutionary connections. Psychotherapy and neuroscience* (pp. 79–115). Karnac.

Waugh, C. E., Zarolia, P., Mauss, I. B., Lumian, D. S., Ford, B. Q., Davis, T. S., Ciesielski, B. G., Sams, K. V., & McRae, K. (2016). Emotion regulation changes the duration of the BOLD response to emotional stimuli. *Social Cognitive and Affective Neuroscience, 11*(10), 1550–1559. https://doi.org/10.1093/scan/nsw067

Weinberg, R., & Butt, J. (2005). Goal setting in sport and exercise domains: The theory and practice of effective goal setting . In D. Hackfort, J. L. Duda, & R. Lidor (Eds.), *Handbook of research in applied sport & exercise psychology: International perspectives* (pp. 129–144). Fitness Information Technology.

Weisberg, D. S., Keil, F. C., Goodstein, J., Rawson, E., & Gray, J. R. (2008). The seductive allure of neuroscience explanations. *Journal of Cognitive Neuroscience, 20*(3), 470–477. https://doi.org/10.1162/jocn.2008.20040

Weiss, M. J., & Harris, S. L. (2001). Teaching social skills to people with autism. *Behavior Modification, 25*(5), 785–802. https://doi.org/10.1177/0145445501255007

Welling, H. (2012). Transformative emotional sequence: Towards a common principle of change. *Journal of*

Psychotherapy Integration, 22(2), 109–136. https://doi.org/10.1037/a0027786

Wenner, M. M. (2018). Sympathetic activation in chronic anxiety: Not just at the "height" of stress. *Journal of Neurophysiology, 120*(1), 7–8. https://doi.org/10.1152/jn.00220.2018

Wesson, D. R., & Smith, D. E. (2010). Buprenorphine in the treatment of opiate dependence. *Journal of Psychoactive Drugs, 42*(2), 161–175. https://doi.org/10.1080/02791072.2010.1040

Wheeler, M. A., Stuss, D. T., & Tulving E. (1997). Toward a theory of episodic memory: The frontal lobes and autonoetic consciousness. *Psychological Bulletin, 121, 331–354. doi: 10.1037/0033-2909.121.3.331*

Wiest, G. (2012). Neural and mental hierarchies. *Frontiers in Psychology, 3*, 516. https://doi.org/10.3389/fpsyg.2012.00516

Wiley, J. F., Bei, B., Bower, J. E., & Stanton, A. L. (2017). Relationship of psychosocial resources with allostatic load: A systematic review. *Psychosomatic Medicine, 79*(3), 283–292. https://doi.org/10.1097/PSY.0000000000000395

Wilkinson, B. D. (2018). The limits of neuroscience in counseling: A humanistic perspective and proposed model. *Journal of Humanistic Counseling, 57*(1), 70–78. https://doi.org/10.1002/johc.12067

Willford, J. A., Richardson, G. A., Leech, S. L., & Day, N. L. (2004). Verbal and visuospatial learning and memory function in children with moderate prenatal alcohol exposure. *Alcoholism: Clinical and Experimental Research, 28*(3), 497–507. https://doi.org/10.1097/01.ALC.0000117868.97486.2D

Williams, D. P., Koenig, J., Carnevali, L., Sgoifo, A., Jarczok, M. N., Sternberg, E. M., & Thayer, J. F. (2019). Heart rate variability and inflammation: A meta-analysis of human studies. *Brain, Behavior, and Immunity 80*, 219–226. https://doi.org/10.1016/j.bbi.2019.03.009

Williamson, J. B., Porges, E. C., Lamb, D. G., & Porges, S. W. (2015). Maladaptive autonomic regulation in PTSD accelerates physiological aging. *Frontiers in Psychology, 5*, 1571. https://doi.org/10.3389/fpsyg.2014.01571

Wilson, G., Farrell, D., Barron, I., Hutchins, J., Whybrow, D., & Kiernan, M. D. (2018). The use of eye-movement desensitization reprocessing (EMDR) therapy in treating post-traumatic stress disorder—a systematic narrative review. *Frontiers in Psychology, 9*, 923. https://doi.org/10.3389/fpsyg.2018.00923

Witkiewitz, K., & Bowen, S. (2010). Depression, craving, and substance use following a randomized trial of mindfulness-based relapse prevention. *Journal of Consulting and Clinical Psychology, 78*(3), 362–374. https://doi.org/10.1037/a0019172

Witkiewitz, K., Bowen, S., Douglas, H., & Hsu, S. H. (2013). Mindfulness-based relapse prevention for substance craving. *Addictive Behaviors, 38*(2), 1563–1571. https://doi.org/10.1016/j.addbeh.2012.04.001

Witkiewitz, K., & Lustyk, M. K. B., & Bowen, S. (2013). Retraining the addicted brain: A review of hypothesized neurobiological mechanisms of mindfulness-based relapse prevention. *Psychology of Addictive Behaviors, 27*(2), 351–365. https://doi.org/10.1037/a0029258

Witkiewitz, K., Marlatt, G. A., & Walker, D. (2005). Mindfulness-based relapse prevention for alcohol and substance use disorders. *Journal of Cognitive Psychotherapy, 19*(3), 211–228. https://doi.org/10.1891/jcop.2005.19.3.211

Woodford, M. S. (2012). *Men, addiction, & intimacy: Strengthening recovery by fostering the emotional development of boys and men.* Routledge.

Woolery, A., Myers, H., Sternlieb, B., & Zeltzer, L. (2004). A yoga intervention for young adults with elevated symptoms of depression. *Alternative Therapies, 10*, 60–63.

Woolf, C. J. (2011). Central sensitization: Implications for the diagnosis and treatment of pain. *Pain, 152*(3 Suppl), 2–15. https://doi.org/10.1016/j.pain.2010.09.030

Wyper, K. R., & Rasmussen, C. R. (2011). Language impairments in children with fetal alcohol spectrum disorders. *Journal of Population Therapeutics and Clinical Pharmacology, 18*(2), e364-e376.

Yager, J., & Feinstein, R. E. (2016). Potential applications of the National Institute of Mental Health's research domain criteria (RDoC) to clinical psychiatric practice: How RDoC might be used in assessment, diagnostic processes, case formulation, treatment planning, and clinical notes. *Journal of Clinical Psychiatry, 78*(4), 423–432. https://doi.org/10.4088/JCP.15nr10476

Yau, J. O. Y., & McNally, G. P. (2018). Brain mechanisms controlling Pavlovian fear conditioning. *Journal of Experimental Psychology: Animal Learning and Cognition, 44*(4), 341–357. https://doi.org/10.1037/xan0000181

Yee, A. X., Hsu, Y., & Chen, L. (2017) A metaplasticity view of the interaction between homeostatic and Hebbian plasticity. *Philosophical Transactions of the Royal Society of London, Series B, Biological Sciences, 372*, 1715. https://doi.org/10.1098/rstb.2016.0155

Yee, J. R., Kenkel, W. M., Frijling, J. L., Dodhia, S., Onishi, K. G., Tovar, S., Saber, M. J., Lewis, G. F., Liu, W., Porges, S. W., & Carter, C. S. (2016). Oxytocin promotes functional coupling between paraventricular nucleus and both sympathetic and parasympathetic cardioregulatory nuclei. *Hormones and Behavior, 80*, 82–91. https://doi.org/10.1016/j.yhbeh.2016.01.010

Yoga Ed. (2018). *The yoga ed curriculum.* http://yogaed.com/resource/the-yoga-ed-curriculum/

Young, S. N. (2007). How to increase serotonin in the human brain without drugs. *Journal of Psychiatry & Neuroscience, 32*(6), 394–399.

Zaidel, D. W. (2014). Creativity, brain, and art: Biological and neurological considerations. *Frontiers in Human Neuroscience, 8*, 389. https://doi.org/10.3389/fnhum.2014.00389

Zengar Institute. (2016). *NeurOptimal advanced brain training systems.* http://www.zengar.com

Zhang, W., Yan, T. T., Barriball, K. L., While, A. E., & Liu, X. H. (2015). Post-traumatic growth in mothers of children with autism: A phenomenological study. *Autism, 19*(1), 29–37. https://doi.org/ 10.1177/1362361313509732

Zimmerman, M. E., Ezzati, A., Katz, M. J., Lipton, M. L., Brickman, A. M., Sliwinski, M. J., & Lipton, R. B. (2016). Perceived stress is differentially related to hippocampal subfield volumes among older adults. *PLOS ONE, 11*(5), e0154530. https://doi.org/10.1371/journal.pone.0154530

Index

About the Contributors

Charmayne Adams, MA, NCC

Charmayne is a doctoral candidate at the University of Tennessee in Knoxville. She has worked for inpatient psychiatric hospitals, residential treatment facilities, correctional facilities, and mobile crisis services. She has extensive clinical experience working with individuals who are in crisis or have experienced significant trauma. In addition to clinical practice, she has presented at regional, state, and national conferences on trauma-informed counselor education and is currently writing her dissertation on andragogy in counselor education programs, specifically concerning trauma theory and practice.

Mohiuddin Ahmed, PhD

Mohiuddin Ahmed received undergraduate and graduate degrees in philosophy in Bangladesh at Dhaka University and was awarded a Fulbright Scholarship to study in the United States. He completed his PhD in clinical psychology at the University of Pittsburgh. He has had more than 40 years of clinical experience working with varied populations of all ages in the Philippines, Bangladesh, and the United States. He has worked in psychiatric inpatient and outpatient facilities, institutions for the developmentally disabled, and nursing homes; in addition, Mohiuddin has provided consultation to mental health agencies, residential programs for adults with behavior disabilities, and special education programs. He has supervised many pre- and postdoctoral level psychology graduate students. He coauthored with Charles Boisvert the books *Mind Stimulation Therapy: Cognitive Interventions for Persons with Schizophrenia* and *Using Diagram in Psychotherapy: A Guide to Visually-Enhanced Therapy*. For his full biography and publication list, please see his website at www.psychologymentalhealth.com.

Sinem Akay-Sullivan, PhD, LPC-S, RPT

Sinem Akay-Sullivan, PhD, LPC-S, RPT is an assistant professor in the Department of Counselor Education at Sam Houston State University (SHSU). After receiving her master's and doctorate degrees from the Department of Counseling and Higher Education at the University of North Texas, she worked at a child advocacy center where she specialized in trauma work and became certified as a trauma-focused cognitive behavioral therapist. She also received training in eye-movement desensitization and reprocessing (EMDR) and is in the process of becoming a certified EMDR therapist. Sinem is currently the assistant director of the Center for Research and Clinical Training in Trauma at SHSU.

Saba Aqel

Saba Aqel is a current graduate student in the clinical mental health counseling program at Northwestern University. She has been involved in research within the fields of immunology, psychology, and neurology for 7 years. She is driven to help others overcome personal obstacles through mental health education and counseling. Saba is additionally interested in medical research, specifically, psychoneuroimmunology research involving the complex intricacies that exist between the psychological, neurological, and immunological responses in the body. Particularly, she is interested in biomarkers and interactions between the brain and gut and their relationship with mental health in the framework of trauma. She is interested in studying the effect of trauma on these connections on a physiological level through in vivo and in vitro research. She has completed a yearlong project pertaining to the effects of both stress and exercise, independently, on lupus nephritis—an inflammatory kidney autoimmune disease caused by systemic lupus erythematous. Saba has also conducted research investigating the immune mechanisms and responses in multiple sclerosis and the role of a small molecule compound in altering disease activity. Overall, she is interested in continuing with her research interests while also working with individuals who have experienced trauma during their lifetimes.

Courtney Armstrong, LPC

Courtney has been a licensed professional counselor (LPC) more than 20 years, with a specialty in treating trauma, grief, and anxiety. She is an approved LPC supervisor and has trained thousands of mental health professionals over the last 10 years in creative techniques for treating trauma and grief that are grounded in evidence-based and neuroscience principles. Courtney has authored several publications, including *The Therapeutic "Aha!": 10 Strategies for Getting Your Clients Unstuck* (2015, W. W. Norton) and *Transforming Traumatic Grief* (2011, Artemecia Press). She also contributed chapters to *Techniques of Grief Therapy: Creative Counseling for the Bereaved*, edited by Robert Neimeyer (2012, Routledge), and *Memory Reconsolidation in Psychotherapy*, edited by Matthew Dahlitz and Geoff Hall (2015, Dahlitz Media), as well as published articles in professional magazines, such as the *Psychotherapy Networker*, *Counseling Today*, and *The Neuropsychotherapist*.

Olivia Bentley, MA, LPCC

Olivia is currently a senior research assistant at the George Washington University Center for Rehabilitation Counseling Research and Education and a doctoral candidate in the counseling program. She has more than 8 years' experience in the field of mental health, with 4 years as a licensed clinician. She has worked in a variety of treatment settings, with most of her time spent doing individual and group counseling at a residential treatment program for women with substance use disorders. She has experience working from both an abstinence-based and harm reduction framework in the treatment of problematic substance use and employs many creative techniques as part of her person-centered approach. Her research interests center on problematic substance use, particularly as it affects women and families, and she has presented on this and other topics at several regional and national conferences and workshops.

Charles M. Boisvert, PhD

Charles M. Boisvert, PhD, received a BS in psychology from Le Moyne College, MA in counseling from Rhode Island College, and PhD in clinical psychology from the University of Rhode Island. Dr. Boisvert has worked in a variety of clinical settings and is a professor of clinical mental health counseling at Rhode Island College. In addition, Dr. Boisvert is a practicing clinical psychologist at the Rhode Island Center for Cognitive Behavioral Therapy in North Kingstown, Rhode Island. His research and clinical interests include science-practice relations in psychotherapy, using multimodal therapy interventions, biopsychology of stress, psychiatric care in primary care, and predictors of psychotherapy outcome. He has several publications in peer-reviewed journals and serves as an ad hoc reviewer for *Professional Psychology: Research and Practice* and *Family Practice*. He has also served as an ad hoc reviewer for *Schizophrenia Bulletin*. He coauthored *Mind Stimulation Therapy: Cognitive Interventions for Persons with Schizophrenia* and *Using Diagram in Psychotherapy: A Guide to Visually-Enhanced Therapy* with Mohiuddin Ahmed.

Christian D. Chan, PhD, NCC

Christian D. Chan, PhD, NCC, is an assistant professor of counseling at Idaho State University, member at large for the Association for Adult Development and Aging, and co-chair of the American Counseling Association (ACA) Branch Development Committee. His interests revolve around intersectionality of cultural and social identity; multiculturalism in counseling, supervision, and counselor education; social justice; career development; critical research methods; acculturative stress; intergenerational conflict; and cultural factors in identity development and socialization. His prior professional experiences include case management with foster care adolescents, career development, higher education administration, intensive outpatient counseling, and outpatient counseling, providing individual, couples, parent-child, group, and family counseling services. In addition to contributions of peer-reviewed publications in journals, books, and edited volumes and over 90 refereed presentations at the national, regional, and state levels, he recently received the ACA Robert

H. Rencken Emerging Professional Leader Award, ACA Courtland C. Lee Multicultural Excellence Scholarship Award, and Association for Counselor Education and Supervision Outstanding Graduate Student Leadership Award.

Szu-Yu Chen, PhD, LPC, NCC, RPT

Dr. Szu-Yu Chen is an assistant professor of counseling at Palo Alto University. She has worked with diverse populations in a variety of settings, including schools, community agencies, private practice, and inpatient and outpatient facilities. She has clinical experience in incorporating basic information about the child's brain in parent and teacher consultations. Her research interests include play therapy and multicultural issues in counseling and supervision.

Savannah Cormier, M.S., LPC, RPT

Savannah Cormier is an assistant professor at Arkansas State University. Her clinical experiences center on providing neuroscience-informed, relational-cultural counseling to adolescents and adults, as well as neuro-informed play therapy to children. Similarly, Savannah infuses brain-based teaching and learning principles into her teaching and supervision with master's level counselors in training. She is currently working on a number of studies, including her dissertation on brain-based counselor training.

Corinna Costello, PhD, LPC (NC), LPC (IL), ATR-BC

Corinna Costello, PhD, LPC, LCPC, ATR-BC, has been a licensed counselor and registered/board-certified art therapist for 20 years. She earned her PhD in counselor education and supervision in 2015 and earned her master of art degree in art therapy from the School of the Art Institute of Chicago in 1994. She has had clinical experiences in a variety of inpatient and outpatient settings and with several different populations. Corinna is a clinical lecturer and core faculty for Counseling@Northwestern University, and her current research is focused on the utilization of creativity and various strength-based approaches to building resiliency levels, reducing trauma-based responses, and altering the neurophysiological affect within the counseling experience.

Doris D' Hooghe

Doris D'Hooghe is a psychotherapist who has been in private practice since 1990. She founded Trauma Centre Belgium in 2009, which specializes in trauma education and attachment for all populations. She is trained in Gestalt therapy, group therapy, and transpersonal psychology, as well as integrative psychology and psychotraumatology. In the last 10 years, she has become interested in the blending of neuroscience with psychology, attachment, and trauma. Her work is based on the integration of neuroscience and psychology and the principles of neuropsychotherapy.

Laurie Dickstein-Fischer, PhD

Dr. Laurie Dickstein-Fischer is an assistant professor and program director for the school counseling program at Salem State University. She was awarded the 2017 Massachusetts Counselor Educator of the Year Award and was recently nominated to be a board member with the Massachusetts School Counselors Association. She received her master's from John Hopkins University and her PhD from Northeastern University in the combined counseling psychology and school psychology program. She has trained and provided psychological interventions at Baltimore City Public Schools, Massachusetts Mental Health Center (Harvard Medical School Department of Psychiatry), Edith Nourse Rogers Memorial Veterans Hospital, Massachusetts College of Art and Design, and Columbia Valley Community Health Department of Behavioral Medicine. Her research focuses on autism and the intersection of social interaction and technology. She is often featured in the newspaper and television for her research pertaining to autism and her robot named Penguin for Autism Behavioral Intervention.

Dalena Dillman Taylor, PhD, LPC, LHMC, RPT

Dr. Dalena Dillman Taylor earned her doctoral degree in counseling and completed her master's degree in counseling from the University of North Texas. She is a tenure-earning assistant professor at the University of Central Florida (UFC), as well as the director of the Center for Play Therapy Training and Research at UCF. Dr. Dillman Taylor is a certified child-centered play therapist supervisor, a certified child-parent relationship therapist supervisor, and a trained Adlerian play therapist. Dr. Dillman Taylor's primary research interests include advancement of Adlerian play therapy field toward evidence-based practice, counseling and educational services for high-need children and families, and counselor development and supervision. Dr. Dillman Taylor has been active in the areas of research, teaching, and service. Dr. Dillman Taylor has published 20 scholarly works in refereed and/or peer-reviewed dissemination outlets. Dr. Dillman Taylor is the co-principal investigator of Project Harmony (90FM0078-01-00), a 5-year federally supported research grant awarded by the Office of Family Assistant.

Deborah L. Duenyas, PhD, LPC

Deborah L. Duenyas received her PhD from Kent State University and her masters from Columbia University. She is a counselor educator at Kutztown University of Pennsylvania teaching courses, including neuroscience for counselors, assessment in counseling, research methods, and field experience, as well as other courses. Deborah is an LPC and has worked in an array of clinical settings. She holds a standard teaching certificate (K–8) and has provided English language instruction in Osaka, Japan.

Diona Emmanuel, MPH, MA, LGPC, NCC

Diona is a doctoral candidate in the counseling program at the George Washington University. Her experience stems from the opportunities presented while obtaining her master of public health and master of arts in clinical mental health counseling. Clinically, she has provided individual, family, and group counseling for adolescents and adults and integrated expressive arts into her work with clients. She has worked with various presenting issues, including grief and loss, career transitions, problems in the workplace, anxiety, depression, and substance addictions with co-occurring disorders. She has worked with adolescent and adult clients in various substance use disorder treatment centers, including residential facilities and intensive outpatient programs. She has experience presenting at regional, national, and international conferences on a variety of topics, including integrating expressive arts into substance abuse counseling.

Thomas A. Field, PhD, LMHC, LPC, NCC, CCMHC, ACS

Thomas Field is an assistant professor of psychiatry in the mental health counseling and behavioral medicine program at Boston University School of Medicine. He also currently sees clients in private practice. Thom has provided counseling services since 2006 and has worked with over 1,000 clients in a variety of settings. He received his PhD in counseling and supervision from James Madison University. His research has received recognition from the American Mental Health Counselors Association (2013 Dissertation Research Award), Council for Accreditation of Counseling and Related Educational Programs (2016–2017 Faculty Research Award), and Western Association for Counselor Education and Supervision (2015 Professional Publication Award). He currently serves as the chair of the American Mental Health Counseling Association's Neuroscience Interest Network, is the associate Editor for the Journal of Mental Health Counseling's Neurocounseling section, and the coeditor of the "Neurocounseling: Bridging Brain and Behavior" column in *Counseling Today.* He was the first editor of the first book that the ACA has published on the topic of neuroscience (*Neurocounseling: Brain-Based Clinical Approaches*).

Russell Fulmer, PhD, LPC

Russell Fulmer received his PhD from Kansas State University in counselor education. He is currently clinical associate professor with the Counseling@ Northwestern program through the Family Institute at Northwestern University. His experience includes time overseas in medical education. Russell's research interests involve artificial intelligence and psychodynamics.

Gary G. Gintner, PhD, LPC-S, NCC

Gary G. Gintner is an associate professor and program leader in the counseling program at Louisiana State University. He has published numerous articles on topics such as *Diagnostic and Statistical Manual of Mental Disorders, 5th Edition* (*DSM-5*), differential diagnosis, mood disorders, substance use disorder, and best practices for the treatment of psychiatric and substance use disorders. He is a nationally recognized trainer on the *DSM-5* and best practice guidelines. His

30 years of clinical experience includes inpatient care, substance use disorder counseling, and outpatient mental health. He is a fellow of the ACA and was the 2007–2008 president of the American Mental Health Counselors Association (AMHCA). He served as the chair for AMHCA's *DSM-5* Task Force. Currently, he is a member of the Global Clinical Practice Network of the World Health Organization and participated in the field trials on ICD-11.

Timothy J. Hakenewerth, EdS, LPC, NCC

Timothy is currently pursuing a PhD in counselor education and counseling (2020) at Idaho State University. He has a master's in mental health counseling and is a licensed practical counselor in both Missouri and Idaho. He has clinical and instructional experience with career counseling and especially enjoys career counseling with the college student population. He is currently researching the effects of work experience on counselor development and preparation.

Shaywanna Harris, PhD, LPC

Dr. Shaywanna Harris received her PhD in counselor education from the University of Central Florida and her master's degree in marriage and family counseling from the University of Akron. She has conducted research using neurofeedback for 4 years and is a certified NeurOptimal neurofeedback provider. She has provided neurofeedback sessions to college students with attention-deficit/hyperactivity disorder and has published the findings of her neurofeedback research in peer-reviewed journals.

Richard Hill, MA, MEd

Richard Hill is a master of brain and mind sciences, a practicing psychotherapist/counselor, an author, an educator, and a professional supervisor. He has developed special training courses for suicide prevention and is the originator of the curiosity oriented approach. His work with Ernest Rossi, PhD, has led to the publication of *The Practitioner's Guide to Mirroring Hands*, which describes their client-responsive therapy, which includes Richard's curiosity oriented approach. He is president of the Global Association of Interpersonal Neurobiology Studies, a select member of the International Psychosocial Genomics Research Group, director of the Mindscience Institute, and managing editor of the *Neuropsychotherapist*. His other books include *Choose Hope* and *How the 'Real World' Is Driving Us Crazy!* he has also published numerous articles, journal papers, and book chapters, including "Perspectives on Coping and Resilience" and "Strengths Based Social Work Practice in Mental Health."

Reginald W. Holt, PhD, LPC

Dr. Reginald W. Holt completed a PhD in counseling/counselor education at the University of Missouri-St. Louis, an MA in clinical psychology at East Tennessee State University, and a 2-year postgraduate training program in advanced psychodynamic psychotherapy at the St. Louis Psychoanalytic Institute. As a core faculty member in the Department of Counselor Education and Family Therapy at Central Connecticut State University (CCSU), Dr. Holt oversees the addictions recovery specialization within the clinical professional counseling program. He also provides graduate-level instruction with a special emphasis on mindfulness-based strategies for mental health and addictions counseling, which coincides with his research interests. He is a LPC in Connecticut, Illinois (licensed clinical professional counselor [LCPC]), and Missouri (LPC) and credentialed as a national certified counselor (NCC) and master addictions counselor through the National Board of Certified Counselors. In addition, Dr. Holt is recognized by the Connecticut Certification Board, Inc. as an advanced alcohol and drug counselor. He is a member of several national and state professional associations and was asked by the Connecticut Counseling Association to co-lead the development of a special interest group in addictions counseling, which received a "Best Innovative Practice" award from the ACA in 2018. His extensive career includes clinical and administrative positions within behavioral health-care hospitals, the correctional system, and a Fortune 500 managed care organization, as well as operating his own private practice.

Justin Jacques, MA, LPC, CAC II, CEAP, NCC, ACS

Justin Jacques is an LPC, certified addiction counselor II, certified employee assistant professional, nationally certified counselor, and approved clinical supervisor. Currently, Justin is a staff clinician at Colonial Health and a PhD student in counselor education and supervision at the George Washington University. In the past, Justin has worked as the assistant director of counseling and wellness at the University of North Texas at Dallas. In 2012, Justin completed a certificate in learning and organizational change from Northwestern University. He also has a master's degree in counseling psychology and education from the University of Colorado and an undergraduate degree in health promotions from the University of Northern Iowa. Justin's research interests include student athletes, veteran populations, health behavior change, sleep behaviors, and stress in emerging adults.

Elizabeth A. Keller-Dupree, PhD, LPC-S, NCC

Dr. Bea Keller-Dupree is an associate professor of psychology and counseling at Northeastern State University, as well as owner, therapist, and consultant at Enrichment Counseling & Consultation in Tulsa, Oklahoma. She is an LPC-S, pk–12 certified school counselor, and nationally certified counselor. Dr. Keller-Dupree researches wellness and well-being practices, social and emotional development, and experiential learning.

Michele Kerulis, LCPC, CMPC

Michele is a doctorate level licensed clinician with 16 years of direct work with clients in multiple settings and 10 years teaching at the graduate level. She is certified through the Association of Applied Sport Psychology (AASP) and a member of the US Olympic Committee Sport Psychology Registry. Michele was the program director of a graduate program (MA in counseling with a specialization in sport and health psychology) and developed the program to meet the Illinois state licensure requirements, AASP certification requirements, and National Board for Certified Counselors (NBCC) requirements. She had a career in the fitness industry as a group fitness instructor for about a decade.

Kevin E. Kip, PhD

Kevin E. Kip, PhD, is a tenured distinguished health professor, epidemiologist, and biostatistician with 18 years of experience in U.S. federal, Department of Defense, and industry-funded studies. He holds a without compensation appointment with the James A. Haley HSR&D Center of Innovation on Disability and Rehabilitation Research, Tampa, Florida. His background is interdisciplinary with more than 170 peer-reviewed publications. With multimillion dollar funding from the U.S. Department of Defense, he established the Research to Improve Emotional Health/Quality of Life of Service Members with Disabilities Center at the University of South Florida. Through this center, he is the leading researcher worldwide in the study of accelerated resolution therapy (ART), an emerging, brief, and evidence-based method of psychotherapy for the treatment of post-traumatic stress disorder (PTSD) and related comorbidities. Dr. Kip is a previous principal investigator of the National Heart, Lung, and Blood Institute Dynamic Registry of Percutaneous Coronary Intervention, which enrolled approximately 10,000 patients. He was a member of the Institute of Medicine Committee to Review the Health Effects in Vietnam Veterans of Exposure to Herbicides. Dr. Kip is the current chair of the Data Safety and Monitoring Board for the NIDDK-funded Look AHEAD (Action for Health in Diabetes) multicenter trial and is a frequent grant reviewer for the National Institutes of Health (NIH).

Susan M. Long, PhD, LPC, CWC

Susan is an LPC, certified wellness counselor in Ohio, and adjunct professor for the graduate counseling program at the University of Toledo. She currently works with children and adolescents who have experienced trauma. In addition, she works in private practice using neurofeedback and biofeedback.

Adriaan Louw, PT, PhD

Adriaan, cofounder and CEO of International Spine and Pain Institute (ISPI), earned both an undergraduate and a master's degree in research and spinal surgery rehabilitation from the University of Stellenbosch in Cape Town, South Africa. He is a guest lecturer/adjunct faculty at Rockhurst University, St. Ambrose University, and the University of Nevada, Las Vegas. In addition, he maintains a clinical practice and is co-owner of the Ortho Spine and Pain Clinic in Story City, Iowa. Adriaan has been teaching postgraduate, spinal manual therapy, and pain science classes throughout the United States and internationally for

15 years. He is a certified spinal manual therapist through ISPI. In addition, Adriaan has presented at numerous national and international manual therapy, pain science, and medical conferences, and he has authored and coauthored articles, books, and book chapters related to spinal disorders and pain science. Recently, Adriaan completed his PhD, which centers on therapeutic neuroscience education and spinal disorders.

Chad Luke, PhD, LPC/MHSP, ACS, NCC, MAC

Chad Luke, PhD, is an associate professor of counselor educator at Tennessee Tech University in Cookeville, Tennessee, and a clinical supervisor. He holds a PhD in counselor education from the University of Tennessee. He teaches courses in career counseling, career development, neuroscience for counselors, theory, multicultural counseling, group counseling, practicum, and internship. He has clinical experience with addictions, children and adolescents, the homeless, college students, and other adults. He has been a career services director and associate dean of student development and has published several articles and book chapters on career, college success, and mental health. He is an LPC specializing in career, addictions, and neuro-informed counseling. His previous books include *Neuroscience for Counselors* (2016, Sage) and *Essentials of Career-Focused Counseling: Integrating Theory, Practice, & Neuroscience* (2017, Cognella).

Gina Martin, MA, LPC, NCC

Gina is a current doctoral student who works as a counselor educator, contributing to master's and undergraduate level training programs. She has clinical experience working with children and adolescents who have experienced trauma and has done research in the areas of trauma, attachment, and neuroscience.

Whitney McLaughlin, MA, LPCA, NCC

Whitney is a board-certified counselor and LPC associate in North Carolina. She earned her master of arts in clinical mental health counseling from Wake Forest University and is currently a doctoral student at North Carolina State University. She currently works as a career counselor at North Carolina State University and does part-time clinical work at Western Wake Counseling and Psychological Services, a private practice in Cary, North Carolina. She has over 5 years of counseling experience serving children and adults, as well as couples and families, in various public and private settings. Her research interests include neurocounseling, integrated care, self-care, multicultural counseling, and racial disparities in mental health. She has often used activities that integrate neuroscience into the counseling experience with clients and psychoeducational groups.

Jennifer E. Mostafa, LGPC

Jennifer Mostafa is a licensed graduate professional counselor (LGPC) in the District of Columbia and received her master's degree in counselor education from the University of Mississippi. Jennifer has also served in the United States Army for over 13 years and is currently serving as the mental health resource coordinator for military affiliated students. Her practice is based on a holistic approach toward healing, working with clients to bring balance into their lives by using a variety of techniques, such as cognitive behavioral therapy, attachment theory, mindfulness, and a reality-based approach that encourages self-acceptance and insight.

Jessie Podolak, PT, DPT

Jessie is a doctor of physical therapy. She is in her 18th year of practice, with experience as a physical therapist in hospital, skilled nursing care, aquatic, and orthopedic outpatient settings. Over the last 12 years, she has developed expertise as a manual therapist, working extensively with patients suffering from low back pain, neck pain, joint injuries, arthritis, fibromyalgia, and other types of chronic pain. Her treatments incorporate manual therapy, therapeutic exercise, and therapeutic neuroscience education. She is currently a part of the faculty at the International Spine and Pain Institute (https://evidenceinmotion.com/). As a part of ISPI, she participates in research and teaches other physical therapists across the country how to best serve people living in pain.

Jennifer Reckner, MA

Jennifer L. Reckner received her master's in mental health counseling from Northwestern University. She is a clinical mental health counselor in private practice in Madison, Wisconsin, and works mostly with complex trauma and personality disorders. Prior to becoming a clinical mental health counselor, Jennifer was a nurse for more than 10 years. Jennifer's research interests integrate her background in nursing with mental health and tend to focus on the integration of the mind, body, and neuroscience. She is also passionate about social justice and multicultural theory to empower clients to reach their full potential.

Danica M. Rodriguez, MA

Danica Rodriguez received her master of arts in counseling at Northwestern University and previously received a bachelor of science degree from the University of Florida. Danica is experienced in using horticulture as a therapeutic intervention with clients.

Eve Rogerson, MA

Eve is a master's student at Northwestern University. In addition to her studies, she is a graduate assistant at Northwestern University and represents graduate students on the board of the LPCANC. She has been a crisis counselor with Crisis Text Line for the past 18 months and has held various volunteer positions supporting people in crisis for organizations, such as Safe Alliance and Samaritans. She has a long-held passion for working with individuals in crisis and the promotion of post-traumatic growth.

Laney Rosenzweig, LMFT

Laney Rosenzweig is the Developer of Accelerated Resolution Therapy (ART) which she created in 2008. Laney is a Licensed Marriage and Family Therapist (LMFT) practicing in the mental health field for over thirty years. She has created and authored training manuals and supplemental materials for her training of clinicians in Accelerated Resolution Therapy. In addition to her current private practice, Ms. Rosenzweig's experience has included working with Crisis Programs and Substance Abuse Programs, Employee Assistance Programs. She works with individuals, couples, children and families. She has been on staff as a researcher at the University of South Florida where research has been conducted on ART. Ms. Rosenzweig is the founder and CEO of Rosenzweig Center for Rapid Recovery (RCRR) and trains therapists in ART worldwide.

Jurie Rossouw

Jurie is a resilience expert and the CEO of Driven, a leading AI-powered platform that assess and improves personal resilience. Having published multiple research papers in the area of the neuroscience of resilience, Jurie's focus is on building resilience at an individual, organisational, and global level. He has consulted with large banks, airlines, education institutions, mining, and more. Projects ranged from building resilience at cultural levels, through to enhancing business resilience at a process and resource level. Most recently Jurie published Executive Resilience, a book which delves into the neuroscience of organisational cultural resilience, and how resilience will become more important as a skill to thrive in a disruptive environment.

Lori A. Russell-Chapin, PhD, BCN, LCPC, ACS, CCMHC

Dr. Lori Russell-Chapin is a professor of counselor education in the Department of Leadership in Education, Nonprofits, and Counseling at Bradley University in Peoria, Illinois. She earned her PhD in counselor education from the University of Wyoming, is licensed in the state of Illinois as an LCPC, and holds several certifications, such as the certification in mental health clinical counseling, approved clinical supervisor, and board-certified in neurofeedback. She teaches clinical graduate counseling courses and is passionate about her part-time private practice with husband, Dr. Ted Chapin. Lori is co-director of the Center for Collaborative Brain Research, a partnership among Bradley University, OSF Saint Francis Medical Center, and the Illinois Neurological Center. Lori enjoys writing and has published and presented extensively in the local, regional, national, and international arenas. She is the author or coauthor of eight books on practicum/internship, supervision, conflict resolution, grief and loss, neurofeedback, and neurocounseling.

Tilman Schulte, PhD

Dr. Tilman Schulte is an associate professor at the Palo Alto University and is the principal investigator of the Neuroscience Program, Biosciences Division SRI International, Menlo Park, California, from 2013 to present. Over the past decade, he maintained externally funded research from National Institute of Alcohol Abuse and Alcoholism (NIAAA) on alcohol use disorder and HIV infection and continue to develop grant ideas that translate cognitive neuroscience for clinical research. Dr. Schulte has strong expertise in neuroimaging methods that includes structural magnetic resonance imaging (MRI), diffusion tensor imaging tractography, functional MRI (fMRI), and functional connectivity (fcMRI). His current clinical research focuses on the identification of neural correlates of cognition and motor functions, and how they are spared or compromised by aging, in neurologically impaired patients with conditions such as HIV infection or age-related neurodegenerative diseases, such as Parkinson's disease. Dr. Schulte's program has attracted graduate students and postdoctoral fellows, seeking training in studying substance use disorders and neurodegenerative diseases.

Kristina Scott, PhD

Dr. Kristina Scott is an assistant professor and program director for the special education and autism programs at Salem State University. She currently teaches courses to prepare early childhood, elementary, secondary, and special education teachers to enter today's diverse classroom environments. Her research focuses on autism spectrum disorder and emotional disabilities. Before coming to the university, she taught in the public schools and helped develop social-emotional learning and autism programs in multiple districts. Since then she has been working to expand opportunities for all students with disabilities in postsecondary education and in the workforce. Her area of research interest is developing social skills for academic success and beyond. Kristina is president of the New Hampshire chapter of Learning Disabilities Association and serves as the state presidents' representative on the National Learning Disabilities Association of America's national board.

Carol Seehusen, MS, TLMHC, NCC

Carol is a current doctoral student who has expertise in somatic pain research, specifically in the mental health field. She is also a counselor educator who has contributed to master's level students' education. She has been practicing since 2008 and has developed a niche in this area.

Amy Shuman, LICSW, DC SW, MSW

Amy Shuman is an ART clinician and practices primarily at her position as a psychological counselor at Western New England University. She is also the lead trainer for the Rosenzweig Center for Rapid Recovery, and as such, she teaches licensed counselors how to practice ART. Ms. Shuman has been working in clinical, administrative, academic, and group social work for more than 20 years. Ms. Shuman has been a coauthor on several research studies related to the efficacy of ART at the University of South Florida, including the study funded by U.S. Army Medical Research and Materiel Command, Telemedicine and Advanced Technology Research Center. This study focused on combat veterans who had previously served in the wars in Iraq and Afghanistan to evaluate ART for the treatment of psychological trauma. This study has been published in the *Journal of Military Medicine.*

Stephannee Standefer, PhD, LCPC

Stephannee Standefer earned her PhD in counselor education and supervision at Northern Illinois University. She is associate program director and core faculty at the Family Institute at Northwestern University. Stephannee is an Illinois licensed clinical professional counselor in private practice. She specializes in complex trauma and sexual abuse survivors. Through her work, she is privileged to walk with survivors as they work toward healing from their trauma using strength-based and neurocounseling practices and techniques.

Megan Stocker Headley, MA

Megan Stocker Headley studied psychology and biology as an undergraduate at the University of Virginia, detouring for dynamic—and not *entirely* unrelated—careers in the arts and food and wine. She recently returned to complete her masters in mental health counseling at Northwestern University. Megan currently works with her mentor in private practice in New York City and incorporates techniques from her yoga teacher certification, believing wholeheartedly that neural integration and embodiment are cornerstones of well-being.

Yoon Suh Moh, PhD, LGPC, CRC, NCC

Yoon Suh earned a doctorate degree in counselor education and supervision from George Washington University. As a certified rehabilitation counselor and nationally certified counselor, Yoon Suh is currently working toward a license in professional counseling in the District of Columbia and certification in neurofeedback through the Biofeedback Certification International Alliance. To partially fulfill the requirement for the acquisition of the certification, Yoon Suh has completed training on neuroscience at the Foundation for Advanced Education in Sciences at NIH in Bethesda, Maryland. Yoon Suh has more than 3 years of clinical experience working with a wide range of individuals and families in vocational, clinical mental health, and community settings, including the deaf and hard of hearing; lesbian, gay, bisexual, transgender, queer, and intersex; individuals with homelessness; asylees; international students; college students; and individuals with a mental impairment. Yoon Suh's research interests involve the effects of chronic or toxic stress on mental health, family caregivers, wellness of professional counselors, suicide in college students, depression prevention interventions, and interdisciplinary studies.

Saranya Sundaram, MRC

Saranya Sundaram is a doctoral student in clinical psychology at Palo Alto University. She has worked with diverse psychiatric and neurological populations in community mental health and hospital settings. Her clinical interests include providing both neuropsychological evaluations and cognitive rehabilitation to individuals presenting with cognitive impairments. Her research interests include psychometric properties of assessment measures and integration of neuroscience and neuropsychological factors in diagnosis and treatment.

Justine Thomas

Justine Thomas is currently a candidate for an MEd in adjustment and school counseling at Salem State University. She has been teaching middle and high school English for the past 6 years. She has experience with students and family members who are diagnosed on the autism spectrum, and her career and research interests include autism and anxiety, as well as the educational experiences of students of color. She can be reached by email (j_thomas12@salemstate.edu).

Dee Wagner, MS, LPC

Dee Wagner is an LPC and board-certified dance/movement therapist and has worked in private practice for 25 years. Dee Wagner has written many articles illuminating the application of polyvagal theory, such as "Polyvagal Theory and Peekaboo: How the Therapeutic Pas de Deux Heals Attachment Trauma in Body, Movement and Dance in Psychotherapy" and "The Big Dance: My Love Affair with the Science of Nervous System Functioning in Voices: The Art and Science of Psychotherapy." *Counseling Today* published her articles "Polyvagal Theory in Practice" and "Using New Nervous System Science to Help Clients with Their Digital Dating." A podcast interview of Dee discussing polyvagal theory is available at TheThoughtfulCounselor.com.

Jordan Westcott, CM-II

Jordan Westcott is a graduate student in the master of science in counseling program at Northeastern State University. Jordan has clinical experience counseling college students through Northeastern State University's college counseling center, cancer patients, and adolescents in the juvenile criminal justice system in Oklahoma. She also has research in minority stress and resilience in lesbian, gay, bisexual, transgender, queer, questioning (LGBTQ+) communities, advocacy competencies in counselors, and historical trauma.

Naomi J. Wheeler, PhD, LMHC (Fl), NCC

Dr. Wheeler is an assistant professor in counselor education at Virginia Commonwealth University. She has extensive clinical and administrative experience providing service to children and families from predominately low-income and racially diverse backgrounds. Her research agenda builds from her professional experiences to examine relational stress across the life span, including early life family adversity and parent/couple stress as contributors to health disparities. Her scholarly products include a book chapter and two published peer-reviewed manuscripts about child mental health and the application of principles of neuroscience in counseling.

Joy S. Whitman, PhD, LPC

Joy Whitman is core faculty in the Counseling@ Northwestern University's master's counseling program and has more than 25 years of clinical experience. Dr. Whitman is an LPC in Missouri and a LCPC in Illinois, as well as an NCC with the NBCC. She was president of the Association for Lesbian, Gay, Bisexual, and Transgender Issues in Counseling. In addition, Whitman serves as an editorial board member for the Journal of Lesbian, Gay, Bisexual, and Transgender Issues in Counseling and served on the editorial board for Adultspan Journal, the journal for the AADA. Whitman's research focus is on LGBTQ counseling issues, specifically on training counselors to provide affirmative therapeutic treatment, and she has published and presented on these issues nationally and internationally. She maintains a private practice in Missouri where she counsels adults and couples and focuses her practice on working with the LGBTQ communities.

Dan Wilsea, MA, ACSM Certified Personal Trainer

Dan Wilsea holds a master's degree in counseling and completed clinical training on an acute psychiatric hospital unit. He is currently earning a certificate in sport and exercise psychology and is an American College of Sports Medicine–certified personal trainer and gym manager of Soho House Chicago. Dan is a military veteran and participant in GORUCK events.

Dawn M. Wirick, PhD, LPC, NCC, ACS

Dr. Dawn Wirick practices in a pain management medical practice and works with clients who have been diagnosed with chronic lower back pain. She received her PhD in counseling and supervision with a specialization in marriage and family therapy from the University of Akron. She is an LPC in New Jersey and has expertise in working with clients who face addictive issues with opioid medications because of chronic pain, manages extensive networks with pain management physicians in a collaborative practice, and works with combat veterans in PTSD group treatment settings. In addition, she conducts individual counseling, group counseling, couple, and family counseling sessions. Her research interests include chronic pain involved with chronic medical diagnoses, chronic pain in post-cancer survival, onset of trauma in caregivers of children diagnosed with cancer, and psychodynamic therapy for delayed onset of PTSD in combat veterans. Dawn comprehends the major "gap" that exists in the neuroscientific treatment of chronic pain as the medical community continues to operate from a biomedical model that focuses solely on tissues and tissue injury.

Mark Woodford, PhD, LPC, MAC

Mark S. Woodford is a professor in the Department of Counselor Education at the College of New Jersey. In addition to teaching courses on counseling boys and men, group and family counseling, and treating addiction and co-occurring disorders, Dr. Woodford has worked in school- and community-based prevention programs, in home-based family counseling programs, and in a residential addictions treatment facility. His research and writing interests are in the application of neuroscience research to counseling practices and gender-specific addiction and family counseling interventions. He is the author of *Men, Addiction, and Intimacy: Strengthening Recovery by Fostering the Emotional Development of Boys and Men* (2012).

Printed in the USA
CPSIA information can be obtained
at www.ICGtesting.com
LVHW081024120224
771619LV00010B/558

9 781516 539482